REPORT UPON THE

COLORADO RIVER OF THE WEST

A Da Capo Press Reprint Series

THE AMERICAN SCENE
Comments and Commentators
GENERAL EDITOR: WALLACE D. FARNHAM
University of Illinois

REPORT UPON THE

COLORADO RIVER OF THE WEST

BY

LIEUTENANT JOSEPH C. IVES

DA CAPO PRESS · NEW YORK · 1969

A Da Capo Press Reprint Edition

This Da Capo Press edition of
Report Upon the Colorado River of the West
is an unabridged republication of the first
edition published in Washington, D.C., in 1861.

Library of Congress Catalog Card Number 69-18459

Published by Da Capo Press
A Division of Plenum Publishing Corporation
227 West 17th Street
New York, N.Y. 10011

Printed in the United States of America

REPORT UPON THE

COLORADO RIVER OF THE WEST

COLORADO EXPLORING EXPEDITION

J.J.YOUNG, from a sketch by H.B.MOLLHAUSEN.

Lith. of Sarony, Major & Knapp, 449 Broadway NY

CHIMNEY PEAK

REPORT

UPON THE

COLORADO RIVER OF THE WEST,

EXPLORED IN 1857 AND 1858 BY

LIEUTENANT JOSEPH C. IVES,

CORPS OF TOPOGRAPHICAL ENGINEERS,

UNDER THE DIRECTION OF THE OFFICE OF EXPLORATIONS AND SURVEYS,

A. A. HUMPHREYS, CAPTAIN TOPOGRAPHICAL ENGINEERS, IN CHARGE.

BY ORDER OF THE

SECRETARY OF WAR.

WASHINGTON:
GOVERNMENT PRINTING OFFICE.
1861.

IN THE SENATE OF THE UNITED STATES, *June* 27, 1860.

Resolved, That there be printed, for the use of the Senate, ten thousand extra copies of the Report of Lieutenant J. C. Ives, Topographical Engineers, upon the survey of the Colorado ; and that five hundred copies be printed for the use of the War Department, and five hundred for the use of the officer commanding the expedition.

   Attest :

ASBURY DICKINS, *Secretary.*

LETTER FROM THE SECRETARY OF WAR.

WAR DEPARTMENT, *June 5, 1860.*

SIR: I have the honor to transmit herewith the report of First Lieutenant J. C. Ives, topographical engineers, upon the Exploration of the River Colorado of the West, with the accompanying maps, called for by the resolution of the House of Representatives of the 1st instant.

Very respectfully, your obedient servant,

JOHN B. FLOYD, *Secretary of War.*

The PRESIDENT OF THE SENATE.

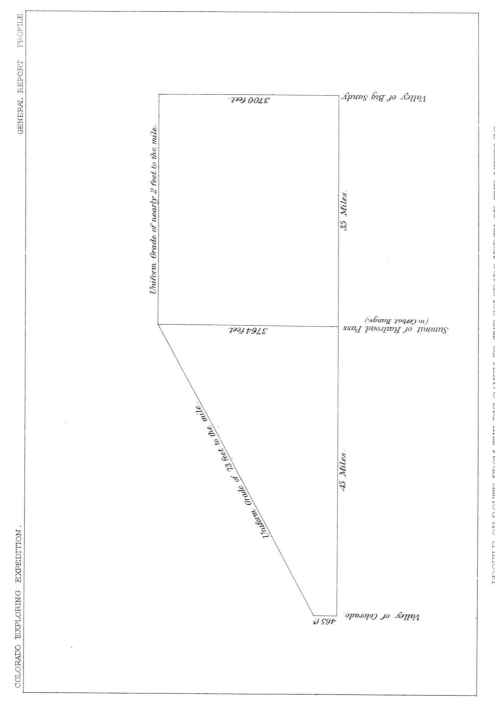

PROFILE OF ROUTE FROM THE BIG SANDY TO THE COLORADO NORTH OF THE NEEDLES

BEING A PORTION OF LIEUT WHIPPLES PACIFIC R. R. ROUTE NEAR 35TH PARALLEL.

Valley of Big Sandy

3700 feet.

35 Miles.

Summit of Railroad Pass
(in Cerbat Range.)

3764 feet.

Uniform Grade of nearly 2 feet to the mile.

Uniform Grade of 73 feet to the mile.

45 Miles.

Valley of Colorado.

465 f.

LETTER TO THE OFFICER IN CHARGE OF THE OFFICE OF EXPLORATIONS AND SURVEYS.

WASHINGTON, *May* 1, 1860.

SIR: I have the honor to submit the accompanying report upon the Exploration of the River Colorado of the West. The presentation of this has been delayed until the maps of the region explored should be completed. A preliminary report was handed in shortly after the return of the expedition from the field; and during the explorations the department was kept apprised of their general progress.

The main object of the work being to ascertain the navigability of the Colorado, detailed information upon that point was also forwarded as the examinations proceeded. It was my desire, in the communications referred to, rather to lay stress upon than to undervalue the difficulties encountered. At the same time the opinion was expressed that the delays and obstacles met with in the first experiment might be in a great measure avoided upon a new trial, conducted with the provisions that experience had suggested.

This view has since received ample confirmation. The outbreak among the Mojave Indians, and the consequent movement of troops into their territory, caused the navigability of the Colorado, at different seasons of the year, to be thoroughly tested. The result has been beyond my most sanguine estimate. The round trip between the head of the Gulf and the Mojave villages—which are 425 miles from the mouth of the Colorado, and but 75 miles from the point which I think should be regarded as the practical head of navigation—has been made in eight days.

I would again state my belief that the Colorado would be found an economical avenue for the transportation of supplies to various military posts in New Mexico and Utah. It may be instanced that the amount of land transportation saved by adopting this route would be: to the Great Salt lake, 700 miles; to Fort Defiance, 600 miles; and to Fort Buchanan, 1,100 miles. The estimate contained in the hydrographic report, of the cost attending the river service, is, I think, a liberal one. The first organization of transportation establishments, to connect the upper part of the river with the interior of the Territories mentioned, would be attended with expense and trouble; but I am convinced that it would ultimately be productive of a great saving in both. The results of the exploration, so far as they relate to the navigability of the river, will be found embodied in map No. 1 and in the hydrographic report.

The region explored after leaving the navigable portion of the Colorado—though, in a scientific point of view, of the highest interest, and presenting natural features whose strange sublimity is perhaps unparalleled in any part of the world—is not of much value. Most of it is uninhabitable, and a great deal of it is impassable. A brief statement could comprise the whole of what might be called the practical results of the land explorations. The country along the Colorado, however, with the exception of a few places, has been almost a *terra incognita*. Concerning the character and value of the portions previously explored, great differences of opinion existed. Between the mouth and the highest point attained are many localities unique and surpassingly beautiful. Some of the Indian tribes, of whom little has been known, are subjects for curious speculation; and it being doubtful whether any party will ever again pursue the same line of travel, I have thought it would be better, in place of condensing into a few lines the prominent facts noticed, to transmit the journal kept during the expedition.

This involves the presentation of what may appear extraneous, and perhaps beyond the limits of a strictly official communication; but a record of the every-day incidents of travel, set down while fresh in the mind, serves to convey a general idea of a country that can scarcely be imparted in any other way, and can hardly fail of reproducing, to some extent, in the mind of the reader the impression made upon that of the traveller.

In passing from the Colorado eastward, an opportunity was afforded of forming a connexion between the Big Sandy, on Lieutenant Whipple's railroad route, and the point upon the river north of the Needles. The examination verified the judgment of Lieutenant Whipple, who, though prevented from actually passing over the country, had selected it for a railroad location. The distance by Whipple's travelled route between the above points was 180 miles, and over a rough and difficult region; by his railroad route it is 80 miles. For 35 miles the line is nearly level; for the remaining 45 miles there is a uniform grade of about 70 feet. During the whole distance there is scarcely an irregularity upon the surface of the ground.

The department of natural history was under the charge of Dr. Newberry, whose name is well known in connexion with such labors. His eminent fitness for the position will appear by an examination of what he has accomplished. His report upon the geology of the region traversed, I regard as the most interesting and valuable result of the explorations. In making the collections Dr. Newberry was zealousy assisted by Mr. Mollhausen, who also prepared the greater portion of the views and illustrations taken during the trip.

The accompanying maps were made by Mr. Egloffstein, who went out with me as topographer. Some of the views, it will be perceived, are also from his pencil. The maps have been drawn directly upon the plates, which will obviate the ordinary expense for engraving. The style is partly new. The system of light and shade has been frequently adopted; but the application of the ruled tints—by which the light sides of the mountains are relieved, and the comparative altitudes of different levels exhibited—is original, I believe, with the artist. The beautiful and effective representation of the topography is the best encomium both upon the style and its projector. The privation and exposure to which Mr. Egloffstein freely subjected himself, in order to acquire topographical information, has resulted in an accurate delineation of every portion of the region traversed.

The survey of the navigable portion of the river was principally conducted by Mr. C. Bielawski, of San Francisco. The duties of meteorologists and assistant topographers were faithfully performed by Messrs. Taylor and Booker.

To Mr. Carroll, the engineer and constructor of the steamer, and to the pilot, Captain Robinson, are due, in great measure, the successful ascent of the Colorado. The report shows how large a share they had in the accomplishment of the work.

The mule train, while following the bank of the river and crossing the country, was in charge of Mr. G. H. Peacock, of California, whose good care and experienced management conducted it safely over as difficult a country as can perhaps be found upon any portion of the continent.

To Lieutenant Tipton, 3d artillery, who commanded the escort, I feel myself under many obligations for voluntary and important assistance rendered in the astronomical and meteorological departments, for the excellent order and discipline maintained throughout the trip among the individuals of his command, and for the uniform cordial co-operation which contributed so much to the pleasure and success of the expedition.

I am, sir, very respectfully, your obedient servant,

J. C. IVES,
First Lieutenant Top. Engineers, Com'g Colorado Exploring Expedition.

A. A. HUMPHREYS, *Captain Top. Engineers,*
In charge of Office of Explorations and Surveys, War Department.

GENERAL TABLE OF CONTENTS.

PART I.

EXPLORATIONS AND SURVEYS.   WAR DEPARTMENT.

COLORADO EXPLORING EXPEDITION, LIEUTENANT J. C. IVES, TOPOGRAPHICAL ENGINEERS, 1857-'58.

GENERAL REPORT.

WASHINGTON, D. C.
1861.

CONTENTS.

INTRODUCTION.

Colorado explorations.—Organization of the Expedition.—Voyage to the mouth of the river.

Position and extent of country drained by the Colorado.—Early explorations of the river.—Expedition of Coronado.—Of Diaz.—Of Fernando Alarçon.—Of Cardinas.—Visits of Jesuit Missionaries.—Foundation of Catholic Missions.—Expedition of Escalante.—Establishment of Fort Yuma.—Expedition of Lieutenant Derby.—Of Captain Sitgreaves.—Of Lieutenant Whipple.—Accounts of Trappers.—Organization of Colorado Exploring Expedition.—Preparations to take the field.—Division of party at San Francisco.—Voyage to the head of the Gulf of California.—Description of the Gulf.—Approach to the mouth of the Colorado.

CHAPTER I.

Mouth of the Colorado.

Approach to mouth of Colorado.—Ship Rock.—Hazardous Reef.—Black Cape.—Entrance to River.—New Channel.—Montague and Goree Islands.—Wild Fowl hunting.—Robinson's Landing.—Scenery at mouth of River.—Return to Schooner.—Rush of Tide.—The Bore.—Difficulty of landing Steamboat.—Novel mooring place.—Overflow of Country.—Landing of Stores.—Boat from Fort Yuma.—Arrangement of Camp.—Atmospheric Phenomena.—Animal and vegetable Products.—Preparation for building ways for Steamboat.—Sunday Excursion.—Completion of Ways.—Defect in build of Boat.—Proposed Remedy.—A Northwester.—Visitors in Camp.—Building of Hull.—New Moon Tides.—Photographic Experiments.—Astronomical Observations.—Extrication of the Monterey.—Fort Yuma Steamboats.—Early navigation of Colorado.—Cocopas.—Suspicions about Expedition.—Mr. Robinson's engagement of Pilot.—Violent Gale.—Overthrow of Observatory.—Departure of Captain Walsh.—Progress of Steamboat towards completion.—Approach of Full Moon Tides.—Arrival of party from Fort Yuma.—Illness of Dr. Newberry.—Launching of Boat.—Preparations to commence ascent of River.

CHAPTER II.

Mouth of the Colorado to Fort Yuma.

Departure from Robinson's Landing.—Perilous Position.—Meeting with Steamer from Fort Yuma.—Kindness of Captain Wilcox.—Description of River.—Camp at Cocopa Village.—Appearance of Indians.—Northwester.—Character of Navigation.—Obstacles and Difficulties Encountered.—Accidents and Detention.—Night Expedition in Skiff.—A Frontier Settlement.—Hospitable Reception.—A Night's Lodging.—Ride to Fort Yuma.—River and Mountain Scenery.—Arrival at Fort Yuma.—Description of Post.—Approach of Explorer.—Operations of Members of Expedition.—Trip of Mr. Peacock to San Francisco.—Recovery of Dr. Newberry.—Yuma Indians.—Rumors of Mormon Movements.—Suspicions and Distrust among Colorado Tribes concerning Expedition.—Difficulty in obtaining Guides.—Low stage of River.—Preparations to start from Fort Yuma.

CHAPTER III.

Fort Yuma to Mojave Cañon.

Departure from Fort Yuma.—Indian Guides.—Yuma Shoals.—A Bad Start.—Purple Hills.—Explorer's Pass.—Arrival of Mail.—Purple Hill Pass.—Reedy Bend.—Varieties of Coloring.—Canebrake Cañon.—Chimney Peak.—Precipice Bend.—Rapid.—Barrier Island.—The Spires.—Chocolate Mountains.—Red Rock Gate.—The Sleeper.—Light-house Rock.—Porphyry Gate.—Great Colorado Valley.—Snags and Sunken Rocks.—Barrenness of Region.—Natural History Collections.—Dismal Flats.—Carroll's Creek.—Halfway Mountains.—Yuma Indians.—Intelligence from Mojaves.—Chemehuevis Indians.—Monument Mountains.—The Monument.—Sand Island Shoals.—Return of Lieutenant Tipton to Fort Yuma.—Impression made upon Indians by Steamboat.—Engagement of Mail Carrier.—Riverside Mountain.—Mineral

CHAPTER IV.

Mojave Valley.

CHAPTER V.

Mojave Valley to mouth of Black Cañon.

CHAPTER VI.

Black Cañon to Great Bend.—Return to Mojave Valley.

CHAPTER VII.

Mojave Valley to Big Cañon, at mouth of Diamond River.

CHAPTER VIII.

Colorado Plateau, near Big Cañon.

CHAPTER IX.

San Francisco Forest to Moquis.

CHAPTER X.

Moquis to Fort Defiance.—Conclusion.

LIST OF ILLUSTRATIONS.

WOOD CUTS. *

* Drawn by Mr. J. J. Young from sketches by Messrs. Mollhausen and Egloffstein.

INTRODUCTION.

COLORADO EXPLORATIONS,—ORGANIZATION OF THE EXPEDITION,— VOYAGE TO THE MOUTH OF THE RIVER.

Position and extent of country drained by the Colorado.—Early explorations of the river.—Expedition of coronado.—Of diza —Of fernando alarçon.—Of cardinas.—Visits of jesuit missionaries.—Foundation of catholic missions.—Expedition of escalante.—Establishment of fort yuma.—Expedition of lieutenant derby.—Of captain sitgreaves.—Of lieutenant whipple.—Accounts of trappers.—Organization of colorado exploring expedition.—Preparations to take the field —Division of party at san francisco.—Voyage to the head of the gulf of california.—Description of the gulf.—Approach to the mouth of the colorado.

The Colorado of the West is the largest stream, with one exception, that flows from our Territory into the Pacific ocean. It has its sources in the southern portions of Nebraska and Oregon, and in its course to the Gulf of California drains two-thirds of the Territory of New Mexico, and large portions of Utah and California, an area of more than 300,000 square miles.

Very little has been known concerning this river. Two streams, Green and Grand rivers, which flow through Utah in a southerly direction, have been supposed to unite somewhere near the southern boundary of that Territory and form the Colorado, but the point of junction has never been visited nor determined. For hundreds of miles below this point the stream has not been seen, till recently, by white men, excepting at one spot, and few Indians, for centuries past, have been near its banks. Notwithstanding this, some portions of the river were among the earliest parts of America to be explored. In less than fifty years after the landing of Columbus, Spanish missionaries and soldiers were travelling upon the Colorado, following its course for a long way from the mouth, and even attaining one of the most distant and inaccessible points of its upper waters. More information was gained concerning it at that time than was acquired during the three subsequent centuries.

In the year 1540 the viceroy of New Spain, interested in the accounts derived from a Franciscan monk of the latter's travels in the Territory now called New Mexico, sent an exploring expedition into that region under the command of Vasquez de Coronado. A detachment of twenty-five men, led by one Diaz, left Coronado's party and travelled westward. They discovered the Colorado and followed it to its mouth. Their description of the river and of the tribes they met upon it is not at all inapplicable to the condition of things at the present day, though the statements concerning the prodigious size of one community of Indians that they encountered are a little exaggerated. The Mojaves, whom, doubtless, they refer to, are perhaps as fine a race of men, physically, as can anywhere be found, but they do not quite come up, in stature and strength, to the descriptions of the Spaniards.

About the same time Captain Fernando Alarçon, by order of the viceroy, sailed up the Gulf of California and ascended the Colorado in boats for a long distance. The account of what he saw agrees with that of his cotemporary explorer.

Another of Coronado's captains, named Cardinas, with a party of twelve men, reached the pueblos of Moquis, and repaired from them, with Indian guides, to a portion of the Colorado, far distant from that seen by the others. The history states that after twenty days' march, over a desert, they arrived at a river, the banks of which were so high that they seemed to be three or four leagues in the air. The most active of the party attempted to descend, but came back in the evening, saying that they had met difficulties which prevented them from reaching the bottom; that they had accomplished one-third of the descent, and from that point the river looked very large. They averred that some rocks, which appeared from above to be the height of a man, were higher than the tower of the cathedral of Seville. This was the first description of the famous Big Cañon of the Colorado.

Several times, during the succeeding two centuries, the lower part of the river was visited by Catholic priests. In 1744 a Jesuit missionary, named Jacob Sedelmayer, went thither, following the course of the Gila, and travelled extensively in both New Mexico and Sonora, and about thirty years afterwards the Jesuits established missions among the Yuma Indians, who live at the junction of the Gila and Colorado. The priests were subsequently massacred by the fierce tribe among whom they had located themselves.

In 1776 another Catholic missionary, Father Escalante, travelled from Santa Fé to Utah, and having explored the region south of the Great Salt Lake, pursued a southwesterly course, towards the sources of the Virgin, and then crossed to the Colorado, which he reached at a point that appears to have been almost identical with that attained, from the opposite direction, by Cardinas, more than two centuries before.

From this time the river was scarcely approached, excepting by an occasional trapper, or some overland party crossing the lower portion, *en route* to California. A considerable part of the emigration, induced by the gold discoveries in that region, passed through New Mexico, by way of the Gila, and the travellers were subjected to molestation from the Yumas. In 1850 a detachment of troops was sent to the mouth of the Gila to keep these Indians under control, and not long afterwards a military post, called Fort Yuma, was regularly established.

The difficulty of furnishing supplies to the garrison, across the desert, was such that, in the winter of 1850 and 1851, General Smith, commanding the Pacific division, sent a schooner from San Francisco to the head of the Gulf of California, and directed Lieutenant Derby, topographical engineers, to make a reconnaissance, with a view of establishing a route of supply to Fort Yuma, *via* the Gulf and the Colorado. The result of the reconnaissance was successful, and the route was at once put in operation. The freight, carried in sailing vessels to the mouth of the river, was transported to the fort—the distance to which, by the river, is one hundred and fifty miles—at first in lighters, and afterwards in steamboats.*

In 1851, Captain Sitgreaves, topographical engineers, with a party of fifty individuals, made an exploration from Zuñi westward. He struck the Colorado at a point about 160 miles above Fort Yuma, and followed the east side of the river, keeping as near to the bank as possible, to the fort. He encountered the Mojaves, and found their appearance and customs generally to agree with the descriptions of the early explorers. The descent was accompanied with hardship and danger. Both the Mojaves and Yumas were hostile, and the difficulty of travelling near the river was extreme, owing to the chains of rugged and precipitous mountains that crossed the valley. The summer heats had parched and withered the face of the country; the stream was low, and what was seen of it did not create a favorable opinion regarding its navigability.

In the spring of 1854 Lieutenant Whipple, topographical engineers, in command of an expedition for the exploration and survey of a railroad route near the 35th parallel, reached the Colorado, at the mouth of Bill Williams's Fork, and ascended the river about fifty miles, leaving it at a point not far below where Captain Sitgreaves had first touched it. The expedition was composed of nearly a hundred persons, including the escort. The Mojaves were friendly, furnishing provisions to the party, whose supply was nearly exhausted, and sending guides to conduct them by the best route across the desert westward. The river was probably higher than when seen by Captain Sitgreaves, and it was the opinion of Lieutenant Whipple that it would be navigable for steamers of light draught. The course of the Colorado northward could be followed with the eye for only a short distance, on account of mountain spurs

_____

* A fuller account of the opening of this route is given in a subsequent chapter.

that crossed the valley and intercepted the view. A high distant range, through which the river apparently broke, was supposed to be at the mouth of the "Big Cañon," which the Spaniards, in 1540, had visited at a place far above.

The marvellous story of Cardinas, that had formed for so long a time the only record concerning this rather mythical locality, was rather magnified than detracted from by the accounts of one or two trappers, who professed to have seen the cañon, and propagated among their prairie companions incredible accounts of the stupendous character of the formation, and it became a matter of interest to have this region explored, and to lay down the positions of the Colorado and its tributaries along the unknown belt of country north of the 35th parallel. The establishment of new military posts in New Mexico and Utah made it also desirable to ascertain how far the river was navigable, and whether it might not prove an avenue for the economical transportation of supplies to the newly occupied stations.

There was no appropriation that would enable the War Department to accomplish this service until the summer of 1857, when the present Secretary of War, having the disposition of a certain amount to be expended in field examinations, set apart a portion of it for the exploration of the Colorado, and directed me to organize an expedition for that object.

To ascertain how far the river was navigable for steamboats being the point of primary importance, it was necessary first to make provision for this portion of the work. The company employed in carrying freight from the head of the Gulf to Fort Yuma were unable to spare a boat for the use of the expedition, excepting for a compensation beyond the limits of the appropriation. A boat of suitable construction had, therefore, to be built on the Atlantic coast and transported to San Francisco, and thence to the mouth of the river. In order that the survey should be made at the worst and lowest stage of the water, I had been directed to commence operations at the mouth of the Colorado on the 1st of December. This left little time for preparation, considering that it was necessary to build a steamer and carry the parts to so great a distance.

In the latter part of June I ordered of Reaney, Neafie & Co., of Philadelphia, an iron steamer, fifty feet long, to be built in sections, and the parts to be so arranged that they could be transported by railroad, as the shortness of time required that it should be sent to California, *via* the Isthmus of Panama. About the middle of August the boat was finished, tried upon the Delaware, and found satisfactory, subject to a few alterations only. It was then taken apart, sent to New York, and shipped on board of the California steamer which sailed on the 20th of August for Aspinwall. Mr. A. J. Carroll, of Philadelphia, who had engaged to accompany the expedition as steamboat engineer, went out in charge of the boat.

The transportation of the steamer was, to the parties concerned, a source of more trouble than profit, but the kind offices of the agents of the Panama Railroad Company, and of the captains of the steamships on both the Atlantic and Pacific coasts, united to the careful supervision of Mr. Carroll, enabled the awkward mass of freight to reach San Francisco in safety by the first of October.

Dr. J. S. Newberry was appointed physician to the expedition, and also to take charge of the natural history department. This gentleman had previously made extensive geological surveys in California and Oregon while attached to the party of Lieutenant Williamson, topographical engineers, in charge of the Pacific railroad surveys in those regions.

Mr. F. W. Egloffstein, who had been attached to Frémont's expedition of 1853, and had subsequently been employed with the party that explored the Pacific railroad route near the 41st parallel, was appointed topographer. Messrs. P. H. Taylor and C. K. Booker were the astronomical and meteorological assistants. A gentleman belonging to the household of Baron Von Humboldt, Mr. Mollhausen, who had been a member of the exploring party of Prince Paul of Wirtemburg, and also of Lieutenant Whipple's expedition, received from the Secretary of War the appointment of artist and collector in natural history.

The members of the expedition were assembled in San Francisco in the middle of October. The interest, which I would here gratefully acknowledge, displayed by General Clarke, commanding the department of the Pacific, and by the officers of his staff, in furthering the necessary preparations, enabled these to be soon completed.   The party was divided into three detachments.   One of them, in charge of Dr. Newberry, started on the 28th of October in the coast steamer to San Diego, at which place some mules were to be procured and taken across the desert to Fort Yuma.   A second detachment, in charge of Mr. Taylor, went by the same steamer to San Pedro, from whence they were to repair to Fort Tejon, collect the remainder of the animals, and cross also to Fort Yuma.   Mr. Carroll and myself, with eight men, were to go by sea to the head of the Gulf of California, there put the steamboat together; ascend the Colorado to Fort Yuma, and join the rest of the party.   Lieutenant Tipton, 3d artillery, and twenty-five men, to be taken from the companies at Fort Yuma, were detailed by General Clarke as an escort to the expedition.

It was on the 1st day of November, 1857, that I sailed from San Francisco, for the mouth of the Colorado, in the *Monterey*, a schooner of 120 tons burden, employed to carry supplies to the head of the Gulf, for transmission to the garrison at Fort Yuma.   There had been almost a full cargo taken in before any of the expedition property was put aboard, and to find room for the latter was a matter of considerable difficulty.   There was no other way, however, of getting my party and stores to their destination, and the quartermaster, Colonel Swords, had, at some inconvenience to himself, kindly allowed me the use of as much shiproom as could possibly be spared.   Every nook in the hold was closely stowed, and much of my property, including the parts of the steamer, had to be carried on deck.   The eight sections of the hull were distributed along on either side of the masts, resting upon piles of lumber, amongst the pieces of the engine and wheel.   The boiler, an unwieldy object, weighing rather more than three tons, was lashed as securely as it could be, amidships.   Two skiffs, a long whale boat, and some boxes completed the deck load, leaving an area of only five or six feet square around the helm, and a still smaller space at the bow, unencumbered.

It was of course necessary that a certain number of mechanics and laborers should accompany me to the mouth of the river to put the steamboat together, and take me up to the fort, but Colonel Swords did not feel authorized to encroach upon the already limited accommodations of the captain and crew by quartering nine persons upon them, and I should have been much embarrassed but for the obliging offices of the master of the vessel, Captain Walsh, who, with much trouble, and at the risk of still more discomfort, succeeded in providing places for the party.   His own small cabin he shared with Mr. Carroll and myself.

We sailed out of the harbor of San Francisco with a brisk breeze, which subsided soon after we had passed the headlands, and for twenty-four hours remained light, allowing but little progress to be made, but then a fresh northwester set in, and continued for several days, during which the *Monterey*, though not in sailing trim, made so good a run along the coast, that on the evening of the seventh day out the land near Cape St. Lucas, the southern extremity of the peninsula of Lower California, hove in sight.

This rapid accomplishment of the first two-thirds of the distance encouraged anticipations of a quick voyage not destined to be realized.   The next morning the wind had died away, and a week of dead calms, of burning tropical days, and stifling nights, found us, at its termination, slowly rolling on the glassy swell, and still in sight of the lower end of the peninsula.

In the Gulf of California the currents of air generally set in the direction of its length, either up or down, according to the season of the year.   During the month of November it appeared that what breeze there was blew *down* the Gulf, and we had to beat slowly up against it, making sometimes little more than twenty miles in the twenty-four hours.   When near the end of the voyage the long-wished-for wind indeed came, and then it blew a gale, and for twelve hours a sea was running that occasioned, in the deeply laden schooner, considerable apprehension for the safety of the property of the expedition, to say nothing of its members; but the *Monterey* rode it through without serious damage, and a few evenings afterwards—three weeks having elapsed since Cape St. Lucas had first been seen—Captain Walsh informed us that we should reach the mouth of the river on the following day.

Tedious as was the last part of the voyage, it had not been entirely destitute of interest, for at no time during the day were we altogether out of sight of land. About Cape St. Lucas the country near the shore is uninteresting, but further north the scenery becomes bolder and more striking. The navigation of the Gulf is nearly free from shoals and reefs, and the sheet of deep water would be unbroken but for lofty volcanic islands, some one of which is nearly always in view. Their sides rise suddenly out of the water, and in thick or stormy nights a vessel might be driven into dangerous proximity to the rocky bluffs before the lead would give notice of their neighborhood.

North of Guaymas these islands are more numerous, and in one place, with narrow channels between, extend across the Gulf in an uninterrupted chain, presenting wild and abrupt outlines, as though formed by spouts of lava hurled up from mammoth submarine craters, and hardened in the air before falling. They are by no means destitute of vegetation, but appear to be uninhabited, and the unbroken solitude adds to their desolate grandeur. It is probable that upon many of their surfaces no human foot has ever trodden. They appear, indeed, almost inaccessible, though among the rugged cliffs an occasional break affords a glimpse of some green valley or cool sheltered glen inviting to the eye, or a narrow vista momentarily opens to view dark and mysterious looking recesses, suggesting the notion, in this region teeming with mineral wealth, that there may be among those secluded nooks places that it would be well worth while to explore.

The main land on the western side has a character very similar, but the bold precipices and steep shelving planes that girt the shore are crowned with jagged peaks piled confusedly above.

During the gale that we encountered, when near the end of the voyage, the remarkable phenomenon was presented of the heavy billows rolling towards us from the portion of the coast that was directly under our lee. I supposed at first that this might be due to some volcanic disturbance, but it is more probable that it resulted from the action of the tides and currents, which increase in strength as the head of the Gulf is approached. A very perceptible change takes place also in the temperature when the valley of the Colorado draws near. Though less warm—at least at the season of our visit—than the latitude of Cape St. Lucas, it possessed a fresh softness not experienced further south, and the islands and mountain peaks, whose outlines, as seen from the Gulf, had been somewhat dimmed by a light haze, appeared surprisingly near and distinct in the limpid medium through which they were now viewed. The whole panorama became invested with new attractions, and it would be hard to say whether the dazzling radiance of the day or the sparkling clearness of the night was the more beautiful and brilliant.

In closing this brief notice of the voyage to the mouth of the Colorado, the recollection of one of its features is so agreeable that I cannot refrain from referring to it. I allude to the hospitality extended to myself and companions by Captain Walsh during the whole of the trip.

In a vessel loaded almost beyond the limits of safety; with a hampered deck, impossible to be kept in order; a crowded cabin, and an inconvenient number of idlers filling up the circumscribed space, enough of the disagreeable must have occurred during the long passage to render it the most uncomfortable experience of seafaring life that our captain had probably ever encountered, and we therefore appreciated the more the unflagging kindness and good humor which contributed so much to our comfort and enjoyment during the thirty days that we were cooped up together on board of the schooner *Monterey*.

CHAPTER I.

MOUTH OF THE COLORADO.

November 28, 1857.—Our near approach to the mouth of the Colorado river was announced, shortly after sunrise this morning, by the appearance of Ship Rock, bearing northwest on the starboard bow. All crowded on deck to see the landmark that indicated the termination of the tedious voyage; but there was no need of haste, for the wind still remained light and uncertain, and dead ahead, affording us an opportunity of inspecting Ship Rock, from different points of view, for nearly fourteen hours. This rather remarkable peak can be distinctly seen twenty or twenty-five miles from the deck of a low vessel, and at that distance bears a great resemblance to a sloop before the wind. It is about two hundred feet high, and covered with guano. It bears nearly south from the mouth of the river, being distant from it twenty-five miles. A reef of low rocks runs from its base in a southwesterly direction for two or three miles. This reef is not noticed upon the charts, and might hazard the safety of a vessel approaching the head of the Gulf by night.

At 4 p. m. we were abreast of a low black-looking cape, beyond which lies the Mission of San Felipe. On the opposite side of the Gulf could be seen the dim outline of a high point, the only land visible in that direction. All of the region in the vicinity is low and flat. On the California side a range of mountains borders the Gulf as far north as Black cape, and then trends towards the northwest. The most elevated peaks appeared from the sea to be from fifteen hundred to two thousand feet in height. The country north of the cape, between the mountains and the water, is so low as to be invisible from the deck of the vessel.

After passing the cape the water began rapidly to shoal, soundings taken during the evening giving a depth of eighteen fathoms. The bottom is a soft ooze, of a grayish-blue color, and feeling like grease to the fingers.

At sunset the tide, which begins now to be strongly felt, became favorable; and though the wind has been light, we have made good progress since nightfall towards the river.

November 29.—The schooner was borne along by the tide last night to the mouth of the Colorado, and, as the ebb set in, came to anchor in five fathoms water, to wait for morning and the returning flood.

The day dawned clear and brilliant, and as the sun rose the temperature became soft and springlike. The transparent purity of the atmosphere, and the light glancing from the unruffled surface of the Gulf, imparted to the scene a dazzling lustre. Ship Rock had entirely disappeared from view. The peaks on the Sonora side were distinctly visible, rising like islands from the surrounding desert. Black cape, low down upon the horizon, and the ragged summits of the California range, limited the view towards the west. Low red hills lay north of this range, beyond the flat country bordering the river, and the irregular outlines were converted by a powerful mirage into fanciful shapes of castles, domes, and giant statues, painted with glowing purple tints and sharply-defined tracery on the blue background of the sky.

At 7 o'clock we started with a head-wind, and, assisted by the tide, commenced beating up the river. In about six miles the water shoaled to three and a half fathoms, and became of a deeper red, and very turbid. The tide making against the wind occasioned considerable swell. The river appeared to be ten or twelve miles broad; but the low, flat banks and bars visible above the surface, combined with the tossing ripples and tremulous motion of the atmosphere, made it impossible to form a correct determination of the lines of the shore.

Captain Walsh informed me that there were two channels; that the eastern one was said to be the deeper, but that, being unacquainted with it, he should follow the other. Standing across to the west, in pursuance of this resolution, in a few minutes the water shoaled very suddenly from three to one and a half fathoms, and the *Monterey* narrowly escaped running aground. A similar result attended an attempt to cross to the eastern shore, and it became evident that we had either entered a centre channel or that it would soon become necessary to retrace our course entirely. The bottom was remarkably flat and uniform, the surface along the middle of the channel being composed of soft mud, and elsewhere of hard clay.

Two glittering islands were now brought into view by the mirage, the narrow stalks of the reeds on their marshy surfaces being magnified into a resemblance to tall and distorted stumps of trees. The localities corresponded to those of Montague and Goree islands. The latter was soon close abeam. It is a quarter of a mile long, and the highest point has an elevation of only a few feet. A green lawn, on which myriads of pelicans were congregated, sloped gently from the centre to the water's edge, and presented a refreshing contrast to the expanse of dark water behind us. No channel had been previously known to exist between these islands; but being headed off by bars from pursuing a course to either side, the only resource was to keep directly on, and as long as the tide served a good channel was found. At noon the tide turned, and the *Monterey* was brought to anchor in four and a half fathoms waters abreast of a point about half a mile from the southern extremity of Montague island.

Attracted by the immense numbers of wild fowl that could be seen fluttering about, the mate and myself had a boat lowered, and taking our guns crossed over to the land. The tide had commenced to run out rapidly, and it was no easy matter to find a place to disembark. Sinking at every step half way to our waists in the soft, gluey mud, we waded slowly and laboriously to the higher ground, and walked a mile inland. The whole island is composed of a fine tenacious brick clay, and bears marks of being entirely overflowed at the spring tides. The surface is covered with a coarse grass, and intersected in every direction by deep gulleys. Innumerable flocks of pelicans, curlews, plovers, and ducks of different varieties, were scattered over the flats. It was easy to shoot them, but almost impossible to get at them afterwards on account of the depth of the mud, and we started back to the schooner but little better provided with game than when we left. The tide was now running out at the rate of about three miles an hour. I took a line of soundings across to the schooner, and continued them to a shoal half a mile further east. This shoal is the foundation of what will probably be before long an extensive island. The surface is now, at low tide, ten feet above the waters. The faces, where exposed, showed that the formation consisted of horizontal layers of clay an inch in thickness, deposited with singular evenness and uniformity. A sheet of water, several miles wide, intervenes between this shoal and the sand hills near the eastern bank of the river. It contains numerous spits and bars, that would seem to present obstructions to navigation.

The day has been warm, and at noon the heat was almost equal to that of midsummer in the northern Atlantic States.

November 30.—Tripped anchor at 11 and drifted up with the tide, it being a dead calm. The reflection of the rays of the sun, the apparent vibration of the atmosphere, the mirage,

COLORADO EXPLORING EXPEDITION.

J.J.YOUNG from a Photograph by LIEUT. IVES.

Lith. of Sarony, Major & Knapp. 449 Broadway.NY

ROBINSON'S LANDING, MOUTH OF COLORADO RIVER.

and the constant shifting of the outlines of the bars, due to the rapidly rising tide, made it impossible to form an accurate idea of the configuration of the shores. After reaching the northeast end of Montague island, a white speck came in sight towards the northwest, which Captain Walsh told me was the house at "Robinson's Landing," near which is the usual anchorage for vessels coming to the mouth of the river. A breeze springing up, sail was made, and we headed directly for it; but when within a mile of the shore the tide turned, and after a vain endeavor to stem the current, which every moment became stronger, finding that we had drifted down stream about two miles, we were compelled to anchor. Mr. Carroll and myself went ashore in a boat, and walked up to the house—a small frame building resting on the tops of piles about four feet above the ground. The owner and builder had been mate of a vessel plying to the mouth of the river; believing that he could do a profitable business by taking blackfish and making oil, he had established his hermit-like retreat by the side of a little gully to which he had noticed that the fish were in the habit of resorting. There is a tradition that, a few miles up the river, a large amount of gold was sunk in a vessel belonging to the ill-fated party of the Count Rousset de Boulbon. After an unsuccessful attempt to revolutionize Sonora, the count tried to escape by way of the Colorado; but, mistaking the channel, got into what is called Hardy's, or the false Colorado, where the vessel was lost, and most of the individuals on board killed by the Indians. The hope of recovering the lost treasure has, it is said, influenced Mr. Robinson in the selection of the singular locality he has chosen for a residence.

The house was now deserted, the proprietor being temporarily engaged in the service of the steamboat company that transport the government stores to Fort Yuma. A note was left upon the door, informing us that the two steamboats were lying at a point fifteen miles above, and requesting Captain Walsh to announce his arrival by sending up a boat.

Lofty columns of smoke could be seen, many miles to the north, which may have been signal fires of the Indians on account of the presence of our vessel, or an accidental conflagration of the prairie.

The whole of the country near the west bank of the river is low and overflowed at the highest tides. Robinson's landing is the most elevated point, and even this, Captain Walsh tells me, is often submerged. The spring tides of this month not having yet become sufficiently high to cover the surface, the ground has had nearly four weeks to become dry, and the walking is, in spots, tolerably good, but the surface is intersected, in every direction, by gulleys, whose bottoms are covered either with water, soft mud, or quicksand. Along the shore the face of the bank is very steep, and it is difficult to see how the boilers and the heavy parts of the steamboat are to be landed. During the spring tides, which are now at hand, the water runs out so rapidly that for only a few moments would the deck of the schooner be above the level of the surface of the ground and near enough to it to discharge freight, and the hands would have to be constantly employed in booming her off, or the hull might catch upon the face of the bluff and the vessel be capsized as the water fell. The government stores are always transferred directly from the deck to the steamboats. The latter were built at a point several miles higher up, at a locality better suited for such an undertaking, but Captain Walsh is not at liberty to run the risk of ascending the river with his schooner any further. By the side of Robinson's house, at the head of the gully previously mentioned, is an excellent position for a vessel to lie, and to which she could easily be floated during the high water that may be expected in the course of the next two days; but as the landing of the property will occupy some time, it would be necessary that she should remain high and dry till the next spring tides came to float her off.

After endeavoring to make an answering signal smoke, but without much success, for want of proper material, Mr. Carroll and myself started about sundown to return to the schooner. The water, from the combined effects of the tide and current, was now running out with great velocity. We allowed the skiff to drift in the direction of the vessel, and while still a long way off could hear the noise of the current striking her stem. We narrowly escaped being swamped as we came alongside, and succeeded with difficulty in getting on board. As the tide fell the swiftness of the flow increased, and soon the mighty volume was surging by with formidable violence. The schooner had come to anchor over a shoal, and owing to the rapid fall was aground before its full force was developed; a fortunate occurrence, as no anchors could have held her much longer. She had no sooner settled down in the sand than a bank commenced forming on the lee side, and in an incredibly short time a mound was raised to a height of several feet, with one or two sluice-ways, through which the water rushed from underneath the keel like a mill-race.

About nine o'clock, while the tide was still running out rapidly, we heard, from the direction of the Gulf, a deep, booming sound, like the noise of a distant waterfall. Every moment it became louder and nearer, and in half an hour a great wave, several feet in height, could be distinctly seen flashing and sparkling in the moonlight, extending from one bank to the other, and advancing swiftly upon us. While it was only a few hundred yards distant, the ebb tide continued to flow by at the rate of three miles an hour. A point of land and an exposed bar close under our lee broke the wave into several long swells, and as these met the ebb the broad sheet around us boiled up and foamed like the surface of a caldron, and then, with scarcely a moment of slack water, the whole went whirling by in the opposite direction. In a few moments the low rollers had passed the island and united again in a single bank of water, which swept up the narrowing channel with the thunder of a cataract. At a turn not far distant it disappeared from view, but for a long time, in the stillness of the night, the roaring of the huge mass could be heard reverberating among the windings of the river, till at last it became faint and lost in the distance.

This singular phenomenon of the ''bore,'' as it is called, is met with but at few places in the world. It occurs here only at the highest spring tides, and is due to the formation of the banks, the rapid rise of the water, and the swiftness of the current. In the course of four or five hours the river falls about thirty feet, and even at the last moment of the ebb runs with considerable velocity. As the torrent suddenly encounters the flood crowding up the narrowing channel, it is banked up and rebounds in a single immense wave that ascends for many miles. In very shallow places, where the rush is suddenly checked, it sometimes rises to a height of ten or twelve feet. When broken by an island it soon reunites. A vessel at anchor, exposed to its full influence, would incur a great risk of being dragged from her moorings and swept along till brought up by a bank or shoal.

December 1.—This morning Captain Walsh made a careful examination to find a place where it would be possible to land the steamboat material and other stores, but the bank at every point was found to be too shelving to admit of the discharge of freight from the deck of the schooner, excepting at high tide, and then the rapid fall of the water and the swift current would render the operation difficult if not impracticable. The gully near the house was again inspected. Near its head the sides are curved and the width and depth are just about sufficient to admit the hull of the Monterey, and bring the deck a proper distance above the level of the surrounding surface. At low water and during the neap tides of the coming fortnight she would have to lie, high and dry, fifteen or twenty feet above the river; a position so new for a shipmaster to place his vessel in that it was with great reluctance that Captain Walsh yielded to the necessity of the case and determined, at high water in the evening, to float his schooner in. At this season the flood during the day is by no means so great or violent as at night, and is unaccompanied by the ''bore.'' The surface at high water was five feet lower than it was last night, and it was impossible to take the schooner to the desired position. She was accordingly anchored near the shore, in the most sheltered place that could be found, and to-night the attempt will again be made to haul her into the gully, and as it will be the tide following the full of the moon, there will probably be water enough to accomplish our object. Owing to our sheltered position the flow of the ebb about the vessel this evening has been quite moderate.

December 2.—The flood came in last night with a violence even greater than that of that preceding. The Monterey, though moored in a place comparatively unexposed, dragged her anchors and was carried a mile up the river; but as high water approached lines were taken out, the necessary preparations made, and, by great exertions on the part of the men, she was floated into position at the head of the gully. This morning, after the water had fallen, she lay snugly encased between the grassy banks, twenty feet above the surface of the river, secure from the effects of tides and storms, but presenting a very odd appearance, and inspiring Captain Walsh with apprehensions lest there should never be another tide that would rise high enough to float her out.

The whole surface of the country was overflowed last night, and the soil, being almost entirely clay, presents an unbroken sheet of soft and tenacious mud, into which one sinks deeply at every step.

The day has been spent in landing the boiler and heavy portions of the steamboat, and it proved a task of no small difficulty to move these unwieldy masses through the saturated surface. As the new moon tides at this season are not so high as those of the full moon, it is not probable that the bank will be again overflowed for a month, and a week's exposure to the warm sun will improve its condition, but a more unpromising place to build a steamboat in could scarcely be imagined. There is no growth of any description. Scattered about in the mud, one or two miles distant, are logs of half decayed driftwood, and from these we have to select the material for building the ways and derricks and to furnish fuel for the camp fires. Some of the men have already commenced this work, and with two or three harnessed to a log and sinking knee deep at almost every step, each stick is hauled through a mile and a half of gulleys and mud into camp.

To-day Mr. Booker, one of my assistants, came down in a skiff from Fort Yuma, bringing with him our letters and papers. He had left the fort on the 29th and had expected to join us on the ebb of last night, but was caught by the flood before he could reach our position and came near being swamped by the "bore," having been barely able to run his boat ashore in time to escape. He reports the safe arrival at Fort Yuma of the party from San Diego.

December 4.—During the last two days the vessel has been unloaded and all of the expedition property discharged. Many things had been injured by salt water getting into the hold, but the essential parts of the steamboat, engine, and the provisions are safe. The unloading being completed, Captain Walsh kindly gave me permission to engage his crew to assist my own small force, for a few days, while accomplishing the heavy labor attending our first operations, and the arduous task of bringing a sufficient quantity of logs is almost completed. The drying of the soil proceeds very slowly, but as the bank has not been again overflowed the tents have been pitched, the provisions and stores securely stowed, and camp fairly established. A spot has been trenched and platformed and prepared with a suitable foundation for a temporary observatory; the observing tent erected and a transit placed approximately in position. Regular astronomical and meteorological observations will henceforward be made and a record kept of the tides, gauges having been put up for that purpose. The tides are now rapidly subsiding and the water runs with greatly diminished velocity.

The days continue warm and delightful, though at night the temperature is low, and a chill wind sometimes sweeps over the wet flats, making the air disagreeable and raw. The atmospheric changes impart variety to a scene that would otherwise be oppressively monotonous. At sunrise the atmosphere is singularly pellucid, and every point on the surface of the water and the land sparkles with light. The distant peaks, that but for the mirage would be scarcely visible, stand out in bold relief above the horizon in curiously elongated shapes, the ever-varying outlines bathed in hues of lustrous purple and gold. As the sun mounts higher, and the light becomes more intense, these grow indistinct, and are gradually lost in a bright mist of grayish blue that seems to blend the earth and sky. The nearer mountains, the water, and the flats, all partake of the same blue cast, and throughout the day are invested with a dazzling azure glare. Towards sunset this, in turn, passes away, the distant summits reappear, but in their true shapes, low down upon the horizon, and the tone of the landscape becomes a cold, leaden gray.

The country is almost destitute of every kind of vegetable growth. Of animal life there are a few varieties. Waterfowl are abundant, and the coyotes are sometimes heard howling about camp after nightfall. A single California lion was encountered to-day by the wood party, but trotted off before any one could get a shot at him.

December 5.—By noon a sufficient number of logs had been brought in, and all hands were set to work to prepare a place for the ways. The formation of the ground along the river is badly adapted for launching a boat. As it is level up to the very edge of the precipitous bluff that forms the western face of the channel, and as the water at the next full moon tides will probably not rise more than a foot above the surface, the ways cannot be built above ground, for they must be at least three feet high to admit of persons working under the bottom of the boat, and their upper surface must be as much as two feet below high water to allow the steamboat to be floated off. The only resource therefore is to make an excavation large and deep enough to contain both the ways and the steamer, and to cut a ditch from it to the river to permit the egress of the boat when it is completed. A spot has been accordingly selected near the brink of the channel, and a space marked out fifty feet by fourteen, which will have to be excavated to the depth of four or five feet. It is a troublesome undertaking, for the digging is exceedingly laborious. The wet, heavy, and tough clay adheres to the spades like glue, and nearly every spadeful has to be scraped off with the hand. The men have, however, gone cheerfully and vigorously to work, and have already accomplished a considerable portion of the task. Mr. Carroll, meanwhile, is overhauling the different parts of the boat and machinery, everything of iron being badly rusted by the long sea voyage.

Much hard work has been accomplished during the past three days, and all are glad that to-morrow will be Sunday, and a day of rest.

December 6.—Not satisfied to pass a quiet day after the labors of the week, many of the men, seduced by the enticing weather and smooth water, started in a boat after breakfast on a clamming excursion towards the Gulf. A furious northwester set in about noon, and continued till dark, occasioning us a good deal of anxiety for the safety of the clam hunters. At sunset the horizon to the south was eagerly scanned, but they were nowhere in sight, and when night fell, and hour after hour passed without their appearance, there seemed to be ground for serious uneasiness. A long interval of painful suspense was at last relieved by the arrival of the missing party. All were safe, and the resentment naturally felt against those who have been the cause of an unnecessary solicitude was appeased when the excursionists came ashore. They were a sorry looking set. They had been caught in the gale, and were exhausted with rowing and bailing. They had not got any clams, but were hungry, wet, and bedraggled, and quite satisfied that it was useless to search for either pleasure or shellfish at the mouth of the Colorado.

December 7.—This morning the excavation of the pit was completed, and from the pile of drift logs that the men had brought in some fifteen or twenty of the straightest and soundest were selected, and a row of posts sunk into the ground, about seven feet apart, along either side of the bottom. Each post is to be united to the opposite one by a cross log fitted upon the tops, making a kind of trestle, of which there will be half a dozen placed parallel to one another, and fastened together by cross and longitudinal braces. The upper surfaces are then to be squared off to a general level, and a rude substitute thus formed for ways, but one which

COLORADO EXPLORING EXPEDITION

H B Mollhausen Del

Lith of Sarony, Major & Knapp 449 Broadway N.Y.

COCOPAS

we hope will well enough answer the purpose. While the carpenter was employed in fitting this rough frame work the other hands undertook the task of moving the boiler up to the side of the pit. It weighs three tons, and though the distance was only twenty-five or thirty yards, there being no convenient moving appliances, it took ten men nearly the whole day to work it along through the deep mud into its place.

The steamboat was built to order in Philadelphia at very short notice, and was put together and tried upon the Delaware river before being taken to pieces for shipment. The trial trip had to be made only three days before the boat was to start for New York in the California steamer, and there was no time to remedy a serious defect that had been developed. The boiler had been ordered, for special reasons, to be of unusual dimensions for the size of the boat, and the weight, resting upon the weakest portion of the hull, occasioned, while the steamer was in motion, a vibration and bending that threatened to break her in two amidships. To guard against this disaster, Mr. Carroll proposed to stiffen the hull by bolting four stout pieces of scantling along the bottom—it being impossible to place them inside—and to fasten others athwart, before and behind the boiler. The timber and the bolts for this object were provided in San Francisco, but nearly sixty holes have to be drilled, by hand, through the thick iron sections, for the bolts to pass through. All day long Mr. Carroll and the blacksmith, perched on a little mound of clay, a trifle less damp than the surrounding surface, have been patiently pounding holes, and have half finished the required number.

A keen and boisterous northwester has roared since morning about our ears, impeding work, and making every one uncomfortable. It has been something like a Texas norther. The temperature fell considerably as it sprung up, and the rapid evaporation from the wet earth added an extra chill.

A little before dark, just as work had been suspended, and the steam from the cook fire was announcing the evening meal to be in an advanced state of preparation, two dirty looking beings hove in sight, and came trotting over the flats, directing their way with unerring sagacity towards that part of camp where the eating arrangements were progressing. The appearance of our party, with the bustle of the camp, and the piles of steamboat pieces and freight lying about must have been rather a novelty, but neither these nor the unusual spectacle of the schooner standing near the top of the bank had any apparent interest for the new comers, but established to leeward of the fire, where they could inhale the odor of the victuals, they sat watching the cook and the supper with an air of mingled wishfulness and veneration. They informed us that they were Cocopas, a tribe that live along the Colorado for fifty miles from the mouth. Directions were given that they should be fed, though those who have had some experience with these Indians say that it is quite impossible to satisfy their hunger. After they had devoured what was conceived to be a sufficient quantity, I endeavored by signs to persuade them to carry a letter to Fort Yuma. They understood what was wanted, but positively declined the duty, informing me, by an expressive gesture, and several emphatic repetitions of the word "Yumas," that if they attempted to execute the commission they would certainly be knocked in the head by the Yuma Indians, amongst whom they would be obliged to pass. They appear to have a great dread of their neighbors, and if our two visitors are fair specimens of the Cocopas the latter are much inferior to the other Colorado tribes. Their figures are not as well proportioned, and their faces are devoid of expression. Their clothing consists of a narrow strip of cotton, tied about the loins, an unseasonable dress for this time of year.

December 14.—The past week has been a monotonous, but a busy one. The ways having been completed the eight sections of the hull were moved upon them, and the fitting and rivetting together commenced. It was a troublesome operation to carry the heavy and awkardly shaped masses of iron to the side of the pit and lower them into position, and great was the satisfaction of the men as each in turn was lodged in its place. The difficulty was increased by the necessity of propping the section up to allow room after they should be rivetted together to slide the timbers beneath. The most hazardous undertaking of all will be to lower the boiler into the hull, and this has not yet been commenced. All kinds of rude expedients have had to be resorted to to make up for the small force of men, and the absence of proper timber and appliances, and the ingenuity of our engineer has several times been severely exercised. The rough handling that the pieces had experienced in the course of the trip from New York, particularly during the Isthmus transit, had bent them so badly out of shape that at first Mr. Carroll viewed them with a kind of despair, but patience and labor have gradually overcome these embarrassments, and the pigmy, but prettily modelled boat, begins now to assume somewhat of its future appearance.

Captain Walsh has been obliged to withdraw his crew in order to have certain work attended to on board the schooner, and every week two of my own half dozen men have to absent themselves for a day, and ascend the river fifteen miles to procure drinking water, which we are compelled to use with great economy.

The new moon tides are now approaching. A few days ago, when the water was at its lowest stage, the surface at high tide was twelve or fifteen feet below the level it attained at the period of full moon, while at low tide it was several feet higher. During the autumn and winter the full moon tides rise higher than those of the new moon, but in spring and summer it is said that the reverse occurs. Similar alternations take place in the comparative heights of the day and night tides at different seasons, but I believe that no opportunity has ever been afforded of keeping a tide-record for a sufficiently long time to exhibit the annual changes and fluctuations.

In a [day or two the boats to take away the *Monterey's* cargo are expected down, and it is desirable that the water should rise before that time sufficiently high to float her out into the stream, so that she can discharge the freight from her own deck to those of the steamers. In spite of all our panegyrics upon the advantages of the position occupied by the *Monterey*, her worthy captain has, for the past two weeks, viewed the situation of his vessel with rueful disgust and forebodings, and is waiting with eager interest for the tide of to-night, which he hopes will set her once more afloat.

The northwester of last week exhausted itself at the end of three days, and since then there has been an uninterrupted succession of the delicious weather experienced before. There being a little photographic apparatus along, I have taken advantage of the mild and quiet interval to experiment, and having constructed out of an india-rubber tarpaulin a tent that entirely excluded the light, have made repeated efforts to obtain a view of camp and the river. The attempt has not met with distinguished success. The chemicals seem to have deteriorated, and apart from this the light is so glaring, and the agitation of the atmosphere near the surface of the ground so great, that it is doubtful whether, under any circumstances, a clear and perfect picture could be secured.

Our two Indian friends have departed. I suspect that there was a rupture of amicable relations between them and the cook, whom, indeed, they must have sadly annoyed by their persevering presence at his fire. All their faculties and thoughts, if they had any, seemed to be concentrated in viewing the preparations for eating. At night, when the cooking operations were concluded, they would indulge in a little conversation and become quite boisterous while laughing and talking over the culinary events of the day. I never caught them asleep; at whatever hour of the night I happened to be about, I would find them still sitting up, glowering over each other and the fire, or peering curiously, with their bright eyes at me and my astronomical instruments. Now that they have gone, the nights are profoundly quiet, excepting for the occasional howling of a wolf, or the low hoarse murmur into which the roar of the spring tide flow has subsided.

The transit has been adjusted in good position, and I have been engaged in testing the rates of the chronometers, and determining the errors of the instrument preparatory to the coming lunation. Though the days have been clear, at night light clouds constantly collect, and often entirely disconcert the observations. There are occasional transitions, however, which compensate for this vexation. The misty wreaths will sometimes suddenly and altogether disappear, unveiling an illuminated sky, upon which the pale constellations of the milky way are clustered in a distinct silver band. The dome of the heaven, reflected from the smooth river, is prolonged far below the horizon, and presents a nearly unbroken sphere of radiant sapphire blue, from whose surface myriads of burnished quivering points emit vivid streams of light, while the steadier rays of the planets seem almost to rival those of the moon in splendor.

December 17.—On the day preceding the night of the highest new moon tide, the surface of the river at high water was several feet below the point which it had to attain before the *Monterey* would float. The prospect for the next tide was, therefore, not encouraging, but shortly after midnight all hands were on the alert, and making ready to assist in the hoped for liberation of the schooner. The boats were manned and provided with tow lines. Anchors were sunk into the bank on either side near the mouth of the gulley. To these blocks and tackle were attached and connected with the schooner so as to secure as strong a pull as possible to move her from her bed in case she should not float entirely free. There was a general excitement as the time of high tide drew near, and the water began to flow about the bulge of the vessel. At last the stern commenced gradually to rise, and then the hull to undulate, and after a few hearty pulls at the ropes, there was a perceptible movement of the whole mass, and in a moment more, to the delight of all engaged, the *Monterey* slid gently out of the bed where she had lain for two weeks, and was restored, with her happy commander, to her proper element. Though the tide rose high enough to bring about this felicitous result, it was far inferior both in height and velocity to that of the preceding full moon, and if accompanied by a bore, the latter was so slight as to be imperceptible from the shore.

The change of the *Monterey's* position was quite opportune, for during yesterday and to-day the two steamboats came down to receive their loads. They started back for Fort Yuma as soon as this was accomplished. Captain Walsh has now only to replenish his water casks and take in a quantity of mud for ballast, and he will be ready to set out on his return voyage.

The arrival of the steamboats and the presence of new faces has formed an event in our monotonous life. These boats are run by two of their owners, Messrs. Johnson and Wilcox, who have been for several years engaged in navigating the lower part of the Colorado. Upon the establishment of Fort Yuma, it was found a measure of economy to supply the post by way of the Gulf and the river instead of by the overland route, and for a year or two freight was carried up in lighters, which were poled along or hauled up by hand. The rapid current, the shoals, the marshy banks, the unknown character of the country, and the presence of hostile Indians, were obstacles in the way of inaugurating navigation that few men would have successfully overcome. As business increased a small steamer was procured, but, owing to some defect in the boiler, blew up before it had been long in operation. Another was then built, and a short time ago a third and larger boat. The two latter now ply regularly between the head of the Gulf and Fort Yuma, and secure profitable returns to their persevering and energetic proprietors. These have the good will of the Indians, and by contributing a certain amount towards staying the cravings of their stomachs, are exempted from thefts and other molestations.

The steamboats brought down a fair stock of passengers of both sexes, from the nearest villages. They were, as a whole, better looking than the pair we had seen. Several of the men had good figures. The women were rather too much inclined to embonpoint, with the exception of the young girls, some of whom were by no means ill-favored. Bright eyes, white teeth, and musical voices, they all possessed. In point of apparel they were about as deficient as the men, a very short petticoat, their only garment, taking the place of the strip of cotton. While the steamboats were unloading both males and females sat in groups about the decks, watching the hands at work, and having a good time themselves doing nothing.

The rumor of the preparation of an expedition to ascend the Colorado was long ago circulated among the adjacent tribes, and has occasioned much interest and excitement. I am told that curious inquiries have been made of the troops by the Indians about Fort Yuma as to the object of the enterprise, and the half understood replies have been transmitted, with many amplifications, up and down the river, occasioning all kinds of surmises concerning our purposes and probable movements. None of the Cocopas were disposed to cultivate us, nor was there much in the appearance of the camp to tempt them from their comfortable quarters on the steamboats. We could see, nevertheless, that our operations engrossed a good deal of their attention and conversation, and that nothing escaped their keen-sighted inspection. The size and appearance of our unfinished boat evidently disappointed them, and I think they regarded it, and the expedition altogether, as rather a poor affair, and derived much amusement therefrom. One or two long-legged fellows, the wits of the party, were foremost in facetious criticism. They seemed to be pointing out to their female companions our makeshifts and deficiency in numbers, and were, no doubt, very funny at our expense, for their sallies were received by the young belles with great favor and constant bursts of merriment.

Before the steamboats left, I was so fortunate as to secure the services of Mr. Robinson, who is to accompany me up the Colorado as pilot, for which duty his experience on the river eminently qualifies him. He has gone to Fort Yuma with Captain Johnson, but intends to join me in a skiff at the end of the month, at which time I informed him that I should be ready to start, though the steamboat people think I will not be able to get the boat launched much before the 1st of February. A great source of anxiety is removed now that I have engaged a capable person for that responsible position.

The work upon the steamboat has meanwhile gone busily on. The riveting of the sections has been completed, and the joists have been bolted upon the bottom, making the hull, to all appearances, abundantly stiff and strong. The arrangements for lowering the boiler into place were entered upon with some trepidation. A pair of ways had first to be made, conducting to the bottom of the boat, and then the heavy mass hoisted upon the upper end, from whence it could slide down into position. The breaking of a rope, or of one of the half rotten sticks of timber, would have brought the whole concern suddenly upon the hull, which it would have crushed like an eggshell; but nothing gave way, and at noon to-day we had the satisfaction of seeing the task safely finished.

The digging of the channel from the pit to the river was then commenced, and the men labored hard at it till dark, almost completing that also.

December 21.—On the morning of the 18th a northwester set in, and, with the exception of a short lull yesterday, has been raging furiously up to the present time. The river has been overspread with a thick haze, a high sea running, and the spray driven by the gale over the flats. The tents were strongly secured, particularly the observing tents, for the transit was in good adjustment, and I hoped that it would not be disturbed. For one day and night the result was doubtful, but yesterday morning a gust came that settled the business, and put an end to a very unpleasant state of suspense. One rope and tent-peg still held on, forming a fixed centre, about which the tent was whirling and waving like a handkerchief, thumping against the transit stand, and undoing the labor of many a long night. The photographic tent made a clean thing of it, apparatus and all, but that was comparatively of little importance.

Our friend, the captain, has had a miserable time getting in his mud ballast, and, I think, has wished himself back in the gulley. The current and shoals and the loose bottom made his position a dangerous one. I suppose he found he could not stand it any longer, for he tripped anchor this morning and made a precipitate retreat, the *Monterey* looking as though she were being cuffed out into the Gulf, while Captain Walsh, with hair and coat skirts standing out horizontally in the gale, pantomimed farewell to us as we watched, regretfully, the disappearing vessel.

The necessity of digging a pit to build the steamboat in has been attended with one advantage, as it has secured a partial shelter to the workmen, without which, for the last day or two, the operations would have been at a standstill. The shaft was yesterday raised to its place. This was the last heavy piece that had to be handled, and the rest of the work will be attended with little risk. An original defect in the steamboat, noticed during the trial trip, was that the connecting rods between the piston and crank played in slots cut so deep into the stern that when the boat was in motion the water would rush in. The lower portions of the slots have had therefore to be covered up, and this has raised the connecting rods and thrown the whole engine out of adjustment, occasioning a most perplexing disarrangement, and one that has given Mr. Carroll two or three days of troublesome work to remedy. He thinks now he has succeeded, and that the parts of the engine are fitted so that it will run smoothly.

Yesterday several Indians appeared suddenly in camp, as though they had been blown from the north by the gale. Fearing lest a too hospitable reception might bring the whole tribe upon us, and make a serious inroad upon our moderate supply of rations, I ordered the cook not to give them anything to eat. As bed time approached they looked blue with disappointment and hunger, and I thought that by morning they would have disappeared; but the latter part of the night was dark, and the sentinel, I suppose, not very wakeful after a hard day's labor, for this morning I found them seated around the fire, shining with repletion, and in a high state of glee. This evening the preparations to guard the provisions were so elaborate that they gave up in despair, and started home in a very unamiable frame of mind.

Now that the *Monterey* has gone, our little party has exclusive possession of the mouth of the Colorado, and the camp looks drearier than ever. Two of the men were compelled to ascend the river this morning for fresh water. They have not returned, and the late hour and the storm make us somewhat anxious for their safety.

December 28.—The last day of the northwester was attended with a pelting rain—the first we have experienced since leaving San Francisco. In the midst of it the men sent for water returned. The boat had several times been on the eve of swamping in the heavy sea, and they were almost worn out with cold and exposure. On the morning of the 23d the gale had subsided, and there was a sudden transition to a cloudless sky and soft summer temperature.

There has been time to place the transit again in the meridian, and to obtain during the last two or three nights some good observations of moon culminations for longitude. Having a small telescope, I have been able also to observe several occultations, and think that the position of the mouth of the river will be accurately fixed.

Game is now abundant. There have been large accessions of ducks and plover to our neighborhood since the storm, but no one has any leisure to shoot them. We are straining every nerve to get the steamboat built before the approaching spring tides. But for the delays occasioned by the defects of her original construction she would have been finished two or three days ago. The essential parts are now complete. On Christmas day the boiler was filled and steam got up. The engine ran beautifully—a great triumph to Mr. Carroll after the trouble he has had with it. The boat is well modelled, and presents a gay appearance now that she has been painted. The word "Explorer," printed in large capitals upon the wheel-house, designates her title and object. Some of the carpenters' work has still to be done, but this will not occasion any delay. It being necessary to provide a stock of firewood before starting, as the men are all busy upon the boat, I told two or three Cocopa Indians, who came to see us yesterday, that if they would go after drift-logs, and haul them to camp until dark, they should have plenty to eat and a large piece of cotton cloth. They were strong, athletic fellows, and after an hour of solemn deliberation, and the further offer of some beads and a fancy tippet, they agreed to go. Having once made the bargain, it is but just to them to say that they performed their part faithfully, though they became heartily sick of the business long before the day was over. Each one, after bringing in a log, would lie on his back to rest, making horrible grimaces, and rubbing his astonished arms and legs. When night came I paid them half as much again as had been promised—thinking that this, and the virtuous consciousness of having for once in their lives done an honest day's work, might induce them to try it again; but I believe that nothing that there is in camp would have prevailed upon them to repeat the experiment.

As the season of high tides draws near, we have had somewhat of the anxiety felt by Captain Walsh lest the rise of water should fall a foot or two short of our expectations, and the Explorer be obliged to remain on top of the bank. Last night's tide quite dispelled any such apprehensions. It still wants three or four days of full moon, and the water rose above the surface of the ways. It is likely that it will be high enough to-night to permit the boat to be launched; but I prefer waiting a day longer for the arrival of Mr. Robinson. He had expected to be here by the 25th, and I am much disappointed at his non-appearance. Every day at sunset we have watched for the appearance of a boat from the north. This evening we thought it was in sight, and collected upon the bank to meet the new comers. The figures were distinctly visible, and we were even confident that there were voices shouting to us. The object had arrived within a few hundred yards before we were undeceived, and the supposed boat and crew turned out to be the trunk of a tree, with short stumps standing upon its surface.

December 30.—Yesterday evening the appearance of a boat in the distance was no delusion, and we had the pleasure of welcoming Mr. Robinson back to his semi-aquatic homestead. He was accompanied by Mr. Bielawski, whom I had engaged in San Francisco as hydrographic assistant, and by Mr. Jasper S. Whiting, the second in command to Captain Stone upon the survey of Sonora. Mr. Whiting is to start with a small party and survey the coast as far as Guaymas, where he is to be joined by Captain Stone and the remainder of his expedition.

The delay in Mr. Robinson's arrival was occasioned by the length of time it took the steamboats to ascend to Fort Yuma. The river is said to be unusually low, even for this season of lowest water, and the difficulties of navigation correspondingly increased. A detachment of my party, sent out by way of Fort Tejon to procure pack mules, had reached the fort in safety. All of the members of the expedition, excepting those that are with myself, are now assembled there. They are not expecting to see us much before the 1st of February. The only unfavorable intelligence was concerning Dr. Newberry, our geologist, who, I regretted to learn, was very ill when the gentlemen left the fort, and entirely unable to join them, as he had hoped to do.

The new comers were surprised to find the steamboat ready for launching. As the water had risen just high enough during the preceding night to float her, we knew that there would be no difficulty in taking her out on the next tide. Steam was gotten up and lines prepared as midnight approached. The water rose almost high enough to overflow the bank. There was enough for our purposes and a foot or two to spare, and the brilliant moonlight enabled the work to be performed as easily as by day. At the instant of high water, before the ebb current could attain much strength, the engines were put in motion, and the little boat backed slowly out into the stream. She was then brought round to the gully and moored securely in a position a little below that which had been occupied by the *Monterey*.

This morning the "Explorer" underwent a critical inspection. She is fifty-four feet long from the extremity of the bow to the outer rim of the stern wheel. Amidships, the hull is left open, like a skiff, the boiler occupying a third of the vacant space. At the bow is a little deck, on which stands the armament—a four-pound howitzer. In front of the wheel another deck, large enough to accommodate the pilot and a few of the surveying party, forms the roof of a cabin eight feet by seven. Nearly every newly-launched craft is supposed by those interested to excel its predecessors; but I imagine few boats have ever been surveyed by their builders with as much admiration and complacency.

The tents were struck this morning, the instruments and movables packed, and the whole day spent in loading. Mr. Robinson was of opinion that all of the provisions and expedition property could not be carried at once, and that two trips would have to be made, at least, as far as the head of tide-water, beyond which point there would be less danger. There was a chance, however, that to-night the bank would be overflowed, and I disliked to leave anything behind; so package after package was stowed away, till the boat was sunk down to the extreme limit that prudence would justify, and what was left it was found that the two skiffs would hold. These are to be towed alongside. A small sloop that belonged to Mr. Robinson, and which the Sonora expedition has purchased from him, we expect also to tow twenty miles up the river, to a point where Mr. Whiting is to join his party. The night promises to be perfectly quiet, or we would not be able to start with our present load. The proper time for a steamboat to leave is two or three hours before the ebb. This evening the tide is coming in with great force and rapidity. At low water the surface was one or two feet below the low-water mark of the last full moon tide, which portends a corresponding increase of elevation at high water.

Our task has not been completed a day too soon, for there is every indication that by 3 o'clock to-morrow morning the country will be entirely submerged. Before that time, however, we trust to have bidden a final farewell to Robinson's Landing and the mouth of the Colorado.

CHAPTER II.

MOUTH OF THE COLORADO TO FORT YUMA.

Camp 2, Cocopa Village, December 21.—At midnight steam was gotten up and all hands roused for immediate departure. The two skiffs, with their heavy loads, were fastened alongside, and Mr. Whiting's sloop attached by a towline astern. The atmosphere was clear and profoundly quiet, and the moon's rays, flashed back from the mirror-like sheet of water, made it almost as light as day. But for the roar of the rushing tide, and the occasional swift passage of some floating substance, the expanse of water would have seemed as still and motionless as a lake. The party was disposed so that the boat would be in perfect trim—a necessary precaution, for the gunwale was scarcely six inches above the surface of the water. The lines were then cast loose, and with a shrill scream from the whistle the Explorer started out into the river, and in a moment was shooting along upon the tide with a velocity that made the high bank seem to spin as we glided by.

For some time all went well. Not a ripple broke upon the surface. We kept at no great distance from the bank, long stretches of which were rapidly passed, till, at last, as we were entering a bend to the west, a little breeze from the north sprang up, and the tide making against it at once occasioned a disturbance. As the wind freshened, waves began to rise, and the water to dash into the boat. The prospect was somewhat alarming, for even throwing overboard the cargo would not have saved the open boat from swamping had the breeze continued long enough to have raised a sea, and though near the land, the strongest swimmer would have stood little chance in such a current, with nothing to cling to but a steep bank of slippery clay. We shipped so much water that we were on the point of commencing to lighten the boat, and I think if the wind had held fifteen minutes longer the Colorado expedition would have come to a disastrous issue; but the breeze died away as suddenly as it had sprung up; the water again became smooth, and in a couple of hours all danger from winds and waves was over; the low banks on the opposite side came in sight, and the broad and hazardous sheet of water narrowed into a moderately sized and shallow stream.

Twenty miles above Robinson's Landing Mr. Whiting perceived near the shore the camp fire of his men, and left with his sloop to join them. A few miles higher up the firewood gave out, and the whole party being exhausted from want of rest and hard labor during two successive days and nights, we stopped for a few hours for sleep and breakfast. Our steamboat does not furnish accommodations for either sleeping or cooking, and every night the men will have to camp on shore, a matter of little importance, as it is quite impracticable at night to navigate the lower portion of the Colorado, and the river will not be likely to improve as it is ascended.

We breakfasted at rather a late hour, and afterwards the men took their axes and laid in a stock of firewood.   As we were making ready to start the sound of paddles was heard, and in a few moments one of the steamboats from the fort shot out from behind a bend which had concealed her approach.   The people on board were so much astonished at the sight of our boat, which they had expected to find still upon the ways at Robinson's Landing, that they had got some distance down the river before they thought of stopping.   Then they rounded to and hauled up alongside of the bank, a hundred yards below.   Captain Wilcox was in command. He had brought letters for our party and newspapers, the latter containing intelligence of the outbreak among the Mormons.   Dr. Newberry had nearly recovered from his attack of illness, and hoped to be able to join me at the fort and accompany the steamboat up the river.   Captain Wilcox gave us a piece of fresh beef and a spare rudder, and notified us that the river below the fort was in a worse condition than he had ever known it to be.   He very kindly proposed to carry to Fort Yuma for me the articles that were in the two skiffs, and told me that I could leave them at a certain place on the bank in charge of the Indians, who would deliver them safely to him as he passed by on his return.   I was glad to accept this offer, for towing the loaded boats had considerably impeded the Explorer's progress.   When this arrangement had been made, he bid us good-by and pursued his way down the river to meet a vessel daily expected from the Gulf, while we steamed along in the opposite direction.   After travelling for a few hours without interruption, we reached the point that had been designated by Captain Wilcox, and as it was becoming somewhat late, made the boat fast to a tree and went into camp.

Between camp and the point above Robinson's Landing, where the Colorado narrows, the character of the river has been generally uniform.   The banks are low—in few places more than eight feet in height—and the country flat for a long distance beyond.   On one or both sides there is usually a fringe of willow and cottonwood, or a thicket of high reeds.   The channel is circuitous, but thus far there have been no very sharp bends.   In few places has the depth of water been less than twelve feet.   Slues branch in every direction, and many of them might mislead a person unacquainted with the localities.   The current has been moderate, averaging about two and a half knots an hour.   At this place, which is forty miles above Robinson's Landing, the tide raises the river two or three feet.   The water is perfectly fresh, of a dark red color, and opaque from the quantity of mud held in suspension.

We found a large party of Cocopas—men, women, and children—waiting on the bank, with grinning faces, for the arrival of the "chiquito steamboat," as they call our diminutive vessel. They have been thronging about the camp fires all the evening, chattering, laughing, begging, and keeping a sharp lookout for chances to appropriate any small articles.   I had no hesitation, however, in leaving the packages of provisions and stores taken from the skiffs piled in a conspicuous place near the edge of the bank, merely notifying them that the things belonged to the other steamboat.   They reap too much benefit from the parties who ply regularly past their villages to risk losing all by a single depredation.   One of the Cocopas seemed to apprehend that my mind might be ill at ease in regard to the safety of the property, and disinterestedly offered to remain and watch it, and deliver a letter from me to Captain Wilcox when he should arrive.   As he expected me to be equally disinterested, I gave him a piece of cotton, of which he was much in need.   A few are provided with blankets, but nearly all, males and females, are on a scanty allowance of clothing.   The women generally have modest manners, and many are good looking.   They have a custom of plastering their hair and scalps with the soft blue clay from the river bank, the effect of which is not at all pretty, but the clay is said to be a thorough exterminator of vermin, and as such must give them a great deal of comfort.

Camp 3, January 1, 1858.—A high north wind has been blowing since morning.   The distance accomplished has been much diminished by it.   On the desert eastward, we have seen the sand, in dusky cloud-like masses and great columns, drifting and whirling towards the Gulf. The difficulties of navigation are increasing, though none are of a character to involve more than a delay. The river is exceedingly crooked, and the current, in some of the bends, has been, at least, four knots an hour. Sharp turns, sand bars, and shoals are constantly encountered. There are no rocks, and the snags, though numerous, are seldom dangerous. The Explorer works admirably, and turns the bad corners with greater facility than a larger craft. We have grounded several times, but in no case have been detained more than a few moments. It is not worth while to make any attempts at speed during the present stage of water. We have been steaming to-day eight hours, exclusive of the time occupied in taking in wood, and are twenty-four miles from last night's camp. This, considering the strong head-wind, we think a good run. The boats that ply to Fort Yuma save time by having regular wood depots at convenient intervals. We are obliged to stop and cut wood whenever it is wanted. There is plenty of excellent fuel all along the bank. The dead mesquite, willow, and cottonwood trees, instead of rotting become seasoned in the pure dry atmosphere. The mesquite has a particularly close, fine grained texture, and makes a hot fire.

While the steamer is in motion a man stands at the bow with a sounding pole, which he keeps constantly employed. Captain Robinson, on the after deck, pilots the boat, and assumes her entire management. One must be a good while upon the river to acquire the experience and skill that are requisite in order to run a boat successfully. A knowledge of the locality of the deepest water cannot be imparted. The rapid current, the loose character of the soil, and the sedimentary deposits occasion great and sudden variations in the river bed, and the channel has been known to shift from one bank to the other in a single night.* From the formation of the banks, from the appearance of the water and the eddies, from the direction taken by pieces of drift-wood and other floating substances, and from the character of the islands and bars visible above the surface the experienced pilot can do much towards selecting the proper course, though at the present stage of water boats rarely pass over even this portion of the river, which is said to be better than any that has been navigated higher up, without running aground many times a day. If there is a chance of finding a better place the boat is backed off. If not, she is forced over the shoal by working her in the sand, with the help of the engine, poles, and lines fastened to anchors or trees, and hauled upon with the windlass. The bars are composed of soft and loose material, and may always be passed with more or less labor, depending, in a great measure, upon the skill shown in the employment of the different methods of extrication resorted to.

Camp 5, January 3.—Two days of hard work have advanced us thirty-one miles. The general appearance of the country and the river undergoes no change. The average depth of water in the channel is becoming less, probably not exceeding nine feet. The bottom is very irregular, the soundings sometimes varying in a distance of a dozen yards from two and a half to twenty-one feet. Last evening we reached a place where the river was very wide and filled with snags. The shoals extended all the way across. While trying to extricate ourselves from a broad sand bar by backing off the rudder got jammed by a snag, and could not be moved. An anchor was then let go, and lines carried in a skiff to the shore. It was some time after dark when the boat was brought alongside of the bank. The rudder was unshipped, and the stock found to be bent, but by heating and hammering with an axe it was at last straightened so as to be serviceable. To-day three hours have been spent on the shoals. We would scarcely be clear of one obstruction, and the boat afloat, before she would run aground

---

* The occurrence of earthquakes has, at times, seriously affected the river banks and bed, entirely changing their form and character, caving in large slices of the bluff, filling up sloughs, forming new channels, uprooting snags, and creating fresh obstructions. In November, 1852, while a schooner was at anchor thirty miles above the mouth of the river, and floating in fourteen feet of water, there came a premonitory rumbling and shock, and the bed of sand was suddenly forced up, leaving the vessel aground, with only three feet of water around her. In that position she remained till floated off by the succeeding spring tides.

upon another.   Captain Robinson tells me that he has never known the navigation to be so difficult.

Fort Yuma, January 5.—Day before yesterday, after making fifteen miles, a broad bar was encountered, over which the boat was gradually worked.   The water above was shallow, and the current swift.   The steamer lost her steerage way, and her head swung round with a good deal of force, and slid some distance upon the highest part of the bar.   An anchor was carried out, but it came home.   Another was placed at a greater distance, but it too failed to hold.   There being no trees near by, a long line was then taken to a snag on the opposite side of the river.   After heaving upon this nearly half an hour the boat was loosened, and her head almost turned up stream, but just then the snag broke, and she swung back harder than ever.   Night fell while she was fast aground.   I was desirous of reaching Fort Yuma on the following day, before the departure of the mail for the next steamer, but as we were still fifty miles distant by the river there seemed little probability of accomplishing it.   Captain Robinson, however, informed me that ten miles higher up was the residence of a white settler, where a horse could be procured, and that he could row me there in a skiff by ten or eleven o'clock, which would enable me, by riding the rest of the night, to reach the fort by daylight.   Taking a man along to pull another oar, we started an hour or two after sunset.   The night was dark, and as usual very cold, and the freezing temperature seemed to us the more piercing after having been all day under a hot sun.   The current would at best have been hard to row against, and the darkness, which made it impossible to keep in the channel, enhanced the difficulty.   After an hour or two Captain Robinson began to suspect that he had gotten off from the river into a slue, but finding that there was still a current determined to keep on, knowing that there must be an outlet somewhere above, though the distance would probably be rendered greater by the deviation.   Hour after hour passed without our being able to form an idea of our position.   The night grew colder as it advanced, and a keen wind from the north set in.   In some places we had to get into the water in order to lighten the skiff over bars where it was too shallow for it to pass.   Our feet were nearly frozen, and our bodies paralyzed with cold when we reached, about one o'clock at night, a portion of the river which Captain Robinson recognized, by the light of the newly risen moon, to be near our destination.   As we drew up to the bank the familiar sound of barking dogs greeted us, and we hurried our benumbed limbs ashore to reach, as soon as possible, the expected haven.   The disappointment we met was a grievous one.   The house of the proprietor of the estate turned out to be a roofless structure surrounding the four sides of a square, the logs of which it was built being placed close enough together to exclude a horse or a cow, but affording no more shelter nor warmth than a rail fence does to the lot it encloses.   Three or four men wrapped in blankets were asleep around the embers of a fire, their feet in close proximity to the coals.   An old Indian, a dog, and a pig having no blankets, and unable to sleep, were couched together near them.   One of the men roused up at our entrance, and put on some more wood.   In reply to my questions, he informed me that the owner was absent; that the horses were out grazing, and could not be caught till morning, and that there was nothing to eat or drink upon the premises.   As a partial protection against the raw blast which rushed through the openings between the logs, he told me that I was welcome to share his couch.   It was an excellent opportunity to realize the proverb about misery and bed-fellows.   I was stiffened with cold, and gratefully accepted the hospitable offer of my new acquaintance, turning in for the remainder of the night between the dirtiest pair of blankets, and, meaning no disparagement, with the dirtiest looking man I ever saw in my life.   Captain Robinson and the men with us were similarly accommodated by the others, and the party settled down into an apparent state of repose, but we were so cold and wet that we were unable to sleep until the arrival of day brought sunlight and warmth.   I woke when the sun was two or three hours high, and it felt then like a summer morning.   Robinson and the boatmen had gone back to the Explorer.   The other men were at their work, cutting wood for the steamboat company. I hunted up my companion of the previous night, and prevailed upon him to try and catch me a horse, which he succeeded after an hour or two in doing. He somewhat objected to my riding the animal he had caught, informing me that it was a stallion of great spirit and value that had been left in charge of his master, and having been running loose for some weeks would perhaps be so wild as to do injury not only to his rider but to himself.

The object of this solicitude did not look at all dangerous, but I mounted him with great caution and started for the fort. I soon found that my charger was not likely to volunteer a faster gait than a leisurely walk, and, with a half dread of rousing some slumbering fires, touched him with the spur. This producing no effect, I dug the spur into his side a little harder, and at last, with the help of a stout cudgel, broken from a tree, urged him into a trot. By an energetic appliance of the stick and both heels, the first twelve miles were accomplished in a little more than three hours, when the brute subsided again into a walk, from which nothing could start him. While pondering over the idea that my friend on the river was a practical joker, I met an ox team and wagon, with two or three Mexicans trudging alongside and a white man lying on his back on top of the load. He roused up as I passed, and inquired, with a muddled air and thick utterance, what I was doing with his friend's horse, from which I inferred that he was the owner of the place where we had passed the night, was the custodian of the animal in question, and was also somewhat intoxicated. On being informed of the circumstances of the case, he expressed great indignation, assuring me that the horse was the most valuable one in that part of the country; had been left with him as a precious charge; that he would not for five hundred dollars have him subjected to a chance of injury, and that I must at once dismount and let him be driven back by the Mexicans. Fort Yuma being nearly fifteen miles distant and the day somewhat advanced, I tried to convince him that no great injury would be done by a few hours of careful riding; but, under a strange infatuation regarding the value of the animal I was bestriding, he persisted, with drunken obstinacy, that he should not be ridden a step further. I was revolving the probability of being able, by a sudden violent attack of whip and spur, to excite the cherished beast into a trot, and thus escape from his guardian, when the latter all at once changed his mind and told me that every horse he had in the world and all that his friends had were at my disposal as long as I wanted, and, after an affectionate squeeze of the hand, gave me a benign smile, and falling upon his back called to the driver to go on.

The road to the fort was through a flat and desolate looking country. A few miles of it passed over a point of the great desert to the east. Bunches of grease wood and stunted cedars composed nearly all the vegetation. A bevy of quail would occasionally start up from the bushes at my approach, and two or three times a coyote ran across the trail. A couple of straggling Yumas, from a village that could be seen at some distance towards the river, came sauntering by and helped to break the monotony, but it was a dreary eight hours ride, and I was glad enough when, a little before sunset, the flagstaff that stands on the parade of the fort came in view. The whole distance was only about twenty-seven miles, and, with a good riding animal, might have been easily made in three hours. By the river the distance between the same points is said to be more than forty miles.

During the latter part of the journey the picturesque and singularly shaped peaks of the range of mountains beyond the fort appeared to great advantage—the beautiful outlines of the dark blue masses being drawn in distinct relief upon the illuminated western sky.

Fort Yuma is built upon the west side of the river, on the top of a gravelly spur that extends with a steep bluff to the edge of the stream. A corresponding precipice upon the opposite side forms, with the other, a gate through which the united waters of the Gila and Colorado flow in a comparatively narrow bed. The mouth of the Gila is just above. The southern emigrant route to California crosses the river at this place. For ten or fifteen miles north and south the valley is inhabited by the Yuma Indians, a few years ago the most powerful and warlike of the Colorado tribes. Opposite to the fort an anticipated town has been located and denominated Colorado City. At present there are but a few straggling buildings, the principal of which are a store, blacksmith's shop, and tavern. A good ferry has been established by means of a rope, which is stretched across the river, and to which a large boat is attached. This I found out of order, and the son of the proprietor of the store rowed me over in a skiff. Ascending the steep acclivity, I reached a level plateau that forms the parade ground, and about which the houses and barracks are built. The sentinel pointed out the officers' quarters, and imparted the intelligence that the gentlemen of the mess were just going in to dinner. I had the pleasure of meeting several old friends among them, and the unpleasant features of the preceding twenty-four hours were soon forgotten in the cordial welcome and hospitable entertainment that I experienced.

January 9.—For two days the arrival of the Explorer was almost hourly expected, and her non-appearance last evening made me uneasy, but about dark the Indians at the fort, who are always the first to get intelligence of what is taking place on the river, imparted the news that she was close at hand. Early this morning the steam whistle was heard blowing, and soon the Explorer came in sight at a turn not far below the fort. The Yumas were out in force to catch the first glimpse of the long expected steamer, manifesting more interest than the Cocopas had done.

I met Captain Robinson at the bank, who informed me that on the day that he had parted from me they had broken a rudder against a snag, and had been obliged to stop and make a new one, which had occasioned the detention.

There are several preparations to be made before we shall be ready to start, and to-day being Saturday we propose to defer our departure till Monday morning.

The different detachments of the expedition are now united. While awaiting the arrival of the boat the two parties from Fort Tejon and San Diego have been encamped on the river a mile below. The interval has not been idly spent. Dr. Newberry, assisted by Mr. Mollhausen, the artist, has made valuable natural history collections, to add to what was obtained while on the way from the coast. Mr. Egloffstein has nearly completed a series of topographical sketches of the adjoining country, and Mr. Taylor has been taking meteorological observations in connexion with those of Mr. Booker at the mouth of the river.

There is no grazing in the immediate vicinity, and the Mexican packers and herders have been sent with the mules, in charge of Mr. Peacock, the master of the train, ten or fifteen miles up the Gila, where they will stay till it is time for the pack-train to start. The express, with letters for the San Diego steamer, had left more than twelve hours before I arrived, and Mr. Peacock volunteered to ride with my letters to Los Angelos, which place he believed he could reach before the steamer should have left. If not, he had determined to continue up the Tulan valley to San Francisco, being confident of arriving there before the 20th, the day when the steamer for the Isthmus sails. It is a formidable ride, but as he preferred undertaking it to remaining idle in the camp I took advantage of his offer.

The pack-train will not leave till some time after the departure of the boat, but will overtake us near the head of navigation, wherever that may be, so as to be ready for the land explorations. Mr. Taylor and Mr. Booker are to wait and accompany the land party. The other gentlemen, with Lieutenant Tipton, who commands the escort, and who will take a few of his men with him, are to go on the steamer. Our party will number twenty-four, which is about as many as the Explorer can conveniently carry. Dr. Newberry, though far from well, has decided to go along with us. He believes that his health may be improved by change of air, and, like all the others of the party, is anxious to be in the midst of new scenery and new adventures. Fort Yuma is not a place to inspire one with regret at leaving. The barrenness of the surrounding region, the intense heat of its summer climate, and its loneliness and isolation have caused it to be regarded as the Botany Bay of military stations. Its establishment, however, has brought into entire subjection the Yuma Indians, who had been a scourge to their neighbors and to California emigrants. They are a fierce and cruel tribe, but a much finer race, physically, than the Cocopas. The men are powerfully built and the women better looking. As is always the case, they have deteriorated since the whites have come among them, and many of their former warriors are now idle loafers about the fort and inveterate pilferers and beggars. At present they are in a state of much excitement. There is a settlement of Mormons not far from the Colorado, a few hundred miles above, and it is rumored that some of that people have been among the upper tribes of Indians, telling them of their difficulties with the other whites and endeavoring to secure their alliance. There is an impression among these Indians that the Mormons contemplate, before long, descending the Colorado, which corresponds with a rumor brought from the east by the latest mail of a projected movement into Sonora. The commanding officer of the fort, Lieutenant Winder, a few days ago, sent Lieutenant White, with a detachment of men, up the river, with Captain Johnson, to make a reconnoissance and endeavor to ascertain the truth of these reports.

The fact that my expedition, just at this time, is preparing to ascend the Colorado, has much exercised the Indians above, who are jealous of any encroachment into their territory. I have tried in vain to secure the services of one or two Yumas to accompany me as interpreters. They all seem to be unwilling to go, but Lieutenant Winder has kindly taken the matter in hand and sent for the chief of the tribe, to prevail upon him, if possible, to make the detail.

The river still continues to fall. The Indians say that they have never seen it so low. We shall be able to test the experiment of navigation at as unfavorable a stage of the water as will probably ever be experienced. The load upon the boat is to be made as light as possible. Only six weeks provisions and such arms, ammunition, and luggage as are indispensable, are to be taken along, but it will be impossible to reduce her draught to less than two and a half feet, owing to her small size and heavy boiler and engine. The fore and aft pieces that Mr. Carroll bolted upon the bottom have answered the purpose for which they were intended, in giving the requisite strength and stiffness to the hull, but they add to the difficulty of working over bars and are apt to catch upon snags. The trip from the mouth of the river has developed several deficiencies which we are to-day endeavoring to have remedied. With the assistance of Lieutenant Winder and the steamboat company some extra lines and rudders have been provided, a few trifling damages that had been sustained repaired, and every possible provision made against the obstacles we expect to encounter in the ascent of the unknown river above.

COLORADO EXPLORING EXPEDITION.

H.B.Mollhausen.Del

Lith. of Sarony,Major & Knapp, 449 BroadwayNY

YUMAS

CHAPTER III.

FORT YUMA TO MOJAVE CAÑON.

Camp 12, *Yuma shoals, January* 11.—It was the intention this morning to make an early start; but the last preparations, as usual, consumed several hours of time, and it was nearly 11 when all of our party were collected at the wharf, everything put aboard, and steam gotten up. Our friends at the garrison came down to see us off, and the sides of the bluff were lined with Indians—men, women, and children—assembled to witness our departure, and, in spite of their distrust, delighted to have something to see and talk about. The urgent request of Lieutenant Winder to the chief had not failed of its effect, and the latter engaged (though reluctantly) that two Indians should accompany us—an old Diegeno, by the name of Mariano, and a young chief who had signalized himself by escaping unhurt from a recent memorable conflict with the Pimas and Maricopas,* and whom it pleased to be called the "Capitan." With an eye to theatrical effect, not at all uncommon with their race, my two recruits delayed making their appearance till the latest moment. We had bidden our friends good-bye, the plank was about to be hauled in, and I had begun to believe that the chief had played us a trick, when they came stalking

---

* The Pimas and Maricopas live upon the Gila, one or two hundred miles above its mouth. They are peaceable, quietly-disposed Indians, and subsist principally upon the products they derive from cultivating the soil. They have always been friendly to whites, but, from the time of the earliest records, bitter foes to the Yumas and Mojaves, who have been disposed to regard them with contempt, as an inferior race.

In the year 1856 the principal chief of the Yumas became mortally ill. Upon his death-bed he charged his tribe not to be remiss in hunting down their hated enemies, and prophesied that if they would, during the following year, organize an expedition against them, it would result in the latter's complete overthrow.

After the chief's death the Yumas, regarding with superstitious reverence his dying injunctions, prepared for a secret attack upon the Pimas and Maricopas villages. They notified the Mojaves of their intention, and a large number of picked Mojave warriors united themselves to the party. The intended victims of the enterprise had meanwhile—through the offices, as is supposed, of the Cocopas—got wind of the meditated attack, and not only mustered the whole of their own force to repel it, but obtained assistance from the Papagos—a warlike tribe living within the province of Sonora.

It was in the month of September, 1857, that the invading force, numbering between one hundred and one hundred and fifty of the most distinguished Yuma and Mojave warriors, set out for the Pimas villages, under the guidance of a prominent and ambitious Yuma chief. They had no suspicion that their movement was anticipated, and the unprotected appearance of the first village they entered convinced them that they had been successful in effecting an entire surprise. The few inhabitants that were sauntering about fled in apparent terror, and were hotly pursued. The attacking party followed them beyond the entrance of a small cañon, where they suddenly found themselves surrounded by an overpowering force. They attempted to fly, but finding that impossible, fought bravely to the last. The advantages of position and numbers were, however, altogether against them, and rendered resistance hopeless. The contest lasted less than an hour. Out of the whole number of assailants only three or four escaped to carry to these tribes the bitter tale of the discomfiture.

The moral effect of the defeat will long be felt. The very name of a Pima or Maricopa now inspires the Yumas and Mojaves with chagrin and dread.

DRAWN BY FRHREW. FCLOFESTEIN

COLORADO RIVER. CHEMEHUEVIS VALLEY

FROM MONUMENT MOUNTAINS TO MOJAVE MOUNTAINS

along, and entering the boat, seated themselves on the rail with an air of indifference that did not altogether conceal that they thought they were embarked in a rather doubtful enterprise. Their friends on the shore, being out of the scrape themselves, were naturally delighted at seeing others in it. The men grinned, and the women and children shouted with laughter, which was responded to by a scream from the Explorer's whistle; and in the midst of the uproar the line was cast off, the engine put in motion, and, gliding away from the wharf, we soon passed through the gorge abreast of the fort and emerged into the open valley above.

Fig. 1.—Yuma Shoals.

The river here spread out over a wide surface, and was, of course, shallow and full of bars and snags. The channel became at each moment more difficult to find, and when we had made but two miles we were brought to a dead stop by a bar. An anchor was put out ahead; but the bed being quicksand, it would not hold. It was necessary to lighten the boat, and finally most of the men got overboard, and having thus further diminished the draught, succeeded, after four hours and a half of hard labor, in forcing the steamer into the deeper water beyond the bar. The delay would have been less annoying if it had occurred a little higher up. We were in plain sight of the fort, and knew that this sudden check to our progress was affording an evening of great entertainment to those in and out of the garrison. As it was nearly dark when the bar was passed, after proceeding a mile we stopped at a point where there was wood, and went into camp.

Camp 13, *Explorer's Pass, January* 12.—A mile and a half of difficult navigation brought us to the end of the Yuma shoals. For ten miles the valley was then traversed without interruption, and at the head of a southeast bend, where the river again turned to the north, we reached the first of several ranges of low purple hills that cross the Colorado with a northwest and southeast trend. The pass through this range was not visible till we were almost at its mouth.

It was quite narrow, and soon after entering it we lost sight of the valley above the fort, and felt for the first time that we were in a new part of the river. The hills are but a few hundred feet in height, and the scenery, though picturesque, by no means grand; but it presents an agreeable change to the broad monotonous flats which we have been surveying for so many weeks. At the bend below the pass, which we call after our little steamboat, the Explorer's Pass, is the first grass camp yet seen on the river. Some rude Indian huts were standing near by, and scattered over the meadow were quite a number of mules and cattle grazing. Above the gap a pleasant valley extends two or three miles to the north. The river crosses it in several channels, in neither of which was there much water, and, after heaving over the first bar, we camped at dark in a little grove on the west bank.

Fig. 2.—Explorer's Pass.

A Yuma runner from the fort overtook us this morning, bringing the mail that arrived from San Diego last night. I quite astonished him by the munificence of the reward I gave him for what he thought a small service. I am in hopes that this encouragement may induce them to continue to act as mail carriers as long as we are upon the river.

Camp 16, *Canebrake cañon, January* 15.—Seven miles from Explorer's Pass another range of the Purple Hills crosses the river, forming almost a cañon. To the south is a long bend, and the banks of the stream for the first time exhibit no appearance of having been recently formed or washed away, but are lined for some distance with a thick growth of tall reeds that hang over and dip into the water. The view from below of the even and sparkling belt of the river, clearly defined by its yellow fringe, and gradually disappearing in the windings of the pass, is exceedingly picturesque. In the Purple Hill Pass the scenery becomes wilder, and the variety of colors assumed by the rocks adds to its beauty.

Passing another basin, and a third and smaller range, we emerged from the Purple Hills and came in sight of an immense valley stretching far to the northwest and southeast, flanked beyond by the lofty summits of the Dome Rock range.   The river swept around to the west, and soon entered a gorge or cañon more rugged and precipitous than any yet traversed.   The overhanging rocks presented combinations of colors still more unusual and striking than those below, and at intervals would recede from and again approach to the brink of the water.   On either side was a border of canes.   The stream was open and unobstructed, and better deserved the name of a river than any part of it we had navigated since leaving Fort Yuma.

Just before reaching our present camp, which is a little more than 20 miles from Explorer's Pass, a sudden turn brought Chimney Peak full in view.   Its turretted pinnacles towered directly in front, and almost seemed to block up the head of the cañon.   The vista was beautiful, and the channel looked promising.   There was a fine head of steam on, and we anticipated making

Fig. 3.—Purple Hills.

at least ten miles before dark, when one of the rudder stocks broke.   We were obliged to haul up to the bank to make a new one, and darkness came on before this was accomplished.

The country through which we have passed is quite destitute of vegetation.   Close to the river is an occasional growth of mezquite, cottonwood, or willow, which furnishes abundant materials for fuel; but the hills are bare, and the gravelly beds of the valleys sustain only desert shrubs.   There are many varieties of cactus, among which the fluted columns of the *cereus giganteus* stand in conspicuous relief.

In the rocks which compose the Purple Hills, Dr. Newberry has discovered the presence of gold, iron, and lead.   Veins of copper and argentiferous galena have been already worked, and with prospects of successful returns.

COLORADO EXPLORING EXPEDITION.

J.J.Young, from a sketch by F.W.Egloffstein.

Lith. of Sarony,Major & Knapp. 449 Broadway NY

CANE BRAKE CAÑON.
FROM NEAR CAMP 16.

Camp 18, *Great Colorado valley, January* 17.—Provided with a new rudder we started yesterday from camp in the Canebrake cañon, with an open looking stretch of water ahead that gave encouragement of a good day's run.   We soon discovered that, as regards the navigation of the Colorado, no dependence can be placed upon appearance, for after proceeding two hundred yards the boat grounded upon a bar with such force that it took nearly two hours to get her off.   After this we pursued our way through the cañon without difficulty.   At a bend two miles above the head of the cañon, the river makes rapidly against and around the base of a massive perpendicular rock 100 feet high.   The water appeared to be whirling and eddying at an unusual rate, and we discovered that the Explorer was making no headway, being just able to hold her own against the current.   There was not a great deal of steam on, so Captain Robinson headed towards the bank, which fortunately presented an abrupt face, and when

Fig. 4.—Purple Hill Pass.

near enough the men sprang ashore with a tow line, and pulled us along for one or two hundred hundred yards, when the current resumed its accustomed flow.   A short distance north of the rapid several high rocks, arranged in a circular form, occupy the centre of the stream, leaving a narrow channel on either side.   A swift current and some isolated rocks above made the passage dangerous, and we were somewhat startled, just as we thought it safely accomplished, by striking rather heavily upon a sunken rock, but fortunately without sustaining any damage. Looking back the rocks seemed to completely block the river, and the place appeared much more formidable than from below.

From the entrance to Canebrake cañon we had been pursuing a due westerly course, but now the river turned again to the north, winding between gravel bluffs that form a portion of the desert mesa which here extends to the water's edge.   Passing out from these we noticed a short distance westward a cluster of slender and graceful spires surrounding a spur that runs out from Chimney Peak, and appears to form a part of the Purple Hills. North of these, rendered conspicuous by lines of serrated peaks, is a range of chocolate colored mountains, from which the river emerges through a gate formed by a huge crag of vivid red rock.

Fig. 5.—Red Rock Gate.

While turning a bend, a little while after passing the gate, we suddenly noticed upon the summit of a little hill on the left bank a ludicrous resemblance to a sleeping figure. The outlines and proportions were startlingly faithful, and the following sketch, hurriedly taken as the steamer passed, scarcely gives a true idea, and certainly not an exaggerated one, of the accuracy of the likeness which presented itself from different positions for nearly a mile.

This portion of the river assumes almost the character of a cañon, and the navigation was attended with some risk to us who knew nothing of the obstacles that were ahead. In one of the bends too sharp rocky points extended from the banks, and another point jutted out midway from the opposite side. The channel glanced by all three, and a lone rock near the middle of the stream embarrassed the passage. Not far above a circular pinnacle of rock, which at a distance resembles a light-house, blocks the centre of the river, leaving a very narrow but fortunately unobstructed channel. A short hazardous pass followed. At its northern entrance are high cliffs of porphyry, through which the Colorado breaks into the range below. Passing these solid portals, we issued from the Chocolate mountains into the great valley that was noticed after leaving the Purple Hills.

For the first time since entering the Explorer's Pass, we are in the desert region, and the river looks very much as it did immediately above Fort Yuma, dissipating any hopes we might have entertained of finding the navigation improve with the ascent. The surface was so spread out, and the sand bars and snags so numerous, that I was a little apprehensive of having reached a premature head of navigation, but one or two miles were accomplished without any trouble before reaching camp.

The snags we have seen are productive of inconvenience, but of little danger, not being heavy or rigid enough to penetrate the bottom of the boat.   Not a great many rocks have been passed, though enough to make it evident that they may at any time be encountered. The low stage of the river permits us to fix the position of those that would be dangerous at

Fig. 6.—Sleeper's Bend.

other seasons.   The water is perfectly opaque, but the rapid current occasions a ripple upon the surface, which, when the atmosphere is still, distinctly marks the presence of either a sunken rock or snag, and enables it to be avoided.   If the wind is blowing, and the surface is agitated, the ripple of course is not perceptible; and when this is the case, while passing a suspicious looking locality, we proceed very slowly and uncomfortably till the danger is over. While the boat is in motion a man is stationed at the bow with a sounding pole, and constantly calls out the depth of the water and the character of the bottom.   This is not so much for the benefit of the pilot as to gratify the anxious curiosity of the passengers, and to enable Mr. Bielauski and Mr. Egloffstein, who sit on the wheel-house with their note-books delineating the river and the surrounding country, to keep an accurate record.   Captain Robinson, for his part, is able, as a general rule, to predict exactly when the water will shoal or deepen, and to select, with unerring accuracy, from a labyrinth of channels, the most practicable.   His success in avoiding difficulties is not greater than the fertility of resource he displays in extricating us from them, and if the ascent of the river is accomplished, it will be due to his skill and good management.   The labor attending the crossing of a bar, carrying out the anchors and lines, heaving upon the windlass, handling the boat poles, and lightening the boat of the cargo by carrying it ashore in the skiffs, is by no means small; and to enable the men to undergo it with less fatigue, they are divided into two gangs or watches, which alternately work and rest for a day.   The working party remains near the bow, and the others distribute themselves as they best can over the limited accommodations afforded by the wood piles on either side of the boiler. What little space is left abaft the boiler, when the luggage is all aboard, is taken up by the fireman and by Mr. Carroll. The latter is incessantly occupied in responding to the hails of the pilot from the deck overhead to go slower or faster, or to stop, or to back, or to go ahead, and thinks the Colorado the queerest river to run a steamboat upon that he has ever met with in his experience as an engineer.

Fig. 7.—Light-house Rock.

Very few Indians have been seen. In the rough and mountainous region that we have traversed they were not likely to be encountered, their villages being confined altogether to the alluvial bottoms. In the valley which we have now entered they will doubtless reappear. Every form of vitality is rare. The scarcity of vegetation has been alluded to; of fish, but a single one—and that a poor variety—has been caught; and game is seldom met with. An occasional flock of ducks or geese is observed flying past, and this morning a dozen mountain sheep ("big horns") were seen scampering over a gravel hill near Light-house Rock, but not within shot from the bank of the river.

At this time of year few reptiles and insects are about; and Mr. Mollhausen finds it hard to make additions to his zoological collections. Dr. Newberry, who is now quite restored to health, has found a more productive field of labor. The mineral wealth of the country somewhat atones for its animal and vegetable poverty, and in a geological point of view possesses a high degree of interest. The steamboat affords facilities for transportation not ordinarily enjoyed by exploring parties nor scientific collectors, and the doctor has already laid in a large assortment of specimens. The mountains passed to-day—Chimney Peak, the Spires, and the Chocolate range—have exhibited a rare diversity of outline, colors, and tints; and the brilliancy of the atmosphere heightens the effect of every shade and line. The weather, since leaving Fort Yuma, has been uniformly pleasant; the nights are becoming sensibly colder, but the days are still warm and delightful.

Mariano and the Capitan have made themselves quite at home in our party, and even evince some interest in our fortunes and progress. They sit all day on a particular portion of the rail, quiet observers of what is going on. The many mishaps and detentions on the bars must give them a low opinion of our skill in navigation; but they are too polite to show it, and when the boat grounds upon a bar will remain by the hour immovable, without manifesting the least impatience, till she is again afloat. When we make a landing to take in wood they instantly disappear, and refresh themselves with the absence of civilization until the whistle signals that it is time to start; and similarly at night, after receiving their rations, they go off to a distance, out of sight of our roaring camp-fires, and cook their food over a few smouldering embers, in the most quiet and secluded nook that they can find. Each has been presented with a pair of blankets, and these, with full and regular rations, doubtless do much to reconcile them to their involuntary trip.

Camp 24, *Half-way mountain, January* 23.—Since leaving the Chocolate mountains we have travelled sixty-five miles, and are still in the Great Colorado valley, entered at Porphyry Gate. The character of the river has been similar to that below Fort Yuma; but the navigation has proved easier than was anticipated. The water has been frequently divided into several channels, or spread over a wide surface, and filled with snags; but several of the most unfavorable looking places have afforded a clear and unobstructed passage. Bars, as usual, have been of constant occurrence, and at a place named the Dismal Flats, ten miles north of Camp 18, the obstacles were numerous, and we experienced a long detention, but got through at last without any worse adventure than the loss of a rudder and some dents made in the wrought-iron hull by thumps from snags. A few miles above the flats a little stream—Carroll's creek—comes in from the west. Through the whole of the Colorado valley the course of the river has been circuitous, and in the bends, along the concave banks, the channel is almost always good.

The greater part of the valley is a desert plain, a hundred feet or more above the river, limited by clay and gravel bluffs that often abut close upon the edge of the water and form little cañons. There is a good deal of bottom land, and some of it is fertile; but much of it, as I am informed by Dr. Newberry, is so charged with alkali as to be unproductive.

The Yumas cultivate the better portions, which are watered during the summer overflow. A well-conducted system of irrigation would wash out the salt from the soil and increase the amount of productive land.

Fifteen or twenty miles above Porphyry Gate we came in sight of some high mountains on the west bank of the river. Mariano informed me that these were half-way between the fort and the Mojave villages. Our present camp is near their southern base; they do not cross the river, but are skirted by it for many miles. Two or three short and low ranges intervene between the Half-way mountains and the foot of the valley, which otherwise extends unbroken southward to the base of the Chocolate mountains, and west to the parallel chains that form the Dome Rock range.

The Yumas have been constantly encountered since we have been in this valley. They collect in knots upon the banks to watch us pass, and their appearance is invariably the precursor of trouble. Whether their villages are near places where the river is most easily forded, or whether they select for points of view the spots where they know we will meet with detention, we cannot tell; but the coincidence between their presence and a bad bar is so unfailing that Mr. Carroll considers it a sufficient reason to slow down the engine when he sees them collected upon the bank. Their fields and villages have not been seen from the river; for wherever there is much bottom land there is a thick growth of trees near the water, that intercepts the view of the country beyond. Large numbers of these trees are dead and sun-dried, and furnish excellent fuel.

The Yumas present a sorry appearance. Many of them, if left in their natural state, would be fine looking; but for everything that resembles clothing they have a passion, and a tall warrior, with a figure like an Apollo, will strut along in a dilapidated hat and a ragged jacket or pair of trowsers, made for a man two or three sizes smaller, and think that he is amazingly beautified by his toilet. A knot of them gathered together exhibits a ludicrous variety of tawdry colors and dirty finery.

Mariano and the Capitan, when we entered the valley, asked permission to go and spend a day or two with their friends, promising to overtake the boat above. It would have been useless to decline giving what they could at any time with perfect ease take; and I told them they could go, with little expectation that they would ever return. Mariano came back, however, yesterday, and Capitan this morning. The former brought along an urchin whom he introduced as his son, and requested me to furnish with some white cotton. As to the first part of his statement, I concluded, from the boy's features and complexion, that either Mariano was trying to impose upon me, or had himself been grossly imposed upon; but the white cotton, or "manta," as the Indians call it, was provided, to the great satisfaction of the young gentleman in question.

Fig. 8.—Riverside Mountains.

The Capitan has late news, through some of his friends, from the Mojaves, and informs me that the chiefs are anxiously expecting our arrival; are disposed to be friendly, and intend to visit us in state as we approach their territory. He states also that two or three white men have been among them lately for some time, which is confirmatory of what we heard below.

A small party belonging to a tribe called the Chemehuevis came into camp this evening. They live in the valley adjoining that which we are now traversing, but are altogether different in appearance and character from the other Colorado Indians. They have small figures, and

COLORADO EXPLORING EXPEDITION

H B Möllhausen Del.

Lith of Sarony,Major & Knapp, 449 Broadway,NY

CHEMEHUEVIS

some of them delicate, nicely-cut features, with little of the Indian physiognomy. Unlike their neighbors—who, though warlike, are domestic, and seldom leave their own valleys—the Chemehueris are a wandering race, and travel great distances on hunting and predatory excursions. They wear sandals and hunting shirts of buckskin, and carry tastefully-made quivers of the same material. They are notorious rogues, and have a peculiar cunning, elfish expression, which is a sufficient certificate of their rascality. One of them tried to cheat me while fulfilling a bargain for a deerskin; but I detected him at it, and, in spite of his denial, proved the fraud upon him. He was highly amused at being fairly caught, and it raised me very much in his estimation; if I had tried to cheat him, and had succeeded, his admiration would have been unlimited.

Camp 32, *Beaver island, January* 31.—Forty-two miles of navigation generally similar to that of the preceding week have brought us to the head of the Great Colorado valley. For twenty miles of this distance the Half-way range bounds the west bank. A broad and even swell extends from the water to the edge of the acclivity. At the northern extremity of the range are two prominent peaks. The most northerly, which is the highest, stands close to the river side, and forms a conspicuous feature in the scenery for a long distance above and below. We are now at the verge of the foot-hills of a continuous chain of mountains, that crosses the Colorado ten miles above, and has been in sight for many days. Among the group of fantastic peaks that surmount this chain is a slender and perfectly symmetrical spire that furnishes a

Fig. 9—Monument Mountains.

striking landmark, as it can be seen from a great way down the river in beautiful relief against the sky. Through a gap in the range some lofty snow-topped summits are visible to the north. Between us and the Riverside mountains the bluffs of the desert come to the brink of the river; but below this confined passage is a stretch of several miles, which we call the Sand Island shoals, where the Colorado is divided by islands into numerous channels, and the navigation is more difficult than any yet experienced. One bar would scarcely be passed before another would be encountered, and we were three days in accomplishing a distance of nine miles. A boat drawing six inches less water, and without any timbers attached to the bottom, could have probably made the same distance in three hours. The ascent of the river, under the circumstances, promises to be a tedious business; and as our provisions are half consumed, Lieutenant Tipton took advantage of an opportunity afforded a few days ago by our meeting Captain Johnson, with Lieutenant White and party, returning to the fort, and went back with them in order to bring up the pack-train.

This slow progress and the long detentions, though dull enough for us, have been a source of intense satisfaction and fun to the spectators on the banks. The Yumas are no longer seen. Our sharp witted friends, the Chemehuevis, seem to have exclusive possession of the upper end of the valley. Not having the same experience in steamers as the former tribe, for they seldom go to Fort Yuma, they have doubtless watched with great curiosity for the long-expected boat. If we had anticipated inspiring them with awe or admiration, we should be sadly disappointed, for I am sure they regard our method of ascending the river with unaffected contempt. They have been demonstrating to Mariano and Capitan—who are disposed to espouse our side, and yet are a little ashamed of being in such ridiculous company—how vastly inferior our mode of locomotion is to theirs. They can foot it on the shore, or pole along a raft upon the river without interruption; and that we should spend days in doing what they can accomplish in half as many hours, strikes them as unaccountably stupid. The gleeful consciousness of superiority at all events keeps them in an excellent humor. When we reached the Sand Island shoals, as usual, they were awaiting the approach of the steamer at points opposite to the bars. At first our troubles occasioned them unqualified delight. They watched the boat with breathless eagerness as we tried in vain to get through one place after another, and every time she ran aground a peal of laughter would ring from the bank; but after a while our mishaps appeared to move their compassion, and some one of them would run ahead, and point out to Captain Robinson the part of the bar that had the greatest depth upon it, which their frequent fording of the stream often enabled them to know. An old woman, among others, endeavored to help the captain along, but as we approached the place she indicated his knowledge of the river showed him that it would not do, and he sheered off without making the trial. The benevolence of the old hag was at once converted into rage, and with clenched fists and flaming eyes she followed along the bank, screaming at the captain, as long as he was in hearing, a volley of maledictions.

At evening, when we go into camp, they come to visit us in great numbers. As long as their women and children are about we know that they have no hostile intentions, but sentinels are always posted, and exactly at sunset I make every Indian leave the camp limits. At first I think they entertained a dim mistrust of my right to eject them thus summarily from their own premises, but habit is everything, and now they all go away at sundown as a matter of course. A few evenings ago, being visited by a chief of apparently some importance, I prevailed upon him to send a runner to Fort Yuma for the mail, and after a little trouble he found a volunteer. A great deal of haggling and changing of mind had to be gone through with before a bargain was concluded, but finally the Indian was satisfied, and promised to return for our letters on the next day. After once making an agreement, I have never known one of them to recede from it, and punctually at the time appointed he came for the package. We were near falling out from his demanding to be paid in advance, but the matter was compromised by his receiving a red blanket, and consenting to wait till his return for the balance of the payment agreed upon. He told me that he would reach the fort in three days, rest a day, return in three days, and that in one more day he could accomplish the distance that we would have made during the intervening seven—not an improbable supposition at our recent rate of travel.

Each successive range of mountains passed presents more striking varieties and combinations of color, imparting a strange and novel beauty to the barren rocks. As the rays of the setting sun fall upon the rugged face of the Riverside mountain, and illuminate its crevices and hollows, tints of purple, blue, brown, almond, and rose color are brought out in gorgeous relief, and contrast singularly with the dull monotonous gray of the desert. Dr. Newberry found, in this mountain, indications of the presence of gold, silver, lead, iron, and copper, and discovered veins resembling the gold-bearing rocks of California. The nature of our duties does not permit any lengthy examinations. A careful search might develop ample stores of treasure, which the close proximity of water transportation would greatly enhance in value.

Camp 33, *mouth of Bill Williams's Fork, February* 1.—A few miles above camp the river wound around the base of a massive rock, into which a deep groove had been cut by the ceaseless flow of the stream. This point may be considered the southern entrance of the cañon

Fig. 10.—Corner Rock.

through the Monument mountains. Immediately above the river grew narrower and deeper, and the hills crowded closely upon the water's edge. The regular slopes gradually gave place to rough and confused masses of rock, and the scenery at every instant became wilder and more romantic. New and surprising effects of coloring added to the beauty of the vista. In the foreground, light and delicate tints predominated, and broad surfaces of lilac, pearl color, pink, and white, contrasted strongly with the sombre masses piled up behind. In their very midst a single pile of a vivid blood red rose in isolated prominence. A few miles higher a narrow gateway opened into the heart of the mountains. On one side of the entrance was a dark red column, on the other a leaning tower of the same color overhung the pass, the ponderous rock seeming ready to fall as we passed beneath. Rich hues of blue, green, and purple, relieved here and there by veins of pink and white, were blended in brilliant confusion upon the sides of the cañon, producing a weird-like and unearthly effect, which the fantastic shapes and outlines of the enclosing walls did not diminish.   For six miles we followed the windings of the river through this fairy-like pass, where every turn varied and heightened the

Fig. 11. — Monument Cañon.

interest of the pageant, and then the lines of cliff stopped, and we issued suddenly from the cañon into a comparatively open valley.   Low foot-hills, from the range on the west side of the river, skirt the bank, but on the east side they recede, leaving a few gravelly spurs, and beyond these a belt of bottom land.   The whole appearance of the country indicated that we had reached the Chemehuevis valley and the mouth of Bill Williams's Fork, which is the only important tributary to the Colorado between the Virgen and the Gila.   Having accompanied, in 1853, the expedition of Lieutenant Whipple to explore for a railroad route along the 35th parallel, and having, with that party, descended Bill Williams's Fork to its confluence with the Colorado, I was confident of the locality.   The mouth of the stream was at that time, which happened to be in the present month, February, about thirty feet wide, and several feet deep.   I now looked in vain for the creek.   The outline of the bank, though low, appeared unbroken, and for awhile I was quite confounded.   My companions were of opinion that I had made a great topographical blunder, but I asked Captain Robinson to head for the left shore, proposing to camp and make an examination.   As we approached the bank I perceived, while closely scanning its outline, a small dent, and after landing repaired to the spot, and found a very narrow gulley, through which a feeble stream was trickling, and this was all that was left of Bill Williams's Fork.   The former mouth is now filled up, and overgrown with thickets of willow.   An unusual drought must have prevailed for two or three years past in the regions that furnish its supply.   The Colorado, according to the Indians, is as low, proportionally, as its tributary.

The party of Lieutenant Whipple contained one hundred men, two hundred mules, and four wagons, but the trail is entirely obliterated.   Not a trace, even of the wagons, remains.

The navigation to-day has been generally good, but we struck one sunken rock, and passed several that are now visible, but that would be dangerous at a higher stage of water unless their position were accurately known.   The iron put into the hull of the Explorer must have been of excellent quality or she would have been sunk long ago by some of the thumps she has experienced.

We met, in the cañon, two Chemehuevis, with their wives, children, and household effects, paddling towards the valley below, on rafts made by tying together bundles of reeds.   There being no bars to interrupt us we passed them under a full head of steam, and made a great impression.   They drew their rafts into a little cave when they saw us coming, and peered out at the steamboat, as it went puffing by, with an amusing expression of bewilderment and awe.   Having, themselves, heavy loads to carry, I imagine they appreciated, better than their friends below, the advantage of being able to stem the current without manual labor.

As Captain Robinson and myself were walking out this evening we suddenly came upon two Indians reclining on the top of the bank, in sight of the steamer.   I at once knew them to be Mojaves.   One of them must have been nearly six feet and a half in height, and his proportions were herculean.   He was entirely naked, excepting the ordinary piece of cotton about his loins, and his chest and limbs were enormously developed.   A more scowling, sinister looking face than that which surmounted this noble frame I have seldom seen; and I quite agreed with a remark of the captain, that he would be an unpleasant customer to encounter alone and unarmed.   His companion was smaller, though a large man, and had a pleasant face.   Neither took the slightest notice of us, but both continued looking at the steamboat, the taller man with an expression that indicated a most unamiable frame of mind.   Doubtless they were sent down from the valley above to learn something in regard to our party.   I am sure that the report of one of the two will be anything but complimentary to the steamboat and ourselves. I can scarcely blame him for his disgust, for he must suspect that this is the first step towards an encroachment upon the territory of his tribe.

Camp 38, *Chemehuevis Bend, February* 7.—For two or three days a norther has been blowing, similar to those experienced almost weekly at the mouth of the river.   At times it has made the boat unmanageable, and the surface of the water having been so agitated that it was impossible to distinguish the channel.   Our progress has been difficult and slow, and scarcely twenty-five miles have been made since leaving the mouth of Bill Williams's Fork.   While the gale lasted we were nearly blinded and choked by drifts of fine sand, that darkened the air and penetrated into the luggage, bedding, provisions, fire-arms, and the very pores of one's skin.

The bed of the stream has been covered in spots with gravel, and two or three times, when the water was shoal, we have had the unpleasant sensation of having the bottom of the boat grinding upon the rough edges of the stones.

Our course has been for some days very much to the west.   A little below camp the river turns to the north, and continues in that direction till it enters a chain of mountains twelve or fifteen miles above.   This chain, which we call the Mojave range, separates the Chemehuevis and Mojave valleys.   A cluster of slender and prominent pinnacles, named by Lieutenant Whipple "The Needles," is in close proximity to the river.   The Monument mountains bar the view towards the south.   The region which we are travelling scarcely deserves the name of valley. It is a basin of the desert, bounded by the Monument and Mojave mountains, and by spurs projecting from them.   There is very little alluvial land or vegetation.   One place was passed to-day that looked somewhat inviting, where wheat and corn fields, dotted with groves of mez-quite, extended to a considerable distance back from the river.

The mountain scenery is beautiful ; with every change of position it presents new varieties of fanciful and bold groupings. The Needles and a high peak of the Monument range, which I have called Mount Whipple, are the most conspicuous landmarks, and designate the points where the river enters and leaves the Chemehuevis valley.

Fig. 12.—Monument Range from the North.

On the evening of the 3d the Indian sent for the mail returned with letters and papers brought by the last express from San Diego. When one day's journey from the fort he had met a Yuma that had been despatched by Lieutenant Winder to bring the letters to us, and had thus been spared a two day's journey. The Yumas, who perhaps have derived an exaggerated notion of our poverty from the Cocopas, had told our messenger that we would take the letters and would not pay him. This I learned during the evening from Mariano, and it accounted for the anxious look that the mail carrier was observed to wear during the hour or two that I was busy in reading the intelligence that had been brought. When I went to hunt him up, I found him seated under a tree a little retired from camp, looking very blue and gloomy. Our stock of Indian goods is large, and selected with a special view to the peculiar tastes of the Colorado tribes, and I was anxious to have it clearly understood that a faithfully performed service would be well paid for; so I conducted him to the boat, a crowd of his friends following with looks of eager expectation, and unlocking one of the boxes of valuables selected and gave him enough manta, beads, mirrors, red cloth, and fancy articles, to overcome for once his Indian stoicism, and make him grin with pleasure and his companions stare with envy.

An old acquaintance came to see me a day or two ago. We were steaming under good headway, abreast of a wooded bank that skirted one of the patches of bottom land, when a

number of the Chemehuevis appeared, earnestly gesticulating and making signs to us to stop.
They displayed so much anxiety and eagerness that I asked Captain Robinson to head for the
bank.   It turned out that a little Chemehuevis chief, who had been a good deal in Lieutenant
Whipple's camp, had taken this cool method of calling himself to our attention, thereby bringing upon himself some reflections from the pilot, which were not complimentary.   Having no

Fig. 13.—Mount Whipple.

time to stop, I asked him to step on board, and before he was aware of the manœuvre he found
himself a passenger and rapidly leaving his tribe and home behind.   Happily both he and his
followers looked upon the proceeding as a high compliment.

We have now been absent from Fort Yuma for four weeks and have but two weeks rations
left.   Should the pack train meet with detention we should be on short allowance, and, unlike
a land party, have no mules to fall back upon.   I have been anxious for some time to increase
the stock of provisions by trading with the Indians, and took advantage of the chief's presence
to open negotiations upon the subject.   He promised before he left that evening that his people
should bring some beans and corn to trade for manta and beads.   Our camp is at the head-
quarters of the Chemehuevis nation, and great numbers of all ages and both sexes have visited
it to-day.   They have been perfectly friendly, and considering their knavish character and
restless inquisitive dispositions, have behaved very well and given little trouble.   The amount
of cultivable land in their valley is so inconsiderable, and they themselves so inclined to
vagrancy, that I could not expect to find them with much provision to spare, but last evening
about two dozen brought baskets and earthen bowls of corn and beans.   I saw that they had
come prepared for a long haggling, and I made them place their burdens in a row on some
boards that were laid out for the purpose; asking each in turn whether he preferred beads or
manta, I placed what I thought a fair amount of the desired article opposite to the proper

heap of provisions. The whole tribe had crowded around to look on, and their amusement, during this performance, was extreme. Every sharp face expanded into a grin as I weighed the different piles in succession in my hand, and gravely estimated their contents; and when, the apportionment being over, I directed two of my men to bag the corn and beans, and coolly walked away, the delight of the bystanders, at the summary method of completing the bargain, reached its climax and they fairly screamed with laughter. A few of the traders seemed not quite to comprehend why they should have had so little say in the matter, but having been really well recompensed, according to their ideas of things, the tariff of prices was established, and this morning, when fresh supplies were brought, they received the same rate of payment without question or demur.

Mr. Mollhausen has enlisted the services of the children to procure zoological specimens, and has obtained, at the cost of a few strings of beads, several varieties of pouched mice and lizards. They think he eats them, and are delighted that his eccentric appetite can be gratified with so much ease and profit to themselves.

There has been lately a remarkable disparity between the temperatures of the day and night. Almost every night it is cold enough to form a thin crust of ice upon the little lagoons and inlets, while at midday the thermometer in the shade sometimes stands at 85°, and in the sun it is oppressively warm.

Fig. 14—Remains of Grand Mesa in Chemehuevis Valley.

Camp 40, *head of Mojave Cañon, February* 9.—The norther continued yesterday, and, as is apt to be the case towards its close, blew with redoubled violence. The force of the gale being felt principally upon the cabin and after deck, it was impossible to steer the boat, and after a day passed in swinging about from one shoal to another, rubbing over bars, and scraping rocks, nightfall found us advanced just three miles.

MOJAVE CAÑON.

J.J.YOUNG, from a sketch by H.B.MOLLHAUSEN.

To-day has been perfectly serene, and the atmosphere indescribably soft and limpid. For several miles the river assumed a new aspect, being straight and broad, having high banks, and presenting a placid unbroken sheet of water—not a bar being visible above the surface. To one viewing the noble looking stream from the bank, it would have appeared navigable for vessels of the heaviest draught, but the depth of water was scarcely sufficient to enable the Explorer to pass without touching.

Entering the foot hills of the Mojave range, the channel was again tortuous, and after traversing a narrow pass the Needles came in view directly in front. As we approached the mouth of the cañon through the Mojave mountains, a roaring noise ahead gave notice that we were coming to a rapid, and soon we reached the foot of a pebbly island, along either side of which the water was rushing, enveloped in a sheet of foam.

Fig. 15.—Mouth of Mojave Cañon.

After ascending a few yards a harsh grating noise warned us that we were upon a rocky shoal, and Captain Robinson at once backed the Explorer out and went up in a skiff to reconnoitre. He found good water, excepting for a short distance at the lower end, where the depth was three feet, and the bottom sprinkled with rocks. There was danger that the after part of the boat in passing might catch upon a rock, and the bow be swung around by the rapid current against another with such violence as to knock a hole in the bottom. An anchor was carried to a point some distance up stream, and a line taken from it to the bow. This line was kept taut, while, with a high pressure of steam, the Explorer was forced up the rapids, once or twice trembling from stem to stern as she grazed upon a rock, but reaching the still water above without sustaining damage.

A low purple gateway and a splendid corridor, with massive red walls, formed the entrance to the cañon. At the head of this avenue frowning mountains, piled one above the other, seemed to block the way.   An abrupt turn at the base of the apparent barrier revealed a cavern-like approach to the profound chasm beyond.   A scene of such imposing grandeur as that which now presented itself I have never before witnessed.   On either side majestic cliffs, hundreds of feet in height, rose perpendicularly from the water.   As the river wound through the narrow enclosure every turn developed some sublime effect or startling novelty in the view. Brilliant tints of purple, green, brown, red, and white illuminated the stupendous surfaces and relieved their sombre monotony.   Far above, clear and distinct upon the narrow strip of sky, turrets, spires, jagged statue-like peaks and grotesque pinnacles overlooked the deep abyss.

The waning day found us still threading the windings of this wonderful defile, and the approach of twilight enhanced the wild romance of the scenery.   The bright colors faded and blended into a uniform dark gray.   The rocks assumed dim and exaggerated shapes, and seemed to flit like giant spectres in pursuit and retreat along the shadowy vista.   A solemn stillness reigned in the darkening avenue, broken only by the plash of the paddles or the cry of a solitary heron, startled by our approach from his perch on the brink of some overhanging cliff.

The obscurity was rapidly increasing, when a turn of the river threw a sudden light upon the way, and we found that we were passing out of the cañon, having reached the low foot hills beyond.   A short distance further, coming to a good camping place, we hauled up to the bank for the night.

CHAPTER IV.

MOJAVE VALLEY.

Camp 41, *Mojave valley*, *February* 10.—The gray rocks that skirted the river for a few miles at the northern entrance to the Mojave range appeared to little advantage, contrasted with the imposing features of the cañon just passed. At every turn we now looked eagerly ahead, expecting to come in sight of the Mojave valley. Our proximity to it was soon announced by

Fig. 16.—Head of Mojave Cañon.

a lofty column of smoke that ascended from the summit of a little peak near the bank, where a watcher had been stationed to warn the inhabitants above of our approach. In a few moments a gap in the side hills revealed a glimpse of an open country, with bright foliage and green trees and a blue range in the distance, and after traversing a short avenue, lined with low

COLORADO RIVER. MOJAVE VALLEY.

FROM MOJAVE MOUNTAINS TO PYRAMID CAÑON.

bluffs, and terminated by a narrow gateway, we issued from the hills and beheld the broad and noble valley of the Mojaves spread before us.

At this season of the year, before the burning heat has withered the freshness and beauty of the early vegetation, this valley, of course, appears in the most attractive aspect. It may be that the eye, weary of the monotonous sterility of the country below, is disposed to exaggerate its charms, but as we first saw it, clothed in spring attire, and bathed in all the splendor of a brilliant morning's sunlight, the scene was so lovely that there was a universal expression of admiration and delight. Towards the north, to the limit of vision, the tortuous course of the river could be traced through a belt of alluvial land, varying from one or two to six or seven miles in width, and garnished with inviting meadows, with broad groves of willow and mezquite, and promising fields of grain. From either border of this glistening expanse, and contrasting with its emerald hue, rose dark gray terraces, leading, with regular steps, to the bases of lofty mountain chains, whose bold and picturesque outlines are so softened by the distance as to harmonize with the smiling scene below. A pale blue haze, singularly transparent and delicate, lends an exquisite tint both to mountain and valley.

As the steamer emerged from the cañon the Mojaves began to cluster upon the banks, and I was glad to see, from the presence of the women and children, that they had no immediate hostile intentions. A chief, with a train of followers in single file, approached the edge of the bank to pay his respects, but as it was not convenient just then to stop, I made signs to him to visit us in camp at evening. All day the Indians have followed us, examining the boat and its occupants with eager curiosity. They, on their side, have been subjected to critical inspection, which they can stand better than any of the tribes that live below. The men, as a general rule, have noble figures, and the stature of some is gigantic. Having no clothing but a strip of cotton, their fine proportions are displayed to the greatest advantage. Most of them have intelligent countenances and an agreeable expression. The women, over the age of eighteen or twenty, are almost invariably short and stout, with fat, good-natured faces. Their only article of dress is a short petticoat, made of strips of bark, and sticking out about eight inches behind. Some of the younger girls are very pretty and have slender, graceful figures. The children wear only the apparel in which they were born, and have a precocious, impish look. Their delight to-day has been to mimic the man at the bow who takes the soundings, every call being echoed from the bank with amusing fidelity of tone and accent. At some of the prominent points as many as fifty women and girls would be collected, presenting, with their brilliant eyes and teeth, an agreeable picture. They regard the steamboat with a ludicrous mixture of amusement, admiration, and distrust. The stern wheel particularly excites remark. It is painted red, their favorite color, and why it should turn around without any one touching it is evidently the theme of constant wonder and speculation. The little babies form a remarkable feature of the group. Those that are very young the mothers, with unusual good judgment, dispose of by tying them in a wooden arrangement, shaped like an old fashioned watch case, which may be carried in the hand as conveniently as a walking stick, or suspended to a tree, and the infant thus be securely and at the same time conveniently put away till required for nursing. When a few months older, they are taken out of the case and carried upon the projecting petticoat, where they sit astraddle, with their legs clasping their mother's waist and their little fists tightly clutched in her fat sides. They have a sharp, wide-awake expression, and their faces may always be seen peering from under their mother's arms, spying out what is going on. They nurse without moving their position, having only to elevate their mouths at a slight angle. It is rare for one of them to utter a cry, which may be attributed to the judicious system of their early training.

When we went into camp large crowds surrounded us, and numbers, both of the men and women, brought corn and beans to trade. Of the latter they have seven or eight varieties. It was difficult at first to fix upon bargaining terms, and they seemed unwilling to come to any

H.B.Mollhausen,Del

IRETEBA.   CAIROOK.

MOJAVES

agreement till the arrival of the chief whom I had seen. He, it seemed, had been several times at Fort Yuma, and had picked up, by ear, about thirty English words, without having an idea of their meaning. These he rung the changes upon with great volubility, producing an incoherent jumble of nonsense, which made him pass, with his admiring friends, for an accomplished linguist. Mariano and Capitan declined to interpret, feeling a delicacy in offering assistance in presence of one who spoke so fluently, and our new friend, with his jabbering, proved a great nuisance. At length, with the help of a little pantomime, in which I have become expert, a system of prices was arranged, and for a small quantity of beads and manta I obtained one or two bushels of corn and twice as many beans.

I discovered that the talking Indian held only a subordinate rank; that he belonged to the clan of José, one of the five principal chiefs of the Mojave nation, and that we are to receive a visit from the great man to-morrow. The minor chiefs wear a white plume, tipped with crimson. I infer that rank is, to some extent, hereditary, for I observed a singularly handsome and well-formed boy wearing the same badge of distinction.

I had some expectation that our visitors would object to being sent away from camp at sunset, but, though a little astonished at the demand, they complied without hesitation.

Camp 42, *Mojave villages, February* 11.—Bright and early the Mojaves were in camp, eager to trade, and while the fuel was being taken in I collected a considerable amount of provision. Our own stock will be exhausted in about a week, and as it may be some time before the train will come up, it is fortunate that we are enabled to lay in a fresh supply. Beans they appear to have in abundance, corn in smaller quantity, a very slender stock of wheat, and a few pumpkins. They raise watermelons, but these are not yet in season. Fuel is not so plenty as it has been, but enough can be found every few miles to answer our purposes. There is plenty of timber growing in the valley, but the dry wood is consumed in meeting the demands of the large population.

A few miles from camp we descried an immense throng of Indians standing upon an open meadow, and Capitan informed me that the chief José was awaiting, with his warriors, our approach. As there was a good wooding place near by, I determined to stop and have an interview, and, landing, sent him word that I was ready to see him. In a few moments he marched up with dignity, his tribe following in single file, the leader bearing a dish of cooked beans. A kind of crier walked a dozen paces in front to disperse from around the spot where I was standing the women, children, and dogs. José is advanced in years, and has rather a noble countenance, which, in honor of the occasion, was painted perfectly black, excepting a red stripe from the top of his forehead, down the bridge of his nose, to his chin. There was, in the first place, a general smoke at my expense, followed by a long conference. I tried to make him comprehend that we were on a peaceful mission; that I had a great esteem for him personally; and that I had certain things to ask of him, viz: that he should have provisions brought in to be traded for; should never permit any of his tribe to come about our camp after sunset; should send guides to conduct Lieutenant Tipton and train up the river by the best route; and should at once detail an Indian to carry a package to Fort Yuma and bring a return package to us. In return, his people should be well paid for their provisions and services, and he himself for his trouble.

My address, which differed from any speech ever yet made to a band of Indians since the formation of our government—inasmuch as it contained nothing about the "Great Father at Washington"—was at last duly comprehended by José and by the crowd that were seated around. It was difficult to satisfy them about the expedition; they could not understand why I should come up the river with a steamboat and go directly back again, nor why it was necessary to keep up a communication with Fort Yuma. I endeavored to explain these suspicious circumstances, and apparently succeeded; for José said that my wishes should be gratified, and that he would visit camp at evening, and meanwhile make the necessary arrangements to provide a messenger. I invited him to go with me on the steamboat; but he declined, and his friends appeared to think that he had done a prudent thing.

All of this occupied some time, and involved a great deal of gesticulation and intricate pantomime, which, even with interpreters, I find it convenient to have recourse to. Oral communication, under existing circumstances, is a complicated process. I have to deliver my message to Mr. Bielawski, who puts it into indifferent Spanish for the benefit of Mariano, whose knowledge of that language is slight; when Mariano has caught the idea he imparts it in the Yuma tongue, with which he is not altogether conversant, to Capitan, who, in turn, puts it into the Mojave vernacular. What changes my remarks have undergone during these different stages I shall never know; but I observe that they are sometimes received by the Mojaves with an astonishment and bewilderment that the original sense does not at all warrant.

A shoal upon which the steamer grounded towards evening prevented us from going into camp till dark, and I had to tell José and his followers that they must go away and return in the morning. I gave the chief a pair of blankets, which, in compliance with what seems to be an imperative law, he at once tore into strips and distributed to those about him; then he told them, in a florid speech, that they must respect our property and treat us as friends; and the crowd started for their homes. One or two stragglers, unable to resist the temptation, caught up some little articles that were lying exposed and tried to run off with them; supposing that, in the dusk, they could do so unobserved. They were detected in the act, and, dropping their plunder, made a precipitate retreat. José appeared to regret the occurrence, and looked a little sheepish at this practical result of his oratory; but some of the tribe were disposed to brave it out, and for a few moments it looked as though our amicable relations were to be dissolved. Capitan, who had witnessed the occurrence, came forward and made them a speech. He has a great reputation both as a warrior and orator, and was listened to with profound attention and respect. His gestures were so expressive, and the tones of his voice so modulated, that I could follow without difficulty his meaning. In glowing terms he represented the impropriety of their conduct, and assured them that he was identified with our party and would espouse our cause in the event of a quarrel. His remarks produced a strong impression, and the result was that José made a formal apology, and assured us that the would-be plunderers were not Mojaves, but some visitors to the valley from a tribe beyond the mountains; of which statement I assured him I did not believe a word. They all left camp, but with serious faces, leaving Mariano and Capitan quite concerned at the turn affairs had taken.

The position of a Mojave chief is one of honor and dignity, but carries little authority with it unless his views happen to coincide with those of a majority of the tribe. There are some turbulent spirits who are disposed to hostilities; and should they commit any overt act, the majority might disapprove, and yet, from unwillingness to give up or punish the offenders, find themselves obliged to sustain their action.

When Lieutenant Whipple passed through this valley one of the five chiefs, whose name was Cairook, and a sub-chief called Ireteba, joined him as a guide, and accompanied him through the country west of the Colorado as far as the Mormon road that leads to Los Angelos. They were noble specimens of their race, and rendered the party invaluable service. I have been making inquiry after them with the hope of meeting them again, and learn that Cairook still lives and retains his authority. The name of Ireteba the Indians do not recognize, and it is probable that some mistake was made about his appellation.

Camp 47, *head of Mojave valley, February* 17.—José and his tribe returned on the following morning, and seemed anxious that the indiscretion of the preceding night should be forgotten. They brought in a good deal of provision, and a runner presented himself to take the Fort Yuma letters. These were prepared and handed to him, and he started off without delay. He made no stipulation about the payment, but was much gratified at receiving in advance a red blanket and a piece of cotton. I gave José—letting him clearly understand that it was in payment for his services—some cloth, beads, cotton, and fancy articles, which he forthwith distributed, retaining nothing for himself but a handsome red scarf; this caught his fancy so strongly that he could not part with it, but twisted it about his head, turban fashion, where it excited general admiration. Their tastes are very arbitrary. Small white beads they highly prize; blue and red beads they will not accept as a gift, with the exception of a single variety of large blue glass beads, which they intersperse with the white in their necklaces; for cloth or blankets, red is the color most esteemed; white cotton and any kind of clothing they are glad to procure. Apart from their fondness for beads, their tastes are generally for things that are useful; and for paints, ribbons, imitation jewelry, feathers, &c., they have a contempt.

We left José and his clan looking very much pleased at the result of the morning's negotiations, and their friendly demeanor has relieved Mariano and Capitan from a load of anxiety. Their position would be a delicate one in the event of hostilities, as it might create unpleasant complications between the Yumas and Mojaves. I think Mariano, though a good-natured old fellow, would run away were there to be any fighting; but Capitan seems disposed to stand by our side. He quite surprised us by the bold and decided ground he took last night. Any outbreak would be a cause for much regret. Besides our reliance upon the Indians for provisions, our little party of twenty-four, in an open boat, half the time stuck upon a bar, could be greatly harassed by six or seven hundred men concealed in the thickets that often line the banks of the river.

On the same day that we bade farewell to José we passed another of the chiefs, whom they call Manuel. He was seated in state on the bank, with his tribe around him; but it was not convenient to stop, and when camp was reached at evening I learned that we were beyond the limits of his domain, and that it would not comport with his dignity to visit us.

The next day we remained in camp. During the morning, while passing in and out of the boat, I remarked an Indian seated for a long time near the end of the plank. At last I observed that he was constantly regarding me with a half smiling, half embarrassed air, and, looking at him more intently, discovered that it was my old friend Ireteba. He had been too modest to introduce himself. He was delighted at being recognized, and at the cordial greeting he received. He told me that his chief, "Cairook," lived across the river, and would soon come to see me. I at once proposed to Ireteba to accompany me on the boat, and upon the arrival of the pack train to go with us eastward; and he expressed his willingness to do so. I judged from his appearance that he was very poor, and gave him some blankets and other articles. When he and Cairook parted from Lieutenant Whipple they were loaded with enough presents to make them rich, according to an Indian's notions, for the rest of their lives; but it is the custom of the Mojaves to burn their property when a relation dies to whose memory they wish to pay especial honor, so that wealth is held by as uncertain a tenure as life.

The appearance of a great crowd upon the opposite bank indicated the presence of Cairook, and in a few minutes a messenger swam the river, and asked me to send a boat over. This it was impossible to do, as the skiff had been hauled upon the bank for repairs that were not yet completed, and there was no steam up. I was, therefore, obliged to send word that he must furnish his own transportation. The river was deep, and it was inconsistent with his dignity to make the first grand entré into camp dripping with water; and after a good deal of commotion and delay he hit upon a truly regal method of crossing. A raft was provided, and four of his tribe, one swimming at each corner, conveyed him over. He stood erect in the centre, and the water, for an acre or two around, was alive with his swimming followers. The meeting was friendly and pleasant. Cairook is a noble looking man. He is nearly six feet and a half high, and has a magnificent figure and a fine open face. He seemed glad to see me, and laughed a great deal as he alluded to former adventures. He inquired particularly for Lieutenant Whipple, for whom he had conceived an exalted opinion. Many of his tribe remember, and have been recalling, incidents of that expedition. Among other things, they were inquisitive to learn something of the man who could carry his teeth in his hand; which brought to mind an amusing recollection of the astonishment with which they had seen a member of the party take out and replace one or two false teeth. Cairook spent the whole day with me. I gave him plenty to eat, and some tobacco, and made as much of him as possible. He was highly gratified at his reception, which he saw added to his importance with the tribe. Like the rest, he required satisfying as to the object of our coming, and desired to know how long we were to remain, and where we were next going. As both he and Ireteba are intelligent men, and quick of comprehension, I drew, upon the ground, a map of the river and the surrounding country, and explained to them our plans, while they interpreted to the others. They seemed, for the first time, to clearly understand and feel at ease about the matter. Their countenances brightened, and there were frequent exclamations of "ahotka," ("good.") I told Cairook what I required of him in regard to the trading for provisions, the rules to be observed by the Indians, and the detail of messengers to carry letters to the fort; also that I wanted Ireteba to accompany me, and that an additional guide must be selected to go with us when we should leave the river. To all of this he gave a ready assent, and delivered a speech upon the subject to his people.

I now gave him some presents, which he forthwith distributed, as José had done, to his friends. The disposition of a few desirable articles that could not be divided occasioned him some perplexity. He made an earnest speech upon the subject, and at some one's suggestion it was decided to submit the matter to the popular vote. A deafening clamor and hopeless confusion was the immediate result of this experiment in universal suffrage, till Cairook, very sensibly, threw the objects of strife into the midst of the crowd, to be scrambled for, which had the effect, after a fierce momentary tussle, of restoring peace.

For two days Cairook, at my invitation, travelled upon the steamboat. He was accompanied, on the first day, by his wife. She is a nice looking squaw, and I allowed herself and her spouse the privilege, accorded to no other Indians, of sitting upon the upper deck. We made a good run, meeting with little detention, and they sat in dignified state, and enjoyed the admiring gaze of their neighbors, who were assembled in crowds along the banks. From the airs that were put on by Madam Cairook in consequence of being the only female thus distinguished, I am afraid that the trip turned her head, and that she must have been quite unbearable to her friends after she left us.

As we steamed away from the Mojave villages we passed a conspicuous conical peak, a few miles east of the river, which stands almost upon the 35th parallel, opposite the initial point of the California boundary. Cairook soon after bid us good bye, and returned home. Ireteba is to remain; and unwilling to be entirely bereft of the society of his tribe, has brought along a lad of sixteen, by the name of Nah-vah-roo-pa, to keep him company. Since the meeting with Cairook, our relations with the Mojaves have been of the most friendly description. They have, at every stopping place, brought provisions to trade, and of beans and corn we have now an adequate supply. Our original rations will be exhausted in a few days, and I have made every exertion to procure some wheat, in order to vary, as much as possible, the fare, but of this they have a limited quantity. The little flour they have brought is mixed with corn meal. It makes an excellent bread.

The zoological collections have been largely added to. Fish, squirrels, rabbits, rats, mice, lizards, snakes, &c., &c., have been brought in—many of them alive.

The behavior of the Indians has been orderly, and every evening, exactly at sunset, they have retired in a body from camp. Mariano and Capitan are delighted with the pacific relations that have been established, and no longer manifest any impatience to return, though, a few days ago, they were becoming importunate upon the subject. Capitan is a great favorite with the Mojaves, particularly with the young ladies. For several nights he has been absent at entertainments given in his honor, and, if what Ireteba says is true, has been taking advantage of his absence from Mrs. Capitan to be altogether too much of a gallant.

There has been a great deal to interest us among the people of this valley, and I regret that we have had to pass so hurriedly, and that we have been unable to learn more in regard to their habits and customs.   Very few parties of whites have visited them, and none have remained longer than a few days.   They are, therefore, in their native state, as they have

Fig. 17.—Boundary Cone.

existed for centuries.   Of their religion or superstitions, I have not been able to learn anything.   Government, they have so little of, that there cannot be much to learn.   They are not at all communicative concerning their institutions.   The marriage tie seems to be respected in more than an ordinary degree among Indians.   I think that few, if any, have more than one wife.

Their minds are active and intelligent, but I have been surprised to find how little idea of the superiority of the whites they have derived from seeing the appliances of civilization that surround those whom they have met.

Fire-arms, and the Explorer's steam-whistle, are the only objects that appear to excite their envy.   In most respects they think us their inferiors.   I had a large crowd about me one day, and exhibited several things that I supposed would interest them, among others a mariner's compass.   They soon learned its use, and thought we must be very stupid to be obliged to have recourse to artificial aid in order to find our way.   Some daguerreotypes were shown to them, but these they disliked, and were rather afraid of.   I heard one or two muttering, in their own language, that they were "very bad."   There being a few musicians and instruments in the party, the effect of harmony was tried, but they disapproved of the entertainment, as of everything else, and when the sounds died away, appointed two or three of their own musicians to show ours how the thing ought to be done. These artists performed a kind of chant, in a discordant, monotonous tone, and after making some of the most unearthly noises that I ever listened to, regarded us with an air of satisfied triumph. I tried, by showing them the boundaries upon a map, to make them comprehend the extent of our nation, as compared with their own, and to explain the relative numbers of the inhabitants. The statements were received simply as a piece of absurd gasconade, and had the same effect as the visits of some of the chiefs of the northwestern Indians to the Atlantic cities, which have resulted in destroying the influence of the unfortunate ambassadors, by stamping them forever, in the estimation of their own tribes, as egregious liars.

Two of the five great chiefs I have not met. One of them, named "Sikahot," lives not far below our present camp, but we passed his territory without stopping, and like Manuel, he does not think it dignified to go beyond his own dominions to visit us. They think it due to their position to receive the first call. I had a long discussion with Cairook, Ireteba, and Mariano about it. They were desirous that I should see Sikahot, and importuned me to stop and visit him. This I was not anxious to do. For the sake of future parties that might visit the valley, I had determined not to encourage the expectation that they were to receive from the whites gratuities, but to exact always some equivalent in return for what should be given them. The others had rendered or agreed to render certain services, for which they had received payment, but of Sikahot there was nothing to be asked. I told Cairook, and the other Indians, that if I met their friend I could not give him anything, but that if he would bring flour I would pay him for it as I had paid them; that Indians never gave white men any presents, and ought not to expect any. This was an idea that had never occurred to them, and they could not help grinning at the fairness of the reasoning. All the crowd laughed when the remark was translated to them.

It is a fact well known to those who have had much to do with Indians, that, as a rule, they never give anything to whites. Gratitude seems to be an element foreign to their nature. The only emotion that benefits excite in their breasts is a desire to receive more. The Mojaves have been uncontaminated by the vices that the approach of civilization engenders among Indians, and are, perhaps, rather superior to the generality of their race, but, as far as we can judge, they have, with few exceptions, certain qualities common to the Indian character. They are lazy, cruel, selfish, disgusting in their habits, and inveterate beggars. Even Cairook is not exempt from this last frailty, though, to do him justice, the things he asks for are seldom for himself. Ireteba is the only one that I have never known to beg for anything.

We have had such agreeable intercourse with the Colorado Indians that it is pleasant to be able to notice one good quality in them, and that is the exactitude with which they fulfil an agreement. On several occasions this has been called to our attention, and I am disposed to give them all credit for so honorable a characteristic.

The Mojaves preserve constant friendly relations with the Chemehuevis and Yumas, and were allied with the latter in the attack upon the Pimas and Maricopas, last September. At that time they lost one of their five chiefs and a great many of their best warriors. The Cocopa Indians they bitterly hate, and make forays into their country, slaying and taking prisoners. The unwarlike habits of that tribe have not permitted them to offer much resistance to these incursions, but they avenged themselves by giving the warning to the Pimas, which resulted in the wholesale slaughter of the attacking force. The animosity of the Mojaves against the Cocopas has been raised to the highest pitch by the disaster which befel the war party from this intervention of their despised foes.*

* The hatred which the Mojaves bear to this tribe, and the ferocity of their passions when excited, are exhibited in the following account, by an eye witness, of the treatment to which they subjected a prisoner belonging to the Cocopa nation. The fearful retaliation which the latter has since visited upon them would seem to be no more than was deserved :

"Among the captives they had stolen from the unoffending Cocopas was a handsome fair complexioned young female,

It is somewhat remarkable that these Indians should thrive so well upon the diet to which they are compelled to adhere. There is no game in the valley. The fish are scarce and of very inferior quality. They subsist almost exclusively upon beans and corn, with occasional watermelons and pumpkins, and are probably as fine a race, physically, as there is in existence.

Before leaving Washington, the late Secretary of War, Mr. Davis, proposed to me to carry out varieties of seeds for distribution to the Mojave tribe, and in accordance with this humane suggestion I provided an assortment of vegetable and fruit seeds, and have given them to the chiefs and some of the leading men, who have promised to try this season the experiment of planting them.

The annual overflow of the river enables them to raise, with little labor, an abundant supply of provisions for the year, which they improvidently consume, allowing the future to take care of itself. The failure of a crop is, therefore, an irremediable calamity. During one season, a few years since, the Colorado did not overflow its banks; there were consequently no crops, and great numbers of the Mojaves perished from starvation. It is quite possible that such visitations are of periodical occurrence, and are among the means adopted by nature to prevent the population of the valley, as there is no outlet for it nor room for its expansion, from increasing beyond the capacity of the country to sustain it. There is no question but that for several centuries, since the first visits of the early Spanish explorers, there has been little or no increase in the number of inhabitants. This number is apt to be overrated. I have discovered that the crowds seen collected at the different points passed during our progress up the river have been composed, to a considerable extent, of the same set of individuals, and suspect that the chiefs in their first formal visits have enhanced their apparent state and importance by borrowing recruits from their neighbors.

A system of irrigation and an improved method of agriculture would make the valley far more productive, but it is not certain that it could ever be a profitable place for white settlements. The shifting of the river bed, which, to the Indians who have a certain community of property, is a matter of little importance, would occasion serious embarrassment to settlers who had established permanent locations and improvements. The rapidity and extent of the changes in the position of the Colorado can scarcely be imagined by one who has not witnessed them.

Having an opportunity to compare the condition of things at present with what it was four years ago, I have been able to appreciate the transformations that are liable to occur, and am satisfied that there are few places in the bottom lands that may not, during any season, be overrun.

Our camp is fifty-two miles from the foot of the valley by the course of the river, though little more than half that distance in a direct line. A few places have been encountered where the navigation is difficult. A rapid, over a gravelly shoal, occurs near the head of the Mojave

about twenty-five years of age. She was as beautiful as any Indian woman I have ever seen, tall, graceful, and lady-like in her appearance.

"A noisy meeting was held, and the night spent in one of their victory dances, during which they would dance around her, shout in her ears, and spit in her face. The next morning a post was firmly planted in the ground, and about eight feet from the bottom a cross beam attached. They then drove rough wooden spikes through the palms of their captive's hands, and by these raised her to the cross-beam, and drove the spikes into the soft wood, extending her arms as far as they would reach. Then with pieces of bark stuck with thorns they tied her head firmly back to the upright post, drove spikes through her ankles, and for a time left her.

"They soon returned, and placing me, with their other captives, near the sufferer, bid us keep our eyes upon her until she died. Then they commenced running around the stake in circles, hallooing and stamping like demons. After a while several supplied themselves with bows and arrows, and at every circlet they would shoot an arrow into her quivering flesh. Occasionally she would utter piteous cries, which would awaken from the mocking crowd taunting yells.

"For two hours she hung in this dreadful condition, bleeding and sighing, her body mangled in a shocking manner. Whenever she would scream aloud they would stuff rags in her mouth to silence her. After she was dead they took her body to a funeral pile and burned it."—*Olive Oatman's Narrative.*

cañon, and one less violent twenty miles above. There are two or three troublesome shoals, where the river is divided by islands into several channels, but as a general rule the navigation has been better in this valley than elsewhere above Fort Yuma. The places that at low water give most trouble are the bars where the bed is covered with pebbles or gravel, but these, with a boat of lighter draught or at a higher stage of the river, would present no difficulty.

The range east of the Mojave valley we call the Black mountains. These mountains run from a point fifteen or twenty miles east of the foot of the valley in a northwesterly direction, and cross the Colorado about fifty miles north of camp. Where the river breaks through this

Fig. 18.—Beale's Pass.

chain there is doubtless a stupendous cañon. Beyond the cañon is the supposed position of the mouth of the Virgen and the Great Bend of the Colorado. Westward, opposite to camp, is the pass through the spur that connects the Black and Mojave ranges, by which the wagon trail of Lieutenant Beale leaves the valley of the Colorado.

The winter has given place to spring. The nights are cool, but ice is no longer found. The days are very warm, but even the rays of the sun have seemed to be more tempered and less oppressive since entering the Mojave valley.

J.J.Young, from a sketch by H.B.Mollhausen.

Lith.of Sarony,Major & Knapp 449 Broadway.NY

DEAD MOUNTAIN, MOJAVE VALLEY.

CHAPTER V.

MOJAVE VALLEY TO MOUTH OF BLACK CANON.

DEAD MOUNTAIN.—TRADITIONS CONCERNING IT.—PYRAMID CAÑON.—DEEP RAPID.—RAPIDS AND ROCKY SHOAL.—LONG DETENTION.—LAND STORM.—DEFECTS IN STEAMER.—TOPOGRAPHICAL AND GEOLOGICAL INVESTIGATIONS.—DEPARTURE OF CAPITAN.—ARRIVAL OF MAIL CARRIERS.—INTELLIGENCE FROM THE PACK TRAIN.—COTTONWOOD VALLEY.—PAINTED CAÑON.—MOUNT DAVIS.—VICINITY OF PAI-UTES.—DIFFICULT RAPIDS.—GRAVEL BLUFFS.—MOUTH OF BLACK CAÑON.—EXPLORER'S ROCK.—ACCIDENT TO STEAMBOAT.—DETENTION.—SCARCITY OF SUPPLIES.—PREPARATIONS TO ASCEND THE CAÑON.—MINERALS IN OPAL MOUNTAINS.

Camp 50, foot of Cottonwood valley, February 24.—An imposing mountain stands near the west bank of the Colorado at the head of the Mojave valley. It is the highest peak in sight, and is regarded with reverence by the Indians, who believe it to be the abode of their departed spirits. Ireteba informed me, with awe in his countenance, that should any one dare to visit it he would be instantly struck dead. This is the first time I have been able to extract any allusion to the religious belief of the Mojaves, and Ireteba was reluctant to speak upon the subject.*

From the Dead mountain a range extends to the northwest and a spur crosses the river and connects with the Black mountains. This spur forms the northern limit of the Mojave valley. For several miles our course lay through the foot hills, when the river narrowed and entered a cañon through a gate, one side of which looked like the head of a bull. The scenery in this cañon was picturesque and beautiful, but nevertheless seemed tame in comparison with the grand and startling effects presented in the cañons through the Monument and Mojave mountains.

Near the upper end a rapid occurred upon a pebbly shoal, and the Explorer received some hard knocks, to which she has become lately quite accustomed. After traversing the Pyramid cañon—so called from a natural pyramid, of symmetrical proportions, twenty or thirty feet high, standing near the rapid just mentioned—rapids were encountered in quick succession, and have been met with, at short intervals, up to camp, which is twenty miles from the head of the Mojave valley. Most of them have been ascended without difficulty. At one (Deep rapid) there was sufficient depth and a channel unobstructed by rocks, but the rush of water was very strong. When we first heard its roar and saw the surging and foaming torrent we were startled, and a little apprehensive that we might have reached the head of navigation. There was less difficulty in making the ascent than had been anticipated. Not knowing what

---

* In the narrative of Miss Oatman this mountain is alluded to, and her description is interesting, as furnishing an additional example of the universality among the tribes of North American Indians of the tradition of a deluge:

"They told me, pointing to a high mountain at the northern end of the valley, that in ancient times there was a flood, which covered all the world except that mountain, and that by climbing it one family was saved from the general deluge; that this family was very large and had great riches, clothing, cattle, horses, and plenty to eat; that after the water subsided one of the family took all the cattle and one kind of clothing and went north, and was there turned from red to white; that another of the family took deer skins and bark, and from him the Indians have descended; that the progenitor of the whites had a red complexion until he stole, and then he became white; that remains of the old 'big house,' in which this ancient family lived, were up there yet; also pieces of bottles, broken dishes, and remnants of all the various kinds of articles used by them.

"They said also that this venerated spot had been, since the flood, the abode of spirits, and that if the feet of mortals should presume to tread their enchanted land a fire would burst from the mountain and instantly consume them. It is their belief that the spirit of every white, whom the Mojaves had been successful in slaying, is held there in their perpetual chains, and doomed to the torment of quenchless fires, while the Mojave, by whose hand the slaughter was perpetrated, is exalted to eternal honors and superior privileges therefor."—*Narrative of Olive Oatman.*

COLORADO RIVER. COTTONWOOD VALLEY.

FROM PYRAMID CAÑON TO PAINTED CAÑON

LITH. OF SARONY MAJOR & KNAPP, 449 BROADWAY N.Y.

depth of water would be found, Captain Robinson had the boat lightened and Mr. Carroll put on a head of steam that made the stern wheel spin around like a top, and a line being taken out ahead, the summit of the rapid was quickly attained.

Abreast of the last camp was a rapid that occasioned more trouble, although the flow was less violent. The river was divided by an island into two channels, and in neither was there more than two feet of water. The shoal extended for some distance and the bottom was

Fig. 19.—Pyramid Cañon.

covered with rocks. A long line had to be taken ahead, in order to reach a place where there was good holding ground. The boat was lightened and, after several hours of hard labor, had been brought to the crest of the rapid, when the line broke and the Explorer drifted down, bumping upon the rocks, and was in imminent danger of having her hull stove. The day's work was undone in an instant, and we were very glad that it was no worse. When she finally brought up, it was upon some rocks, where she was wedged so fast that it occupied half of the next day to extricate her. The remainder of the day was spent in a second and more successful attempt, and at dark we had the satisfaction of seeing our steamer safely anchored above. That same night the fiercest norther sprang up that has yet been experienced, and continued throughout the following day. We ate, drank, breathed, and saw little but sand for twenty-four hours, and the gale was so violent that the Explorer was dragged from her anchorage and driven upon the rocks. At night the wind subsided, but recommenced the next day, though with diminished force, and we got the steamboat, by evening, into deep water. To-day we had made one or two miles when the wind once more sprang up and blew with such fury that we were but too happy to find a cove where the boat could lie in safety. We have spent the day sitting on a bank, blinded and choked by masses of sand that have been beating upon us without an instant's cessation.

The timbers fastened to the Explorer's hull are a greater hindrance to her progress in this part of the river than below. They become wedged in the rocks, and render it difficult to extricate the boat, besides increasing the draught by the amount of their thickness, which is four or five inches. As has been the case at places in the lower portions of the Colorado, the bar that has here detained us three days would not have stopped a boat of six inches less draught, with a smooth bottom, as many hours. It is probable that there is not one season in ten when even the Explorer would encounter one-fourth of the difficulty that she has during the present unprecedentedly low stage of water.

Fig. 20.—Deep Rapid.

Ireteba has become warmly interested in our hopes of reaching the Great Bend. He had thought that the Deep rapid would put a stop to the steamboating, and since that has been passed entertains a higher opinion of the capabilities of our craft. He told me this evening that there are yet four difficult rapids this side of the Great Bend; that the last of these occurs in an immense cañon, where the channel is filled with huge rocks, through which the water rushes in a furious torrent. Here, he informs me in emphatic pantomime, we shall come to a dead stop. Not far above, according to his account, the Colorado makes the bend to the east and a stream comes in, the water of which is salt. This, it would seem, must be the Virgen, for the upper waters of that river are known to have a brackish taste.

The late detentions have afforded Dr. Newberry and Mr. Egloffstein excellent opportunities to pursue their respective avocations. The doctor has had leisure to make a very full and perfect mineralogical collection, and become thoroughly conversant with the geological characteristics of the region. Mr. Egloffstein has taken panoramic views of the river and the adjacent country, and has now completed a set that extends from Fort Yuma to the present camp. The ascent of a prominent peak on the opposite side of the river (Mount Newberry) has given him a view of the whole of the Black mountain range.

The position of the cañon through the Black mountains is nearly north. The walls of the entrance are plainly visible. East of the cañon the mountains present an impassable barrier to all progress in that direction. The only break that has been seen by which it seems possible to cross, in order to pursue the land explorations, is near the 35th parallel, where the gap is apparent, by which Captain Sitgreaves and Mr. Beale must have both descended to the Colorado.

Not far west of the Black cañon, a low place in the same range designates a pass through which a good wagon route may be found between the portion of the river south of the mountains and the road to Utah. This connexion it will be important to make, if the head of navigation turns out to be, as Ireteba says it will, in the Black cañon.

Apart from the volcanic upheavals, as exhibited in the ranges of mountains, Mr. Egloffstein thinks that he has been able to distinguish a great and general rise of the whole region towards the north and east along a line within fifty miles of us.* If this be correct the grade of the river will soon become so steep that it will be impossible to ascend further.

Four days ago Capitan begged permission to return, and his services being no longer required since Ireteba has joined us, I told him he could go. He has been with the party so long that we really regretted parting from him. Before he left he was loaded with as many presents as he could carry, and was also charged with a package of letters to be taken to Fort Yuma. Mariano is inclined to see the issue of the exploration of the navigable portion of the river, and decided not to accompany Capitan back.

For several days we have been expecting the return of the Indian expressman. These runners regulate their marches so as to reach their destination at the close of day, and every evening at sunset we have looked anxiously towards the Pyramid mountains, with the hope of descrying some one crossing the summit. This evening a moving figure was discerned in the distance, that turned out to be the long-expected messenger with the letters. He brought intelligence from Lieutenant Tipton that the arrangements for the departure of the pack-train were progressing favorably, and that he should commence the ascent of the river from the fort on the 15th of this month.

The Mojave was dust-begrimed and weary. He has had a hard time footing it in the face of the gale and the driving sand during the past three days, but after he had received the payment that was allotted to him, did not appear to regret having undertaken the trip.

An occasional lull in the blast has permitted the partial subsidence of the sand clouds, and afforded glimpses of a valley immediately above camp. Groves of cottonwood trees, of a larger growth than any seen before, indicate that there is some alluvial land, but the valley does not appear to be of great extent.

Camp 53, *Round island, March* 1.—The Cottonwood valley was found to be only five or six miles in length and completely hemmed in by wild-looking mountains. The belt of bottom land is narrow, and dotted with graceful clusters of stately cottonwood in full and brilliant leaf. The river flows sometimes through green meadows, bordered with purple and gold rushes, and then between high banks, where rich masses of foliage overhang the stream, and afford a cool and inviting shade. From the edges of this garden-like precinct sterile slopes extend to the bases of the surrounding mountain chains. A few isolated black hills break the monotony of the ascent. There is no vegetation ; the barren surfaces reach to the very summits of the lofty ranges and impart to the grandeur of the scene an air of painful desolation.

We have now entered a region that has never. as far as any records show, been visited by whites, and are approaching a locality where it is supposed that the famous "Big Cañon" of

---

* This impression subsequent examinations entirely confirmed.

the Colorado commences; every point of the view is scanned with eager interest. We can distinctly see to the north the steep wall of one side of the gorge where the Colorado breaks through the Black mountains. Whether this is the "Big Cañon" or not it is certainly of far grander proportions than any which we have thus far traversed.

Fig. 21.—Cottonwood Valley.

At the head of the Cottonwood valley we threaded a cañon formed by the passage of the river through a spur that connects the Black and Dead mountain ranges. It was only two or three miles in extent, and the sides were of moderate height, but the gorgeous contrast and intensity of color exhibited upon the rocks exceeded in beauty anything that had been witnessed of a similar character. Various and vivid tints of blue, brown, white, purple, and crimson, were blended with exquisite shading upon the gateways and inner walls, producing effects so novel and surprising as to make the cañon, in some respects, the most picturesque and striking of any of these wonderful mountain passes.

The country above and adjoining the river is tolerably open. There is no more alluvial land, but low gravel hills can be traced as far north as the base of the Black mountains. Just above the Painted cañon, and forming a part of the spur that has been alluded to, is a symetrical and prominent peak, Mount Davis, which presents the most conspicuous landmark north of the Dead mountain. At the base of Mount Davis the river divides and forms a round island of considerable extent, at the foot of which is a rapid that has created some trouble and detention.

A few scattered Mojave families inhabit the Cottonwood valley. We saw no fields under culti-vation, and the residents brought neither corn nor beans to trade. One of them agreed to take a letter for me to Lieutenant Tipton, and to guide the pack-train from the Mojave valley until it should overtake us. This may be at no great distance ahead, for Ireteba, while admitting that we may reach the mouth of the Black cañon, still maintains that we can never get the steamboat through it. Since leaving the Cottonwood valley he has appeared uneasy, and has given me constant warnings to exercise precaution, for that the "bad Pai-utes" are prowling about. He says that great numbers of them live near the Mormon road, from which we are not far distant; that there are many white men among them, and that some Pai-utes who lately visited the Mojaves told them that they intended to destroy our party as soon as it should enter their territory. He thinks that we are too few in number, and looks dubiously at us and then at the bank, when we come to places where the river is narrow and the formation of the gravel hills is favorable for an ambuscade. There is seldom difficulty in selecting a spot for camp that

Fig. 22.—Painted Cañon.

would be impregnable against almost any number of Indians armed only with bows and clubs; and as full moon is approaching the nights do not invite attack.

The view this evening of the island, the river, the labyrinth of low hills, the great chains of mountains that interlock from the north and south, and Mount Davis, towering directly overhead, all bathed in the brilliant moonlight, is indescribably magnificent.

The Indians are seated at the verge of camp, earnestly observing the Dead mountain. Its hoary crest is draped in a light floating haze, and misty wreaths are winding like phantoms among its peaks and dim recesses. The wondering watchers see the spirits of departed Mojaves hovering about their legendary abode, and gaze reverently at the shadowy forms that circle around the haunted summit.

Camp 57, *mouth of Black cañon, March* 8.—The twenty miles of distance between Round island and the present camp required five days to accomplish. A dozen or more rapids, of all descriptions, had to be passed; some were violent and deep, others shallow. At a few the bed of the stream was sandy; but generally it was composed of gravel and pebbles. Below the crest of one rapid the current forked, forming two eddies. Several attempts were made to

F.W. EGLOFFSTEIN, from a sketch by LIEUT. IVES.

BLACK CAÑON

ascend; but the bow was not pointed exactly towards the centre of the fork, and, being thrown off by the eddy, the boat would go down stream, whirling around like a teetotum.   After four or five unsuccessful trials, Captain Robinson struck the right point, and we got through without further trouble.   The worst places encountered have been where the banks were low and destitute of vegetation, and the rocky bed of the river afforded no holding ground near by for an anchor.   The lines have become almost worn out by hard service; the skiff is badly battered, and scarcely able to float, and all the oars are broken.   The last seventy miles will, perhaps, be

Fig. 23—Mount Davis.

the best part of the Colorado to navigate when the water is not at so exceedingly low a stage. The rapids will be less violent, and the bottom being gravelly no new bars will be formed as the river rises.

Between Mount Davis and the Black mountains the river flows between gravel bluffs and the foot-hills of the latter chain.   The view in all directions was intercepted, and before we were conscious of its neighborhood a sudden turn around the base of a conical peak disclosed the southern portal of the Black cañon directly in front.   The Black mountains were piled overhead in grand confusion, and through a narrow gateway flanked by walls many hundreds of feet in height, rising perpendicularly out of the water, the Colorado emerged from the bowels of the range.

A rapid, a hundred yards below the mouth of the cañon, created a short detention, and a strong head of steam was put on to make the ascent.   After passing the crest the current became slack, the soundings were unusually favorable, and we were shooting swiftly past the entrance, eagerly gazing into the mysterious depths beyond, when the Explorer, with a stunning crash, brought up abruptly and instantaneously against a sunken rock.   For a second the impression was that the cañon had fallen in.   The concussion was so violent that the men near the bow were thrown overboard; the doctor, Mr. Mollhausen, and myself, having been seated in front of the upper deck, were precipitated head foremost into the bottom of the boat; the fireman, who was pitching a log into the fire, went half-way in with it; the boiler was thrown out of place; the steam pipe doubled up; the wheel-house torn away; and it was expected that the boat would fill and sink instantly by all, but Mr. Carroll, who was looking for an explosion from the injured steam pipes.   Finding, after a few moments had passed, that she still floated, Captain Robinson had a line taken into the skiff, and the steamer was towed alongside of a gravelly spit a little below; it was then ascertained that the stem of the boat, where the iron flanges of the two bow sections were joined, had struck fair upon the rock, and that, although the flanges were torn away, no hole had been made, and the hull was uninjured. The other damages were such as a day or two of labor could repair.

Fig. 24.—Gravel Bluffs south of Black Mountains.

After making these unexpected and welcome discoveries, the captain and myself went out in the skiff and examined the rock.   It stands in the centre of the channel; has steep sides and a conical shape.   The summit, which comes almost to a point, is about four inches below the surface of the water; and if the boat had struck half an inch to one side or the other of the flanges, the sheet of iron that forms the bow would have been torn open as though it had been a strip of pasteboard.

Nearly three days have elapsed since the accident, and everything is restored to its former condition.   I have thought it would be imprudent, after this experience of sunken rocks, to attempt the passage of the cañon without making a preliminary reconnaissance in the skiff.   A second escape of the boat, in the event of a similar encounter with a rock, would be too much to hope for; and should she be sunk in the cañon, and there be nothing to swim to but perpendicular walls five hundred or a thousand feet high, the individuals on board would be likely to share the fate of the steamer.   The carpenter has been working at the skiff, to put it in a more serviceable condition, and two or three oars have been mended; to-morrow the captain, the mate, and myself, are going to make an attempt to ascend the cañon.

The arrival of the pack-train is looked forward to with much eagerness.   Rockets were sent up this evening from the summit of the cliff above camp, and the southern horizon was watched for the appearance of similar signals in that direction, but without result.   For two or three weeks we have been subsisting upon the corn and beans obtained from the Indians; the corn is ground in coffee-mills, and makes a tolerable bread, upon which and boiled beans, washed down with water from the river, we breakfast, dine, and sup.   This diet agrees wonderfully

Fig. 25 —Mouth of Black Cañon.

with the Mojaves; but either our stomachs are not sufficiently trained to it, or it is not wholesome fare for whites, for some of the men suffer a good deal.   The labor for the past two or three weeks has been excessive, involving the necessity of standing, sometimes for hours, waist-deep in the chilling water; and strong food has been particularly craved.   The want of coffee is generally found, on such occasions, to be the severest privation, even more so than that of meat.   But the greatest trouble our party has had to put up with has been the absence of salt. The bag containing the whole supply was lost or stolen a fortnight ago.   No one can imagine, who has not tried the experiment, how tasteless and disagreeable food may become when prepared without this common but indispensable ingredient.   A well-salted dog or mule soup would be received with delight in exchange for the insipid dishes of beans and corn which we are compelled daily to swallow.

Ireteba volunteered yesterday to go back to the Mojave valley and ascertain the whereabouts of the pack-train.   He thought he would be able to learn the news and return by the time

Captain Robinson and myself should have made the reconnaissance of the cañon; and I willingly acceded to his proposition.   Before leaving he again warned me against the Pai-utes. Their tracks have been discovered in the immediate neighborhood, and one of them was seen an evening or two ago watching us from a thicket on the opposite side of the river.   It would be no easy matter to surprise us in camp; but there is a prospect that the doctor and Mr. Egloff-stein, who spend much of their time in geological and topographical excursions, may be carried off some day by a straggling party.

The mountains west of the river are rich in mineral curiosities.   Along the bottoms of the ravines are found crystals of quartz, in curiously grouped clusters, and great numbers of opals. Some of the latter are of considerable size, and promise to prove, when polished, valuable gems.

CHAPTER VI.

BLACK CANON TO GREAT BEND—RETURN TO MOJAVE VALLEY.

Camp 59, *head of Black cañon, March* 10.—The skiff having been put in tolerable order, a bucket full of corn and beans, three pairs of blankets, a compass, and a sextant and chronometer were stowed away in it, and a little before sunrise the captain, mate, and myself commenced the exploration of the cañon. My companions each pulled a pair of sculls, and with considerable vigor; but as the current has a flow of three miles an hour we could not make rapid progress. We had proceeded a quarter of a mile, and had just rounded the first bend, when one of the sculls snapped, reducing by half our motive power. There was, fortunately, a current of air drawing in the right direction through the narrow gorge, and, with the odd scull and a blanket, an apology for a sail was rigged, which, at intervals, rendered great assistance.

In a few minutes, having passed what may be called the outworks of the range, we fairly entered its gigantic precincts, and commenced to thread the mazes of a cañon, far exceeding in vastness any that had been yet traversed. The walls were perpendicular, and more than double the height of those in the Mojave mountains, rising, in many places, sheer from the water, for over a thousand feet. The naked rocks presented, in lieu of the brilliant tints that had illuminated the sides of the lower passes, a uniform sombre hue, that added much to the solemn and impressive sublimity of the place. The river was narrow and devious, and each turn disclosed new combinations of colossal and fantastic forms, dimly seen in the dizzy heights overhead, or through the sunless depths of the vista beyond. With every mile the view became more picturesque and imposing, exhibiting the same romantic effects and varied transformations that were displayed in the Mojave cañon, but on an enlarged and grander scale.

Rapids were of frequent occurrence, and at every one we were obliged to get out of the skiff, and haul it over. Eight miles from the mouth of the cañon, a loud sullen roaring betokened that something unusual was ahead, and a rapid appeared which was undoubtedly the same that had been described by Ireteba. Masses of rock filled up the sides of the channel. In the centre, at the foot of the rapid, and rising four or five feet above the surface of the water, was a pyramidal rock, against which the billows dashed as they plunged down from above, and glanced upwards, like a water spout.

The torrent was swifter than at any place below, but a steamboat, entirely emptied of its cargo, which could be deposited upon the rocks alongside of the rapid, could, if provided with long and stout lines, be hauled up. During a higher stage of the river the difficulty of the place would be much diminished. With our nearly worn out ropes it would be very hazardous to attempt the ascent.

DRAWN BY FRH᷐ F. W. v. EGLOFFSTEIN.

COLORADO RIVER. DAVIS VALLEY

FROM PAINTED CAÑON TO BLACK CAÑON.

Several rapids followed, at short distances, all of which would be troublesome to pass at the present depth of water. The constant getting out of the boat, and the labor of dragging it through these difficult places, made our progress for some miles exceedingly tedious and fatiguing. As sunset was approaching we came to a nook in the side of the cañon, four miles above the Roaring rapid, where a patch of gravel and a few pieces of drift-wood, lodged upon the rocks, offered a tolerable camping place, and we hauled the skiff upon the shingle, and stopped for the night. There was no need of keeping a watch, with two grim lines of sentinels, a thousand feet high, guarding the camp. Even though we could have been seen from the verge of the cliff above, our position was totally inaccessible.

Darkness supervened with surprising suddenness. Pall after pall of shade fell, as it were in clouds, upon the deep recesses about us. The line of light, through the opening above, at last became blurred and indistinct, and, save the dull red glare of the camp-fire, all was enveloped in a murky gloom. Soon the narrow belt again brightened, as the rays of the moon reached the summits of the mountains. Gazing far upward upon the edges of the overhanging walls we witnessed the gradual illumination. A few isolated turrets and pinnacles first appeared in strong relief upon the blue band of the heavens. As the silvery light descended, and fell upon the opposite crest of the abyss, strange and uncouth shapes seemed to start out, all sparkling and blinking in the light, and to be peering over at us as we lay watching them from the bottom of the profound chasm. The contrast between the vivid glow above, and the black obscurity beneath, formed one of the most striking points in the singular picture. Of the subsequent appearance of things, when the moon rose higher, I do not think any of our weary party took particular notice.

This morning, as soon as the light permitted, we were again upon the way. The ascent of the river was attended with as much labor as it had been the day before; for though none of the rapids were of so violent a character, they were of constant occurrence. The wind still held to the south, and the blanket sail was again set to great advantage.

The cañon continued increasing in size and magnificence. No description can convey an idea of the varied and majestic grandeur of this peerless water-way. Wherever the river makes a turn the entire panorama changes, and one startling novelty after another appears and disappears with bewildering rapidity. Stately façades, august cathedrals, amphitheatres, rotundas, castellated walls, and rows of time-stained ruins, surmounted by every form of tower, minaret, dome, and spire, have been moulded from the cyclopean masses of rock that form the mighty defile. The solitude, the stillness, the subdued light, and the vastness of every surrounding object, produce an impression of awe that ultimately becomes almost painful. As hour after hour passed we began to look anxiously ahead for some sign of an outlet from the range, but the declining day brought only fresh piles of mountains, higher, apparently, than any before seen. We had made up our minds to pass another night in the cañon, and were searching for a spot large enough to serve as a resting-place, when we came into a narrow passage, between two mammoth peaks, that seemed to be nodding to each other across the stream, and unexpectedly found, at the upper end, the termination of the Black cañon.

Low hills of gravel intercepted the view, and prevented us from seeing far into the unknown region beyond. A mile above the cañon the river swept the base of a high hill, with salient angles, like the bastions of a fort. At the base was a little ravine, which offered a camping place that would be sheltered from observation, and we drew the skiff out of the water, determining not to proceed any further till to-morrow. Leaving the mate to take charge of the boat, the captain and myself ascended the hill, which is over a thousand feet high. A scene of barren and desolate confusion was spread before us. We seemed to have reached the focus or culminating point of the volcanic disturbances that have left their traces over the whole region south. In almost every direction were hills and mountains heaped together without any apparent system or order. A small open area intervened between camp and a range to the north, and we could trace the course of the river as it wound towards the east, forming the Great Bend. In the direction of the Mormon road to Utah, which is but twenty miles distant, the country looked less broken, and it was evident that there would be no difficulty in opening a wagon communication between the road and the river. We tried to discover the valley of the Virgen, but could see no indication of any stream coming in from the northwest. The view in that direction was partially obstructed by another summit of Fortification rock.

Not a trace of vegetation could be discovered, but the glaring monotony of the rocks was somewhat relieved by grotesque and fanciful varieties of coloring. The great towers that formed the northern gateway of the cañon were striped with crimson and yellow bands; the gravel bluffs bordering the river exhibited brilliant alternations of the same hues, and not far to the east, mingled with the gray summits, were two or three hills, altogether of a blood-red color, that imparted a peculiarly ghastly air to the scene.

The approach of darkness stopped further observations, and we descended to camp, having first taken a good look, in every direction, for the smoke of Indian camp-fires, but without discovering any. In making the sixteen miles from last night's bivouac, we have had to labor ha d for thirteen hours, stemming the strong current, and crossing the numerous rapids, and being thoroughly exhausted, depend for security to-night more upon our concealed position than upon any vigilance that is likely to be exhibited.

Camp 57, foot of Black cañon, March 12.—Skirting the base of Fortification rock, we ascended the river a couple of miles, and came to the mouth of a stream about the size of Bill Williams's Fork, as the latter was when we passed it. We disembarked, and followed for some distance along its border. The appearance of the bed and the banks indicated the existence, during some seasons, of a wide and deep river. It was now but a few inches deep. The water was clear, and had a strong brackish taste. This fact, and its position, led me to suppose that we were at the mouth of the Virgen, but I could scarcely believe that that river could ever present so insignificant an appearance.

I now determined not to try to ascend the Colorado any further. The water above the Black cañon had been shoal, and the current swift. Rapids had occurred in such quick succession as to make navigation almost impossible, and there would be no object in proceeding beyond the Great Bend. The difficulties encountered in the cañon were of a character to prevent a steamboat from attempting to traverse it at low water, and we had seen drift-wood lodged in clefts fifty feet above the river, betokening a condition of things during the summer freshet that would render navigation more hazardous at that season than now. It appeared, therefore, that the foot of the Black cañon should be considered the practical head of navigation, and I concluded to have a reconnaissance made to connect that point with the Mormon road, and to let this finish the exploration of the navigable portion of the Colorado.

As we were going back to the boat we saw fresh Indian tracks in the sand, and hastened to get possession of the skiff, not knowing in how close proximity our unpleasant neighbors might be. A bright lookout was kept upon the nearest bank as we sailed down stream towards the cañon, which was reached, however, without accident or molestation.

The descent of the river was a much easier and pleasanter operation than going up, and the rapidity of the progress added an additional charm to the scenery. One or two of the rapids had to be passed with caution, but down most of them we shot with exhilarating velocity. It was nearly ten o'clock when we started to return; but we had accomplished the thirty miles to the steamboat camp by four or five in the evening.

The first question asked was, if any news had been received from the pack-train; and the reply was not favorable. Ireteba had returned from the Cottonwood valley, and brought the unwelcome tidings from the Mojaves who live there that neither they nor their friends in the valley below had heard anything in regard to its approach. It behooved us, therefore, to commence the descent of the river as soon as possible; for even the stock of corn and beans was found to be running very low. To-day we have been getting everything in readiness for the move, and are going to start to-morrow morning.

At sunset a halloo was heard from the opposite bank, and a couple of Indians were seen making signs for the skiff to be sent to them. Ireteba, who had come to the edge of the water when he heard the shout, informed me that one of the Indians was the Mojave runner that I had last sent with letters to Fort Yuma. The skiff was at once despatched to bring him over, and as he landed he handed me a large package of letters and newspapers. He told me that he had passed the pack-train in the mountains, below the mouth of Bill Williams's Fork. He bore a note from Lieutenant Tipton, dated on the 5th of March, from that locality, informing me that the country along the river had been very difficult to travel, and that the progress of the train had been slow, but that he should push on as fast as possible to join us. Unless some accident occurs we are likely to meet him before we reach the Mojave valley.

The news from the train, the receipt of letters and papers from home, and the prospect of a speedy change of diet, have occasioned much hilarity in camp, and our Mojave messenger finds that he can get from almost any of the party pretty much what he chooses to ask for—a circumstance of which I observe he is not slow in taking advantage.

Camp 52, *Cottonwood valley, March* 16.—Thirty miles of the descent have been easily accomplished. A pelting storm of rain, accompanied with violent gusts of wind, compelled us to lie over for a day, but had the good effect of raising the river a few inches, and enabled the steamer to glide down the rapids without delay or danger. During the night of the storm a party of Pai-utes came to the opposite side of the river. A large number of Indian tracks were found that had been made subsequently to the fall of rain.

The Mojave who brought the letters was so delighted with the reception his services received that he volunteered to go again to Fort Yuma. His offer was closed with at once, and a package was prepared, with which he trotted off an hour or two before the departure of the boat. I had to send an order to the fort for his payment, and a direction not to give him anything to bring to our party. We hope to be far distant from this portion of the river by the time he would be able to return.

While steaming around the base of Mount Davis we overtook the expressman, who called out to us that there were fresh tracks of horses and mules on the west bank, leading down the river, that had been made only a few hours before. At the first wooding place the trail was searched for and examined. There appeared to be four persons; and we concluded that they were Mormons, from the Vegas, who had come to look after our movements.

This evening an individual called to us from across the river to send a boat over. As soon as the visitor made his appearance we perceived that he was a Mormon. A member of my party who had been in Utah said that he recognized him as one of their bishops. For some reason he chose to make a mystery of his personality, and told a clumsily contrived and impossible story; representing himself and companions as California emigrants *en route* to Los Angelos. He said they had taken this detour of a couple of hundred miles to avoid meeting Indians; and, according to his own account, they had already passed all of the Indians that were to be encountered on the regular trail, and by coming to the Colorado would be obliged to run the gauntlet of one or two thousand more. This and several similar discrepancies did not argue well for the bishop's sanctity; but we gave him a night's lodging—that is, a pair of blankets to sleep upon—and entertained him as well as the corn and beans would permit. An old Indian had, a few hours before, brought some beautiful crystals of rock salt to trade for beads. If he had known the market value of salt in our camp he could have enriched himself; there was not a man who would not have given half his wardrobe, if necessary, for a lump of it.

The bishop departed with early dawn to join his companions, first extracting all the information he could concerning our expedition and the practicability of navigating the river. A reconnaissance is being made, under the guidance of Nah-vah-roo-pa, to connect the head of navigation with the Mormon road, and we have remained in the valley to-day awaiting the return of the absent party. Ireteba has preceded us to the Mojave villages to look after the pack-train, of which there are still no tidings. Old Mariano is the only Indian left. Those who live in this neighborhood have suddenly become shy, and refuse to approach camp; Mariano has been among them, and reports that the Mormons have created a prejudice against us by informing the already suspicious Mojaves that we have come to take away their lands. Mariano further states that they have proposed to these Indians to commence hostilities, promising the assistance of themselves and the Pai-utes, and that they bribed Ireteba this morning, by the offer of a mule, to conduct the scouting party to the Mojave villages, the visit being intended for our especial disadvantage; all of which is to be received with due allowance, though the coincidence is singular between the appearance of the Mormons and the sudden change of manner adopted by our neighbors.

The latter are extremely sensitive about the possibility of strangers invading their domains. I learned from Ireteba that the Mormons had on several occasions made friendly overtures, but that his tribe suspected them of looking with a covetous eye on the beautiful Mojave valley. Certain zealous divines, eager to make proselytes, had baptized a number of the Indians. Ireteba told me, with a grin, that Cairook was among the number, and that the big chief was greatly disgusted when they tried to duck his head in the river.

Foot of Pyramid cañon, March 20.—The morning after the departure of the Mormons Mr. Peacock, with an advanced portion of the pack-train, rode into camp; on the following day Lieutenant Tipton and the remainder of the detachment joined us. The trip from Fort Yuma had been a rough one; the trails across the mountain ranges were difficult even for pack-mules to follow. Grass had been very scarce; only five good grazing camps had been found during the whole distance, and the mules consequently were not in the best condition to commence the land explorations.

The conduct of the Mojaves had been friendly till within a day or two, when their behavior became suspicious. They remained at a distance from camp, and at night attempted to set fire to the grass. Lieutenant Tipton had been strongly tempted to attack them, but felt reluctant to have any outbreak while ignorant of the condition of my party. Two Yumas, who had acted as guides, had a talk with the Mojaves, and told Mr. Tipton that the Mormons had been endeavoring in every way to excite the hostility of the last-mentioned Indians against the expedition, and had urged them to commence an attack by stampeding the animals. This statement coincides entirely with what Ireteba and Mariano have repeatedly told me. I have found these two Indians invariably truthful, and know not what object they could have had in manufacturing a false story. Corroborated as it is by the Yumas and by many circumstances that have occurred, I hardly know how to discredit it, though I feel reluctant to believe that any white men could be guilty of such unprovoked rascality.

An early and satisfactory event after the arrival of the train was the having a hearty meal cooked; and when this was disposed of, preparations were made to return immediately to the Mojave villages. The reconnoitring party had come in, having found a practicable line of communication between the river and the Mormon road. For the first nineteen miles, to the summit of the Opal mountains, some work would be required to make a roadway practicable for wagons; beyond the summit a sloping plain extends to a gap a short distance north of the Vegas.

Another storm of rain, and the necessity of giving the mules a rest, caused a day's postpone-ment of our departure. As we commenced the descent from the Cottonwood valley, two Indians, who had been watching our movements, started upon a run along the trail leading to the south. We saw them, through the pure atmosphere, long afterwards, on the side of a distant mountain, still maintaining their rapid gait towards the villages of the Mojaves. This performance argues that the latter Indians, as well as the Mormons and Pai-utes, entertain a lively interest in all our proceedings.

Violent gusts of wind have retarded our progress, and the temporary loss of some of the mules that had strayed off in a useless search after better fare delayed the pack-train. We have camped together at the foot of the Pyramid cañon, under the lee of the Bull's Head rock. There is no grass, and the half-starved animals are trying to fill their stomachs with dry twigs of the desert growth.

Ireteba has not returned. It appears that even this steadfast old friend has deserted us. I have sent Nah-vah-roo-pa to tell Cairook and the chiefs that we shall be at their villages to-morrow, and that they must come into camp and have a talk.

For the last week the days have been raw and blustering, in uncomfortable contrast to the delightful, balmy weather experienced during the month of February.

Camp 60, *Sitgreaves's Pass, March* 23.—A cold, raw wind followed us from the Pyramid cañon until the bottom lands of the Mojave valley were reached, and then, as if by magic, the temperature became soft and warm. Not an Indian appeared upon the banks—a great contrast to the scene of our departure, when a crowd of friendly looking faces occupied every little promontory and knoll. One or two bars caused detention, and the pack-train arrived a little before us. Camp was made on the east bank, at the point where the wagon road of Mr. Beale strikes the river. A few of the Mojaves made their appearance before dark, with an air as though doubtful of the reception they might meet. They had little to say, and seemed to have come principally to spy out the condition of things. I received them as usual, and told them to let Cairook know that I wanted to see him.

A strong guard was kept till morning, but the night passed without disturbance. The next day the Indians came straggling into the vicinity until a large number were collected. They were all armed, and unaccompanied by women and children. Our own party had their weapons ready, and were in too good a position for defence to tempt an attack from a party provided with nothing better than bows and arrows and clubs. About noon Cairook came to see me. He was much embarrassed, and it was some time before I could get any satisfactory explanation of the changed state of affairs. After a vast amount of beating around the bush, and pantomime, and interpreting, he at last, however, told a distinct story. While in the Cottonwood valley I had given a Mojave a note to carry to Lieutenant Tipton, in which I asked him to push on and join us as rapidly as possible. The Indian had delayed his departure, and by so doing had encountered the scouting party of Mormons, one of whom had taken the note from him and destroyed it. The startled messenger communicated the fact to the rest of his tribe, and they believing that we would blame them for the breach of faith and be disposed to resent it, and half persuaded by the Mormons that we had evil designs against them and their possessions, were prepared for immediate hostilities. I inquired of Cairook, with anxiety, whether the other messenger, who had taken our mail from the Black cañon and had afterwards met the Mormons, had likewise allowed his bundle of letters to be torn up. Cairook assured me that he had not. That, on the contrary, fearing lest the package in his charge might be tampered with, he had made off as fast as he could, and was far advanced on the road to Fort Yuma.*

When Cairook had made a clean breast of it, he opened a pouch that he held in his hand, and taking from it a folded paper, handed the latter to me. I found that it was a kind of recommendation that had been given to him many years before by one of the Mormon leaders. To any paper of this description Indians attach a superstitious value, and Cairook evinced no slight degree of magnanimity when, in a spirit of fair dealing, he informed me by signs that

---

* I afterwards learned that this was strictly true, and that the letters had been safely delivered.

I was at liberty to destroy it. His face beamed with delight when I told him that I had no wish to do so, and restored it to him. I further assured him that he had been humbugged by the Mormons, and that so far from having designs upon the Mojave valley, we intended to at once take our departure from it. Upon this he delivered to his people an earnest speech, which was respectfully listened to, and had the effect of altogether restoring harmony. Before night the Indians were about camp as usual, without weapons, and in company with the women and children. Ireteba came back after the interview with his chief, greatly pleased that good feeling had been restored. He told me that he and two other Mojaves had been detailed by Cairook to accompany the land party, and were to guide us to some point on the Colorado above the Great Bend.

I now hastened the preparations for departure, being anxious to leave before anything could happen to interrupt the harmonious relations with our fickle neighbors. A rupture with the Mojaves would have seriously interfered with the progress of the expedition. The land explorations would have been delayed and perhaps altogether disconcerted. With foes on the bank, it would have been impossible for the steamboat party to descend the river without a detachment on either shore to defend them from attack, and this would have necessitated the return of all the members of the expedition to Fort Yuma. I now made an almost equal division of the force. The officers of the Explorer, with Messrs. Taylor, Bielawski, and Booker, half of the escort, and all but three of my men, were selected to go back with the boat. Dr. Newberry, Messrs. Egloffstein, Mollhausen, and Peacock, three laborers, the Mexican packers, together with twenty soldiers, commanded by Lieutenant Tipton, composed the land party. The notes and collections were placed in charge of Mr. Taylor to transport to Washington. The preparation of maps, reports, and letters, the division of provisions, and selection of the articles to be carried across the plains, occupied a large portion of the night. By eight this morning the steamboat detachment was ready to leave, and our friends on the Explorer bid us good by and were soon out of sight beyond a turn of the river.

The first arrangement and adjustment of the packs occupied two or three hours, and it was almost noon by the time we were prepared to start. Ireteba and his two friends appeared punctually and took their place at the head of the train. A Yuma Indian, who had accompanied Lieutenant Tipton from the fort, expressed a desire to go along, and was allowed to do so.

Cairook came to bid us farewell. I was never before so struck with his noble appearance. When he shook hands his head was almost on a level with mine as he stood beside the mule on which I was sitting. He indicated his wishes that we might have a successful trip, and remained watching the train till it was out of sight, waving his hand and smiling his adieus. We all felt regret at parting with him, for he had proved himself a staunch friend.*

* This excellent chief is no longer living. Not many months after our departure a difficulty occurred between the Mojaves and a party of emigrants, in which some of the latter were killed. A detachment of troops, subsequently ordered to the valley, was fired upon by the Indians, and a large force was sent to obtain satisfaction. The Mojaves made peace by surrendering eight or nine of their principal men as security for the future good behavior of the rest. Cairook volunteered to go as a hostage, and was taken to Fort Yuma and confined, with his companions, in the guard-house. The restraint soon became irksome and galling to their wild natures, and to Cairook in particular it was almost intolerable. His faithful follower, Ireteba, visited him several times during his confinement, and one day made an eloquent appeal in his behalf to Lieutenant Tipton, who was again on duty at the fort. He recounted in moving terms the services Cairook had rendered, both to Lieutenant Whipple's party and to my own, and begged that he might be set free. Of course Lieutenant Tipton had no power to grant the request, but this Ireteba could not comprehend, and went away grievously disappointed, saying that if the "commandante" (a title he had formerly applied to me) were there he knew the favor would not be refused. When the chief learned the failure of the mission he made a characteristic proposition to his brother captives for the termination of his own and their confinement. At certain hours they were all permitted to come out for fresh air upon the porch of the guard-house, and he agreed, being a very powerful man, to seize and hold the sentinel and allow the rest to escape. The heroic and generous project was executed. The following morning, as the Indians were taking an airing in front of the guard-house, they made a sudden rush down the hill towards the river, Cairook at the same instant pinioning the sentinel in his arms. He was bayoneted on the spot by the members of the guard. The fugitives were fired upon. Some were killed and some escaped. None were retaken alive. The survivors carried to the tribe the story of their chief's self-sacrifice, and the only son of Cairook, a fine boy, has since been regarded by the Mojaves almost with veneration.

Ascending to the first slope of the Gravel desert, we directed our course towards the gap in the Black mountains, by which Captain Sitgreaves and Mr. Beale approached the river. This gap appears to be the only pass that exists in the portion of the range south of the Black canon.

For nine or ten miles the road was good, and led over a succession of gravel terraces and slopes to the base of the mountains. Before entering the pass I turned to take a last look at the Mojave valley. The view was extensive, comprising the whole region between the Needles and the Black cañon. The Dead mountain range, the Pyramid and Painted cañons, and Mount Davis, were raised in bold relief upon the low country near the river. The beautiful valley was enveloped in the delicate blue haze that imparts to it so softened and charming a glow, and the windings of the Colorado could be traced through the bright fields and groves till the river disappeared in the Mojave cañon.

Following Sitgreaves's Pass we traversed a rocky ravine for two or three miles, and, coming to some water holes and a patch of grass, at the advice of Ireteba made a halt, and, for the first time during the expedition, pitched camp out of sight of the Colorado.

CHAPTER VII.

MOJAVE VALLEY TO BIG CAÑON, AT MOUTH OF DIAMOND RIVER.

MEADOW CREEK.—IRETEBA'S MOUNTAIN.—VALLEY.—RAILROAD PASS.—PROFILE OF CUT-OFF FROM BIG SANDY, VIA RAILROAD PASS, TO COLORADO.—CERBAT RANGE.—TOPOGRAPHY NEAR GREAT BEND.—AQUARIUS MOUNTAINS.—PEACOCK'S SPRING.—HUALPAIS GUIDES.—APPEARANCE OF GAME.—COLORADO PLATEAU AND CAÑON.—NEW RIVER.—SIDE CAÑON OF DIAMOND RIVER.—HUALPAIS RETREATS.—APPEARANCE OF INHABITANTS.—DIAMOND RIVER.—BIG CAÑON OF THE COLORADO.—GEOLOGICAL EXPOSURES.—ASCENT OF SIDE CAÑON.—TEMPORARY EMBARRASSMENT.—ARRIVAL AT HUALPAIS SPRING.—DEPARTURE OF IRETEBA AND MOJAVE GUIDES.— SIDE CAÑONS OF THE COLORADO.

Camp 61, *Meadow creek, March* 25.—The grazing at the camp in Sitgreaves's Pass was poor, and the mules were ill prepared for the rough road before them. A few miles brought us to the base of a steep and difficult ascent that led to the summit of the Black mountains. The path was narrow and devious, and attended with hazard to the weak and heavily-loaded beasts. All of the party had to clamber up on foot, leading their riding animals; and as the ascent was accomplished under a burning sun, it was a matter of some congratulation when the top of the

Fig. 26.—Meadow Creek.

pass was attained. A wide and beautiful valley divided the Black mountains from a high snow-capped chain called by Lieutenant Whipple, who had seen it from the east, the Cerbat range. A rapid descent led through a ravine to the eastern base of the range we were crossing. When nearly down the hill the head of a creek was encountered, and half a mile from the valley the ravine spread out for a few hundred yards, forming a snug meadow carpeted with

DRAWN BY FRHⁿ F.W.v FGLOFFSTEIN.

BIG CAÑON

FROM NEAR HUALPAIS SPRING.

good grass, and fringed on one side by a growth of willows that bordered the stream. The half-starved animals would hardly allow the saddles to be removed in their impatience to enjoy the unaccustomed plenty. They ate greedily for the rest of the day, and nearly all night, and this morning still seemed so ravenous that I have remained in camp to let them appease their appetites. The delay has permitted me to set up a transit and get some observations on moon culminations for longitude.

Ireteba informed me after breakfast that there were a few Hualpais living at no great distance, and that he would hunt them up, and endeavor to engage one to accompany us beyond the point where he himself would be compelled to go back. He has not yet returned from his mission. He has told me that in a few days we shall strike the Colorado and come to a large settlement of Hualpais Indians ; that it would be unsafe for himself and companions to proceed further, and that we must secure Hualpais guides to conduct us to another tribe that reside upon a tributary of the Colorado, a long distance above. Between the two villages he says the river is inaccessible and the country sterile, with few watering places, and those difficult to find.

Fig. 27.—Ireteba's Mountain.

I can converse with Ireteba with considerable readiness, notwithstanding the absence of our interpreter, Mariano. The Mojave has acquired a few familiar words, and is expert in drawing maps on the ground. His pantomime is expressive and intelligible. He is invaluable as a guide, having had enough experience with mules to teach him their rate of travel, and enable him to select the most favorable routes and the best grazing camps. I tried to persuade him to consent to remain with the expedition till its return to Fort Yuma, but when he learned that we might have to pass through the villages of the Maricopas, on the return route, he positively refused; making no secret of his terror at the idea of encountering any members of

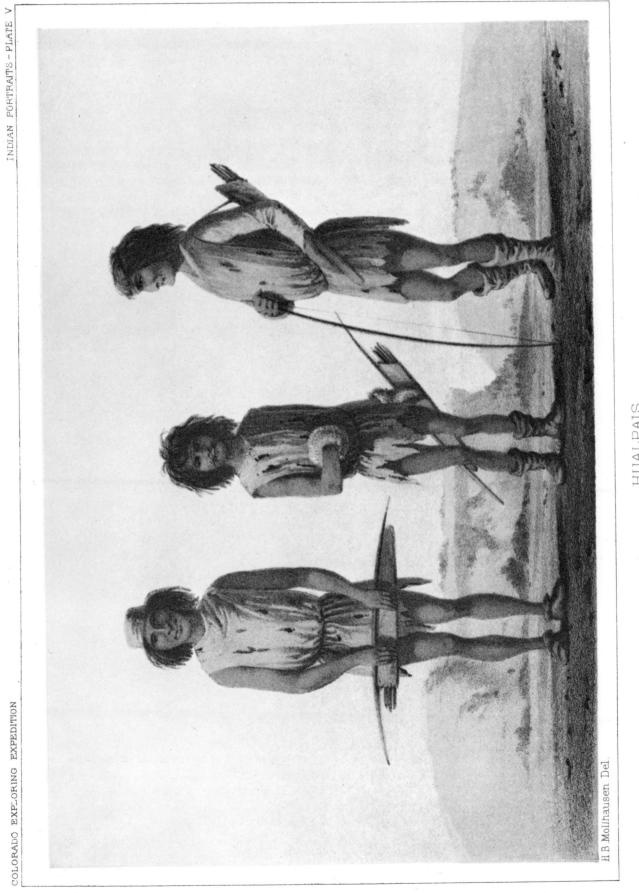

H B Mollhausen Del.

HUALPAIS.

that tribe.   I told him we would protect him, but he thinks if they could slaughter so easily a hundred of the best Yuma and Mojave warriors, our little party would stand a poor chance against them.

Opposite to camp is a conical hill four or five hundred feet high, surmounted by a cylindrical tower.   It is a conspicuous feature among the other summits, and would be a good landmark to guide the traveller from the east to the pass, and to the excellent camping place at its mouth.

Camp 64, *spur from Cerbat range, March* 29.—Leaving Meadow creek and its abundant pasturage, we descended to the valley, which is of immense extent, and runs in a northwest and southeast direction, extending either way beyond the limit of vision.   Toward the south, below the Black mountains, it unites with the Mojave valley, and from the base of the Cerbat range the eye could follow the gentle slope for over forty miles till it terminated near the head of the Mojave cañon.

The pass by which we were to cross the Cerbat mountains was apparent as soon as we left the Black range, and Ireteba, who had joined us early in the morning, headed directly for it. The pure atmosphere made it seem close by, and it was disappointing to plod through the hot sand hour after hour, and find it appearing as far off as ever.   When the base of the mountains was at last reached, it was found that the ascent was scarcely perceptible.   A place more like

Fig. 28.—Railroad Pass.

a cañon than an ordinary mountain pass presented itself, and we penetrated the range for a few miles through the windings of a nearly level avenue.   In a pretty ravine, hemmed in by picturesque bluffs, our guide pointed out a good spring of water, with grass enough near by to afford a tolerable camping place.

The next day, after proceeding one or two miles along the pass, which we called the Railroad Pass, we emerged from the Cerbat range, and came into what was at first supposed to be a broad valley, but which turned out to be a basin formed by the chain we had passed, and spurs extending from it.   There was a low divide on the rim of the basin nearly opposite the eastern entrance to the Railroad Pass.   The altitudes of these opposite edges are about the same. Lieutenant Whipple, while locating a railroad line near the 35th parallel, had reached a point a short distance east of this divide, where he struck the headwaters of Bill Williams's Fork, at that time an unexplored stream.   Supposing that it would conduct directly to the Colorado, he followed it till it was too late to return, and was compelled to pursue a difficult and circuitous route to its mouth.   He was confident, however, from a careful study of the country at either end, that the direct route from the divide to the Colorado would be practicable for a railroad, besides greatly shortening the distance.   The observations of the past two days have demonstrated the accuracy of his judgment.   A uniform slope extends from the foot of Cactus Pass, a point on Lieutenant Whipple's line, to the divide, the altitude of which has been stated. From the divide the road can follow the rim of the basin along an unbroken ridge to Railroad Pass, from which place there is a smooth slope to the Colorado.   The distance from Cactus Pass to the Colorado, by this line, is about eighty miles.   For the whole of this distance there scarcely exists an irregularity upon the surface of the ground.

Instead of crossing the basin, Ireteba took us north, for ten or fifteen miles along the eastern base of the Cerbat range, to an excellent grazing camp, but where there was only a small

Fig. 29.—Cerbat Basin.

spring of sulphurous water.   This he told me was the last water we should have for two days. The mules had become so much weakened that I found it again necessary to remain a day in camp to permit them to graze.   A violent hail-storm, followed by a raw and piercing sleet that kept them huddled all day with bent backs, shivering in the blast, counterbalanced the good effects that might have otherwise resulted from the delay.

A weary twenty miles of travel through a soft yielding soil have brought us to the northeastern rim of the basin, where we have camped without water. For two or three days we have been passing through a good grazing country. In the valleys and mountain slopes the blue grama and pin grass, both highly nutritive, grow luxuriantly. The want of water renders the region valueless.

Each successive valley crossed has been twelve or fifteen hundred feet higher than the preceding, and we have attained now an elevation of nearly four thousand feet above the level of the sea. Thus far the scenery has been monotonous and rather uninteresting; the valleys and ranges possess the same general character, and all appear to head somewhere about the mouth of the Virgen. The appearance of the country just passed over, and what I saw from the top of Fortification rock, have led me to suppose that at the Great Bend of the Colorado there may be a focus from which quite a number of mountain chains radiate; but the observations have been too limited to warrant a decided opinion.

Ireteba was unsuccessful in finding his Hualpais friends. There are certainly a number of the tribe in the neighborhood. The smokes from their fires have been repeatedly seen on the mountain sides, and fresh tracks upon our route showed that several persons had preceded the train by only a few hours.

Camp 65, *Peacock's spring, March* 31.—Leaving the Cerbat basin, the course lay towards a low point in the extension of Aquarius mountains—another chain almost parallel to the Black and Cerbat ranges. The gap much resembles the Railroad Pass. After entering it the trail took a sudden turn to the north, in which direction it continued. The sun was very hot, and the mules, not having had a plentiful drink of water for four days, showed marks of distress. Ten or twelve miles from camp, Mr. Peacock, who was riding in advance, discovered a large spring of clear, sweet water in a ravine near the road. There were no signs of the place having been used as a camp, and even Ireteba did not appear to have known previously of its existence. A Mexican subsequently found a running stream a mile or two further on, where the Indians passing this way had been in the habit of stopping.

Ireteba, at my request, again went in search of some Hualpais tractable enough to enlist for a few days in our service. After an absence of several hours he came back and reported that he had discovered two who were willing to go. In a little while, from the top of a neighboring hill, a discordant screaming was heard, proceeding from two Indians who were suspiciously surveying camp. It was some time before our Mojaves could persuade them to approach, and when they did they looked like men who had screwed up their courage to face a mortal peril. They were squalid, wretched-looking creatures, with splay feet, large joints, and diminutive figures, but had bright eyes and cunning faces, and resembled a little the Chemehuevis. Taking them into the tent occupied by Lieutenant Tipton and myself, with many misgivings as to how many varieties of animal life were being introduced there, I brought out some pipes and tobacco and told Ireteba to proceed with the negotiations. These were not soon arranged. The sentiousness belonging to Mr. Cooper's and other story-book Indians is not a gift of the tribes that one encounters in travelling. Our old guides and the two new candidates talked all at once, and with amazing volubility; they seemed to be recounting their personal histories from birth to the present date. The conclusion arrived at was that they knew nothing about the country—neither a good road nor the localities of grass and water; that they were out hunting and had lost their way, and had no idea of the direction even of their own villages. This very probable statement I correctly supposed to be a hint that they were not to be approached empty-handed; for when Ireteba had been authorized to make a distinct offer of beads and blankets, one of them recollected where he was, and also that there were watering places ahead to which he could guide us. It was thought advisable to again lie over for a day; and they went away, agreeing to be in camp on the day but one following.

A third Hualpais turned up this morning; he had features like a toad's, and the most villainous countenance I ever saw on a human being. Mr. Mollhausen suggested that we should take him and preserve him in alcohol as a zoological specimen; and at last he became alarmed at the steadfast gaze he was attracting, and withdrew to the edge of a rock overhanging the cook's fire, where he remained till dark, with his eyes fixed in an unbroken stare upon the victuals. The Hualpais are but little removed from the Diggers. They present a remarkable contrast to our tall and athletic Mojaves. The latter, as I discovered to-day for the first time, have suspected that the object of the expedition was to make war upon the others; and I had some trouble in convincing Ireteba that this was not the case. That we have come out to fight somebody he has fully made up his mind.

Deer and antelope are now frequently seen, but they are shy and hard to approach. A single antelope one of the Mexicans succeeded in killing; they are just in season, and the flesh was tender and delicately flavored.

Fig. 30.—Colorado Plateaus from near Peacock's Spring.

Camp 67, *Big cañon of the Colorado, April* 3.—The two Hualpais preserved the credit of the Indian employés by being punctual to their engagement, and led off in company with the Mojaves as we ascended the ravine from Peacock's spring. It was a cool lovely morning, and a favorable day for travel. After proceeding a mile or two we issued from the hills and entered a region totally different from any that had been seen during the expedition. A broad table-land, unbroken by the volcanic hills that had overspread the country since leaving Fort Yuma, extended before us, rising in a gradual swell towards the north. The road became hard and smooth, and the plain was covered with excellent grass. Herds of antelope and deer were seen bounding over the slopes. Groves of cedar occurred, and with every mile became more frequent and of larger size. At the end of ten miles the ridge of the swell was attained, and a splendid panorama burst suddenly into view. In the foreground were low table-hills, intersected by numberless ravines; beyond these a lofty line of bluffs marked the edge of an immense cañon; a wide gap was directly ahead, and through it were beheld, to the extreme limit of vision, vast plateaus, towering one above the other thousands of feet in the air, the long horizontal bands broken at intervals by wide and profound abysses, and extending a hundred miles to the north, till the deep azure blue faded into a light cerulean tint that blended with the dome of the heavens. The famous "Big cañon" was before us; and for a long time we paused in wondering delight, surveying this stupendous formation through which the Colorado and its tributaries break their way.

Our guides, becoming impatient of the detention, plunged into a narrow and precipitous ravine that opened at our feet, and we followed as well as we could, stumbling along a rough and rocky pathway. The Hualpais were now of great assistance, for the ravines crossed and forked in intricate confusion; even Ireteba, who had hitherto led the train, became at a loss how to proceed, and had to put the little Hualpais in front. The latter, being perfectly at home, conducted us rapidly down the declivity. The descent was great and the trail blind and circuitous. A few miles of difficult travelling brought us into a narrow valley flanked by steep and high slopes; a sparkling stream crossed its centre, and a gurgling in some tall grass near

Fig 31 —Side Cañons of Diamond River.

by announced the presence of a spring. The water was delicious. The grass in the neighborhood was sparse, but of good quality.

This morning we left the valley and followed the course of a creek down a ravine, in the bed of which the water at intervals sank and rose for two or three miles, when it altogether disappeared. The ravine soon attained the proportions of a cañon. The bottom was rocky and irregular, and there were some jump-offs over which it was hard to make the pack animals pass. The vegetation began to disappear, leaving only a few stunted cedars projecting from the sides of the rugged bluffs. The place grew wilder and grander. The sides of the tortuous cañon became loftier, and before long we were hemmed in by walls two thousand feet high. The scenery much resembled that in the Black cañon, excepting that the rapid descent, the increasing magnitude of the collossal piles that blocked the end of the vista, and the corresponding depth and gloom of the gaping chasms into which we were plunging, imparted an unearthly character to a way that might have resembled the portals of the infernal regions. Harsh screams issuing from aerial recesses in the cañon sides, and apparitions of goblin-like figures perched in the rifts and hollows of the impending cliffs, gave an odd reality to this impression. At short distances other avenues of equally magnificent proportions came in from one side or the other; and no trail being left on the rocky pathway, the idea suggested itself that were the guides to desert us our experience might further resemble that of the dwellers in the unblest abodes—in the difficulty of getting out.

Huts of the rudest construction, visible here and there in some sheltered niche or beneath a projecting rock, and the sight of a hideous old squaw, staggering under a bundle of fuel, showed that we had penetrated into the domestic retreats of the Hualpais nation. Our party being, in all probability, the first company of whites that had ever been seen by them, we had anticipated producing a great effect, and were a little chagrined when the old woman, and two or three others of both sexes that were met, went by without taking the slightest notice of us. If pack-trains had been in the habit of passing twenty times a day they could not have manifested a more complete indifference.

Seventeen miles of this strange travel had now been accomplished. The road was becoming more difficult, and we looked ahead distrustfully into the dark and apparently interminable windings, and wondered where we were to find a camping place. At last we struck a wide branch cañon coming in from the south, and saw with joyful surprise a beautiful and brilliantly clear stream of water gushing over a pebbly bed in the centre, and shooting from between the rocks in sparkling jets and miniature cascades. On either side was an oasis of verdure—young willows and a thick patch of grass. Camp was speedily formed, and men and mules have had a welcome rest after their fatiguing journey.

A hundred yards below camp the cañon takes a turn; but as it was becoming very dark, all further examinations were postponed till to-morrow. In the course of the evening Ireteba came into my tent, and I asked him how far we had still to travel before reaching the great river. To my surprise he informed me that the mouth of the creek is only a few yards below the turn, and that we are now camped just on the verge of the Big Cañon of the Colorado.

Camp 69, *Cedar Forest, April* 5.—A short walk down the bed of Diamond river, on the morning after we had reached it, verified the statement of Ireteba, and disclosed the famous Colorado cañon. The view from the ridge, beyond the creek to which the Hualpais had first conducted us, had shown that the plateaus further north and east were several thousand feet higher than that through which the Colorado cuts at this point, and the cañons proportionally deeper; but the scene was sufficiently grand to well repay for the labor of the descent. The cañon was similar in character to others that have been mentioned, but on a larger scale, and thus far unrivalled in grandeur. Mr. Mollhausen has taken a sketch, which gives a better idea of it than any description. The course of the river could be traced for only a few hundred yards, above or below, but what had been seen from the table-land showed that we were at the apex of a great southern bend. The walls, on either side, rose directly out of the water. The river was about fifty yards wide. The channel was studded with rocks, and the torrent rushed through like a mill-race.

The day was spent in an examination of the localities. Dr. Newberry has had opportunities for observation seldom afforded to the geologist. This plateau formation has been undisturbed by volcanic action, and the sides of the cañons exhibit all of the series that compose the table-

J.J.YOUNG, from a sketch by F.W.EGLOFFSTEIN.

BIG CAÑON AT MOUTH OF DIAMOND RIVER.

lands of New Mexico, presenting, perhaps, the most splendid exposure of stratified rocks that there is in the world.

A few of the Hualpais paid us a visit, but their intelligence is of so low an order that it is impossible to glean information from them, and their filthiness makes them objectionable. Our new guides seemed to think we should have difficulty in ascending to the portion of the plateau which they traverse on the way to higher points upon the river. The route they ordinarily pursue follows the cañon of Diamond creek, but this they pronounced impracticable for mules, and said that we must retrace our course for several miles in order to strike a more circuitous, but easier trail, that ascended one of the branch cañons.

Following their advice and guidance, yesterday morning we toiled up the rough road by which we had come, for six miles, when they struck off into a side ravine that led towards the southeast. Half a mile from the mouth, the Hualpais told Ireteba that our camping place was just ahead, and scrambling over the summit of a hill, in a minute were both out of sight. For a mile we kept on, every few moments coming to a fork, where the selection of the right road was left to chance. There was a network of cañons, and the probabilities were that nine out of ten would lead to an impassable precipice. The ascent became so rough that it was already

Fig. 32.—Side Cañons of the Colorado.

almost impracticable for the mules, and at last the Mojaves stopped, declaring that they had lost their way, and had no idea how to find the camping place or the water, and that the Hualpais were a very bad set. This opinion no one was inclined just then to dispute. I however asked one of the Indians to go back and endeavor to find the deserters or some other member of their tribe. We waited impatiently half an hour, and then the order was given to countermarch, for I intended to search for the route by which we had come; but before going far, the little Hualpais came back. He seemed amused that we should not have been able to find the water, and again took his place at the head of the column. He conducted us for two miles through a difficult and intricate maze of ravines, and then climbed a side hill, and in a most unexpected place pointed out a little spring. There was a sufficiency of water, and tolerable grass near by. The second Hualpais came back during the evening, and seemed also to be astonished that we should have had trouble in finding what to him was so familiar. They both professed a determination to accompany the train, and Ireteba told me that it was time for himself and companions to return.

This morning the Mojaves left us. I gave them three mules, and a large part of the remaining stock of Indian goods. Ireteba in particular was loaded with presents, every one being desirous to give him something. He is the best Indian that I have ever known. He is perfectly unobtrusive, and is the only one that has never begged for anything. He has proved to me, as he did to Lieutenant Whipple, a faithful guide. He seemed sorry to separate from us, but informed me, in a confidential way, that the Hualpais were great scoundrels, and that it would not be safe for himself and friends to go further from their own tribe. He said that they would certainly be watched during their return; and if not vigilant, would lose both their presents and their lives, and that they were going to travel, for two days, without rest or sleep. I gave them a bag of provisions and some cooking utensils, and packing all of their presents upon the mules they departed, much gratified with the termination of their expedition.

The Hualpais spring was upon one of the hills that form the southwestern boundary of the great plateau through which the Colorado and its tributaries flow. In these hills the side cañons head, and their course can be traced for a long distance, as they bury themselves deeper and deeper in the bowels of the mesa.

A bluff nearly a thousand feet high had to be ascended in order to reach the summit of the plateau. It was so steep that some of the mules gave out, and had to have their packs removed, and all were so much exhausted that we were compelled to stop when only an hour's journey from a camp where the Hualpais told us we would find water.

Since attaining the summit the road has been good, and has traversed a slightly undulating park, covered with luxuriant grass, and interspersed with cedar groves, where deer, antelope, and hare have been startled by the approach of the train from their shady coverts. The whole system of cañons has again been visible, extending in immense perspective to the north and east.

CHAPTER VIII.
COLORADO PLATEAU, NEAR BIG CANON.

Camp 71, *Pine forest, April* 10.—Four miles from the camp, in the Cedar forest, were some large pools of water in a rocky ravine. There was no spring. The supply had been derived from melting snows, and the place would be dry a little later in the season. The Hualpais seated themselves upon the ground as though they had made up their minds to camp. I questioned them as well as I could about the marches ahead, and they assured me that no more water would be found for three days. This did not agree with a former statement, but they adhered positively to it, and it was possible that it might be true. We thought it better, therefore, to go no further. The next morning both the Hualpais were missing. They had run away during the night, taking with them a little flour and a pair of blankets. It was expected that many of the mules would be missing. They were at once counted, but the number was found to be correct. What had frightened the guides off we could not imagine. I was sorry they had deserted, for the presence of some one that could be relied upon to point out the watering places had prevented a great deal of anxiety.

We had now entered the region of pines. The growth was thicker, and trees of considerable size began to be mingled with the low cedars. The ascent from the Hualpais spring, though gradual, had been rapid, and the barometer indicated an altitude of about six thousand feet. The increase of elevation was felt very sensibly in the changed temperature, which had become wintry and raw.

For the first time black-tailed deer were seen, and some of the soldiers took advantage of the early arrival at camp to go out hunting. One of them had not returned at dark, and two days passed before he was found. Signal fires by night and smokes by day were kept up, and searching parties scoured the country in every direction. A light snow storm, that occurred the night after the man's disappearance, had covered up his footprints and made it impossible to follow him. During the storm he wandered to a great distance from camp, and when the snow melted there was a break in the trail which it was difficult for our most experienced trailers, the Mexicans, to connect. They at last got upon the track, at a time when the man was completely bewildered, and by mere accident was travelling in the right course. He had given himself up for lost, and was wandering in a state of desperation bordering on insanity, when he happened to see one of the signal smokes, and followed its direction to camp, which the Mexicans reached an hour afterwards, having traced him over the whole line he had pursued since his departure.

The next day an early start was made. We had to select our own way through the forest, being for the first time without the guidance of those who were familiar with the country, and what was more important, in this arid region, with the whereabouts of watering places. It was an unfortunate morning for the experiment. Dark clouds covered the sky, and masses of

DRAWN BY FRH. F.W. v. EGLOFFSTEIN.

BIG CAÑON

NEAR DIAMOND RIVER.

mist were drifting through the glades of the forest, enveloping the landscape in obscurity. We held a course a little east of north. The pine trees became larger and the forest more dense as we proceeded. A heavy gale roared among the branches overhead, and about noon it commenced snowing. For some time we kept at the bottom of a ravine that afforded a partial shelter from the blast, but the surface of the ground was rough, and the snow fell so thick and fast that it was impossible to select the way.

Ascending to the table-land, we happened upon an open portion of the forest and encountered the full violence of the storm. The fall of snow was accompanied with thunder and lightning, an unusual phenomenon at such a time. The flashes were vivid, and the reverberations loud and frequent. The scene would have been beautiful had it not been so thoroughly uncomfortable. The storm at last became so vehement that we were unable to proceed. Men and mules huddled together under such trees as afforded the best shelter, and waited as resignedly as possible till the fury of the tempest had somewhat abated. The day was nearly spent; the packs were therefore taken off, camp made, fires kindled, and the mules driven into a ravine. About sunset it promised to clear off, but the clouds reassembled, the wind and sleet again drove past, and the night was bleak and raw. The unfortunate mules, benumbed with cold, stood shuddering about the fires that were made in the ravine. The sudden change from hot summer weather was a severe test of endurance, and there was danger that in their weak condition they would not be able to stand it. The snow and the gale continued nearly all of the next day. The grass was entirely covered. The animals had to fast for twenty-four hours longer, and I thought that last night would have finished the majority of them, but singularly enough not one has died.

This morning the sky was cloudless and the wind had abated. When the sun rose it became as warm as it had been in the Mojave valley, and the snow melted even more rapidly than it had fallen.

Our altitude is very great. During the last march the ascent was continuous, and the barometer shows an elevation of nearly seven thousand feet. A still higher plateau rises towards the north. The Colorado is not far distant, and we must be opposite to the most stupendous part of the "Big Cañon." The bluffs are in view, but the intervening country is cut up by side cañons and cross ravines, and no place has yet been seen that presents a favorable approach to the gigantic chasm.

Camp 73, *Colorado plateau, April* 12—Two miles beyond the snow camp some lagoons were discovered—one of them large enough to be called a pond. I recognized the place as having been described by the Hualpais to Ireteba, but of the position I had not been able to form a correct idea. As we advanced towards the northeast, long undulating swells followed each other and intercepted the view. The snow storm had extended over but a limited area, and the road, at first heavy, in the course of an hour or two became dry and good. The pines disappeared, and the cedars gradually diminished. To our regret the patches of grass also were less frequently met with, and the little seen was of poor quality. Each slope surmounted disclosed a new summit similar to that just passed, till the end of ten miles, when the highest part of the plateau was attained, and a sublime spectacle lay spread before us.

Towards the north was the field of plateaus and cañons, already seen and described, and shooting out from these a line of magnificent bluffs, extending eastward an enormous distance, marked the course of the cañon of the Little Colorado. Further south, eighty miles distant, towered the vast pile of the San Francisco mountain, its conical summit covered with snow, and sharply defined against the sky. Several other peaks were visible a little to the right, and half way between us and this cluster of venerable and mightly volcanos was the "Red Butte," described by Lieutenant Whipple, standing in isolated prominence upon the level plain. On the north side of the Colorado appeared a short range of mountains, close to the cañon, which had been previously hidden by the intervening plateaus.

A march of twenty miles having been made, and no sign of water appearing, we had to put up with a dry camp. The grass was miserable, and altogether the mules fared badly. During the night the herders were negligent, and at daybreak nearly a hundred of the animals were missing. They had taken the back trail for the lagoons, but having started late and travelled leisurely were overtaken not many miles from camp. The trip did not render them better fitted for the day's journey, which had to be delayed until they were brought back.

The sun was oppressively warm, and every place whose appearance gave promise of water was carefully searched, but without success. Ten miles conducted to the head of a ravine, down which was a well-beaten Indian trail. There was every prospect therefore that we were approaching a settlement similar to that of the Hualpais, on Diamond river. The descent

Fig. 33 —San Francisco Mountain from Colorado Plateau.

was more rapid than the former had been, and in the course of a few miles we had gone down into the plateau one or two thousand feet, and the bluffs on either side had assumed stupendous proportions. Still no signs of habitations were visible. The worn-out and thirsty beasts had begun to flag, when we were brought to a stand still by a fall a hundred feet deep in the bottom of the cañon. At the brink of the precipice was an overhanging ledge of rocks, from which we could look down as into a well upon the continuation of the gorge far below. The break reached completely across the ravine, and the side walls were nearly perpendicular. There was no egress in that direction, and it seemed a marvel that a trail should be found leading to a place where there was nothing to do but to return. A closer inspection showed that the trail still continued along the cañon, traversing horizontally the face of the right hand bluff. A short distance off it seemed as though a mountain goat could scarcely keep its footing upon the slight indentation that appeared like a thread attached to the rocky wall, but a trial proved that the path, though narrow and dizzy, had been cut with some care into the surface of the cliff, and afforded a foothold level and broad enough both for men and animals. I rode upon it first, and the rest of the party and the train followed—one by one—looking very much like a row of insects crawling upon the side of a building. We proceeded for nearly a mile along this singular pathway, which preserved its horizontal direction. The bottom of the cañon meanwhile had been rapidly descending, and there were two or three falls where it dropped a hundred feet at a time, thus greatly increasing the depth of the chasm. The change had taken place so gradually that I was not sensible of it, till glancing down the side of my mule I found that he was walking within three inches of the brink of a sheer gulf a thousand feet deep; on the other side, nearly touching my knee, was an almost vertical wall rising to an enormous altitude. The sight made my head swim, and I dismounted and got ahead of the mule, a difficult and delicate operation, which I was thankful to have safely performed. A part of the men became so giddy that they were obliged to creep upon their hands and knees, being unable to walk or stand. In some places there was barely room to walk, and a slight deviation in a step would have precipitated one into the frightful abyss. I was a good deal alarmed lest some obstacle should be encountered that would make it impossible to go ahead, for it was certainly impracticable to return. After an interval of uncomfortable suspense the face of the rock made an angle, and just beyond the turn was a projection from the main wall with a surface fifteen or twenty yards square that would afford a foothold. The continuation of the wall was perfectly vertical, so that the trail could no longer follow it, and we found that the path descended the steep face of the cliff to

Fig. 34. Precipice leading to Cataract Cañon.

the bottom of the cañon. It was a desperate road to traverse, but located with a good deal of skill—zigzagging down the precipice, and taking advantage of every crevice and fissure that could afford a foothold. It did not take long to discover that no mule could accomplish this descent, and nothing remained but to turn back. We were glad to have even this privilege in our power. The jaded brutes were collected upon the little summit where they could be turned

J.J.YOUNG, from a sketch by H.B.MOLLHAUSEN.

CAMP – COLORADO PLATEAU

around, and then commenced to re-perform the hazardous journey. The sun shone directly into the cañon, and the glare reflected from the walls made the heat intolerable. The disappointed beasts, now two days without water, with glassy eyes and protruding tongues, plodded slowly along, uttering the most melancholy cries. The nearest water, of which we had knowledge, was almost thirty miles distant. There was but one chance of saving the train, and after reaching an open portion of the ravine the packs and the saddles were removed, and two or three Mexicans started for the lagoons mounted upon the least exhausted animals, and driving the others loose before them. It was somewhat dangerous to detach them thus far from the main party, but there was no help for it. Some of the mules will doubtless give out before the night march is over, but the knowledge that they are on their way to water will enable most of them to reach it in spite of their weariness and the length of the way.

I gave directions to the Mexican not to return for a couple of days. This will give the beasts time to rest, and afford us an opportunity of exploring the trail beyond the precipice, where we had to stop. Several cañons head near us, all leading into the mighty avenue which forms the main water-way. Each branch has its subordinate tributaries, that interlock with one another, and cut away more than half of the original plateau.

Camp 73, *Colorado plateau, April* 14.—Lieutenant Tipton, Mr. Egloffstein, Mr. Peacock, and myself, with a dozen men, formed the party to explore the cañon. It was about five miles to the precipice. The descent of the latter was accomplished without serious trouble. In one or two places the path traversed smooth inclined ledges, where the insecure footing made the crossing dangerous. The bottom of the cañon, which from the summit looked smooth, was covered with hills, thirty or forty feet high. Along the centre we were surprised to find an inner cañon, a kind of under cellar, with low walls at the starting point, which were soon converted into lofty precipices, as the base of the ravine sank deeper and deeper into the earth. Along the bottom of this gorge we followed the trail, distinctly seen when the surface was not covered with rocks. Every few moments, low falls and ledges, which we had to jump or slide down, were met with, till there had accumulated a formidable number of obstacles to be encountered in returning. Like other cañons, it was circuitous, and at each turn we were impatient to find something novel or interesting. We were deeper in the bowels of the earth than we had ever been before, and surrounded by walls and towers of such imposing dimensions that it would be useless to attempt describing them; but the effects of magnitude had begun to pall, and the walk from the foot of the precipice was monotonously dull; no sign of life could be discerned above or below. At the end of thirteen miles from the precipice an obstacle presented itself that there seemed to be no possibility of overcoming. A stone slab, reaching from one side of the cañon to the other, terminated the plane which we were descending. Looking over the edge it appeared that the next level was forty feet below. This time there was no trail along the side bluffs, for these were smooth and perpendicular. A spring of water rose from the bed of the cañon not far above, and trickled over the ledge, forming a pretty cascade. It was supposed that the Indians must have come to this point merely to procure water; but this theory was not altogether satisfactory, and we sat down upon the rocks to discuss the matter.

Mr. Egloffstein lay down by the side of the creek, and projecting his head over the ledge to watch the cascade, discovered a solution of the mystery. Below the shelving rock, and hidden by it and the fall, stood a crazy looking ladder, made of rough sticks bound together with thongs of bark. It was almost perpendicular, and rested upon a bed of angular stones. The rounds had become rotten from the incessant flow of water. Mr. Egloffstein, anxious to have the first view of what was below, scrambled over the ledge and got his feet upon the upper round. Being a solid weight, he was too much for the insecure fabric, which commenced giving way. One side fortunately stood firm, and holding on to this with a tight grip, he made a precipitate descent. The other side and all the rounds broke loose and accompanied him to the bottom in a general crash, effectually cutting off the communication. Leaving us to devise means of getting him back he ran to the bend to explore. The bottom of the cañon had been reached. He found that he was at the edge of a stream, ten or fifteen yards wide, fringed with cottonwoods and willows. The walls of the cañon spread out for a short distance, leaving room for a narrow belt of bottom land, on which were fields of corn and a few scattered huts.

A place was found near the ledge where one could clamber a little way up the wall, and we thus got a view of the valley. The river was nearly as large as the Gila at low water, and, with the exception of that stream, the most important tributary of the Colorado between its mouth and our position. The cañon Mr. Egloffstein saw could not be followed far; there were cascades just below. He perceived, however, that he was very near to its mouth, though perhaps at a thousand feet greater altitude, and an Indian pointed out the exact spot where it united with the cañon of the Rio Colorado.

The Yampais did not differ much from the Hualpais in general appearance. They were perhaps a trifle cleaner and more respectable. It is probable that, all told, they do not number more than two hundred persons. One of them accompanied Mr. Egloffstein to the foot of the ledge, and intimated a willingness to go with us to camp, but when he saw the broken ladder gave up his intention. The accident did not appear otherwise to concern him. There must have been some other trail leading to the retreat, for the use of the ladder had evidently been long abandoned.

Having looked at all that was to be seen, it now remained to get Mr. Egloffstein back. The slings upon the soldiers' muskets were taken off and knotted together, and a line thus made which reached to the bottom. Whether it would support his weight was a matter of experi_ment. The general impression was that it would not, but of the two evils—breaking his neck or remaining among the Yampais—he preferred the former, and fastened the strap around his shoulders. It was a hard straight lift. The ladder pole was left, and rendered great assistance both to us and the rope, and the ascent was safely accomplished. We invited the Indian to follow Mr. Egloffstein's example, but this he energetically declined. The examination being finished, it was time to return. On leaving camp we had expected to be back before night, and had brought along neither provisions nor overcoats. An hour or two earlier, finding that the day was rapidly slipping by, two of the party were directed to go back and tell those who had remained that we might be detained till the next day, and in that case to forward in the morning something to eat. We walked as fast as possible, in order to get out of the cañon before dark, but the ascent was laborious, and the trail, made in coming down over the rocks, difficult to follow. Numerous branch cañons, all looking alike, would have rendered it easy to become lost had the trail been once departed from. Night came before the foot of the precipice where the train had stopped was reached. It was impossible to distinguish the way in the dark, and we had to halt. A few minutes previously the tracks of the two men that had been sent ahead had been noticed diverging from the proper course, and it was concluded that they were wandering astray somewhere in the labyrinth. After nightfall, as is always the case in these regions, it became bleak and cold. Some of the party, attired for a walk under a hot sun, had not even their coats. The cañon was as dark as a dungeon. The surface of the ground being covered with rocks, a recumbent position was uncomfortable, and the rocks being interspersed with prickly pear and some other varieties of cactaceæ it would have been unwise to walk about. The choice, therefore, lay between sitting down and standing still, which two recreations we essayed alternately for twelve hours that might have been, from the sensations of the party, twelve days. As soon as it was light enough to see the way we put our stiffened limbs in motion. Climbing the precipice was severe work. The summit once attained, it was but five miles to camp, but the violent exercise of the ascent, coming after a twenty-four hours' abstinence from food and rest, and a walk of more than thirty miles over a difficult road, proved

J.J.YOUNG. from a sketch by F.W.EGLOFFSTEIN

UPPER CATARACT CREEK, NEAR BIG CAÑON.

so exhausting that, during the last stretch, two or three of the men broke down, and had to have coffee and food sent back to them before they could proceed.

The messengers, as expected, had not arrived, and our non-return had occasioned some anxiety. The Mexicans were immediately despatched in search of the missing men. Directions had been given that if at any time a person should perceive that he was lost, he should wait quietly in one place for the arrival of the searching party. The two men had had the nerve to follow this plan, and, as soon as they were convinced of the hopelessness of finding the lost path, had selected a comfortable place and patiently waited during the rest of the day, all night, and till noon of the following day, when the Mexicans found them. Their trail could scarcely have been traced for any great distance over the rocks, and had they continued wandering through the mazes of the cañons they would probably have never again been heard from.

The region east of camp has been examined to-day. The extent and magnitude of the system of cañons in that direction is astounding. The plateau is cut into shreds by these gigantic chasms, and resembles a vast ruin. Belts of country miles in width have been swept away, leaving only isolated mountains standing in the gap. Fissures so profound that the eye cannot penetrate their depths are separated by walls whose thickness one can almost span, and slender spires that seem tottering upon their bases shoot up thousands of feet from the vaults below.

Fig. 35.—Side Cañons of Flax River.

Towards the southeast, also, for a great distance, the surface is furrowed by these abysses. They appear to extend nearly to the San Francisco mountains, and bar all progress eastward. Northward we can proceed no further, and the only course is to go back to the nearest water as a starting point, and from thence strike south, and, heading these formidable barriers, cross Flax river, and again travel north upon the opposite side of that stream.

The mules were brought back this evening; only two were lost; the others reached the Lagoon. To-morrow morning we shall return to that place, and after making an examination of the cañons northwest of the trail proceed to follow the remaining route now open to us.

Camp 74, *Forest lagoons, April* 18.—Midway between the last camp and the lagoons, a trail was encountered leading towards another point of the Big cañon. With a small detachment I left the main party and followed its course. It headed directly for the north side mountains—the peaks already spoken of as seen upon the opposite bank of the Colorado. We travelled till dark; the trail ended near some deserted huts that resembled those seen at the Yampais village; they were in the midst of a pine grove; there was no water in the neighborhood, and the Yampais, who doubtless make this place their summer resort, must be compelled to send to the bottom of the cañon for their supply.

The country became rough and so much cut up by ravines that it was impossible to approach very closely to the main river. A good view was obtained of the walls of the Flax river cañon, and its mouth approximately located. The junction was below the mouth of Cascade creek, showing that that stream is not, as had been supposed, a tributary of the Colorado, but of its smaller affluent.

We had to camp without water, and it being the second day that the animals had had nothing to drink, a great part of them broke from the herders as soon as their saddles were removed, and made a stampede for the lagoons. Barely enough were left to pack the few articles that had been brought.

Another reconnaissance has since been made on foot from the lagoons westward. A line thirty miles in extent was traversed, with results similar to those previously obtained. An excellent view was had of the Big cañon. The barometric observations upon the surface of the plateau, and at the mouths of Diamond and Cataract rivers, showed that the walls of this portion of the cañon were over a mile high. The formation of the ground was such that the eye could not follow them the whole distance to the bottom, but as far down as they could be traced they appeared almost vertical. A sketch taken upon the spot by Mr. Egloffstein does better justice than any description can do to the marvellous scene.

Our reconnoitering parties have now been out in all directions, and everywhere have been headed off by impassable obstacles. The positions of the main water-courses have been determined with considerable accuracy. The region last explored is, of course, altogether valueless. It can be approached only from the south, and after entering it there is nothing to do but to leave. Ours has been the first, and will doubtless be the last, party of whites to visit this profitless locality. It seems intended by nature that the Colorado river, along the greater portion of its lonely and majestic way, shall be forever unvisited and undisturbed. The handful of Indians that inhabit the sequestered retreats where we discovered them have probably remained in the same condition, and of the same number, for centuries. The country could not support a large population, and by some provision of nature they have ceased to multiply. The deer, the antelope, the birds, even the smaller reptiles, all of which frequent the adjacent territory, have deserted this uninhabitable district. Excepting when the melting snows send their annual torrents through the avenues to the Colorado, conveying with them sound and motion, these dismal abysses, and the arid table-lands that enclose them, are left, as they have been for ages, in unbroken solitude and silence. The lagoons by the side of which we are encamped furnish, as far as we have been able to discover, the only accessible watering place west of the mouth of Diamond river. During the summer it is probable they are dry, and that no water exists upon the whole of the Colorado plateau. We start for the south with some anxiety, not knowing how long it may be before water will be again met with.

Camp 77, *Partridge ravine, April* 21.—On the day of our departure from the lagoons it was, for the first time during more than a week, warm and clear. Both the heat and the dryness were regretted. Even a snow-storm would have been welcome, assuring a supply of water.

J.J.YOUNG. from a sketch by F.W.EGLOFFSTEIN.

BIG CAÑON.

The mules, ignorant of what was before them, refused, as mules often do, to drink on the morning before leaving camp. A southeast course was followed, which led over an undulating surface, where the travelling for a while was tolerably good. A thick growth of cedars and pines offered occasional obstructions to the pack animals, who would get their loads tangled among the low branches. As the day advanced the heat became more oppressive, and a tract was entered where, the soil being loose and porous, the animals sank to their fetlocks at every step. Finally a small but impassable cañon was reached. After several ineffectual and fatiguing attempts to cross, we had to head the ravine by climbing the face of a high bluff in which it rose. The growth on the side of the ascent was dense, and the ground strewed with sharp rocks. Darkness came on before we had quite accomplished the descent upon the opposite side, and it was necessary to camp, not only without water, but on a very short allowance of grass. All the mules had to be hobbled to prevent them from stampeding back to the lagoons, which rendered it still more difficult for them to pick up enough to eat.

We had made as much easting as possible, being in constant fear, however, of meeting some insurmountable cañon that would require a long detour, and lengthen the distance to the belt of country south, where we were expecting to find water.

In spite of all the precautions some of the mules strayed, and while hunting for them a man got lost. By the time all were found the sun was high in the heaven, and shining with even more fervor than on the previous day. The face of the country continued much the same. The trees generally intercepted the view, and the landscape, where seen, was sufficiently monotonous, consisting of interminable slopes, broken here and there by a line of low bluffs that marked the edge of some higher plateau. At the end of ten miles of weary travel a steep ascent brought us to the summit of a table that overlooked the country towards the south for a hundred miles. The picture was grand, but the cedars and pines kept it shut out during most of the time, and the road was heavier than ever. No place could be descried, far or near, that gave a promise of containing water. A more frightfully arid region probably does not exist upon the face of the earth. Some difficult ravines were crossed a little before nightfall. The wretched and broken-down animals, now forty-eight hours without drinking, and that, too, while making long marches under a burning sun, were brought to a halt. They had to be tightly hobbled, for, in their frantic desire for water, nothing else could have restrained them from rushing back to the only place where they were certain of finding it. Too thirsty to graze, they stood all night about camp, filling the air with distressing cries. This morning the weakened brutes staggered under their packs as though they were drunk, and their dismal moaning portended a speedy solution of their troubles should water not soon be found.

For the third time the sun rose hot and glaring, and as the great globe of fire mounted the heavens its rays seemed to burn the brain. The condition of things was desperate should no water be discovered during the day. A single bad cañon or ravine, to turn us from the course for any great distance, would be unquestionably the destruction of the train. The scanty supply brought in kegs and canteens was exhausted. In this hot, dry atmosphere, when exercise is taken, the evaporation from the system is very great, and unless this is compensated for the body soon becomes intensely parched. The men now suffered as well as the beasts. Mile after mile the dreary ride continued, and the flagging pace of the mules showed that they were on the eve of exhaustion, and still the unvarying character of the plateau held out no promise of relief. The ground, fortunately, was smooth and level, and the travelling easy. While unconscious of the vicinity of any break in the surface of the plain, we came to the edge of a steep declivity, at the bottom of which was a ravine, whose sides displayed the volcanic rocks that are met along the 35th parallel, but from which we had been so long absent. Our hopes rose upon seeing surfaces not composed of loose pebbles or porous earth, and we urged the fainting animals down the hill. A fresh bear trail crossing the slope was a good sign that the almost despaired of element was not far distant. Green grass carpeted the bottom of the ravine, and a few hundred yards from its mouth a projecting ledge threw a deep cool shadow over an extensive pool of clear, delicious looking water.   The crazy beasts, crowding and huddling upon one another, plunged into the pond and drank till they were ready to burst.   A few yards above smaller basins of rock filled with the delightful beverage furnished an ample supply for the men.

A large grizzly bear—the animal whose tracks we had observed—was seen quietly ascending a hill near by, and half of the company rushed after the grim monster.   He was unconscious of pursuit till the party was close upon him.   Then he commenced to run, but the hill retarded his pace, and a volley of balls made the fur fly in all directions from different parts of his hide. Twice he turned as though meaning to show fight, but the crowd of pursuers was so large, and the firing so hot, that he continued his flight to the top of the hill, where he fell dead, riddled

Fig. 36.—Mount Floyd.

with bullets.   His skin was taken off to be preserved, and the flesh divided among the party. It is rather too strong flavored to be palatable when roasted or broiled, but makes capital soup.

We have now left the arid and desolate cañon region, and a due east course can be pursued as far as Flax river.   The belt of country now to be traversed is perhaps, at some seasons of the year, as dry as the district northward, but at this time the melting snows from the San Francisco and other volcanic mountains send fertilizing streams through the valleys and ravines, occasioning an abundant growth of grass; and the surface being covered with volcanic rocks, natural tanks are formed, that preserve supplies of water for a considerable period.

We anticipate, therefore, a few days of travel undisturbed by the anxieties that have attended the march since leaving the Mojave valley.   The only difficulty now to be apprehended is that the sharp and vitreous masses of hardened lava overspreading the ground may injure the feet of the animals.   The rough country traversed has been so hard upon shoes that nearly all of the mules are now unshodden.

A few miles south is a peak that forms one of the most prominent objects in this region.   We recognize it as the Mount Floyd laid down by Mr. Beale.

CHAPTER IX.

SAN FRANCISCO FOREST TO MOQUIS.

Camp 80, *Bill Williams's Mountain, April* 25.—Partridge ravine widened as it was descended, till it became a beautiful valley, covered with grassy slopes and clumps of cedars. It contained neither springs nor a running stream, but among the rocks along the base of the bluffs many pools were discovered. The pasturage was excellent. The place is a great resort at this season for grizzly bear, antelope, deer, and wild turkeys, large numbers of whose tracks were seen leading to and from the water holes.

For ten or fifteen miles we followed the course of the valley, and then, allowing the mules a day to rest and graze, struck off directly to the east. The surface of the ground was sprinkled with lava rocks. Before advancing far a steep bluff obstructed the way. The growth of cedars was so dense that we could scarcely get the riding animals and packs through, much less see to select a good place to ascend. Dismounting and going directly at the face of the precipice we clambered blindly up, driving the mules ahead. The sharp stones made the footing additionally insecure. Breathless and exhausted, at last we attained the summit, and found that it was only the first of a series of similar ridges that were also to be crossed. Descending to the ravine we were soon engaged in another upward scramble, and the process had to be repeated till animals and men were scarcely able to stand.

The eastern crest overlooked a beautiful rolling country, in the midst of which towered the volcanic mountains that have long formed so conspicuous a feature in the scenery. A pool of water surrounded by grass afforded a good camp.

This morning we re entered the region of pines, and have travelled all day in the midst of picturesque and charming scenery. The valleys are covered with a bright green sward, and open groves are disposed gracefully upon the lowlands and ridges. Heavy masses of snow are still piled upon the San Francisco summit, and this close proximity of winter heightens and gives a zest to the enjoyment of spring.

Our camp is in the midst of an extensive meadow at the northern base of Bill Williams's mountain. This peak, though the second in importance of the cluster, is far less lofty than its collossal neighbor, and the snows that whitened its crest a few weeks since have nearly disappeared. A sparkling brook now dashes down the ravine and meanders through the centre of the meadow, which contains perhaps five hundred acres, and is covered with a luxuriant growth of grama grass. Stately pines and spruce are scattered upon the surrounding slopes, and afford a delightful shade. We found in possession of the spot a herd of antelope that scoured over the mountain like the wind when they saw the train approaching.

To eyes that have been resting upon the deserted and ghastly region northward this country appears like a paradise. We see it to the greatest advantage. The melting snows

DRAWN BY FRH.R F.W.v.EGLOFFSTEIN.

BIG CAÑON

FROM COLORADO PLATEAU.

have converted it into a well-watered garden, and covered it with green meadows and spring flowers.   The grass, even when dried by the summer's sun, will remain nutritious.   The groves of trees will at all times give the region a habitable appearance, and, though it is not known how great the supply of water would be during the summer, the country can never present the arid wastes that are spread along the belts of territory both north and south.   One only source of trouble is that which we anticipated encountering.   The vitreous rock rasps off the hoofs of the unshod mules like a file, and they will be disabled if we have long to travel over the lava region.

Fig. 37.—Bill Williams's Mountain.

Camp 84, *April* 30.—The route continued through an open park, dotted with flowery lawns and pretty copses, and then reached the edge of the great forest that surrounds the San Francisco mountain, and entered its sombre precincts.   It was delightful to escape from the heat of the sun, and travel through the cool underwood.   Across the dark shady glades a glimpse would sometimes be caught of a bright tinted meadow glowing in the sunlight.   Antelope and deer were constantly seen bounding by, stopping for a moment to gaze at us, and then darting off into the obscure recesses of the wood.

Half-way to the mountain we passed an open prairie—a natural clearing in this vast expanse of pines—and camped upon the eastern edge.   Water was found in a ravine close by.   The amount of snow melted from the mountain sides during the past fortnight has been immense, and every water-course is filled with a cold, clear rill.   During the march to-day the effects of the thaw have been found somewhat inconvenient.   Some of the ground passed over has been comparatively low, and so soft between the rocks that the mules were in danger of miring at every step.   Nothing frightens a mule or makes him more obstinate than this, and it was with great difficulty that we compelled the unwilling animals to proceed.   As we approached the great volcano, the jagged rocks, with which the surrounding surface was strewn, so bruised their feet that they were hardly able to walk.

Under the southwest base of the San Francisco peak we camped at a spring, known to be permanent. It is in a sheltered nook almost buried in the side of the impending mountain. There is abundant grazing. The water is cold and delicious. The surrounding forest furnishes shade in summer, and material for warmth in winter, and at all seasons of the year the place doubtless affords an excellent camp.

On the following day, while skirting the base of the mountain, the tender-footed beasts stumbled and staggered upon the sharp rocks till it seemed inhuman to drive them any longer, but the delays and short marches had so reduced our stock of provisions that it was absolutely necessary to keep on. As we turned our backs upon the imposing pile the road became a little better, and by degrees the lava disappeared. The eastern border of the pine forest was soon reached, and a belt of cedars entered similar to that growing upon the other side.

The grass and the scoriæ go together, and after being rid of the latter the former also became scarcer. We made the first camp, after leaving the forest, with plenty of water, but with little pasturage. As the evening approached there was a sudden change of weather. From summer heat it became intensely cold. A roaring gale sprang up, accompanied with snow and sleet. Yesterday morning the ground was covered with snow to the depth of nearly a foot, and the storm was driving so furiously that it was impossible to move from camp. These violent transitions from a July to a January temperature are very trying both to men and animals. The half-frozen beasts were exposed to the keen blast for twenty-four hours without a mouthful to eat. That they were able, in their weakened and emaciated condition, to survive it was a matter of astonishment. Several times during the past two weeks they have appeared to be on their last legs, but an occult store of vitality has always turned up at the critical moment to meet the emergency.

The tempest had sufficiently subsided to-day to enable us to continue the journey. The storm had spread over only a small area, and the descent to Flax river being rapid, we were removed from its effects by a few hours of travel, and brought into a lower country and a less inclement atmosphere. We have camped at the first grazing place encountered, and expect to reach Flax river to-morrow.

Dense and black masses of clouds are still drifting past the San Francisco summit and the surrounding slopes and icy cold blasts reach us at intervals from that quarter. The storm seems to have burst out again with increased violence, and we congratulate ourselves on having escaped from its influence.

Camp 85, Flax river, May 2.—The wide valley of Flax river could be recognized a long way off by the line of cottonwoods that skirt the banks of the stream. The river is smaller than the Colorado, but at this season, when the water is becoming high, much resembles the other at its low stage. There are the same swift current, chocolate colored water, shoals, snags, sand bars, and evidences of a constantly shifting channel. The width opposite to camp is about fifty yards, and the depth five or six feet. The banks and bottom are composed of quicksand, and we have been unable to find a ford. The bottom lands are in places several miles wide. Here and there are to be found patches of a coarse grass, which at this season is green and nutritious.

Before proceeding with the examinations northward, it became necessary to look into the condition of the train and the supplies. The inspection developed unsatisfactory results. Most of the mules are in such a state as to preclude the possibility of their going much further. Several that I was unable to supply with the Mexican pack-saddle, or arapaho, have had to carry army pack-saddles, which, according to invariable experience on long marches, have mangled their backs shockingly. The sudden and severe snow-storms, coming in the midst of hot weather, the scarcity, and, at times, absolute deprivation of food and water, the difficult country and rocky surface, have reduced them to a sorry plight. They look and move like slightly animated skeletons.

The stock of provisions is nearly gone. While traversing the thick forests the branches have torn the packs and occasioned unavoidable wastage. There is barely enough left to take the party to Fort Defiance, which is the nearest military post. I am loth, however, to forego a short exploration of the country to the north, if only to visit the towns of the Moquis, which cannot be more than seventy or eighty miles distant. The impassable cañons west of the territory of these Indians have thrown them out of the line of travel and exploration, and there has been no record concerning them since the accounts of the early Spanish missionaries, who visited the country, and described the "seven cities" which they found there.

It has been finally arranged for Lieutenant Tipton to take the train and follow Lieutenant Whipple's trail to Zuñi, and thence go to Fort Defiance, while Dr. Newberry, Mr. Egloffstein, and myself, with ten men and a few of the least exhausted mules, are to proceed northward. A reduction throughout the command in the amount of the accustomed ration will enable our small number to be kept in the field for a week or two longer than the time it would require to go directly to the fort.

The day has been passed in preparing to carry out this arrangement. The mules, provisions, &c., for the use of my detachment, have been crossed to the north side of the river. Owing to the quicksand, and the want of tools and materials to construct a raft, this would have been a difficult if not an impracticable undertaking, had we not been provided with one of Buchanan's portable boats.* As it is, there has been no trouble. Enough pack-straps were tied together to reach across, and a single person could easily pull over the boat and a load weighing a couple of tons. The mules swam over. To enable them to reach and emerge from the river across the quicksand banks, an approach was prepared on either side with logs and branches of trees covered with earth.

The gale has blown itself out, and a cloudless sky has succeeded, bringing with it a return of summer weather.

Camp 89, *Flax river*, *May* 6.—We made an early start, and signalling good-bye to our friends upon the opposite side of the river, struck off towards the bluffs that border the bottom lands. The direction taken was a little east of north. The alluvial earth was soft and difficult to traverse; the slope that followed composed of material still softer, and when, after crossing several ridges, the top of the plateau was reached, the soil became so light and friable that every step of the way was attended with labor and fatigue. The day was the hottest that had been experienced.

The summit being attained, a vast extent of country—sweeping from Flax river around to the northeast—was brought into view. It was a flat table-land, from which wide tracts had been eroded to a moderate depth, leaving exposed lines of low bluffs and isolated fragments of

---

❋ This admirable invention was patented by Colonel R. C. Buchanan, 4th infantry, in 1857. The boat consists of a portable skeleton frame, sheathed with *unprepared* canvas, secured to the framework by lashing. It was first used during the campaign in Southern Oregon against the Rogue River Indians, in 1856.

Expecting to carry everything, during my land explorations, upon pack-mules, I had a boat made of smaller dimensions than had been before constructed. It was eleven feet long, five feet wide, and about two feet deep. The frame was of pine, and the whole weight, including the canvas and cords, but 150 pounds—a light load for a single animal. Twelve men could cross a river in it with perfect safety. It could be unpacked and put together in about ten minutes.

A few years before I had had experience, while in the same country, and under much the same circumstances, of one of the ordinary pontoon boats. Its liability to rot, to get stuck together when packed and carried under a hot sun, and to be injured by the attrition of pack-ropes, other packs, and branches of trees, rendered it, after a short time, almost valueless.

The Buchanan boat was found to be free from these objections. After being packed for four months over a rough and wooded country, it was found in a perfectly serviceable condition. The canvas covering I used when required to protect the packs from rain. This rendered it unnecessary to carry a tarpaulin.

My experience has convinced me that the boat is admirably adapted for field service, and will be found to possess the advantages of lightness, durability, and staunchness, in a superior degree to any now in use.

the removed stratum. The scene was one of utter desolation. Not a tree nor a shrub broke its monotony. The edges of the mesas were flaming red, and the sand threw back the sun's rays in a yellow glare. Every object looked hot and dry and dreary. The animals began to give out. We knew that it was desperate to keep on, but felt unwilling to return, and forced the jaded brutes to wade through the powdery impalpable dust for fifteen miles. The country, if possible, grew worse. There was not a spear of grass, and from the porousness of the soil and rocks it was impossible that there should be a drop of water. A point was reached which commanded a view twenty or thirty miles ahead, but the fiery bluffs and yellow sand, paled somewhat by distance, extended to the end of the vista. Even beyond the ordinary limit of vision were other bluffs and sand fields, lifted into view by the mirage, and elongating the hideous picture. The only relief to the eye was a cluster of blue pinnacles far to the east that promised a different character of country. It was useless, however, to take the risk of proceeding directly thither. The experience of the day had demonstrated the hopelessness of trying to drive the mules for any length of time through an untrodden and yielding soil, and it was determined, as a last chance, to go back to Flax river and ascend the bank, at the hazard of having to make a long circuit, till some Indian trail should be encountered leading in the desired direction, and affording a beaten way practicable to be followed.

The night spent upon the desert showed that this condemned region was not entirely devoid of life. As the sun declined and a pleasanter atmosphere succeeded to the oppressive heat, scorpions, spiders, rattlesnakes, and centipedes emerged from their retreats to enjoy the evening air. A collector in that department of natural history could have reaped a harvest of these reptiles in almost any part of our camp-ground.

The next day we went back to the river, striking it ten miles above the place where we had left it. The return was attended with the same difficulties as the march of the day before, and I think nothing but the knowledge on the part of the thirsty mules that they were approaching water could have made them hold out till the distance was accomplished. The valley seemed like an Eden, in contrast with the region that had just been visited, though a sorry looking place if compared with the more favored parts of the continent.

During yesterday we have travelled up the river twenty-five miles. The valley is much cut up by ravines and sloughs. There are indications that, at some seasons, there are storms which send torrents of water from the plateau across the alluvial lands. The soil in many places is impregnated with alkalies and the surface covered with an efflorescence.

The blinding glare of the sun upon the white ground seriously affects the vision, and it has been found necessary to screen the eyes with muslin shades.

The bottom is filled with black-tailed deer. A buck was killed to-day measuring six feet from the nose to the base of the tail. The venison was of delightful flavor, and, though not in season, quite tender. Ruins of ancient pueblos have been passed. These vestiges of a former race of inhabitants, which are found so widely scattered over the table-lands of New Mexico, may be taken as evidence either that the country where they exist can or that it cannot now sustain a population; depending upon the theory adopted to account for the disappearance of the previous residents.

At noon to-day we came to the object of our search—a well-beaten Indian trail running towards the north. Camp was pitched at the place where it strikes the river, and it is the intention to make the second attempt to-morrow to penetrate the unexplored region. Near by are several salt springs, and scattered over the adjacent surface are crystals of excellent salt. This accounts for the position of the trail, for it is doubtless here that the Moquis obtain their supply of that article.

Camp 91, *Pottery Hill, May* 9.—The Indian trail pursued a straight line almost due north, and had been sufficiently used to form an easy, well-beaten path, which could be travelled without difficulty or fatigue. Eighteen miles brought us to the line of bluffs by which the valley slopes are bounded.   There was no appearance of a break till the face of the precipice was reached, when a narrow entrance was disclosed that conducted into a ravine bounded by walls of brilliant red marl.   The road was level for some distance along the gorge, and then a steep ascent was reached which brought us, after some difficult climbing, to the summit.

About us and extending westward as far as the eye could reach, were the red bluffs, yellow sand, and all the direful features previously encountered upon the desert, but in front, only a few miles distant, a line of beautiful blue peaks stood like watch-towers upon the verge of a pleasant looking region.   A green slope between two prominent summits directly ahead led

Fig. 38—Blue Peaks.

to an undulating ascent, seen in far perspective and dotted with fantastic crags, the most distant of which were tipped with snow.   The cool, soft tints of this picturesque landscape were in refreshing relief to the glaring colors and desolate monotony of the foreground.

The march having extended to twenty-five miles, and darkness approaching, we were compelled to camp just before reaching the entrance to this land of promise.   The day had opened bright and hot, but taught by experience we were not astonished when at noon a storm set in, accompanied with hail and rain and a piercingly cold atmosphere.   The rain at night might have been an advantage had not the porous soil instantly absorbed every drop.   We had nothing in which to catch enough water to supply the animals.   The icy blast would have prevented them from grazing even had there been anything to eat, and they looked, if possible, more wo-begone than ever when morning came.

We gladly left the desert and ascended the slope.   While advancing, the Blue Peaks rose up in front, like ships approached at sea—some in cones and symmetrical castellated shapes, and others in irregular masses.   We had made six miles, and were looking out eagerly for water when we reached a little spring issuing from a rock by the side of the trail.   At the

COLORADO EXPLORING EXPEDITION.

MOQUIS PUEBLOS.

J.J.YOUNG from a sketch by F.W.EGLOFFSTEIN

foot of the rock was an artificial basin nine or ten feet in diameter, which was filled with clear and sweet water.   The mules slaked their thirst, the kegs were filled, and we proceeded on the way, but not with the same ease as the day before.   The rain had softened the path and made it hard to travel.   Eight miles from the spring half of the animals, having been without food for nearly two days, broke completely down, and camp was made at the base of a hill where a clump of cedars furnished a supply of fire-wood.

It was again necessary to rest for a day, and not knowing how far ahead it might be to the next water, in the early morning we sent the mules back to the spring to drink and graze. The men reported, when they returned with the herd this evening, that the spring had filled the basin so slowly as only to furnish water to one or two of the animals, and they must start thirsty on their journey to-morrow.   The failure of the spring is a source of anxiety.   We are forty miles from the river.   Another day's journey without water would make it impossible to return, and at any risk it would be necessary to keep on.

The supposed position of the Moquis towns turns out to have been erroneous.   We should already, according to the maps, be in sight of them; but a view from the top of the hill, by which we are encamped, discloses no signs of habitations.   The Blue Peaks in the direction of the trail are nearly passed, and the country northward looks arid and unpromising.

Camp 92, *Limestone spring, May* 10 —It was resolved to make a long march should no water be reached, and we started at an early hour.   Three miles from camp, while passing through some hills that exhibited every indication of utter dryness and sterility, we found, at the bottom of a ravine, a growth of young willows surrounding some springs, and a patch of fresh, green grass.   The packs were removed.   A trench was dug across the ravine, which filled slowly, but in a few hours had enabled all the mules to drink.   It did not take them long to eat up the grass, and an hour before noon the packs were replaced and the march resumed. The path had again become hard, and thirteen miles were accomplished without trouble.   This brought us to a rough ravine that led through a limestone ridge to the edge of a broad valley. Some tolerable grass and a little spring of water offered sufficient inducement to camp.

As the sun went down, and the confused glare and mirage disappeared, I discovered with a spy-glass two of the Moquis towns, eight or ten miles distant, upon the summit of a high bluff overhanging the opposite side of the valley.   They were built close to the edge of the precipice, and being of the same color as the mesa, it would have been difficult to distinguish them even with a glass, but for the vertical and horizontal lines of the walls and buildings.   The outlines of the closely-packed structures looked in the distance like the towers and battlements of a castle, and their commanding position enhanced the picturesque effect.   When darkness fell, camp fires—probably those of the Moquis herdsmen—could be seen scattered along the further side of the valley.

Camp 93, *Moquis pueblos, May* 11.—The trail crossed the valley, making straight for the pueblos.   For six miles not a sign of life was perceived; but while ascending a hill near the base of the bluff two mounted Indians and one small horse charged suddenly upon us, the riders shouting vociferous welcomes, and each insisting upon shaking hands with the whole company.   One of them was respectably dressed.   He had on a blue coat, cotton pants, a hat, a belt of circular brass plates, and a variety of ornaments.   In his hand was a flint-lock musket of ancient pattern.   The little horse they rode was nearly as thin as our mules, but garnished with red trimmings and a Mexican saddle and bridle.   The most remarkable feature about both was their neatness.   Their hair was finer than is usual with the race, and carefully combed. They were arrayed, to be sure, in their best attire, but cleanliness is seldom considered by Indians as forming any part of the most elaborate toilet.

I asked the leader to be directed to water, and he pointed to a gap where a ravine appeared to run up the bluff rather behind the pueblos, and signified that there we would find an abundance. He further informed me that there was an excellent grass camp at the same place.   A great deal of pantomime brought about this understanding, and then he signified that we must leave the trail and follow him, which we accordingly did, diverging a little to the left from our former course. It was the first time we had had a guide since the departure of Ireteba, and it was pleasant to be able once more to shift the responsibility of conducting the train to a third party.

Our new friend had a pleasant, intelligent face which expressed, however, misgivings as to our character and object in coming into that unvisited region. He rode along humming to himself, with a palpable affectation of being cool and unconcerned, occasionally glancing back with a dubious air to see what was going on behind. The two who had been selected to bear the brunt of the first interview had, I suppose, brought the horse as a means of escape, for soon others of the tribe, satisfied of our pacific intentions, came up on foot. All were running at the top of their speed. They approached to the very sides of the mules, greatly to the alarm of those animals, and suddenly brought up to shake hands, commencing with me, and continuing through the train. They were clean and nice looking; no particular costume prevailed. Every available article acquired by trading with other Indians—for they have no communication with whites—had been converted into raiment or material for personal adornment. Their figures were of medium size and indifferently proportioned, their features strongly marked and homely, with an expression generally bright and good-natured. Thirty or forty joined us, and the cortege in a little while became of considerable length.

The face of the bluff, upon the summit of which the town was perched, was cut up and irregular. We were led through a passage that wound among some low hillocks of sand and rock that extended half-way to the top. Large flocks of sheep were passed; all but one or two were jet black, presenting, when together, a singular appearance. It did not seem possible, while ascending through the sand-hills, that a spring could be found in such a dry looking place, but presently a crowd was seen collected upon a mound before a small plateau, in the centre of which was a circular reservoir, fifty feet in diameter, lined with masonry, and filled with pure cold water. The basin was fed from a pipe connecting with some source of supply upon the summit of the mesa. The Moquis looked amiably on while the mules were quenching their thirst, and then my guide informed me that he would conduct us to a grazing camp. Continuing to ascend we came to another reservoir, smaller but of more elaborate construction and finish. From this, the guide said, they got their drinking water, the other reservoir being intended for animals. Between the two the face of the bluff had been ingeniously converted into terraces. These were faced with neat masonry, and contained gardens, each surrounded with a raised edge so as to retain water upon the surface. Pipes from the reservoirs permitted them at any time to be irrigated.

Peach trees were growing upon the terraces and in the hollows below. A long flight of stone steps, with sharp turns that could easily be defended, was built into the face of the precipice, and led from the upper reservoir to the foot of the town. The scene, rendered animated by the throngs of Indians in their gaily-colored dresses, was one of the most remarkable I had ever witnessed. My state of admiration was interrupted by the guide, who told me, to my astonishment, that we had reached the camp-ground. Besides the danger of the mules trampling upon and ruining the gardens, it was no place to stop, inasmuch as there was not a blade of grass. I called the attention of the Indian to the latter fact, which he did not appear to have considered. While he was reflecting upon the matter, we were joined by a pleasant looking middle-aged man, with a handsome shell suspended to his neck, and a kind of baton in his hand, whom I supposed to be a chief. Like the rest, he shook hands all around, and held a consultation with the guide and with the crowd generally about the grass. They finally concluded that there was plenty a little further ahead, and we proceeded around the ascent by a side trail that led away from the pueblo. In ten minutes a spot was reached which all agreed was the best grazing camp the country afforded. I no longer wondered that their one horse looked so thin. A single animal could scarcely have existed for three days upon all the grass in the neighbor-

H.B.Mollhausen, Del.

Lith. of Sarony,Major & Knapp, 449 Broadway,N.Y.

MOQUIS.

J.J.Young, from a sketch by F.W.Egloffstein.

INTERIOR OF A MOQUIS HOUSE

hood.   Some distance back in the valley I had seen a small patch of grass, and now signified to the troubled looking Indians that I would send the train back, and let the mules be driven to the reservoir when they needed water.   I also told them that Dr. Newberry, Mr. Egloffstein, and myself would visit their houses before following the rest of the party to the camp.   This arrangement seemed satisfactory, and the chief, accompanied by several friends, led the way with an inconvenient alacrity, considering the steepness of the ascent.   The stone steps being surmounted, we came upon a level summit, and had the walls of the pueblo upon one side and an extensive and beautiful view upon the other.   Without giving us time to admire the scene, the Indians led us to a ladder planted against the centre of the front face of the pueblo.   The town is nearly square, and surrounded by a stone wall fifteen feet high, the top of which forms a landing extending around the whole.   Flights of stone steps led from the first to a second landing, upon which the doors of the houses open.   Mounting the stairway opposite to the ladder, the chief crossed to the nearest door and ushered us into a low apartment from which two or three others opened towards the interior of the dwelling.   Our host courteously asked us to be seated upon some skins spread along the floor against the wall, and presently his wife brought in a vase of water and a tray filled with a singular substance that looked more like sheets of thin blue wrapping paper rolled up into bundles than anything else that I had ever seen.   I learned afterwards that it was made from corn meal, ground very fine, made into a gruel, and poured over a heated stone to be baked.   When dry it has a surface slightly polished, like paper.   The sheets are folded and rolled together, and form the staple article of food with the Moquis Indians.

As the dish was intended for our entertainment, and looked clean, we all partook of it.   It had a delicate fresh-bread flavor, and was not at all unpalatable, particularly when eaten with salt.   After we had eaten and drank, Mr. Egloffstein took a pipe from his pocket, which was filled and passed around.   I noticed, then and afterwards, that the Moquis, when commencing to smoke, bow with solemnity towards each point of the compass.   While they were engaged with the pipe we had a chance to examine the contents of the apartment.   The room was fifteen feet by ten; the walls were made of adobes; the partitions of substantial beams; the floor laid with clay.   In one corner were a fireplace and chimney.   Everything was clean and tidy.   Skins, bows and arrows, quivers, antlers, blankets, articles of clothing and ornament, were hanging from the walls or arranged upon shelves.   Vases, flat dishes, and gourds filled with meal or water were standing along one side of the room.   At the other end was a trough divided into compartments, in each of which was a sloping stone slab two or three feet square for grinding corn upon.   In a recess of an inner room was piled a goodly store of corn in the ear.   I noticed, among other things, a reed musical instrument with a bell-shaped end like a clarionet, and a pair of painted drumsticks tipped with gaudy feathers.   Another inner room appeared to be a sleeping apartment, but this being occupied by females we did not enter, though the Indians seemed to be pleased rather than otherwise at the curiosity evinced during the close inspection of their dwelling and furniture.

While Mr. Egloffstein was making a sketch of the place and its owners, I had a talk with the latter.   Spreading out a map of the country we had been exploring, I pointed out our route and the places with which I supposed they were familiar.   They seemed to comprehend, and the chief designated upon the map the positions of the six Moquis pueblos.   I told him that we wished to go further to the north, and he signified that four days' travel in that direction would bring us to a large river.   Whether there were watering places between it was difficult from his signs to determine.   I then asked for a guide, promising a mule to any one that would accompany me, whereupon he said that he would be ready to go himself early the next morning.   A bargain was likewise made for some sheep, which they agreed to send to camp, receiving a blanket in exchange for each animal.

Then we went out upon the landing, and by another flight of steps ascended to the roof, where we beheld a magnificent panorama.   The San Francisco mountain, the valley and cañon of Flax river, and the plateaus to the north and east were all visible, the most distant objects appearing distinct and well defined through the transparent atmosphere.   Several trails radiated from the foot of the bluff in perfectly straight lines, and could be traced a long way over the level surface.   One conducted to the cañon of Flax river and doubtless to the Yampais village; another, the chief told us, was the trail of the Apaches; another, that of the Coyoteros; a fourth came from Zuñi, and still further east was the Navajo trail leading to Fort Defiance.

We learned that there were seven towns; that the name of that which we were visiting was Mooshahneh.   A second smaller town was half a mile distant; two miles westward was a third, which had been seen from camp the evening before.   Five or six miles to the northeast a bluff was pointed out as the location of three others; and we were informed that the last of the seven, Oraybe, was still further distant, on the trail towards the great river.

From these heights, the ascent to which is so difficult and so easily defended, the Moquis can overlook the surrounding country, and descry, at a vast distance, the approach of strangers.   The towns themselves would be almost impregnable to an Indian assault.   Each pueblo is built around a rectangular court, in which we suppose are the springs that furnish the supply to the reservoirs.   The exterior walls, which are of stone, have no openings, and would have to be scaled or battered down before access could be gained to the interior.

The successive stories are set back, one behind the other.   The lower rooms are reached through trap-doors from the first landing.   The houses are three rooms deep, and open upon the interior court.   The arrangement is as strong and compact as could well be devised, but as the court is common, and the landings are separated by no partitions, it involves a certain community of residence.   The strength of the position unfortunately does not protect the animals upon the plains below, and our friends informed us, with rueful faces, that the Comanches and Navajoes had driven off a great deal of their stock during the previous year.   The Moquis do not look warlike, and but for their natural and artificial defences would doubtless long ago have been exterminated by their powerful and aggressive neighbors.

Curious faces were peering at us from the openings and landings during these observations.   Many of the women and girls made their appearance; all but one or two having previously kept out of sight.   The hair of the young girls is gathered into large knots, or rather knobs, one at each corner of the forehead, which gives them an odd appearance, but their skins are rather fair and their faces pretty.   They are quiet and retiring; were neat in their appearance, and prepossessing in expression and manner.   The whole tribe are of a much lighter hue than any Indians met upon our route.

Having made a long visit, we descended to camp, inviting the chief and two of his friends to go with us, which they did, taking us down by a more direct route than that by which we had ascended.   The sheep were soon forthcoming, according to agreement, and several brought bags of corn and little packages of dried peaches to trade.   Some beautiful and really valuable Navajo blankets were also offered, and readily exchanged for a woollen shirt, or some common article of apparel.

The three who accompanied us down I invited into my tent and regaled with bread and molasses, which they ate greedily.   They had scarcely commenced when as many as the tent could hold entered without invitation and joined in the repast.

Like the Zuñi Indians, the Moquis have albinos among them.   A woman with a fair light complexion and hair has been in camp this evening.   It seemed incredible that she could be of Indian parentage, but the cases are by no means rare in the pueblos of New Mexico.

Satisfied with the conduct of the chief, I gave him a red sash, which excited great admiration.   He then departed, promising to be in camp early in the morning, ready to accompany us as guide.

The day has been still and clear, and the heat intense.   It is hard to realize that the region about us was covered with snow but forty-eight hours ago, and that we were nearly frozen by the cold wind and pelting sleet.

CHAPTER X.

MOQUIS TO FORT DEFIANCE.—CONCLUSION.

Camp 94, *Oraybe, May* 12.—This morning the Moquis were in camp exhibiting an insatiable curiosity to see everything that was going on. Our promised guide did not come with the others, and I supposed he was preparing himself for the journey. Corn meal was brought in for trade, and one individual opening his blanket disclosed a dozen fresh eggs, for which he found a ready sale.

The mules had to be driven to the reservoir and it was late before the train was in readiness to move. The chief still did not appear. I began to fear he was going to disappoint us; and after watching the place of descent from the town for a quarter of an hour, finding that he did not come in sight, determined to wait no longer.

It was difficult to decide which direction to take. I inquired of the Indians for the trail to Oraybe, but they could not or would not understand, and no one would consent to lead the way. Concluding to pursue a northwest course, we started through the sand-hills; following, as nearly as possible, that direction, but had scarcely ridden a hundred yards when the chief appeared over the brow of a hill, running, as the Indians had done on the day before, at full speed. He rushed to the head of the train, shook hands, told me that he had to go back to his house, but would soon overtake us by a short cut; ordered a boy near by to guide us meanwhile, and disappeared as rapidly as he had approached.

Under the guidance of the lad we followed a sinuous and difficult road through the hills that form the slope from the bluffs to the plain below. The trail led close to a second town whose inhabitants were gathered on the walls and housetops to gaze at us as we passed.

Two more reservoirs were seen, and several gardens and peach orchards. A few miles of tedious travelling brought us to the edge of the valley. The chief here overtook us, and a mule was furnished to him upon which he mounted and led the way.

The country now traversed was the most promising looking for agricultural purposes of any yet seen. It had nearly all been under cultivation. Immense fields were passed, and our guide stopped constantly to gossip with his neighbors who were busy planting corn.

Their method of doing this was very primitive. With a sharp stick a hole was punched in the ground a foot deep, and the corn dropped in and covered up. No women were engaged in the labor. Unlike other tribes of Indians, the men do the out-of-door work, leaving to the females the care of the households, the spinning, weaving, sewing, &c. At the end of a few miles Oraybe came in sight; it was larger than the other pueblos. Though we had made but a short march, several mules gave out and could not be driven even without their packs. The scanty grass of the three preceding days had taken away the remnant of strength left to them. We had to camp, though the pasturage was neither good nor abundant.

The Oraybe reservoirs are a mile or two distant, but we shall pass one to-morrow and be

COLORADO EXPLORING EXPEDITION.

DRAWN BY FRHᴿ F.W. v. EGLOFFSTEIN.

CAÑON OF CATARACT CREEK AND FLAX RIVER.

able to water the animals and fill the kegs as we go by. A large number of the citizens came to see us. I subsequently learned that one of them was the chief, but he did not accost any one nor seem desirous of making acquaintances. It was apparent that he was out of humor, and the chief that had guided us informed me that the other, who seems to be the senior of all, had objected to any of the tribe accompanying the expedition north, on the ground that there was no water, that the country was bad, that we would have to travel several days before we would come to a river, and that if we did reach it the mules could not get to the bank. Arguments and promises were vain. The Oraybe continued to express disapproval, and his influence seemed to be all-powerful. His ill temper increased as the discussion proceeded, and at last he left in a sulk and went home. I then had a talk with the other. He was friendly in his manner, but said that he could not go while his superior objected, and intimated, if I understood him aright, that the Oraybe captain had some reason for not being well disposed towards Americans. He said that there was a water hole a long day's journey off where we could get a small supply; that to this point he would guide us, and that there was a trail beyond which could be followed as well without guidance as with it. He persisted that there would be a march of three or four days without water before reaching the river. As nearly as I have been able to judge, they consider a day's march thirty miles. If his statement is true, the question of crossing this desert in the present condition of the mules may be considered as settled.

The Oraybe Indians are more quiet than their brethren of Mooshahneh. They collect in a circle to witness anything that may be going on, but are almost silent, and when they speak or laugh do so in a suppressed tone, like children under restraint. There is much uniformity of dress. All are wrapped in Navajo blankets, with broad white and dark stripes, and a crowd at a distance looks like the face of a stratified rock.

The external and internal arrangements of the houses are like those of the other town, but there is generally less neatness and thrift in the appearance both of the place and its inhabitants.

Camp 95, Oraybe gardens, May 13.—Neither of the chiefs appeared in camp this morning, nor many of their tribe. They are late risers, and we were off soon after sunrise. Not expecting to be furnished with a guide, it had been determined what course to take, and we skirted the eastern base of the bluff in order to follow a deep depression that has been noticed extending towards the northwest. We had proceeded a mile, when an Indian came running after us. He said that he had been despatched by the Oraybe chief to conduct us to the next water, and we began to think the old fellow less churlish than he had appeared, and gladly availed ourselves of his civility and of the new-comer's knowledge.

Selecting a course amongst numerous intersecting trails, that would have puzzled a stranger considerably, he led the way to the east of the bluff on which Oraybe stands. Eight or nine miles brought the train to an angle formed by two faces of the precipice. At the foot was a reservoir, and a broad road winding up the steep ascent. On either side the bluffs were cut into terraces, and laid out into gardens similar to those seen at Mooshahneh, and, like them, irrigated from an upper reservoir. The whole reflected great credit upon Moquis ingenuity and skill in the department of engineering. The walls of the terraces and reservoirs were of partially dressed stone, well and strongly built, and the irrigating pipes conveniently arranged. The little gardens were neatly laid out. Two or three men and as many women were working in them as we passed.

The steep hill completely broke down the animals, and we had to camp upon the brink of the mesa above. I rewarded the Indian handsomely, and tried to persuade him to continue with us to-morrow. He has consented, but looks as though he meant to break his word. Our Mojaves would have persisted obstinately in refusing, or, having once agreed to go, would have adhered to their bargain.

While on the road to-day the guide pointed out a place where the Navajoes had recently made a descent upon the Moquis flocks.   He had himself been herding at the time, and showed me two scars upon his sides from wounds received in the engagement.   The herders had been utterly routed, and retreated to their pueblo, while the conquerers made off with all their stock.

The country to the north and northwest is rolling for some miles, and then there are elevated plateaus rising in successive steps.   The most remote appears to be sixty miles off, and higher than any table-land that has been passed.   Distant peaks can be seen a little east of north.   The Indians have said that the trail runs northwest, and that it is the only practicable route by which upper portions of the river can be attained.   Such a course would bring us, at the end of ninety miles, opposite to the point where we struck the Cascade river, and only about fifty miles distant from it, though we would have travelled, in heading the cañon and side cañons of Flax river, nearly three hundred miles.

Fig. 39.—View north from Oraybe Gardens.

Camp 97, *Oraybe gardens, May* 15.—No Indians came again to camp.   The guide, before leaving, had told a Mexican that the distance to the river was more than a hundred miles, and that the only watering place was about twenty-five miles from Oraybe.   Preferring to see for ourselves the condition of the country, we pursued the same general course as before, towards the northwest.   The top of the mesa on which we had been encamped proved to be very narrow, and before we had travelled a mile we came to its northern edge, where there were the usual precipice and foot-hills forming the descent to a broad valley.   Here, also, the bluffs had been formed into terraced gardens and reservoirs.   The descent was steep and difficult.   The valley furnished better grass than any seen since leaving Flax river, but the soil was soft and the travelling laborious.   We crossed the low land and ascended the opposite mesa.   The trail was found, and its course followed for ten or eleven miles, when most of the mules again gave out, and became unable to proceed. It was cloudy and cool. They had had rest, tolerable grazing, and water during the previous day and night, but it was evident that their strength was gone.

There were no indications of water ahead. The country could be seen for a great distance, and, as far as the eye could reach, exhibited only line after line of arid mesas. In a ravine, not far from camp, appeared to be the watering place spoken of by the Moquis. Water had recently existed there, but there was none to be found now.

To fully test the practicability of proceeding further, and at the same time to avoid what might be an unnecessary march of the whole train northwards, two experienced water hunters, mounted on the least broken down mules, rode ahead to explore. If they found water they were to send up a smoke as a signal for the train to advance. They travelled about twenty miles, finding a deserted Indian encampment, where water had been at some seasons, but which was then perfectly dry. From the point where they halted, on the summit of a lofty plateau, the country could be overlooked for fifty or sixty miles, and there was every indication that it was a waterless desert.

There was no alternative but to return; and the next morning we retraced our way and encamped near the northern Oraybe gardens, at the edge of the large valley. We have remained here for a day to let the mules rest and graze before undertaking the trip to Fort Defiance. As it is, we half anticipate reaching that place on foot.

The Oraybe chief, gratified at the fulfilment of his prediction in regard to the impracticability of the trip northward, has been to visit us, and comported himself with much amiability. He told me that he would send a guide to show us the best route to Fort Defiance, and I accordingly regaled him with the best the camp afforded. He ate till he could eat no more, and then stowed away what was lelft in the folds of his blanket.

Several of the tribe have been working in the gardens and tending the sheep during the day. In the former labor the women as well as the men assist. The walls of the terraces and the gardens themselves are kept in good order and preservation. The stone and earth for construction and repairs they carry in blankets upon their shoulders from the valley below. The soil is of a poor character, and the amount which they extract from it speaks well for their perseverance and industry. Both turkeys and chickens have been seen in the pueblos. They have the material for excellent subsistence if they choose to avail themselves of it.

In the neighborhood are beds of coal, which Dr. Newberry thinks of a character to burn well, but they appear to have no idea of the value of these deposits, although wood for culinary and other purposes has to be transported from a distance of several miles. We have tried, but with doubtful success, to make them comprehend the worth of the fuel close at hand.

Camp 98, *near Tegua. May* 17.—Climbing the bluff south of camp and descending the opposite side of the mesa, we were joined by the promised Moquis guide, who came up, according to what appears an invariable custom, at the last moment and in a great hurry.

When the place was reached where the trail turned west to go to Oraybe, I asked the guide if he could not take a short cut to Tegua, (the most eastern pueblo,) which the Moquis chief had said was on the trail to Fort Defiance. He said that he could, and struck off toward the east. In ascending a mesa, five or six miles beyond, an almost impassable precipice was encountered, but the mules, after sundry falls, succeeded in reaching the summit. Beyond was a valley nine or ten miles wide, and upon the opposite side a plateau with three Moquis towns standing in a line upon the top. We camped three miles from them; sending the mules to their reservoir for water. The valley was well covered with grass. Large flocks of sheep attested the wealth of the citizens of this department of Moquis. Almost the entire population came to see us, evincing the greatest curiosity at everything they witnessed. In dress and general appearance they have a smarter look than the citizens of the other towns, and seem to be more well-to-do in the world. All the Moquis have small hands and feet, but ordinary figures. Their hair is fine and glossy. Many have an Italian physiognomy. The men wear loose cotton trowsers, and frequently a kind of blouse for an upper garment, over which they throw a blanket. The dress of the women is invariably a loose black woollen gown, with a gold-colored stripe around the waist and the bottom of the skirt. The stripe is of cotton, which they grow in small quantities. The material of the dress is of their own weaving.

They seem to be a harmless, well-meaning people, industrious at times, though always ready for a lounge and gossip. They are honest, so far that they do not steal, but their promises are not to be relied upon. They want force of character and the courageous qualities which the Zuñians and some other Pueblo Indians have the credit of possessing. Their chiefs exercise a good deal of authority, but by what tenure they hold their power, or how many there are, we could not learn.

A singular statement made by the Moquis is, that they do not all speak the same language. At Oraybe some of the Indians actually professed to be unable to understand what was said by the Mooshahneh chief, and the latter told me that the language of the two towns was different. At Tegua they say that a third distinct tongue is spoken. These Indians are identical in race, manners, habits, and mode of living. They reside within a circuit of ten miles, and, save for the occasional visit of a member of some other tribe, have been for centuries isolated from the rest of the world, and it would seem almost incredible that the inhabitants of the different pueblos should not preserve a system of intercourse. If what they say is true, it would appear that this is not done. Tegua and the two adjacent towns are separated by a few miles from Mooshahneh and another pair. Oraybe is at a little greater distance from both. Each place, depending upon its internal strength, is independent as regards defence. The people are indolent and apathetic, and have abandoned the habit of visiting each other till the languages, which, with all Indian tribes, are subject to great mutations, have gradually become dissimilar.

Camp 99, *Peach Orchard spring, May* 18.—Passing by the reservoir to water the mules and fill the kegs, we were joined by the Teguan chief and several of his friends. The guide having disappeared during the night, I asked for him, and was told by the chief that it would be unsafe for one or two of them to take the trip alone, but that he himself and nine others were going to the fort as soon as they could have some corn ground, and make other preparations, and that they would join us at the first watering place, which we would reach about noon. There was little doubt in the minds of any who heard this statement that it was a wholesale fiction, but he pointed out the direction of the best route to Fort Defiance, and, bidding the Moquis good-bye, we followed the course that had been designated. The chief accompanied us a short distance, and at parting renewed the assurance that ten of his people would overtake us before night. Crossing the valley in a nearly easterly direction, at the foot of the bluff upon the opposite side we reached a large and excellent spring about the time our friend had indicated.

The ravine is the prettiest spot seen for many a day, covered with rich turf, shaded by peach trees and surrounded by large gooseberry bushes. The water is clear and cold; the trail from Tegua has been plain and deeply cut, showing constant travel. After reaching camp two Navajoes rode in upon horses that we had seen yesterday hobbled near the Moquis pueblo. I supposed at first that they had stolen them, but a soldier told me that he had seen one of the men at Mooshahneh, and that the Moquis had told him that there were two or three Navajoes there on a visit.

That the latter should have the face to go to Moquis so soon after the recent foray speaks well for their boldness, but does not indicate much spirit on the part of the others. The two that came to see us were merry, impudent looking knaves; they ate, and smoked, and laughed, and finally asked for a glass of liquor as independently as though they were at a tavern. It was impossible to put them down: favors or rebuffs made the same or rather no impression; they received all with a grinning indifference that would have been good-natured, had it not been so impertinent. A third joined them after a while, also from the direction of Moquis, and the first two, after a rest, saddled their ponies and departed, informing me that the other would stay and accompany us. They perpetrated one act of civility, however, before leaving, presenting me with a cheese of dirty exterior, but almost white inside and very good. Two Moquis Indians came into camp at sunset and told us that they were going on with us.

Camp 100, *White Rock spring, May* 19.—We had proceeded but a few miles this morning when a shouting was heard behind, and looking back we saw the Moquis chief and eight of his followers running to overtake us. They had left Tegua before daylight; with the Navajo leading off upon his pony, the company of Indians formed a respectable looking retinue, doubling the size of the party. I was glad to see that each had brought his own provisions tied up in the corner of a blanket and swung over the shoulder. From their description we inferred that it was about fourteen miles to the next water; but that distance was accomplished, and the Indians being interrogated, said that it was still a little way ahead; mile after mile was passed, and still the water was a little way ahead, till we had at last made twenty-four miles, when they signified that it was the place to camp.

We were in a level, grassy ravine, a mile deep, with low rocky walls; an excellent spring was found at the lower end. The country crossed to-day has been a rolling mesa overgrown with cedars, which have contracted the view; occasional lines of bluffs break the smoothness of the surface. We are now in the Navajo region; a little way back of camp in a broad valley were herds of horses and flocks of sheep. A great many Indians have come into camp, both male and female, all mounted, the women riding astraddle like the men; there being little to distinguish them apart excepting that the former wear a blanket and carry the luggage when there is anything to be transported. They are rather a fine looking race, with bold features, but look like rascals, and undoubtedly are such. Fortunately our camp and grazing ground are enclosed on three sides by the walls of the ravine; the camp is pitched near the mouth; the mules are inside, and cannot be taken out without passing by us.

The Moquis and the Navajoes have the semblance of being on good terms, and have been talking and laughing together in the most friendly manner. But the Tegua chief privately informed me during the evening that these same men had stolen their stock, and that they were a bad set.

The spring is beneath a projecting rock of white sandstone that almost forms a cave. It is in a recess at the extreme end of the ravine, and the ravine itself is a mile from the trail, and surrounded by so many similar formations that we should have probably missed the place but for the Moquis guides. The Navajo left us on the opposite side of the valley as soon as he came in sight of his own territory. The green plain is studded with isolated white rocks—remnants of the mesa—which stand in bright relief upon the dark surface, and form the most striking feature of the landscape.

Camp 101, *Pueblo creek, May* 20.—Several Moquis who have been visiting the Navajoes swelled the train to-day. There are now twenty-three accompanying us, and as we proceed mounted Navajoes fall into the ranks till we find ourselves moving in great force. The Moquis assured me that the next water was but a little distance from the last camp, but we travelled nearly twenty miles before reaching it. We found there a pretty creek running between steep earth banks ten or twelve feet high. The water is good, though warm. The country passed over has preserved generally the same features—a rolling mesa covered with a cedar forest—the bluffs, however, being seldomer encountered than on the previous days. The crest of a plateau a few miles from the creek overlooked an extensive and lovely valley, a brilliant sheet of verdure dotted with clumps of cedars, and extending far to the north and south.

Countless herds of horses and flocks of sheep were grazing upon the plain. The Moquis said that we were entering one of the most thickly populated sections of the Navajo territory.

H.B. Mollhausen. Del.

NAVAJOS

Lith. of Sarony, Major & Knapp. 449 Broadway NY.

Hundreds have come into camp, and, considering their natural impudence and the weakness of our party, have astonished me by the correctness of their behavior.

One old fellow was pointed out by a companion who spoke pretty good Spanish as the chief. They were curious and a little concerned to know why we had come from the west. No party of whites had ever entered their country from that direction. The chief said that we must have just left the country of the Apaches, who had lately stolen the Moquis horses, of which act the Navajoes had been wrongfully accused ; that the Apaches had plundered them also, and that, as our animals were safe, we must be friends to the Apaches, which proved that the Apaches, the Moquis, and the Americans were all leagued against "the poor little Navajoes," to use his own expression. The reasoning was logical, but the throng of saucy vagabonds that

Fig. 40.—Navajo valley.

were listening to the speech with grins that they took no pains to conceal were not calculated to enlist much sympathy, and we concluded that the pitiful harangue was intended for the benefit of the Moquis, to disarm them of their suspicions in regard to the perpetrators of the late theft. I perceived, however, that the Moquis were as unconvinced as ourselves by the plausible reasoning. We asked how far we had still to travel before reaching Fort Defiance, and they said that a single day's march would take us there. We supposed that it must therefore be about thirty miles distant. They had not heard of the arrival of any party of Americans from the direction of Zuñi.

The Navajoes displayed one trait of character which I had never seen exhibited by Indians. A crowd of women surrounded the place where the doctor and myself were sitting, and were amusing themselves by inspecting the remnant of the Indian goods and trinkets that had been brought along. Having no further occasion for the articles, as the expedition was now so nearly ended, and pleased with the unexpected civility we had experienced, I distributed most of the things to those standing about. The women were highly delighted, and not long after some of the men, whom I supposed to be their husbands, brought into camp a quantity of cheese and joints of mutton—enough to have lasted our company a week. I offered to pay for what we required, but they insisted upon my accepting all as a gift.

Camp 103, *Fort Defiance, May* 22.—A mile or two from Pueblo creek the trail passed a little south of a lake more than a mile long and half a mile broad. A little beyond was a stream of considerable size, and sixteen miles further a ravine with a large deep body of water. The

Fig. 41—Valley of Fort Defiance.

region traversed was covered with well-beaten trails, and parties of Indians were constantly riding by. Near all the watering places were immense numbers of horses and sheep, attesting the wealth of the tribe.* Pines were mingled with the cedars, and the latter became larger as we travelled east. At the end of twenty-three miles we camped. Fort Defiance is not yet in sight, but the Indians have pointed out the crest of a mesa a little way ahead which overlooks the post.

CONCLUSION.

Early the following morning we reached Fort Defiance, and the field labors of the expedition terminated. Lieutenant Tipton with his detachment we found encamped in the valley a mile or two below the fort. The night but one before our arrival a Navajo had eluded the vigilance

---

* An interesting and valuable memoir respecting the Navajo tribe was prepared a few years since by Dr. J. Letherman, assistant surgeon United States army, and published in the annual report of the Smithsonian Institution for the year 1855. It presents a graphic description of the character and habits of the Navajoes, as well as of the appearance and resources of the country which they inhabit, and conveys to the reader an excellent idea of a large portion of the Territory of New Mexico and its aboriginal inhabitants.

of the sentinel, and succeeded in abstracting from the camp a trunk containing a portion of the field-notes; but the energetic measures at once taken by Major Brooke, commanding the post, led to the recovery of the property, and the only result was a slight detention.

The Navajoes at this time began to exhibt symptoms of disaffection. Our arrival at Fort Defiance was none too soon. Only a fortnight afterwards hostilities broke out between the tribe and the United States troops, which would have seriously imperilled our safety had they commenced while we were passing through the Navajo territory. At it was, we reached the settlements upon the Rio Grande without interruption.

All of the party, excepting myself, continued on towards the east, crossing the plains from Santa Fé to Fort Leavenworth, and repairing thence to the seaboard. It was necessary for me to dispose of the steamer and certain property at Fort Yuma, and to settle the accounts of some members of the expedition who had gone back in the boat, and I accordingly took the stage from Santa Fé to El Paso, and from that place followed the southern overland mail route to San Diego.

Stopping for a day or two at Fort Yuma, I found Captain Robinson still in charge of the Explorer, and learned from him that the trip down the river had been accomplished without accident or any molestation from the Indians. In order not to run any risk of losing the collections and the field-notes, the descent had been made slowly and with great caution. Fort Yuma was reached on the 16th of April, twenty-five days from the time of starting.

After disposing of the little boat that had done us such good service to the transportation company at the fort, I bid farewell to Captain Robinson and the Colorado, and proceeding to San Francisco took the first steamer for New York.

PART II.

EXPLORATIONS AND SURVEYS. WAR DEPARTMENT.

COLORADO EXPLORING EXPEDITION, LIEUTENANT J. C. IVES, TOPOGRAPHICAL ENGINEERS, 1857-'58.

HYDROGRAPHIC REPORT.

WASHINGTON, D. C.
1861.

CONTENTS.

HYDROGRAPHIC REPORT.

HYDROGRAPHIC REPORT.

[Note.—Throughout this report, in stating facts bearing upon the navigability of the Colorado, the river is described as it appeared at its lowest and worst stage. It is probable, however, that not once in twenty years would the navigation be attended with so many obstructions as during the season of unprecedentedly low water when the survey was made.]

GULF OF CALIFORNIA AND MOUTH OF THE COLORADO.

The Gulf of California, into which the Colorado river empties, is six hundred miles long, and averages about eighty miles in width. The navigation is good, particularly along the western or Lower California shore, where the coast is bold and rock-bound, and the water deep. Along the northern half of the eastern side the country is generally low, and the adjacent soundings shallow.

The surface of the Gulf is dotted with islands, some of which are twenty or thirty miles in extent. The faces of these islands are usually precipitous, and there are many, in the lower part of the Gulf, where, to the very base of the cliffs, there are no soundings. As the lead would not give notice of their proximity, during dark nights, unless caution was observed, their neighborhood might be attended with hazard. There are no currents that prove a hindrance to navigation. Between the islands and along the shore, particularly near the head of the Gulf, the tides are sometimes strongly felt.

The prevailing winds blow either up or down the Gulf. During the autumn and winter they are generally from the northwest. In summer southeast breezes are more frequent. The worst gales come from this quarter. Calms are liable to be encountered at all seasons. In the vicinity of Cape St. Lucas, which is at the southern extremity of Lower California, they occur oftenest and are of longest duration. It is in the same neighborhood that the most furious storms and tempests are experienced. The length of the voyages of sailing vessels from San Francisco to the mouth of the Colorado is from fifteen to thirty-five days.

The greater portion of the harbors is upon the coast of Lower California. They are at Cape St. Lucas, San José, La Paz, Port Escondido, Loreto, Molega, Angeles bay, San Louis, and the bay of San Felipe. At Cape St. Lucas harbor there is sufficient depth for vessels of the heaviest draught. The harbor is protected from southeast winds, but is exposed towards the north and west. It is a dangerous anchorage, for there is a high surf, and no bottom at a hundred fathoms, till within a short distance of the beach. The locality can be distinguished a long distance off by the white cliffs that border the coast. At San José the harbor is exposed from east northeast to southwest, and would be unsafe during the summer and early autumn. The holding ground is good. The harbor of La Paz is land-locked, but vessels of large size cannot approach within three miles of the town. At Loreto, Port Escondido, Molega, a little beyond Point Conception, and at Angeles bay vessels of moderate draught can find a good anchorage. Angeles bay has been seldom resorted to. It is towards the head of the Gulf, and not far from the southwestern extremity of Angeles island. It is four miles wide and opens towards the east. There are springs of slightly brackish water near the southern end, at the base of a high mountain. An excellent bed of oysters exists in the vicinity. There are said to be lead mines in a valley at no great distance. At San Louis and San Felipe there is anchorage for small vessels. The latter place is only fifty miles from the mouth of the Colorado.

On the eastern coast, twenty-five miles from the head of the Gulf, is a small bay. The harbor of Guaymas is entirely land-locked, and is secure and spacious. The depth of water is from four to six fathoms, permitting the ingress of ships of the heaviest draught.

Upon some of the islands in the Gulf there is guano, and several are known to contain valuable metals. Upon Carmen island are valuable deposits of salt. The waters of the Gulf abound in whales, seals, turtles, &c.

Below the harbor of San Felipe is a low black cape, and at this place the lofty and barren mountains, which border the shore as far as Cape St. Lucas, leave the coast and trend towards the northwest. Ten or fifteen miles northeast of Black cape, and a little east of south from the mouth of the river, is a rock one or two hundred feet high, white with guano, the sides rising abruptly from the water. Approaching from the south it bears a strong resemblance to a vessel sailing before the wind. A reef runs from the base in a northwest direction for at least one or two miles, and not being laid down upon the charts might hazard the safety of any craft passing near at night. Abreast of Ship Rock I found between seventeen and eighteen fathoms. Lieutenant Derby states that in 1850 he found the depth in the same locality twenty fathoms. The bottom being remarkably flat and uniform, it would appear from this that the Gulf towards its head is rapidly filling up.

Beyond the rock the shores on both sides come in sight, and the Gulf narrows till it is only four or five miles in breadth. The water gradually shoals to two and a half or three fathoms, and becomes red and turbid. The bottom is a soft ooze, feeling like grease to the fingers. Two islands, Montague and Goree islands, and a bar twelve or fifteen miles wide, obstruct the mouth of the river. In the channels across the bar there are only ten feet of water. In the channel of the river, above the bar, as far as the head of tide water, the depth varies from twelve or fifteen to thirty-five feet.

The country on both sides is a flat expanse, entirely overflowed by the spring tides, which render it, during much of the time, a sheet of soft mud. The lines of the shore and the channels upon and beyond the bar are shifting and changeable, and shoals and islands are in constant progress of formation and removal. For twenty miles above the mouth the navigation is rendered periodically dangerous by the strength and magnitude of the spring tides. These have a rise and fall of from twenty-five to thirty feet, and a flow of extraordinary velocity, varying from five to seven or eight miles an hour. The flood is preceded by a "bore" or huge tide wave, from four to seven feet high. In the bends around Point Invincible and Howard's Point it is very powerful and violent, but loses its force as it ascends, and at a distance of thirty miles is scarcely felt. There are curves of the shore, as at Robinson's Landing, where the rush of water is broken, and vessels may lie at anchor in comparative safety. Upon the shoals are formed what are called "tide rips," where the sudden check to the surging mass causes it to bound along in high successive waves. The neap tides have a rise and fall of only ten feet, and a velocity of two and a half or three miles an hour.

No opportunity has ever been afforded of making continuous observations upon these tides. At some seasons of the year the full moon, and at others the new moon tides are greatest and most violent. Similar alternations take place in regard to the day and night tides. There is no slack water. The ebb running out encounters the flood and is turned back, the current instantly setting in the opposite direction.

The draught of vessels plying to the mouth of the river should not exceed eight or ten feet. If they carry freight that is to be discharged upon the decks of the river boats, they usually anchor near the west bank, in the vicinity of Robinson's Landing. The best approach across the bar can be determined by experiment only. On several occasions vessels have crossed along the western shore. Lieutenant Derby followed the California coast. At the time I passed the deepest channel appeared to be between Montague and Goree islands. The most sheltered spot should always be selected for an anchorage, and where there is sufficient depth to insure the vessel from grounding at the lowest tide. In this part of the river, owing to the formation of the steep shelving banks and the rapid rise and fall of the water, it would be difficult and dangerous to land freight from the vessel directly upon the shore. The best course would be to ascend the river for twenty or thirty miles. It would be impossible to sail up. The vessel should take advantage of the tides, and, an hour or two after the passage of the "bore," or the setting in of the flood, drift along the channel, keeping near the highest bank, and constantly sounding; care being taken to select a secure place for an anchorage before the approach of the ebb. The time of high water at "full and change" is, at the mouth of the Colorado, 3*h*. 15*m*., p. m.

When a steamboat is to be built for service upon the river the materials should be carried at least twenty-five miles above the mouth, in order to secure a place not overflowed at the highest tides, to be beyond the effects of the bore, and to be near fresh water.

Enough drift-wood can be found strewed over the flats to afford a supply of fuel, and some miles higher up there is a growth of cottonwood, willow, and mesquite along the banks, but the country furnishes no timber suitable to be used in building a boat, or even material of which the ways could be constructed.*

MOUTH OF THE COLORADO TO FORT YUMA.

It is about one hundred and fifty miles by the river from the head of the Gulf to Fort Yuma, though only half that distance in a direct line. Concerning no particular locality can any special information be given that would be of value to the navigator. The shifting of the channel, the banks, the islands, and the bars is so continual and so rapid that a detailed description, derived from the experiences of one trip, would be found incorrect, not only during the subsequent year, but perhaps in the course of a week, or even a day. A few facts of a general character can alone be stated.

The width of this portion of the river varies from one-eighth to half a mile. The course is exceedingly tortuous. The depth in the channel is from eight to twenty feet, but bars are frequently encountered where there are not more than two feet of water. The current, during the low stage of the river, which is from October till the early part of May, has an average velocity of two and a half miles an hour. In some of the bends it is perhaps a mile an hour swifter. The period of highest water is in the early part of July, when this velocity is increased to five or six miles. The average height is then ten feet greater than during the summer months, but the depth is not in all places proportionally increased. New bars at once form when the river begins to rise, and the obstructions to navigation, though not as numerous, are still encountered.

No rocks are met with below Fort Yuma. The bed of the river is composed of quicksand and soft clay. The bars are yielding, and any agitation upon their surface causes them speedily to wash away. A boat may frequently be forced over places where there was, at the time of its striking, six or eight inches too little water.

For several years the Colorado has been regularly navigated by steamboats between its mouth and Fort Yuma. At low water trips are rarely made without the boat grounding many times a day. A sounding pole is constantly employed. Different points upon the bar are tried till the least difficult is found. The steamer is then worked backwards and forwards to loosen the sand. Lines are attached to a tree, snag, or to an anchor taken out ahead, and are heaved upon with the windlass or capstan. As a last resource the boat is lightened of a portion of the cargo, and by these expedients the bars may always be passed, with more or less difficulty and

*The above information has been gathered from my own observations, from the report of Lieutenant Derby, Topographical Engineers, from Captain C. P. Stone, of the Sonora survey, from Captains Johnson and Wilcox of the Colorado steamboat company, and from Captains Naghel, Jayne, and Walsh, who have commanded vessels running from San Francisco to the mouth of the Colorado.

delay, depending in a great measure upon the address shown in the employment of the different modes of extrication resorted to. The snags are numerous, but being flexible or brittle are seldom dangerous.

Experience alone can impart the knowledge required to enable one to navigate successfully. Memory assists but little in selecting the channel, for it has been known to change from one bank to the other in a single night. Generally, along a steep bank and a concave bend the deepest water is to be found, but the rule is not invariable. The water being turbid and perfectly opaque, it is impossible to determine the depth as in the case of a clear stream. From the formation and relative positions of the islands and banks, from the eddies, the direction of the currents, from the pieces of drift-wood and other floating substances, the experienced navigator can generally determine the proper course to be selected.

During the months of May and June, while the Colorado is rising, and before new bars have had time to form, the navigation is most easy. At the worst stages of the river the round trip from Fort Yuma to the Gulf, allowing a day or two for taking in the cargo, can be accomplished in two weeks. During high water it is frequently made in three days.

FORT YUMA TO MOUTH OF BILL WILLIAMS'S FORK.

This section of the river is one hundred and ninety miles in extent. The Yuma flats reach from the fort to the first chain of hills that crosses the river. At very low water the navigation at this place will doubtless always be found difficult and tedious. There is nothing to confine the channel, and the water is spread over a wide surface filled with bars and snags. The bed is quicksand, and does not afford good holding ground for an anchor. There are no trees to which lines can be attached, and the snags are not strong enough to render much assistance. The least depth of water encountered was twenty-two inches.

A low range is now entered, and for forty-four miles—from Explorer's Pass, at the entrance of the Purple Hills, to Hazard Pass, at the foot of the Great Colorado valley—the river flows generally between hills and rocky bluffs. The average depth of the channel is less than below Fort Yuma, being not more than eight or ten feet. The velocity of the current is about the same. The bed of the stream is still composed of sand, but for the first time rocks are encountered. The banks are more permanent, as might be expected, than in the flat country below, and the position of the channel more fixed. The bed of the river, however, being composed of the same shifting material, bars are met with that present the same difficulties that characterized the previous navigation. They are not so numerous as in the open country. The more precipitous the banks the deeper, as a general rule, is the channel. In the Purple Hill Pass and through the Cane-brake cañon the navigation is pretty good, though at the lower end of the latter pass there are one or two bars with but twenty inches of water, and at the upper end a cluster of rocks near the left bank that project slightly above the surface. At a higher stage they would be dangerous were their position not known. A mile above the first rapid occurs. The river, at its foot, impinges against the face of a vertical wall and then bends sharply to the left. Some caution should be exercised in making the turn. The channel over the rapid is good, a d the current not swift enough to occasion trouble.

A short distance above are the Barrier islands. Several high rocks, arranged in a circle, occupy the middle of the stream, leaving a narrow channel on either side. That near the left bank is the more favorable, but the current is swift, and two or three isolated rocks just above add to the difficulty of the passage. A single rock, two and a half feet below low water mark, stands in the channel at the head of the narrowest place. Below Red Rock Gate is a difficult bar and then a stretch of good river. The velocity of the current in this portion is about three and a half miles an hour.

At Three Points Bend two sharp rocks project from one bank, and a third juts out midway from the other side. The channel glances by all three, and the passage requires care. Immediately above is a lone rock, fifty feet from the left bank, the top visible a little way above the surface. A difficult shoal occurs beyond. A few miles further the centre of the river is again occupied. A rock shaped like a light-house stands midway between the banks. The channel on the east side is the proper one to be followed. It is but thirty feet wide, but presents no obstructions. Some sharp turns around rocky corners make the next pass a little hazardous, and then, through a narrow porphyry gate, the Great Colorado valley is entered.

The head of this valley is one hundred and ten miles from Porphyry Gate, and the navigation throughout its whole extent is similar to that below Fort Yuma. The current has the same velocity. The average depth of the channel is seven or eight feet. The best water is usually found close to the concave banks. In several places flats are encountered similar to those above Fort Yuma. They are generally filled with snags; the water divided into numerous channels, and the navigation troublesome. In the vicinity of the Half-way and Riverside mountains the river is better than in any other portion of the valley, excepting at one place, the Sand island shoals, where two channels are formed by an island, and these subdivided, occasioning a succession of difficult bars that require much time and labor to pass. There are few places in this valley where the condition of the river is at all permanent, and it is therefore impossible to describe in detail the different localities.

Beaver island is at the commencement of the foot hills of the Monument mountains—a range intervening between the head of the valley and the mouth of Bill Williams's Fork, twenty miles above. At the foot of the island is a little cove, which affords a good place for a steamboat to lay by. In the cañon formed by the foot hills and mountains the river is narrow and the water generally deep. The navigation could be pronounced better than at any place above the mouth were it not for the occasional appearance of sharp, jagged rocks, projecting a foot or two above the surface, and indicating danger when the water is two or three feet higher. Four miles from the mouth of the fork there is a sunken rock near the right bank. All of the rocks observed were quite close to the shore. During the high stage of the river, unless the current should be very swift through the confined passage, the navigation of this cañon would be attended with no trouble.

Throughout the section just described the character of the Colorado differs little from the portion below Fort Yuma. Though isolated rocks are met with, the bed is composed of sand, and the bars have about the same depth upon them. The obstructions are, however, much more numerous than they are below the fort, and the navigation attended with more delay.

BILL WILLIAMS'S FORK TO PYRAMID CAÑON.

This section, one hundred miles in extent, comprises the Chemehuevis and Mojave valleys and the cañon through the range which separates them. The navigation in this cañon is somewhat like, though much better, than in the cañon through the Monument mountains. The river is narrow and deep, and free from bars. There are neither sunken rocks nor any that are visible above the surface. There are indications that during the freshet the water rises to a prodigious height in some of the narrowest portions, and at that time the ascent or descent should not be made without great caution. At other seasons no obstacle will be encountered.

In the lower part of the Chemehuevis valley are many shoals, where the bottom is composed of coarse gravel, and it is hard to force a boat over the unyielding surface. A slight difference in draught would be a matter of great importance in this part of the river. The least depth found was twenty-two inches. Upon all of these bars there is a swift current, which enhances the difficulty of crossing. Through much of the valley the river flows between gravel bluffs, one or two hundred feet high, and here the navigation is good. Where the banks are bold and rocky there is nearly always a good channel and a sandy bed. If the land on either side is low, pebbles are washed down into the steam and overspread the bottom.

At the mouth of the Mojave cañon the Colorado is divided by a pebbly island, on both sides of which are sharp rapids. The eastern channel is preferable to the other. The water has a depth of three feet, but the bottom is gravelly, and some scattered pebbles of large size come within two or two and a half feet of the surface. The rapid is one or two hundred yards in length. In ascending, a line should be taken from the bow to an anchor ahead, to prevent the boat. in case she should catch upon a rock, from being swung around. If the bow were to be whirled back it would be with such violence that an encounter with a rock would occasion serious damage.

In the Mojave valley the river generally is good. At the entrance from the Needles is a broad, difficult shoal, covered with pebbles. Four miles above Camp 41, abreast of Camp 45, and at the very head of the valley, are also rocky bars, attended with slight rapids. The bed generally is less gravelly than in the Chemehuevis valley. The channel is little obstructed by sand bars. One only was found near Camp 44, where for fifteen or twenty yards there were but eighteen inches of water. The average depth of the channel continues to decrease. In the Mojave valley it is about six feet.

This section of the Colorado, it will be seen, differs from the two preceding, principally in the character of the river bed, which, as high as the mouth of Bill Williams's Fork, is composed entirely of sand, but is afterwards found to be partially covered with gravel. At all of the gravelly bars the current is swift, and frequently assumes the character of a rapid. Such places present, of course, more difficulty than the sand bars; but though, from this reason, the bad places are worse, the channel generally is freer from obstructions than it is below. When the water rises the gravel bars do not experience any change, and during a higher stage they would occasion no trouble. At such times the navigation of this section would doubtless be easier and better than that of any other portion of the Colorado.

PYRAMID CAÑON TO BLACK CAÑON.

This section comprises the remainder of the navigable portion of the Colorado. It is sixty miles in length. In the Pyramid cañon, which is five or six miles long, the navigation is good. Above, the bed of the stream is composed generally of coarse gravel and rocks. Rapids occur at short intervals throughout the whole distance. The first, at the head of the cañon, has a depth of two and a half feet. Two or three small rapids which follow present no great difficulty. At Deep rapid the channel is narrow, and the rush of water stronger than at any place below the Black cañon, but in the centre of the channel there is a depth of six feet, and there are no rocks to obstruct the passage. There is good holding ground above for an anchor, to which a line may be attached to keep the bow steady. The rapid above occurs at a sharp turn of the river, but is not difficult to pass.

At Shallow rapid there are only twenty-two inches of water. An island divides the river into two channels. The current is rather stronger on the west side, but the river is narrower, and the abrupt bank, covered with trees, offers better places to which to attach a line. The two rapids above Camp 50 are easy. At the first there is plenty of water, and at the second nearly two and a half feet. The other rapids below the head of Cottonwood valley have at least three feet of water and a moderate current. Through the Painted cañon the navigation is good. Near Mount Davis the edges of the channel are obstructed by rocks, but a sufficiently wide space in the middle is left clear.

Round island should be passed on the eastern side. There is a pair of rapids abreast of the island. At the first there is plenty of water, but at the second, for several yards, a depth of only eighteen inches. At the rapids between Camps 53 and 54 there is sufficient depth. At the last a line should be taken ahead to prevent the possibility of the boat swinging against some rocks that project near the channel.

The rapids between Camps 54 and 55 are neither shoal nor very swift; but abreast of the latter camp is a long rapid, where there are only two feet of water. No others are now encountered till the Black cañon is reached. At the mouth of the cañon there is a short deep rapid, above which, in the centre of the channel, is a sharp conical rock, the top of which is about four inches below the surface.

During the season when the river is high the current in this part of it would be swifter than below, but excepting for this, the navigation of this section of the Colorado would present little difficulty or hazard after the position of the sunken rocks should become known. A boat drawing not more than eighteen or twenty inches could at all times ascend and descend, without being lightened of its cargo, and perhaps experience less trouble from the rapids than from the sand bars in the lower part of the river.

BLACK CAÑON.

The black cañon is twenty-five miles long. It contains twenty-five or thirty rapids. The presence of large rocks in the centre and along the edges of the channel renders many of these rapids dangerous. At two or three, and at Roaring rapid in particular, the fall is considerable, and the rush of water violent. Over any one of them, however, a steamboat of proper construction, partially or entirely lightened of the cargo, could be taken with the assistance of lines, but the passage of the cañon, at low water, would be tedious, and attended with much labor, hazard, and expense.

In some of the narrowest portions of this gigantic defile, drift-wood was seen lodged in crevices fifty feet above the surface of the river, an evidence of the astonishing height to which the water has banked up during the summer freshets. The attempt to go through the cañon at any season when a sudden rise might be apprehended would be accompanied with grave peril. At the beginning of the warm weather, when the water has risen only one or two feet, the cañon might be navigated without serious trouble or danger; but the uncertainty and risk attending the passage, for the greater portion of the year, are such that the mouth of the cañon should be considered, for all practical purposes, the head of navigation of the Colorado.

Above the Black cañon the river soon becomes a continuous rapid, utterly impracticable to be ascended in boats.

DESCRIPTION OF BOAT TO BE USED UPON THE COLORADO.

With a boat of proper construction the Colorado can be navigated without trouble, at all seasons of the year, between the head of the Gulf of California, and the mouth of the Black cañon. The most essential conditions in regard to the boat are as follows:

1st. That she should not draw more than twelve inches when light.

2d. That the boiler should be of large capacity and the engines of great power.

3d. That she should have a large stern-wheel.

4th. That the bottom should be perfectly flat and smooth.

5th. That the hull should be divided by water-tight bulkheads.

For service upon the river I would recommend iron boats in preference to wooden ones. In the hot climate of New Mexico the former would be more durable; they can be built of lighter draught for the same capacity; are cheaper, and more easily and rapidly put together. A good description of boat would be an iron stern-wheel steamer, with the hull one hundred feet long, and the greatest breadth of beam twenty-two feet; built sufficiently full to insure a draught, when light, not exceeding twelve inches; if in sections, the flanges, where the sections meet, to be turned inwards, in order that the bottom may be perfectly smooth and flat; to have a large boiler and a powerful high-pressure engine, with two fourteen-inch cylinders of five feet stroke; a stern-wheel eighteen feet in diameter; the hull to be separated into four water-tight compartments, one at the bow, one enclosing the boiler, a third behind the space set apart for stowing the cargo, and the fourth near the stern; to be steered by three wooden rudders; the bottom to have such a sheer aft that the lower edge of the transom may be, when the boat is loaded, about two inches above the surface of the water, so that the pilot can see by looking over the rail if any of the rudders are bent or foul; to be provided with a capstan; with two anchors of one hundred and twenty-five pounds weight, and a small kedge anchor; with plenty of extra rudders, wheel buckets, and stout lines.

The water of the Colorado holds in suspension a large amount of fine silicious sand, sharp as emery, that cuts away the valves almost as rapidly as it could be done with a file. Unless the boiler is made large it would require but a week's service to disable the engine so as to render it impossible to run the boat.

A steamboat, built as above described, and run by an experienced pilot, would occupy, in making a round trip from the mouth of the river to the head of navigation, from twelve days to five weeks; depending upon the season of the year and the stage of the water.

FUEL.

Wood of excellent quality for the purpose of fuel can be obtained in abundance, alongside of the bank, at short intervals, between the mouth of the river and the Painted cañon. It is principally mesquite, willow, and cottonwood. There are large groves of sun-dried trees, ready for instant use. The mezquite wood makes the hottest fire, but, if much used, injures the boiler. Between the Painted and Black cañons, wood is less frequently met with, and were this part of the river to be constantly navigated, it would be necessary to establish depots, which would derive their supply from below.

ESTIMATE OF COST OF TRANSPORTATION.

A suitable boat, capable of carrying sixty tons, should be able to make fifty trips between tide water and the head of navigation before becoming unserviceable. Such a number ought certainly to be accomplished within six years, which would enable 3,000 tons of freight to be carried to the highest navigable point during that period. A boat of the character described could be built and put together at the mouth of the river for................ $20,000 00

The annual expenses of running her would be—

For pay of captain..	$2,000 00
For pay of pilot...	2,000 00
For pay of two engineers, at $1,500 each......................	3,000 00
For pay of eight hands, at $450 each..........................	3,600 00
For rations of twelve men, at 30 cents per day, about..........	1,300 00
For repairs..	1,100 00
	_____
Annual expenses..	13,000 00

Expenses for six years 78,000 00

Total expense of transportation of 3,000 tons of freight...................... 98,000 00
 Or about $30 per ton.

No estimate is made for expense of fuel. The boats are unable to run at night. As has been stated, there is abundance of wood along the banks, and eight men, while at camp, would be able to lay in a sufficient amount for a day's consumption.

It is believed that the above estimate is a liberal one, and rather exceeds than falls below the expenditure that would be actually involved were a sufficient amount of transportation business done upon the river to keep the boats in service constantly employed.

PART III.

EXPLORATIONS AND SURVEYS, WAR DEPARTMENT.

COLORADO EXPLORING EXPEDITION, LIEUTENANT J. C. IVES, TOPOGRAPHICAL ENGINEERS, 1857–'58.

GEOLOGICAL REPORT.

BY Dr. J. S. NEWBERRY, GEOLOGIST TO THE EXPEDITION.

WASHINGTON, D. C.,
1861.

CONTENTS.

CHAPTER I.

Geology of the coast of Southern California.

Comparison of structure of Coast Mountains north and south of San Francisco.—Evidences of identity.—Infusorial beds and bitumen of Monterey, Santa Barbara, San Luis Obispo, &c.—Origin of bituminous exudations.—Relative age of the Coast Mountains —Miocene strata of Coast Mountains wanting in Sierra Nevada —Sierra Nevada oldest.—Mr. Marcou's description of the "Coast Range System."—Raised sea bottoms and shell beds at San Luis Obispo, San Pedro, and San Diego.

CHAPTER II.

Geology of route from San Diego to Fort Yuma.

General features.—The Peninsular Mountains.—Their relations to the Sierra Nevada.—Prevalence of granitic and gneissoid rocks.—Character of the granites.—Modern deposits skirting their bases proof of recent elevation.—Principal upheaval after Eocene and before Miocene period.—Local geology.—Vicinity of San Diego.—Miocene strata and fossils.— Modern trap eruption east of the Mission —San Diego to the Desert.—Trap near Penasquitas.—Granites with felspathic veins of San Pasqual and Laguna.—Santa Isabel.—Warner's.—The Oaks.—San Felipé.—Tertiaries of Carisso Creek.— Ostreas, Anomias, Gnathodons, contained in them.—The Colorado Desert.—Arroyos or "Washes."—Transported blocks.—Eroded and polished pebbles.—Structure and origin of the Desert.—Ancient fresh-water lakes.—New River, Alamo Mocho, Cooke's Well.—Desert gravel transported from Upper Colorado.

CHAPTER III.

Geology of country bordering Lower Colorado.

General features of Colorado Basin —Desert Plains and network of Mountains.—Volcanic character of the district.—Local geology.—Mouth of the Colorado to Fort Yuma.—Transport and deposition of sediment by the river.—Fort Yuma.— Purple Hills.—Highly colored porphyries, trachytes, and tufas.—Explorer's Pass.—Granite.—Gold, copper, iron, and lead of Purple Hills.—Chimney Peak.—Turreted summits of volcanic mountains in this region.—Theory of their formation.—Barrier Islands —Quaternary and Tertiary conglomerates.—Spire Range.—Light-house Rock.—Metamorphosed red sandstones.—Gneissoid rocks of Chocolate Mountains.—Gravel beds bordering river.—Great Colorado Valley.— Stratification of sediments.—Origin of cross and curved stratification.—Alternations of layers of sand and clay.—Suncracked clay seams.—Half way and Riverside Mountains.—Metamorphic limestone.—Talcose slate.—Metalliferous rocks.—Monument Mountain and Cañon.—Tertiary conglomerates.—Granite with metalliferous veins.—Metamorphic limestone.—Silver, copper, lead, iron.—Geological scenery.

CHAPTER IV.

Geology of region between Bill Williams's Fork and Rio Virgen.

Infusorial strata of White Rock.—Chemehuevis Valley.—Mojave Mountains.—Mojave Cañon.—Metamorphosed Tertiary rocks.— Porphyries and trachytes.—Mojave Valley.—Black Mountains.—Prevalence of erupted rocks.—Dead Mountain.—Pyramid Cañon.—Cottonwood Valley.—Tertiary and modern gravels.—General structure of valleys traversed by Colorado.— Mount Davis.—Tertiary conglomerate.—Quaternary deposits.—Elephant Hill.—Trough of the Colorado at entrance of Black Cañon.—Black Cañon.—Great variety of erupted rocks.—Amygdaloids containing chalcedony and crystallized quartz.—Plutonic character and scenery of the Black Mountains.—Rock salt and gypsum from Rio Virgen.

CHAPTER V.

General view of the structure of the Great Central Plateau.

Common geological character of all the country between the Mississippi and Colorado.—Source and course of the Upper Colorado.—Table lands between Rocky Mountains and Cerbats.—Great Cañon.—Geological elements of its section.— Basin of the Little Colorado.—Its outlines and structure.—Ancient granitic barriers which limit it.—High mesa about San Francisco Mountain.—Valley of the Little Colorado.—Structure of mesa bounding it on the north and east.— Cretaceous mesa of the Moquis villages.—Great white mesa resting on the last.—Snowy mesa bordering the Colorado.—Origin of the peculiar topography of the table lands referred to a vast system of erosion.—All the cañons of Western New Mexico due to aqueous action.—Mesa wall boundaries of broad valleys of erosion.—Area and limits of the Palæozoic continent.—Sources of the sediments forming the strata of the table lands and conditions of their deposition.—Outlines of North American continent approximately defined in the earliest Palæozoic ages.

CHAPTER VI.

Geology of the country between the Mojave Valley and Flax River.

Quaternary deposit of Mojave Valley.—Tertiary strata.—Black Mountains.—Sitgreaves's Pass.—Plutonic rocks with silicious minerals.—Tertiary rocks of eastern base of Black Mountains.—Long Valley.—Cerbat Mountains.—Yampais Valley.— Eastern chain of Cerbat Mountains.—First plateau of the table lands.—Cañon of Diamond River.—Great Cañon of the Colorado.—Detailed sections of its walls.—Silurian, Devonian, and Carboniferous rocks.—Granite pinnacles of ancient sea bottom.—High mesa west of Flax River.—Section of mesa wall at Camp 70.—Middle and upper Carboniferous strata.—Valley of Flax River, its general features and mode of formation.—Cañon of Cascade River.—Detailed sections of its cliffs.—Origin of gypsum.—Companionship of sulphate of lime and peroxide of iron.

CHAPTER VII.

Geology of region about San Francisco Mountain.

General features.—Relations of the San Francisco group to the Mogollon system.—General aspect and isolated character of San Francisco mountain.—Its purely volcanic origin.—Isolated mountains usually composed of erupted materials and chains of metamorphosed rocks.—Theory of this difference.—Traces of recent eruptions about the San Francisco Mountain.— Modern volcanic phenomena of Rocky Mountains and Pacific region.—Oscillations of level on the coast.—Earthquakes.— Continued agitation of western half of the continent through all geological ages.—Local geology.—Drift of Valley of Little Colorado.—Trap plateaus west of San Francisco Mountain.—Ancient surface covered by it.—Section of strata from Picacho to Bill Williams's Mountain.—Partridge and Cedar Creeks.—Upper Carboniferous limestone.—Cross stratified sandstone.—Age of rocks described by Mr. Marcou on Pueblo and Cedar Creeks.—No Devonian or Permian strata in this vicinity.—Bill Williams's Mountain, Mount Kendrick, and Mount Sitgreaves.—Carboniferous limestone.—Modern volcanic cones, Camp 44.—Magnesian limestone west of Little Colorado.—Probably Carboniferous.

CHAPTER VIII.

Geology of region between the Colorado and Fort Defiance.

Valley of the Little Colorado at crossing.—Red sandstone formation.—Its parallelism.—Variegated marls.—Painted Desert.— Mesa walls of red stone.—Variegated marls.—Section of mesa between Little Colorado and Moquis villages.—Parallelism of group of rocks filling interval between the Carboniferous and Cretaceous formations.—Trias of Marcou not identified.— Detailed sections of the variegated marls and red sandstones, salt springs of the latter series, silicified wood of the marl beds.—Lignite with fossil plants.—Probably Jurassic.—Eroded sandstones near Moquis villages.—Geology of the Moquis country.—Lower Cretaceous rocks.—Detailed section of Cretaceous mesa.—Cretaceous fossils.—White mesa north of Moquis villages.—Upper Cretaceous strata.—Geology of Navajo country.—Prevalence of Lower Cretaceous rocks.—Fresh water Tertiary beds.—Valleys of erosion.—Navajo Valley.—Cañon Bonito.—Anticlinal axis west of Fort Defiance.— Elevated and indurated Saliferous sandstones.

CHAPTER IX.

Geology of the route from Fort Defiance to Santa Fé.

CHAPTER X.

Geology of the route from Santa Fé to Fort Leavenworth.

CHAPTER XI.

PALÆONTOLOGY.

CATALOGUE OF THE GEOLOGICAL COLLECTION.

LIST OF ILLUSTRATIONS.

LITHOGRAPHS.

PALÆONTOLOGY.

WOOD CUTS.

GEOLOGICAL MAPS.

CHAPTER I.

GEOLOGY OF THE COAST OF SOUTHERN CALIFORNIA.

COMPARISON OF STRUCTURE OF COAST MOUNTAINS NORTH AND SOUTH OF SAN FRANCISCO.—EVIDENCES OF IDENTITY.—INFUSORIAL BEDS
AND BITUMEN OF MONTEREY, SANTA BARBARA, SAN LUIS OBISPO, &c.—ORIGIN OF BITUMINOUS EXUDATIONS.—RELATIVE AGES OF
THE COAST MOUNTAINS.—MIOCENE STRATA OF COAST MOUNTAINS WANTING IN SIERRA NEVADA.—SIERRA NEVADA OLDEST.—MR.
MARCOU'S DESCRIPTION OF THE "COAST RANGE SYSTEM."—RAISED SEA BOTTOMS AND SHELL BEDS AT SAN LUIS OBISPO, SAN PEDRO
AND SAN DIEGO.

That portion of California lying south of San Francisco has been so fully explored by the geologists of the Pacific Railroad Surveys, Dr. Antisell and Mr. Blake, that, in the hasty examination I was able to make of parts of it, I could hardly hope to furnish any considerable additions to the knowledge of its geology already possessed by the public. It was, however, a matter of extreme interest to me to continue the line of observation which I had carried from the mouth of the Columbia to San Francisco, from that point to the southern line of the State, with particular reference to the structure of the Coast mountains, and to determine the coincidences or differences which might be presented by their northern and southern extensions.

In my report to Lieutenant Williamson on the geology of Northern California and Oregon, (*Pacific Railroad Surveys, Vol. VI,*) I ventured to assert the identity of the Tertiary sandstones and shales of Astoria, Coose bay, and Port Orford, with those of the San Francisco group, and suggested the unity of structure of the Coast mountains throughout the interval between these points; confirming, so far as my observation extended, the opinion which had already been advanced, that the superficial sedimentary rocks of the Coast mountains, from the mouth of the Columbia to the bay of San Francisco, were of Miocene age. It is known, however, to those who are familiar with the subject, that palæontological evidence of this identity was for the most part wanting; the strata in most localities being destitute of fossils, and where those had been found, absolute identity of any species had not been proven.

The indications of geological parallelism in the different parts of the Coast mountains, from San Francisco northward, consisted, first, in the general resemblance of their molluscous fossils—more careful study of which would, it was to be presumed, furnish positive proofs of identity; second, in the lithological characters of the sandstones and shales to which I have referred, as exhibited at their various points of exposure; third, in the beds of lignite which they include; and fourth, in the continuity of the strata.

Going south from San Francisco, we stopped at Monterey, San Luis Obispo, Santa Barbara, San Pedro, and San Diego. The geology of all these points has been quite fully illustrated in the luminous reports of the gentlemen before mentioned, as well as in those of Dr. Trask, the geologist of the State of California. It is, therefore, quite unnecessary that I should give in detail even the observations which my limited time permitted me to make. It was, however, a source of no little satisfaction to trace in the geological exposures of such points on this coast as I examined a striking parallelism with those of the coast line north of San Francisco. Some local features are presented in the infusorial beds of Monterey, the asphaltic effusions of Santa Barbara, San Luis Obispo, and San Pedro, which, at first sight, would seem to militate against the general harmony which I have suggested; but these discrepancies are rather apparent than real.

I have mentioned in my former report, speaking of the section presented on the southern shore of San Pablo bay, the association of the shales and sandstones of San Francisco with a series of fossiliferous and infusorial strata of great thickness. During my recent visit, in an examination of the coast line south of Point Lobos, I discovered strata of white infusorial rock and beds of lignite in still more immediate proximity to the strata underlying San Francisco, and, torn up by the surf, masses of a shell conglomerate, in which are imbedded large numbers of *Scutella interlineata*. Following down the coast, we observed the same, or a similar geological series, exposed at a thousand different points where the waves of the Pacific had eaten deeply into the bases of the Coast mountains. This series has suffered great displacement and considerable metamorphosis through the proximity or protrusion of igneous rocks along the many lines of uplift marking the spurs and parallel ranges of the Coast mountains.

At San Luis Obispo the disturbance of the Tertiary series is particularly marked. The prevailing rocks at this point are fine argillaceous, probably infusorial, shales, sandstones, and shell conglomerates. Many of these strata are highly charged with bitumen, which is caused to exude by the sun's heat, and drips down from the cliffs, forming masses of considerable size and of great purity. Of these strata the shales to which I have referred are much disturbed; in places standing quite vertical, and in some instances are so highly metamorphosed as to become almost vitreous, resembling a fine white or light gray porcelain.

At various points between Monterey and San Diego the bituminous exudations form a feature so striking as to attract the attention and excite the curiosity of all who visit that region, whether learned or unlearned; but, as yet, no satisfactory theory has been advanced to account for their existence. From the fact, however, that beds of lignite are so characteristic of the geology of the Coast mountains, and are inseparably associated with the Miocene strata from Bellingham bay to San Diego, it seems to me the most simple explanation of the existence of these bituminous exudations to refer their origin to that source. It is true that exposures of strata of lignite are not frequently observable in the region where the asphaltum is most abundant; but they exist even as far south as San Diego, as is proved by the borings made near Point Loma, where operations have been commenced for reaching the coal by shafts. The district marked by these bituminous springs and accumulations has suffered a greater amount of volcanic disturbance than any other portion of the coast; and while the application of volcanic heat to beds of lignite would produce precisely similar results, by driving off the bituminous matter which they contain, we can hardly imagine any other adequate cause for the phenomena. The deposits of bitumen of Trinidad and Cuba, which closely resemble those of the Pacific coast, have been, I believe, uniformly considered by those who have studied them most carefully, to be the result of a similar process. The objection to this theory which has been advanced, derived from the absence of lignites from the sedimentary series at some points where the contact with the underlying igneous rocks has been observed, is hardly conclusive; for we know that the lignite beds are by no means continuous, but are far more local than the coal strata of the carboniferous series, and are probably the results of a somewhat different process. The coal seams were formed from plants which grew on the spot where their remains are found; but the Tertiary lignites of the Pacific coast have in many cases been derived from transported materials. My examination of the strata in the vicinity of San Luis Obispo led me to suspect that the asphaltum had been driven up by volcanic heat, and had thus impregnated the more porous strata for a long distance from its point of origin.

The labors of the geologists to whom I have referred have clearly proven the general identity of structure of the Coast mountains throughout Southern California; and yet many questions of interest remain to be settled in reference to the connexion between the Coast mountains, properly so called, and the Sierra Nevada. The ranges of this latter system, as we approach the southern boundary of the State, come constantly nearer the ocean till one of its great subdivisions usurps the place of the ranges forming the coast line northward, and in the peninsula of Lower California becomes itself the boundary between the ocean and the continent. From the vicinity of San Pedro to San Francisco, and thence northward, the nearly uniform northwesterly trend of the parallel serpentine axes, the continuous series of Tertiary strata exhibiting similar lithological characters, and, in many cases, an identity of fossils, give a unity to the whole coast system. But at Point Concepcion the coast line leaves the general trend which it had preserved from San Francisco south, and is deflected far eastward, as though the Coast mountains had been cut away by the action of the ocean; and south of this point they ceased to exist, or were only represented by the islands which border the coast.

At Los Angeles, and thence to San Diego, though still upon the Miocene Tertiaries of the Coast mountains, we were on their eastern, rather than, as before, their western base, and had approached to within a few miles of the Sierra Nevada.

At San Diego the Tertiary rocks are exposed for several miles in the eroded channel of San Diego river. Here they are nearly horizontal, entirely unchanged, and contain great numbers of fossils. In speaking of the age of the Sierra Nevada, I shall perhaps have occasion to return to this subject, and to treat more fully of the geology of the coast near the southern boundary of the State. I may here say, however, in reference to the comparative ages of the Coast mountains and the Sierra Nevada, that while Tertiary strata, for the most part Miocene, but probably also including those of still more recent date, envelope the igneous axes and crown many of the highest summits of the Coast mountains, indicating that the elevation of this system was altogether posterior to the Miocene epoch; the Sierra Nevada bears no strata so recent on its summits, and scarcely on its sides, but is skirted on either base by Miocene rocks not much disturbed. This proves that the great mass of this latter mountain system, though doubtless in some degree elevated during or subsequent to the deposition of the Miocene series, had a distinct existence anterior to that epoch, and raised its summits far above the Miocene sea, to which it formed the boundary.

The latest work which contains any notice of the geology of this region (*Marcou's Geol. N. Amer.*, p. 79) presents so different a view of the structure of the Coast mountains from that which I have given that I am compelled to refer to it. Mr. M. says of the "*Coast Range System*," that it is composed of chains of mountains of slight elevation, generally from 500 to 1,200 feet high; that it extends from Cape Mendocino to Cape St. Lucas, and probably includes the mountains of Sonora and Western Arizona; that its rocks are chiefly eruptive and metamorphic, containing mercury, silver, copper and iron, but no gold; that it is older than the Sierra Nevada system, and is characterized by *Eocene* fossils found south of Monterey and at Mount Diablo; and that hence the date of its elevation was after the Eocene and before the Miocene period." In reference to these points, I have been led by my own observations, and by reliable testimony, to very different conclusions, namely:

1st. The Coast range system is composed of mountains of 2,000 to 6,000 feet in height; extends from San Diego, California, to Washington Territory; does not reach Cape St. Lucas, nor enter the peninsula; and is not found in Sonora or Arizona.

2d. Its surface rocks are chiefly sedimentary; gold *is* found in many parts of it, while silver, copper and iron are, like gold, much more abundant in the Sierra Nevada.

3d. It is of later date than the Sierra Nevada, and, so far as now known, has yielded no Eocene fossils; those of Mount Diablo and of the region south of Monterey, (Santa Barbara, San Pedro, San Diego, &c.,) considered such by Mr. Marcou, being all Miocene; hence the date of elevation of the Coast mountains is subsequent to the Miocene epoch.

Of special interest in connexion with the elevation of its mountain chains are the more recent oscillations of level of which the southern coast of California bears evidence. I have elsewhere noticed the existence of a bed of recent shells upon the shores of San Pablo bay, many feet above the present water level; and have referred the profound erosion of the Golden Gate and the straits of Carquinas to a period of still greater elevation than the present. At several points on the coast of southern California I found evidences of recent elevation still more

striking than that afforded by the shell bed of San Pablo bay.   At San Luis Obispo, a former
sea beach, marked by accumulations of shells, such as now exist in the ocean below, runs along
the bluff, some 80 or 90 feet above the present high-water mark.   At San Pedro a similar
accumulation of shells crowns the perpendicular banks near the landing, at an elevation not
very different from that of the shell bed of San Luis Obispo.   On the hills back from the landing
other beds of shells indicate a still greater elevation of comparatively recent date; and marine
shells are said to exist beneath the surface of many portions of the plain over which the road
passes from San Pedro to Los Angeles.   On this surface I found stones bored by *Pholas*; as I
also did in the ancient sea bottoms at San Pedro, San Luis Obispo, and the bay of San Pablo.

The alluvial plain to which I have referred, lying between Los Angeles and the Pacific,
seems to have been formed at the mouth of Los Angeles river, when the ocean was at a higher
level than now.   By the subsequent elevation of the coast the stream has cut its way deeply
into this plain, and now makes its exit many miles from its former mouth.

At San Diego there are several beds of shells, having the same origin with those of San
Pedro, but occurring at different elevations.   Of these, the lowest, visible for a long distance
on the north side of the Loma, lies but about twenty feet above the present ocean level, and is
composed of a vast number of shells, of which some have not lost their colors.

CHAPTER II.

GEOLOGY OF ROUTE FROM SAN DIEGO TO FORT YUMA.

GENERAL FEATURES.—THE PENINSULAR MOUNTAINS.—THEIR RELATIONS TO THE SIERRA NEVADA.—PREVALENCE OF GRANITIC AND GNEISSOID ROCKS.—CHARACTER OF THE GRANITES.—MODERN DEPOSITS SKIRTING THEIR BASES, PROOFS OF RECENT ELEVATION.—PRINCIPAL UPHEAVAL AFTER EOCENE AND BEFORE MIOCENE PERIOD.—LOCAL GEOLOGY.—VICINITY OF SAN DIEGO.—MIOCENE STRATA AND FOSSILS—MODERN TRAP ERUPTION EAST OF THE MISSION.—SAN DIEGO TO THE DESERT.—TRAP NEAR PENASQUITAS.—GRANITES WITH FELSPATHIC VEINS OF SAN PASQUAL AND LAGUNA.—SANTA ISABEL.—WARNER'S.—THE OAKS.—SAN FELIPE.—TERTIARIES OF CARISSO CREEK.—OSTREAS.—ANOMIAS AND GNATHODONS CONTAINED IN THEM.—THE COLORADO DESERT—ARROYOS OR "WASHES."—TRANSPORTED BLOCKS.—ERODED AND POLISHED PEBBLES.—STRUCTURE AND ORIGIN OF THE DESERT.—ANCIENT FRESH-WATER LAKES.—NEW RIVER.—ALAMO MOCHO.—COOKE'S WELL.—DESERT GRAVEL.—TRANSPORTED FROM UPPER COLORADO.

GENERAL FEATURES.

The geology of this region, like that of the coast of Southern California, has been so freely treated of in the reports of Dr. Antesill and Mr. Blake, that little remains for me to say in reference to it.

The trail which leads from San Diego to the Colorado, almost immediately after leaving the Pacific coast, ascends the foot-hills of the Peninsular mountains, and thence for a distance of one hundred miles is constantly involved in the labyrinth of ranges and valleys which compose this broad mountain belt. At Carisso creek the road emerges from the mountains, and for another hundred miles leads across the level and barren wastes of the Colorado desert, when, without other preparation than that afforded by a belt of timber visible at the distance of many miles, the traveller finds himself standing upon the low, alluvial banks of a broad and rapid river, the waters of which are loaded with a reddish sediment, suggestive of the name it bears.

Both portions of the route, the mountain and desert, though contrasting so strongly in their physical features, are surprisingly harmonious in the desolate monotony of their geological structure and their animal and vegetable life.

THE PENINSULAR MOUNTAINS.

This mountain belt forms, in Southern California, the main prolongation of the Sierra Nevada system, and, to the eye of the common observer, would seem to be its only representative, crossing a line drawn eastward from San Diego towards the interior of the continent. As will be seen, however, in the description of the country bordering the Colorado, there are many other and important mountain ranges which properly belong to the Sierra Nevada system ; having much in common, both in their structure and trend, with the Peninsular ranges, and, in fact, uniting with them at a point further north.

The great mass of the Peninsular mountains east of San Diego is composed of granitic and gneissoid rocks, to the almost entire exclusion of unchanged sedimentary strata, or other forms of metamorphosed material than such as the former present. These granitic rocks, in nearly all localities, exhibit a common character, which they share, as will be seen hereafter, with most of the granites of the other ranges of the same system on the Colorado ; that is, a predominance of the felspathic over the hornblendic ingredients, and particularly in the quantity of albite which they contain. As a consequence of their mineral composition they are usually light-colored and soft, yielding readily to the decomposing action of the elements, and presenting few of the bold and picturesque escarpments usually associated with mountain masses of like magnitude. Little vegetation covers the surface of their slopes, and their geological structure may be read at a glance, even at the distance of miles.

I have mentioned as proofs of the different ages of this mountain system, and that which forms the coast line throughout the entire length of the State of California, that the Miocene Tertiaries; composing so large a part of the coast ranges, are here, above the foot-hills, entirely wanting. This is true, without exception, in all parts of the Peninsular mountains adjacent to the Fort Yuma and San Diego trail; and, from the recorded observations of others, we learn that such is the case in all parts of the Sierra Nevada where these mountains have been crossed in the State of California.

In 1855, when attached to the surveying party of Lieutenant Williamson, United States Topographical Engineers, we crossed the Sierra Nevada from the head of the Sacramento valley to the valleys on Upper Pit river, without anywhere, after leaving the vicinity of Fort Reading, seeing traces of Miocene Tertiary rocks. In our subsequent examinations of the summits and eastern slopes of the Cascade mountains, we met with no strata of that age till we had recrossed this mountain chain in Oregon, and descended into the Willamette valley. Throughout the whole length of the Sierra Nevada system, from the southern line of California to the Columbia, the Tertiaries of the coast cover its western base, but are nowhere, so far as at present known, found crowning its summits, or resting in its higher valleys.

On the western border of the Colorado desert is a series of strata which contain fossils regarded by Mr. Conrad as indicative of Miocene age; and at least one species, the gigantic oyster, (*Ostrea Titan*,) characterisic of the Miocene beds of the coast. This formation skirts the eastern bases of the Peninsular mountains in the same manner that those of San Diego border them on the west; the strata in both cases being somewhat elevated and disturbed, yet reaching but little way up their sides, and being entirely wanting in the interval. These facts seem to prove conclusively that the Sierra Nevada was raised at a period considerably anterior to the elevation of the Coast mountains, and disprove the statement of a recent writer that the latter are the older.[*] This author, as was previously mentioned, assigns to the elevation of the coast range a period anterior to that of the Sierra Nevada, placing it at the end of the Eocene epoch.

The sedimentary rocks to which he refers are doubtless of different ages. The white and red sandstones and conglomerate contain no fossils, but probably should be included in the same category with the Miocene, Pliocene, and modern deposits which are found along the *bases* of the Sierra Nevada, where they have been elevated at a comparatively recent date.

These strata furnish illustration of a truth of wide application, viz : *that the elevation of most of our important mountain ranges cannot be referred to a single epoch, but has been due to a series of elevatory paroxysms, or to processes of upheaval, continuing to act through long periods of time.*

The metamorphic limestone, of which M. Marcou speaks, is a conspicuous feature in the geological structure of most of the numerous ranges of the Sierra Nevada system. It is usually associated with metallic veins, and, for reasons that will be given more fully hereafter, I have referred it to the Carboniferous epoch.

The discovery, by Mr. Blake, of strata in the Sierra Nevada containing Eocene fossils, proves the date of the principal elevation of that range to be subsequent to the Eocene. This fact, taken in connexion with the relations which the Sierra Nevada sustains to strata known to be of Miocene age, permits us to refer the principal elevatory paroxysm of this system to the interval between the Eocene and Miocene.

Such facts as have a bearing on the elevation of the Peninsular mountains, subsequent to the deposition of the Miocene strata, will best be communicated in connexion with the local geology.

[*]Marcou's Geology of North America, p. 79.

VICINITY OF SAN DIEGO.

The traveller entering the harbor of San Diego sees before him a long line of table-land, of which the edge presents a somewhat abrupt declivity, preserving a general parallelism with the line of the beach ; its summit elevated from two to three hundred feet above the present level of the ocean ; the entire landscape devoid of trees ; the contour of the surface, visible for miles, everywhere exhibiting a picture of monotonous barrenness.

This table-land extends, without interruption and with a very gentle ascent, to the foot-hills of the Peninsular mountains, a distance of from twelve to fifteen miles. Through this plateau the San Diego river has eroded a narrow and winding valley, from the point where it issues from the hills till it reaches the ocean. On the sides of this valley the cut edges of the strata composing the table-land are very fully exposed. They consist of soft, yellowish sandstones ; white, chalk-like, infusorial earths, conglomerates and clays ; and include concretions and thin bands of limestone, in great part composed of shells, which are frequently preserved in a beautiful and perfect condition. The best exposure of these fossiliferous beds is across the valley immediately opposite the mission of San Diego, and from this locality I collected a large number of species of both bivalve and univalve shells, and a single echinoderm. Some of these species are new to science, but many are identical with those found in the fossiliferous portions of the Miocene series further up the coast.

The rocks represented in this section are probably equivalents of the middle and some part of the upper portion of the series exposed on the shore of San Pablo bay. They overlie the massive non-fossiliferous sandstones and shales of San Francisco, and are doubtless of the same age with a portion, at least, of the infusorial and fossiliferous deposits of Monterey, Santa Barbara, &c. In looking up the valley of the San Diego river the outcrop of a single stratum may be traced for several miles. The beds are thus seen to be entirely undisturbed, all gently dipping towards the ocean.

Following up the San Diego river, about five miles above the mission, we find it issuing from a narrow cañon cut in a mass of augitic trap, which forms the first of the series of ranges composing the Peninsular mountains. By the protrusion of this trap the Tertiary strata have been somewhat elevated and disturbed, though in no considerable degree metamorphosed. I am inclined to regard the trap exposed at this point as much more modern than the great mass of the mountain system with which it is connected, and its eruption as marking a paroxysm of elevation long subsequent to the upheaval of the chain. The existence of masses of modern trap along the bases of the different ranges of the Sierra Nevada system—a fact to which I shall have occasion to refer repeatedly in treating of the geology of the banks of the Colorado— has seemed to me of especial interest, as showing the continued and comparatively recent action of disturbing and elevating forces along these ancient lines of upheaval.

SAN DIEGO TO THE DESERT.

A mass of trap, similar to that just described, is seen in passing from San Diego to San Pasqual, near Penasquitas. The Tertiary strata are there upheaved by it, but are not again seen, going eastward. From San Pasqual the trail passes over a high ridge, from which the ocean is distinctly visible. This ridge is composed of gray felspathic granite, traversed by veins of felspar of great size. These often include large quantities of schorl, frequently exhibiting handsome crystallizations.

On the east side of San Pasqual mountain we descended to Laguna, a valley on the Pacific side of the main divide, and drained through a cañon cut in a portion of the San Pasqual mountain. From Laguna, continuing eastward, the road follows up a valley to the third range from the ocean. This range, like the two before passed, has nearly a NW. and SE. trend, and is composed of gray granite and mica slate, traversed by veins of felspar several feet wide, which are visible for long distances. The felspar is pinkish white, in large tabular crystals containing schorl. From the summit of this range we descended into the beautiful valley of Santa Isabel, which, surrounded by picturesque summits, with its green meadows and beautiful groups of oaks, presented a charming picture, contrasting strongly with the general sterility of the surrounding region.

From "Warner's Ranch" the road leads by a gentle ascent to "The Oaks," the divide between the waters of the Pacific and the desert. From this point to Carisso creek we followed the windings of the draining stream, which gradually becomes more intermitting and alkaline, until it entirely disappears in the sands of the desert. Throughout this distance the geological features of the route remain constantly the same; the aspect of the country becoming more barren and repulsive at every step.

Tertiary strata.—Approaching Carisso creek, we saw, for the first time in many days, strata of unchanged sedimentary rock. These consist of shales and clays, of a light brown or pinkish color, forming hills of considerable magnitude at the base of the mountains. From their soft and yielding texture they have been eroded into a great variety of fantastic and imitative forms. This series of beds has been greatly disturbed, in many places exhibiting lines of fracture and displacement. Where they are cut through, in the bed of Carisso creek, they contain concretions and bands of dark brown ferruginous limestone, which include large numbers of fossils, *Ostreas* and *Anomias*. These have been already described by Mr. Conrad, and are considered of Miocene age. In the debris of these shale beds I found fragments of the great oyster, (*Ostrea Titan*,) characteristic of the Miocene beds of the California coast.

A few miles north of this point similar strata, probably of the same age, were noticed by Dr. Leconte, but there they contain *Gnathodon*, an estuary shell; showing that the portion of the desert where they are now found was once covered by brackish water.

THE COLORADO DESERT.

That which is called by courtesy Carisso creek is usually, throughout the greater part of its course, a dry gravelly or sandy trough, which in its form gives evidence of being at times traversed and flooded by a stream of water. It is the natural avenue of escape for the rain which falls over a large area on the eastern slope of the Peninsular mountains; and along its rocky bed, beneath the sands, a meagre and alkaline stream at all times percolates, rising at intervals to the surface, and saving from absolute death those who are condemned to traverse this inhospitable region. This stream makes its last appearance near the station-house at the edge of the desert, where, for a few hundred yards, it flows over the sands, encrusting them with the salts it holds in solution, and is then absorbed by the porous soil. The continuation of its bed forms a broad and dusty avenue, cut through the accumulations of debris washed down from the mountains above, and gives easy access to the plains which constitute the desert proper. At rare and uncertain intervals a wild and impetuous torrent, caused by some storm in the mountains, rushes through this excavated channel and spreads itself, with a vast amount of gravel and sand, over the surface of the desert. Yet so infrequent and fitful are these supplies of water that they fail to redeem any portion of the wide area into which they flow from the stern and unrelenting sterility which there reigns supreme.

The flanks of the mountains and the slopes of the higher lands which surround the Colorado desert, as well as those which lie in and about an extensive territory bordering the Colorado on either side, are marked by these dry water-courses, which have received from those who are most familiar with this region the technical name of "washes;" in Spanish they are called "arroyos." They form a striking feature in the topography of the country, and are generally formed by sudden storms bursting upon surfaces covered with loose material, but bare of vegetation.

Emerging from the bed of Carisso creek, where its walls are formed of green, pink, brown, and white marls—the series of Miocene strata already mentioned, which are filled with shells and plates of selenite—the road, crossing the desert, descends for many miles along the slope formed by the materials washed down from the mountain. These materials consist of representatives of the granitic rocks of which I have spoken, with the addition of fragments of metamorphic silicious slate, and a highly crystalline blue, or white limestone. The blocks which strew the surface in the vicinity of the mountains are generally angular, and frequently of considerable size. Further out in the desert they are smaller, and are usually rounded, evincing in their form the attrition to which they have been subjected during their transport. Most of the stones which cover the surface are polished and blackened in a peculiar manner, many of them reflecting the sun's rays like glass. All have been exposed to the action of a common influence, by which they have, in some cases, been curiously weathered and eroded. The blocks of limestone have been most affected by this influence, and the surfaces of all the calcareous fragments are etched into singular and sometimes beautiful figures. This is probably in great degree owing to the action of drifting sand, as we find nowhere else, upon similar material, exposed to ordinary weathering, a like effect produced.

At Carisso creek we were at an elevation of about four hundred and fifty feet above the level of the sea. Within the first twenty miles after leaving the base of the mountains we had descended nearly to the sea level, and had left behind us the accumulations of boulders and gravel, and had come on to the fine alluvial clays and sand which form the desert surface for the greater part of the distance between the peninsula Sierra and the Colorado.

This depressed area doubtless exhibits nearly the same features that it did before it was elevated to its present level. It is everywhere underlaid by a series of Tertiary strata, probably continuous with that containing the *Ostreas*, *Anomias*, and *Gnathodons*, about the mouth of Carisso creek, and of Miocene age. The fossils I have enumerated prove the strata which include them to have been, in part at least, deposited in brackish water, showing that the area of the desert was then occupied by a narrow arm of the sea into which was poured the fresh water drainage of a large surface. In other words, that the present gulf of California formerly extended much further north than now.

The Tertiary strata underlying the central portion of the desert are fine clays and sands, and are doubtless the sediments deposited from comparatively deep and still water, precisely such as are now being deposited at the head of the Gulf of California. Like them, too, they are without fossils.

A portion of the Colorado desert is now scarcely higher than the sea level, and we have evidence that since the retreat of the Gulf much of it has been covered by a continuous sheet of fresh water. The evaporation of moisture has, however, in modern times, exceeded the precipitation, and most of the surface is now constantly dry; though at the lagoons there still remains a miniature representative of the wide-spread fresh water lake which once occupied the area surrounding them.

From Sackett's Wells to the Alamo Mocho, a distance of nearly forty miles, we were almost constantly travelling over a surface strewed with fresh water shells—*Anodonta*, *Planorbis*, *Physa*, and *Amnicola*—showing plainly that we were traversing the bed of a former lake. These shells are very abundant, the *Amnicolæ* being sometimes drifted by the wind till they cover and whiten the ground, and look like miniature snow wreaths. They have generally lost their epidermis, and the *Anodontas* are considerably broken and decayed, but on the whole are so well preserved that it seems impossible that many years have elapsed since they were inhabited by living animals.

Through the depressed portion of the desert New river, which has been already fully described, sometimes flows.   This stream is formed by the surplus water of the Colorado, which occasionally, during the summer freshet, overflows the banks and runs northward towards the lowest portions of the desert, which are many feet below the surface level of the river.

The soil of the area of which I have spoken is fine, rich, and deep, and wants only a supply of water to sustain a vigorous growth of vegetation.

Along the banks of New river we saw the stems of "Careless Weed," wild sunflower, &c., which had grown up subsequent to the last overflow of the Colorado, a few years since, and which had attained a magnitude I have never seen elsewhere exhibited by any annual plants.

At Alamo Mocho we reached the eastern border of the dry lake, and rose on to a terrace composed of fine stratified clays, covered with small rounded pebbles, which include representatives of many rocks subsequently found in place on the upper Colorado.   Pebbles of this character cover the desert surface on both sides of the river, except where occupied by mountain chains throughout the lower five hundred miles of its course; and, as our subsequent observations conclusively demonstrated, a large part of them have been removed from the cañons through which the main stream and its tributaries now flow, and have been transported by its waters often many hundred miles from their point of origin.

The route from Alamo Mocho to the Colorado exhibits few points of geological interest.   The road runs either over the gravel-covered terrace just mentioned, or descending to a lower level traverses a surface of more recent material formed by the action of streams which have cut away the higher and older portions of the desert.   The superficial phenomena of the Colorado desert, the large area which it includes, formerly covered by fresh water, but now dry, the character and origin of the transported materials, which strew the older desert surface, the physical conditions with which both were associated, are matters of peculiar interest and intimately related to the wonderful phenomena of the surface geology of the country bordering the upper Colorado, and in that connexion will be again referred to.

CHAPTER III.

GEOLOGY OF COUNTRY BORDERING THE LOWER COLORADO.

GENERAL FEATURES.

The geological structure of the banks of the Colorado, from the Black cañon, near the mouth of the Rio Virgen, to the head of the Gulf of California, though exhibiting considerable local diversity, has a common character throughout; a character shared by all parts of a wide area bordering the Colorado through the lowest five hundred miles of its course. This area is bounded on the west by the peninsular extension of the Sierra Nevada, and on the east by several ranges belonging to the same system, of which the Mojave and Black mountains, the Cerbat, and, perhaps, even the Aquarius ranges, may be considered as examples; the mountains of Sonora and those crossing the Gila east of Fort Yuma holding the same relation to the southern portion of this area that the former ranges do to the northern, some of them being but the southeastern prolongation of the same lines of upheaval.

As a whole, this area is one of depression; a synclinal trough lying between the principal mountain ranges I have mentioned, the lowest positions of which are scarcely elevated above the ocean level. It is a continuation northward of the great valley, if such it may be called, now occupied by the Gulf of California. It is only, however, when viewed as a whole, and taken in connexion with the great physical features of the region which surrounds the trough of the Colorado, that it deserves the term I have applied to it; and the traveller who passes through it, unless carrying from side to side a line of barometric observations, will be very likely to be deceived by the local variety which its surface presents, and fail to receive a just impression of its general configuration. The greater part of the surface of the Colorado basin is composed of arid sand or gravel plains, exhibiting but little variation of level, of which the Colorado desert, and that lying east of the Colorado and south of the Gila, ("the great Sonora desert,") afford the most striking examples. These plains are enclosed in a net work of bare and rugged mountain chains, not of great altitude, but exceedingly picturesque in their outlines. Of these chains, the most important and most continuous have the northwest and southeast trend of the Sierra Nevada system; the others are but interlocking spurs; the whole forming a series of isolated basins which usually are longest in a northwest and southeast direction, and of which the surfaces, composed of gravel or sand, form the desert plains before described. Into this labyrinth the Colorado pours, as it issues from its trough cut in the great table-lands which skirt the western base of the Rocky mountains, where it takes its rise. Doubtless in earlier times it filled these basins to the brim, thus irrigating and enriching all its course. In the lapse of ages, however, its accumulated waters, pouring over the lowest points in the barriers which opposed their progress towards the sea, have cut them down from summit to base, forming that remarkable series of deep and narrow cañons through which its turbid waters now flow, with rapid and almost unobstructed current, from source to mouth.   The effect of the removal of the barriers which once checked the flow of the Colorado has been to confine the stream to the channel occupied by its current; to limit its vivifying influence to a narrow margin along the banks, leaving the open areas through which it flows—and which were once lakes and afterwards fertile valleys—arid and sterile wastes.   Instead of the broad sheets of water which once, by evaporation, filled the air with showers, covering with verdure all the southern portion of the "Great Basin," it now presents but a narrow thread hastening to the Gulf, and yielding almost no moisture to the region through which it flows.

The mountain chains that traverse the Colorado basin exhibit throughout a marked similarity of geological structure.   The more important ranges are, in great part, composed of granitic and metamorphic rocks, similar to those which form the mass of the Peninsular mountains. With these are associated nearly every known phase of erupted material—porphyries, trap, trachyte, obsidian, tufa, scoria, &c., in endless variety.   Some of these volcanic products are evidently of modern date, and show that the eruptive forces which have left on all that region such surprising evidences of their energy were but recently in vigorous action.

The solfatara west of the mouth of the river, and the mud volcanoes of the desert, prove that the fires below are not yet wholly extinguished.

The general features of the Colorado basin seem to have existed previous to the deposition of the later Tertiary strata, for nearly all its area is underlaid by rocks of that age, which, though generally covered and concealed by Quaternary deposits of gravel and sand, are upheaved and metamorphosed around the bases of most of its mountains.

LOCAL GEOLOGY.

MOUTH OF THE COLORADO TO FORT YUMA.

The geology of that part of the valley of the Colorado lying between Fort Yuma and the Gulf is precisely that of the Colorado desert and of the country south of the Gila.   There are broad plains of gravel and sand, from which rise here and there detached mountains of moderate elevation, like islands from the surface of the ocean.   Through this area the river flows in a tortuous channel, widening near the mouth, and, as its waters are checked in their flow, gradually depositing the material held in suspension, forming wide stretches of monotonous mud flats.   At Fort Yuma and above, the sediment consists of fine micaceous sand and red clay, and at all seasons of the year exists in such quantity as to render the water both red and opaque. Throughout several hundred miles of its course the river alternately, with the seasons, deposits or removes the material it has eroded from its channel in the highlands above.   As we approach the mouth the sandy portions of the sediment are first deposited, forming the bars which everywhere obstruct navigation.   When it meets the tide water of the Gulf the finer and more argillaceous portions alone remain in suspension, and these, when permitted to settle to the bottom, form the broad surfaces of mud of which I have spoken.

Fort Yuma is built upon a granite hill, which projects slightly above the more recent strata surrounding it.   Pilot Knob and the Black mountain, lying west of the fort, are similar granitic masses of greater dimensions.   The view eastward is limited by two ranges of mountains, marking lines of upheaval, which, running northwestward from Sonora, cross the Gila many miles above its mouth, and the Colorado at some distance above the fort.

THE PURPLE HILLS.

Twelve miles above Fort Yuma the Colorado issues from the first of the series of passes which I have spoken of as giving character to its course.   This pass is cut through the most

J.J.Young, from a sketch by H.B.Möllhausen.

Lith. of Sarony, Major & Knapp, 449 Broadway N.Y.

SHORE ON LOWER COLORADO.

southwesterly of several neighboring and parallel ranges, to which, from the general color they exhibit, the name of Purple Hills was given. They are composed of granite and mica slates, associated with which are purple porphyries and trachytes, in sufficient quantity to impart to them their prevailing color. Where we passed through the first of these ranges, it has nearly a northwest and southeast trend, and in the immediate vicinity of the river is composed of a gray, massive granite, which, yielding somewhat readily to the action of the elements, as most of the granites of the Sierra Nevada system do, has formed slopes receding from the river, giving the pass an outline strikingly in contrast with that of most of the cañons cut in the porphyritic rocks higher up. Boot Mountain, a prominent peak in this range on the east side of the river, is composed of trap.

Traversing Explorer's Pass we entered an oval valley cut in various channels by the river. Of this valley the higher portion is occupied by beds of gravel deeply cut by washes and covered with the giant cactus, (*Cereus giganteus*,) and other characteristic forms of the vegetation of the desert. The gravel beds are made up of material of two different classes: first, angular fragments of granite, trap, porphyry, &c., brought down from the neighboring hills, and forming long slopes about their bases; second, rolled and rounded pebbles of various sizes, composed of all forms of erupted rock, with silicified wood, jasper, chalcedony, and occasionally chert containing corals and crinoidal stems; the latter derived, as I subsequently ascertained, from the Carboniferous limestone many hundred miles above. The channel of the river, where it cuts through the second range of the Purple Hills is bordered on either side by walls of trap, trachyte, and porphyry, exhibiting a great variety both of color and consistence, though purple trachytes and porphyries predominate. Toward the upper end of this passage the scenery becomes bolder; the hills higher and more craggy, showing considerable variety and contrast of color. The materials which compose them are porphyries, trachytes, and tufas, pink, purple, white, blue, yellow, brown, &c. The colors are all vivid, and obscured by no vegetation form a landscape very different from any before presented to our eyes.

Proceeding up the river we traversed another valley similar to the one just described, bordered on the east by the desert, with its characteristic geology and botany. We then entered the pass through the third range of the Purple Hills, which are here, however, not purple, but gray; being composed of mica slate, with conspicuous veins of quartz and hornblende. Many parts of the Purple Hills are rich in metallic minerals. In the second range a vein of argentiferous galena has been opened by Mr. Halsted, of Fort Yuma, and promises well. In the immediate vicinity of the river, the third range of the Purple Hills affords the most unmistakable evidence of the existence of valuable minerals. Gold, copper, iron, and lead are found there; the gold in small quantities, and probably not in such abundance as to compensate the miner. Some of the veins of copper are, however, rich, and have already attracted the attention of the residents at the fort. From the claim of Messrs. Hooper, Halsted, and Johnson, I received specimens of erubesite and black copper, not inferior in quality to the ores from the copper mines of the Gila.

Above the mica slate hills, the red, white, green, pink, and blue tufas, porphyries, and trachytes, described as occurring below, reappear, giving the same fantastic appearance to the scenery. These rocks, with trap and scoria, extend from the river to Chimney Peak.

Chimney Peak is a remarkably picturesque double pinnacle which crowns a mountain chain, probably the northwestern prolongation of the middle range of the Purple Hills. Like the other peaks of the range it is composed of trap, and affords a striking example of the tendency to form columnar summits exhibited by all the mountains of this vicinity. Dome mountain on the east of the Colorado, present the same features in nearly an equal degree. The mountains which have this form are all trappean in character, and doubtless owe their peculiar outlines to the manner in which this material yields to the action of the elements. The trap is usually ore or less columnar in structure, the cleavage planes which bound the columns being perpendicular to the cooling surface. When, as most frequently occurs, these planes are vertical, by the erosion of rains and flowing streams, perpendicular walls are formed, and large masses usually exhibit mural faces. This will account for the peculiar outline which many of the trappean summits of the mountains of the Colorado basin present. Their great altitude, as compared with the mass of the ranges which they crown, is doubtless due to the resistance offered by their material to the atmospheric influences which have removed perhaps several hundred feet of the more yielding tufas and trachytes once surrounding them.

About the bases of some of the isolated mountains of the Colorado basin the material washed from the sides and summits has accumulated, and where these detrital slopes have been opened in the beds of the "washes" I have described, I was able roughly to measure the amount of denudation the mountains had suffered. From these data it would appear that many of them have once been fully twice their present size.

At Precipice Bend and Barrier islands the river impinges against huge masses of red trachyte, west of which the highly colored rocks before described are very conspicuous, and extend for many miles along the base of Chimney Peak range.

Fig. 1.—CHIMNEY PEAK FROM THE NORTH.

A mile or two above Barrier islands are high perpendicular bluffs of stratified and consolidated gravel, forming a conglomerate of great thickness. The upper part of these hills is composed of uncemented gravel, and is continuous with the desert surface, which here forms a mesa about one hundred and fifty feet above the level of the river. The consolidated portion of these bluffs is horizontally stratified and not at all metamorphosed. Its constituents do not materially differ from those of the gravel above. They are rolled and angular fragments of porphyry, trachyte, trap, scoria, jasper, &c., in great variety, cemented by carbonate of lime. It may not be possible to determine the exact age of these beds of conglomerate, but I am disposed to regard them as entirely Quaternary.

A portion of the Tertiary series which underlies most of the Colorada basin closely resembles this deposit, being composed of similar materials doubtless accumulated under the same physical conditions. But in most of the exposures of the Tertiary conglomerates they are much more metamorphosed and consolidated than those under consideration, and are associated with infusorial strata, which are here wanting. I have been disposed to regard the stratified gravels exposed at Conglomerate Bluffs, as well as those which underlie the desert surfaces of all the subordinate basins traversed by the Colorado, as accumulations of materials transported by its waters, or derived from the adjacent mountains, and stratified in the bottoms of these basins when occupied by bodies of water. The Colorado having since greatly deepened its channel, the materials formerly deposited by it are now left standing in high bluffs on either side of its course.

A few miles above Conglomerate Bluffs, (Camp 17,) a high crag overhangs the water on the east side of the river, composed of stratified conglomerate, similar, in general character, to that of the bluffs, but metamorphosed, greenish in color and highly inclined. This conglomerate is overlaid by a thick bed of purplish trachyte, which has apparently been the agent of its metamorphosis.

Fig. 2.—SPIRE RANGE.

This bed of conglomerate I was at first disposed to regard as identical with that forming the bluffs below, but subsequent observation led me to consider it the equivalent of the metamorphosed conglomerates exposed at various points higher up the river, which are older than the quaternary, being probably the representatives of a portion of the miocene series of the Californian coast.

We here obtained a fine view of a remarkably picturesque chain of mountains on the west side of the river, stretching away toward the northwest. It is crowned by a range of pinnacles, not unlike Chimney Peak in form and apparently composed of similar material, which suggested the name given it of Spire range. This chain bears an intimate relationship in its geological structure, its trend, and position to Chimney Peak range, marking, however, a distinct line of upheaval, perhaps but a continuation of the more northern ranges of the Purple Hills.

The river here bends abruptly to the east and skirts the base of another prominent and continuous range of mountains, which it bursts through at Porphyry Gate. That portion of this chain which lies west of the river is composed of porphyries, tufas, and trachytes, of which the prevailing color is a dark brownish purple, and hence they have received the name of Chocolate mountains.

The cliffs which border the river at the point where it passes through this range are of similar composition with the western portion of the chain, that on the right bank consisting of a deep purple porphyritic trachyte. In the middle of the stream stands a picturesque conical rock, composed of purple trachyte, and called, from its form, Light-house rock. The adjacent hills upon the left bank are formed of trachyte, porphyry, tufa and volcanic conglomerate, of varied colors and consistence, closely resembling the colored rocks of the Purple Hills. In these hills I discovered a series of highly metamorphosed red sandstones, very distinctly stratified, the strata standing nearly vertical. Where most changed these beds seemed to be converted into purplish trachytes and porphyries, similar to those which I have described as characteristic of this range where we had before observed it. At the time of making these observations I was entirely unable to determine the age of these strata; but to whatever epoch they might belong, I was disposed to consider them as the source from which had been derived, by fusion, a portion, at least, of the purplish trachytes and porphyries so characteristic of the region I had recently traversed. Long subsequently, when we had left the basin of the Colorado, and had descended from the surface of the high table-land lying east of it to the bottom of the Great Cañon of the upper Colorado, in the red sandstones and shales which there form the base of the sedimentary series, I thought I saw the equivalents of the sandstones of the Chocolate mountains. Some of the tufas about Porphyry Gate are highly charged with alkaline salts, and their decomposed portions frequently contain plates of selenite.

Eastward from the point at which the Colorado cuts through the Chocolate mountains they assume a new aspect. They are no longer purple, but gray, and are composed of gneiss traversed by veins of granite and quartz. The gneissoid rocks are frequently foliated in structure and much convoluted; even a hand specimen including curved layers of hornblende and felspar with veins of quartz, well representing the structure of the chain. The aspect of these rocks is such as to lead an observer more readily to refer them to a metamorphic origin than any other granitic rocks seen on our route.

At Camp 18, located near the base of the granitic portions of the Chocolate mountains, the Quaternary strata are very fully exposed. They consist of beds of gravel and sand with brown and white clays, which form low table-hills, extending as far as the eye could reach toward the east in an accurately horizontal line along the mountain bases. The sides and summits of these terraces are covered with rolled pebbles of various sizes, packed so closely as to occupy the entire surface. The harder of these pebbles are curiously polished and blackened, as though with plumbago, while the softer ones, particularly those composed of limestone, are etched and eroded much in the same manner as those found on the surface of the Colorado desert. This effect may be due to blown sand, but at present no sand is here visible, and the erosion seems rather attributable to chemical action.

GREAT COLORADO VALLEY.

For several days after leaving the Chocolate mountains we were occupied in crossing a broad valley, of which the geological structure exhibited a perfect monotony throughout. On either side of the river are broad, gravel, desert plains; that on the southeast occupying all the interval between the parallel ranges of the Chocolate and Monument mountains. The surface of this plain is about one hundred feet above the level of the river, and the bluffs formed by the cut edges, limiting the bottom lands, are composed of gravel, sand, and clays; sometimes partially cemented by lime. In this, as in most of the subordinate basins traversed by the Colorado, its course is exceedingly tortuous; and as the water level is subject to great oscillations the channel is constantly changing, and the sediment, with which its current is always loaded, undergoing deposition or removal. The sections of these alluvial deposits formed along the channel afforded me, at the time we passed—the water then being at its lowest stage— many instructive examples of the mode of formation of false bedding and cross stratification so frequently observed in the older rocks. Several sketches illustrative of this subject, and taken from my note-book, are given in the accompanying wood cuts.

Fig. 3.— SECTION OF ALLUVIAL BANK OF THE COLORADO.

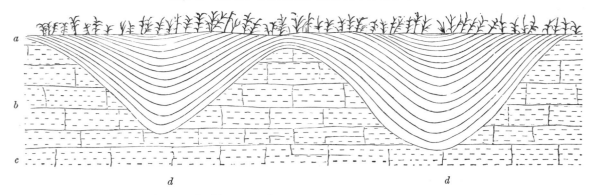

    a Surface of bottom lands covered with grass and canes.
    b Beds of clay and sand horizontally stratified.
    c Water line of Colorado.
   d d Channels eroded in *b*, subsequently filled with curved layers of clay and sand.

Fig. 4.—CROSS STRATIFICATION FORMED BY CHANGING CHANNEL..

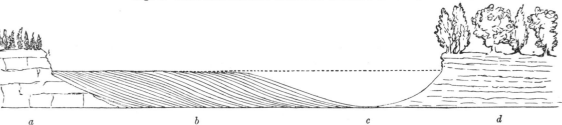

    a Old bank covered with small willows, receiving additions from receding channel.
    b New bank, or sand bar, cross stratified, being added to *a*.
    c Present channel moving from *a* to *d*; the dotted line representing the surface of the stream.
    d Oldest bank, being now cut away by current, covered with large cottonwood and willows.

Sections like this are not unfrequently exposed, where the present stream has cut across its former bed—flowing from *a* to *d*, and crossing *c*.

The nature of the sediment deposited, whether clay or sand, depends upon the velocity of the water in which it was suspended. The bayous and deserted channels, in which the water has very little motion, are gradually filled up with argillaceous sediment, while the first deposit made by the current water, when its motion is but partially arrested, is sandy—as in the formation of sand bars.

The alternations of strata of clay and sand which compose the alluvial banks are simply a record of the varying velocity of the current which deposited them. Not unfrequently I noticed in a section of the bank a thin stratum of clay which, when it formed the surface layer, had been exposed to the sun's rays, and had cracked and contracted till its fragments were widely separated from each other; sand had subsequently been deposited upon and around them, and now the cut edge of the stratum appeared only as a line of detached and imperfectly quadrangular masses of clay in a sand bank.

Fig. 5.—EDGE OF SUN-CRACKED STRATUM OF CLAY IN ALLUVIAL BANK OF COLORADO.

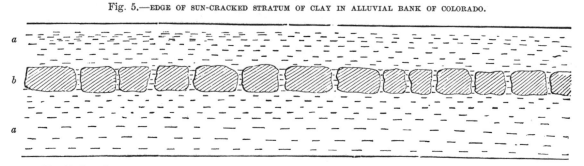

a a Stratified sand.
   b Detached masses of clay, formerly united.

The bottom lands of the river here, as below, are in many localities fertile; but are generally charged with alkalies, which frequently appear in the form of a snow-like efflorescence on the surface. Where there is little alkali, the Indians successfully cultivate corn, beans, pumpkins, wheat and melons. Little rain falls here, and the necessary moisture is supplied to the cultivated lands from the annual overflow of the river. If a larger amount of water could be secured at intervals throughout the season, by irrigation, a portion of the salts would be removed, and much of the alkaline soil be redeemed from its sterility.

HALF-WAY AND RIVERSIDE MOUNTAINS.

These mountains do not cross the Colorado, but their eastern bases are washed by it for many miles. The Half-way mountains we had little opportunity to examine; but the spurs of this range which reach the river are composed of coarse, gray, felspathic granite, with masses of dark cellular trap.

Riverside mountain exhibits a greater variety of constituent material than any other range which we had an opportunity to examine. It is composed of granite, gneiss, mica, and talcose slate, basaltic and amygdaloid traps, with masses of quartzite and veins of quartz. With the micaceous and talcose slates are associated highly crystalline limestones, blue and yellow in color, and containing many veins of iron. These latter rocks are all, doubtless, metamorphic in character, and I have supposed them to be the representatives of the Palaeozoic limestones, micaceous grits, and perhaps dolomites forming the table-lands east of the Colorado.

This group of rocks composing the Riverside mountain is such as leads me to suppose they will be found to contain rich mineral veins. I had an opportunity of examining only a very small portion of the range, but I shall be surprised if gold, silver, and lead are not found in it. Iron and copper are known to exist there, and the rocks which I have enumerated very closely resemble those containing the auriferous veins of California. Argentiferous galena is contained in greater or less quantity in all the ranges of this system, from Sonora northward, wherever the granitic and metamorphic rocks appear. In the porphyries, traps, trachytes, and tufas which, over large areas, replace or conceal the metalliferous rocks to which I have referred, I was able to detect no metallic minerals, except black oxide of manganese, and cobalt.

The variety of materials which compose Riverside mountain is made evident by the striking contrast of colors which they exhibit. This mountain is entirely destitute of vegetation, and, when seen at the distance of several miles, the patches of purple, brown, blue, ash, cream, red, &c., form a picture which would scarcely be exaggerated if represented by the colored diagrams of the geological lecture-room.

When the mountain is illuminated by the rising or setting sun this variety of color produces a novel and pleasing effect, redeeming, in some degree, the scene from the aspect of sterility and desolation which it would otherwise bear.

MONUMENT MOUNTAINS AND CANON.

For several miles above the Riverside mountain, the Colorado is bordered by the bluffs formed by the erosion of the desert plain. They are composed of conglomerate, sand, and clay, but slightly consolidated and entirely undisturbed. In some places the upper stratum, forming the desert surface, is filled with nodular concretions of calcareous tufa. At Beaver island we reach the foot-hills of the Monument mountains. The immediate banks of the river are composed of strata of a peculiar tufaceous conglomerate, apparently formed of volcanic ashes stratified by the action of water, above which are layers of white infusorial earth and beds of gravel and sand. Just above the head of Beaver island these strata are seen, much disturbed and metamorphosed by masses of trap that have been thrown up into low rounded hills.

Corner Rock is a large mass of metamorphosed conglomerate, a portion of the series which I have just described, against which the river impinges, and by which it is deflected from its course. The conglomerate is overlaid by a thick bed of dark blue basaltic trap, which has here been the agent of metamorphosis. On the trap lies a bed of Quaternary gravel.

The series of strata exposed in this vicinity, including the conglomerate and the chalk-like infusorial rocks, I have supposed to be older than the beds of gravel and sand which border the river at so many points below, and to represent the Tertiary epoch. I shall have occasion frequently to allude to the recurrence of similar strata, in describing the geology of the banks of the Colorado between this point and the Rio Virgen.

Soon after passing Corner Rock we entered Monument cañon, which is cut through the Monument mountains by the Colorado, its northern entrance being at the mouth of Bill Williams's Fork. Throughout the whole of its course this cañon abounds in wild and picturesque scenery, the effect of the varied outline of its walls being heightened by the vivid and strongly contrasted colors which they exhibit.

The great mass of Monument mountains is granitic, a rather coarse, massive, felspathic granite, in which the crystals of felspar are pink and the hornblende green. This granite is traversed in every direction by veins of different kinds. The largest and most conspicuous are quartzite and epidote, in which I detected no metallic substances. Other are composed of limonite and specular iron ore, of which great quantities are visible in the cliffs bordering the river. The veinstone associated with the iron is usually crystallized carbonate of lime. Another class of veins contains a greater or less quantity of copper, frequently combined with iron and manganese. Argentiferous galena was also found, but in small quantities.

On either side of the granitic axis of the chain are thick beds of highly metamorphosed conglomerate and sandstone, which, according to the amount of iron contained, are deep blood red, pink, drab, or white. These beds of conglomerate compose the red and precipitous walls which form the southern entrance to the cañon, as also the lower portions of the tabular trap hills at the northern entrance on the east side. Overlying the conglomerates and sandstones, on the same side of the river, are thick masses of stratified trap, which form high and table-topped summits. Near the southern entrance the conglomerates are mingled with masses of blue, green, purple, white, and red trap, trachyte, and tufa, which furnish the most striking elements in the particolored pictures formed by the scenery of the cañon. Associated with the granite in many localities are exposed masses of highly crystalline pinkish, white, or cream-colored limestone. If this rock was at any time fossiliferous, its organisms have entirely disappeared in its metamorphoses. It, however, closely resembles the crystalline limestones of Riverside mountain and that which occurs at various points in the Sierra Nevada of California. A limestone, in some localities highly metamorphosed and resembling this, has been found in the southeastern extensions of the mountain ranges which cross the Colorado, and perhaps in the continuation of Monument range itself. From the relation which these mountain chains bear to the great table-land lying east of them, of which the western portion consists mainly of Carboniferous limestones, there is little doubt that the limestones which they contain are of Carboniferous age.

The view represented by the following cut, taken from a point above the mouth of Bill Williams's Fork, is one of peculiar geological interest, as illustrating the dependence of scenic

Fig. 6.—VIEW OF NORTHERN ENTRANCE TO MONUMENT CAÑON.

character upon geological structure. On the left it is bounded by hills of soft Tertiary conglomerate, covered with quaternary gravel, of which the yielding materials, fashioned by atmospheric erosion, have assumed the form of low, broad-based cones, whose outlines present a series of graceful curves. In front rises a table-topped mountain, of which all the upper portion is trap, with its characteristic mural faces. On the right masses of granite descend to the water's edge, exhibiting the rugged and irregularly rounded outlines which this rock is so prone to assume.

CHAPTER IV.

GEOLOGY OF REGION BETWEEN BILL WILLIAMS'S FORK AND RIO VIRGEN.

Infusorial strata of white rock.—Chemehuevis valley.—Mojave mountains.—Mojave cañon.—Metamorphosed tertiary rocks.—Porphyries and trachytes.—Mojave valley.—Black mountains.—Prevalence of erupted rocks.—Dead mountain.—Pyramid cañon.—Cottonwood valley —Tertiary and modern gravels.—General structure of valleys traversed by colorado.—Mount davis.—Tertiary conglomerate.—Quaternary deposits.—Elephant hill —Trough of the Colorado at entrance of black cañon —Black cañon.—Great variety of erupted rocks.—Amygdaloids containing chalcedony and crystallized quartz.—Plutonic character and scenery of the black mountains.—Rock salt and gypsum from rio virgen.

For many miles above the mouth of Bill Williams's Fork the Colorado is bordered on the west by Monument mountains. For the first five or six miles little but granite is seen. This is similar to that exposed in the cañon, but contains fewer veins. Mount Whipple, which belongs to the Monument range, is apparently granitic throughout. Near where we left these mountains the spurs which approach the river exhibit, in addition to the granite, porphyries, trachytes, and tufas, of various colors, but principally red and purple. Much of the porphyry is exceedingly beautiful, very hard and fine grained, and of a deep purple specked with white.

On the east side of the river, in the immediate vicinity of the stream, for several miles above the mouth of Bill Williams's Fork, are low hills of Tertiary sandstone and conglomerate, covered with loose gravel. This gravel is called by Mr. Marcou "quaternary drift," but it is necessary that this and all similar deposits in the valley of the Colorado should be carefully distinguished from the Drift, technically so called, of the Mississippi valley, as true Drift is wholly wanting in all parts of the route of the expedition west of the Rio Grande.

The beds of recent transported materials which we met with all belong to what has been called "valley drift," being alluvial rather than diluvial in character.

At our Camp 35 the Tertiary strata of which I have spoken are very fully exposed, forming bluffs in some places one hundred and fifty feet high. They are here considerably disturbed, being inclined at a high angle, and exhibit many dislocations. The most conspicuous member of the series is a soft dark red sandstone; but at one point a series of about twenty-five feet in thickness is exposed, consisting almost entirely of white chalk-like infusorial rock. This occurs in layers from a few lines to a foot in thickness, interstratified with which are beds of rounded and frequently large boulders. The infusorial strata are inclined at an angle of 30°, and rest upon the red sandstone of which I have spoken. A bed of yellow clay horizontally stratified lies upon the upturned edges of the infusorial rocks. This is a Quaternary deposit which occurs in many localities in this vicinity and higher up the river, forming bluffs and terraces sometimes two hundred and fifty feet above the present bed of the stream.

Several lines of upheaval cross the river in the vicinity of Camp 36, connected with a range of hills which crosses Bill Williams's Fork a few miles east of the Colorado. The igneous axes of these lines of elevation are greenstone and granite. By them the Tertiary rocks are thrown up into hills of fantastic outlines and vivid colors.

CHEMEHUEVIS VALLEY.

This is a basin of limited extent, enclosed by the Monument and Mojave mountains, and the spurs given off from these chains. The Tertiary infusorial strata, which have been mentioned, reappear in several localities in this valley, but much disturbed. They are covered by thick beds of gravel, sand, and clay, which form bluffs at the margin of the bottom lands, and extend to the bases of the surrounding mountains.

MOJAVE MOUNTAINS.

This important chain bounds Chemehuevis valley on the east. Where it crosses the Colorado its picturesque pinnacles were called by Captain Whipple "The Needles." Though continuous, these mountains exhibit considerable variety of structure. The most southern portion observed by us is composed of porphyries and trachytes, purple, blue, pink, gray, and green in color. The principal mass of the range east of the Chemehuevis valley is light gray or white granite, traversed by numerous veins of quartz. This is skirted by a range of foot hills, composed of highly colored porphyries and trachytes, similar to those which predominate in the more southern portion of the range. Below these, and rising from the base of the chain, is a line of rounded hills, composed of black scoria, which have thrown up and changed the Tertiary rocks, and seem to be more recent than the granites and porphyries. This line of hills diverges from the general trend of the Mojave mountains, and runs down to connect with the erupted masses of which I have spoken as bordering the Colorado. Between the mountains and the river is a broad sloping mesa, composed of the debris of the adjacent ranges, and of transported pebbles. Among these pebbles I found masses of Carboniferous limestone, with characteristic fossils.

MOJAVE CAÑON.

Toward the upper part of the Chemehuevis valley the gravel hills gradually encroach upon the bottom lands until they form precipitous bluffs bordering the river. These bluffs seem to compose two terraces, of which the surface of the lower is about 75 feet, and the upper 120 feet above the river bed. Near the entrance to the cañon, in a westerly bend of the river, is exposed a large mass of erupted rock, evidently quite recent. By this the beds of sand and gravel are much disturbed and metamorphosed, but only locally.

The foot-hills of the mountains are composed of trap, with Tertiary sandstones and conglomerates, the latter highly metamorphosed and thrown about in the greatest confusion, exhibiting a variety of colors quite as vivid and as strongly contrasted as those of similar strata at the southern entrance to Monument cañon. The colors are here, however, not precisely the same, the most conspicuous being bright red, green, and white of the stratified, and brown and purple of the erupted rocks.

The cañon itself presented the most varied and interesting scenery we had met with, its walls being particularly ragged and picturesque in outline, and the colors such as to produce the most unusual and surprising effects. The southern part of the cañon is cut through the trap and metamorphic rocks just mentioned; the gateway by which we entered it being composed of trap and a massive and highly metamorphosed conglomerate, which varies in color from umber brown to blood red.

The most elevated portion of the chain through which the cañon passes is composed of granite and porphyry, and is apparently older than the hills of trap and metamorphosed Tertiary rocks which skirt it on either side. The Needles themselves are formed of purple porphyry and trachyte. Our Camp 40 was located midway of the cañon. The highest summits in the vicinity are composed, on the north and west, of granite; on the south and east, of porphyry. The lower hills, immediately adjacent to camp, consist of metamorphic conglomerate, or rather breccia, containing firmly cemented angular fragments of granite, similar to that of the neighboring summits, and probably derived from them, with intruding masses of purple and brown trachyte and porphyry. These latter materials, with green volcanic tufa, form the picturesque hills which rise from the water's edge on the left bank. Some of the trachytes contain numerous scales of mica, (phlogopite,) and masses of black oxide of manganese.

That part of the cañon which lies north of Camp 40 is formed by the passage of the river

Lith. of Sarony, Major & Knapp, 449 Broadway N.Y.

THE NEEDLES.
(MOJAVE RANGE)

through a distinct mountain range, one of several (four or five) which compose the chain. This range is much higher west than east of the river, and borders the Mojave valley on the southwest and west. Its principal component rocks are gray or greenish and serpentinoid granite, containing a large proportion of hornblende, and traversed by many quartz veins. The greenish granite is scarcely distinguishable from much of that in Monument cañon. North of these granitic mountains are hills of conglomerate, &c., similar to those near the southern entrance to the cañon.

MOJAVE VALLEY.

This is one of the largest of the basin-like areas to which I have so frequently referred. It is elliptical in form; some thirty miles long and fifteen wide, and is bounded on all sides by ranges of rugged and picturesque mountains. From the bases of these mountains long slopes, composed of their debris, extend toward the river. These slopes terminate in gravel mesas similar in character to those which have been described as occurring below, and which here form four and in some places five distinct terraces. Forty feet below the lowest of these terraces the alluvial bottom lands, forming a narrow belt on either side of the river, follow it in its sinuous course.

The mountains are entirely bare of vegetation, and their geological structure is visible at the distance of many miles. The slopes and gravel mesas contain a few clumps of cactus *Larrea* and other desert-loving shrubs, but are generally exceedingly arid and sterile. The bottom lands, though frequently highly charged with alkalies, are usually fertile, the better portions sustaining a luxuriant growth of willows, cottonwoods, "mezquite," (*Algarobia glandulosa*,) and "tornilla," (*Strombocarpa pubescens*,) the more saline surfaces being covered by dense thickets of arrow-wood (*Tessaria borealis*) and *Obione canescens*.

A section from the river westward to the mountains bordering the valley is: 1st. Alluvial bottom lands bordering the stream, of which the general level is about fifteen feet above its bed, and which are usually covered by the annual midsummer inundation; 2d. First terrace, 40 feet, gravel and clay; 3d. Second terrace, 25 feet, gravel; 4th. Third terrace, 25 feet, gravel, with angular fragments of granite; 5th. Fourth terrace, angular fragments washed down from the mountain above; 6th. Mountain of white granite, with strata of clay, mica, and hornblende slates. The granite, which is generally white and compact, contains a few quartz veins with copper.

The mountains which surround the Mojave valley exhibit considerable diversity of geological structure and trend, and while they should all, perhaps, be classed as belonging to one system, (Sierra Nevada,) a part of them exhibit a tendency to depart from the normal trend of that system and approach that of the Wahsatch and Rocky mountains. Of these ranges the most continuous and important is that of the

BLACK MOUNTAINS.

This range seems to take its rise opposite the southern extremity of the Mojave valley, twenty miles east of the river. From the Mojave mountains, which it would cross if prolonged, it is separated by an interval of plain connected with an extensive valley lying east of this range; a valley which seems to be drained through a broad arroyo, terminating near the northern entrance to the Mojave cañon. From their southern point of origin the Black mountains extend without break or interruption for more than one hundred miles, with a trend a little west of north. They constantly approach nearer to the Colorado, and cross it below the mouth of the Virgen, forming the walls of the Black cañon.

This range of mountains is of peculiar interest, from the difference which its trend exhibits from that of most of the mountain chains crossing the Colorado below. Like the Cerbat mountains, a range parallel to and eastward of this, it approaches quite as nearly to the trend of the

Wahsatch mountains as to that of the Sierra Nevada system. Its geological relations are also interesting, from the fact that it forms the first of the series of steps by which the ascent is made from the trough of the Colorado to the surface of the high table-lands occupying the central portion of the continent.

The intimate structure of the Black mountains does not differ essentially from that of some of the ranges which have already been described; particularly that upon which Chimney Peak is set. As a whole, it is characterized by a predominance of rocks of a distinctly eruptive character, such as massive granite, trap, porphyry, and trachyte, and the rarity of gneiss, mica slate, clay slates, &c., which are probably metamorphic.

That portion of the range which forms the eastern boundary of the Mojave valley is composed principally of trap, trachyte, and porphyry, of which the prevailing dark colors have suggested the name given to the entire chain. Further north its composition is more varied, embracing granite, porphyries, trachytes, and tufas in great variety, whose colors are scarcely less striking than those of the Purple Hills.

DEAD MOUNTAIN.

On the west side of the river, near the north end of the Mojave valley, is a high and picturesque mountain, which forms a prominent landmark for all this region. This mountain is supposed by the Mojaves to be the dwelling-place of their disembodied spirits, and hence it has received the name it bears. From this great mass, as a starting point, a continuous mountain chain stretches to the northwest, in harmony with the other ranges of the Sierra Nevada system which we have already described. A spur from Dead mountain extends across to the Black mountains, forming the northern limit of the Mojave valley. This valley is bounded on the west by a range of granitic mountains, which, at first sight, seems to be a spur running off towards the northwest from Dead mountain, but which is, in fact, formed by several distinct lines of upheaval parallel with that of the Dead mountain range, and of which the southeastern termini are *en echelon*. Dead mountain, like all those on the west side of the Mojave valley, is composed mainly of granite. This is generally white and massive, highly felspathic, and frequently friable. In some localities it is gneissoid, and is associated with clay slate, mica slate, &c. In several places low hills of trap and scoria rise near the base of the range.

PYRAMID CAÑON.

As has been stated, a spur from the Dead mountains crosses the Colorado, forming the northern boundary of the Mojave valley. The river cutting through this range has produced Pyramid cañon, a name suggested by a remarkable monument-like pinnacle of porphyritic rock which crowns the left bank near the northern entrance. This range has nowhere a great altitude, nor does the cañon cut through it bear comparison, in point of magnitude, with several others which we traversed. Yet, in this locality, I was furnished with the most satisfactory proof of the truth of the theory I have advanced to explain the mode of formation of the cañons of the Colorado. The walls of Pyramid cañon are, for the most part, formed of massive granite, which exhibit perpendicular faces two hundred feet or more in height. On either side of the stream, among the summits of the granite hills, full two hundred and fifty feet above its bed, are masses of stratified gravel, identical in composition, and continuous with the gravel terraces which border the river both above and below the cañon. Here, then, we have conclusive evidence that where now is Pyramid cañon was once an unbroken barrier, stretching across the course of the Colorado, and raising its waters to an elevation of at least two hundred and fifty feet above their present level. This barrier has been cut through by the action of the river, but these beds of gravel and sand remain as monuments of the time when the valley above Pyramid cañon, as well as that of the Mojaves below, were in great part covered by sheets of water.

Similar deposits would doubtless have been found on the sides of the other cañons of the Colorado; but such accumulations have generally, from the greater height of the barrier, been less in quantity, longer exposed to atmospheric degradation, and, as a consequence, have disappeared.

COTTONWOOD VALLEY.

For some miles above Pyramid cañon the river flows through an area which, though occupying the space between mountains on the east and west, scarcely deserves the name of valley. Granitic masses connected with the Dead mountain form the immediate or remote bank on the west side, while on the east a succession of gravel terraces rise abruptly from the water's edge, and extend in table-topped hills to the base of the Black mountains.

These hills have been eroded from the mass of the terraces by the water which sometimes flows down through them from the summits of the mountains. The material which composes the gravel beds is usually considerably indurated, and cut, as they are, by water flowing from a distance, their erosion has assumed the form of a labyrinth of narrow ravines or cañons, of which the opposite perpendicular walls, though often one hundred feet in height, approach each other so closely that they may be touched at the same time by the outstretched hands.

In many localities the erosions of these Quaternary beds—for of this age I must regard them— have exposed underlying masses of porphyry, trap, or tufa similar to those visible in the higher parts of the Black mountains. Upon the irregular surface of these rocks the consolidated gravels are deposited in nearly horizontal stratification.

A section of the table-hills in this vicinity is as follows: The summit rock is a cream-colored limestone, six feet in thickness, nearly pure above, but becoming a breccia below. The structure of this limestone is waved, like that of ripple-marked clays or sandstones, and its upper surface is most curiously weathered, exhibiting on a great scale something of the same style of erosion as that of the blocks and pebbles of limestone collected on the desert. Usually it presents a naked surface, without soil, upon which, here and there, rest large boulders of black basalt or scoria. Of the few rolled pebbles observed upon it, some were of Carboniferous limestone, and had evidently been transported from a great distance. I observed no fossils in this rock, but there is little doubt that it is of lacustrine origin.

Below the limestone is a succession of strata of indurated gravel, or conglomerate beds of coarse or fine, rounded or angular, fragments of rock, enveloped in sand and cemented by lime. There is much less clay in this series here than in any similar deposits observed below, showing that the currents which deposited them were comparatively rapid. The variety in the composition of the bars in the present river in different parts of its course is dependent on the same cause. Here they are of gravel; lower down, of sand, and at the mouth, of clay.

The boulders and angular fragments included in these conglomerates exhibit great diversity of composition, and have been derived from widely different sources. They may be classed as follows:

First. Angular blocks of all sizes of porphyry in endless variety, granite, sienite, trap, scoria, trachyte, &c., brought down formerly, as now, from the adjacent mountains.

Second. Smaller rolled boulders and pebbles of limestone, generally fossiliferous, but sometimes metamorphic. The most common is a blue unchanged limestone, of Carboniferous age, containing crinoidal columns of large size, *Productus*, *Spirifer*, and *Pecten*, with *Fenestella* and many corals. These, as our subsequent explorations demonstrated, were derived from the Carboniferous limestones of the Great Cañon of the Colorado; the limestone boulders without fossils representing the strata which underlie the Carboniferous series.

Third. Rolled pebbles of quartz, jasper, silicious slates, granite, carnelian, &c., which have been transported from a great distance. Many of these are derived from the Black cañon, especially the quartz and the granite with garnets. The jasper and carnelian are, principally, fragments of the masses of metamorphosed chert, so common in the limestones of the upper Colorado.

As far as observed, these conglomerates contain no fossils properly their own, except the silicified trunks of trees. These are abundant, generally broken; their extremities more or less rounded—as is usually the case with drift-wood—and are principally coniferous.

The trough which the Colorado has excavated in the series I have described is partially filled with accumulations of loose gravel of still more modern date. It is quite impossible to draw the line separating these two formations, although a long time must have elapsed between the eras of their deposition—the time occupied by the Colorado in deepening its bed two hundred feet.

I am disposed to class these conglomerates with the more recent Tertiaries; but resting, as they do, horizontally and undisturbed on the traps and porphyries of the Black mountains, rocks which have thrown up and metamorphosed the Tertiary strata, both above and below this locality, they may be more recent. The identity of composition which their enclosed pebbles exhibit with those of the modern gravel beds, though affording presumptive evidence of their common Quaternary age, is not entirely conclusive, as similar topographical features

Fig. 7.—HILLS OF TERTIARY CONGLOMERATE AND MODERN GRAVEL, CAMP 49.

were exhibited by this portion of the continent during the Tertiary era to those of the present epoch. The lines of drainage were, in general terms, the same, and, consequently, the sources from which transported materials were derived.

In several excursions to the base of the Black mountain range, made from our Camps 49, 50, 51, &c., I procured a very complete series of the rocks which compose these mountains. Among them the porphyries are very conspicuous, including at least a hundred varieties, of which some are unequalled in beauty by any I have elsewhere seen.

Cottonwood valley is formed by the continuation of the Black mountains on the east and north; by the Dead mountain range on the south and southwest; on the northwest by mountains extending into the desert, and which seem to connect the range which runs from Dead mountain with that part of the Black mountains lying west of the Colorado.   The area enclosed by these mountain chains, though large, contains but little level or alluvial land; none, indeed, except that embraced within the limits of Cottonwood valley; a narrow space near its centre, where the conglomerate bluffs recede for a few miles, permitting a growth of vegetation, conspicuous in which are many beautiful groups of cottonwoods.   These trees, at the time of our visit, (February 25,) clothed in the vivid verdure of their spring dress, afforded a most agreeable contrast to the surrounding sterility, and suggested the name given to the valley.

The alluvial bottom lands are bordered on every side by a broad inclined plain, which extends to the bases of the surrounding mountains, and gives a peculiar aspect to the scenery.   There is, however, nothing in the structure of Cottonwood valley radically different from that of the other subordinate basins of the Colorado.

The long slope which I have described as extending from the mountains to the river is only an exaggeration of the similar slope which borders the Mojave valley, and is visible on the sides and around the island-like mountains of the Colorado desert.

As we ascend the river the basins through which it flows become smaller, and the slopes formed by the debris of the mountains bear a constantly increasing ratio to the level surfaces of the gravel mesas.   On the Colorado desert the slopes of the mountains terminate below in level surfaces, which stretch away like the sea, till, perhaps, far beyond the limit of human vision, they meet similar slopes coming down from the opposite enclosing mountain wall.   As the basins narrow, however, the bases of the slopes are brought nearer and nearer each other, until they meet; when, if, as is usual, the basin is of elongated shape, a valley is formed whose sides slope from the bottom on either hand.   In Cottonwood valley the bases of the slopes are separated only by the bottom lands of the river, and from this centre they rise, with an inclination of 2° to 2° 30', to the mountains, from five to ten miles distant.   The amount of debris required to form these slopes proves that we now see only the stumps—if the expression is admissible—of the lofty mountains which once surrounded these areas.   The relief of the mountains has also been greatly reduced by the partial filling of the dividing valleys by the materials removed from their sides and summits.

MOUNT DAVIS.

Above Cottonwood valley is an interval of about twenty miles, extending to the entrance of Black cañon, which, though enclosed in the same great natural barriers with the area last described, is entirely without alluvial land, is set with several isolated mountains, and is traversed by many lines of upheaval, marked by protruded ridges or masses of volcanic rock. The first of these lines of disturbance crosses the Colorado, with a northwest trend, only four or five miles above the lodges of the Mojaves in Cottonwood valley.   The river has cut through this ridge in a cañon of limited extent, whose walls are nowhere more than a hundred feet in height, having none of the grandeur of many of the cañons of the Colorado; yet the variety and intensity of the colors which the rocks forming it display, render it one of the most picturesque and interesting of the series, and well deserving of the name (Painted cañon) given it.

The materials composing its walls are traps, trachytes, tufas, and porphyries; blue, white, brown, crimson, purple, &c., all the colors remarkably vivid, and the contrasts striking.

The detached mountains referred to are usually composed of trap.   They are nearly black in color, and, rising abruptly from the slopes which descend from the distant granitic chains, form peculiar features in the landscape.   They suggested comparisons, in the minds of different members of the party, with colossal whales, raising their black and massive heads above the ocean surface, or lines of Titanic elephants crossing a plain; either of which gives a good idea of their appearance.

Of these trappean mountains the most conspicuous is Mount Davis, which stands immediately on the left bank of the river. Like the others of the group it is composed of trachyte, tufa, porphyry, &c., covered by a thick mass of trap. In some cases this trap covering is horizontal; in others, as Mount Davis, it is highly inclined; its surface forming one of the slopes.

All this group of mountains have the appearance of being upheaved fragments of an ancient lava-plain, but their forms have been greatly modified by degradation, and I am rather disposed to regard them as only the remnants of broad rounded masses of erupted rock, each marking the sight of a volcanic vent, worn into the angular forms which they exhibit by the erosion to which they have been exposed.

Tertiary rocks.—The intervals between these trap mountains is occupied by a series of beds of indurated gravel, usually covered by detrital matter, forming the long slopes which have been referred to.

These gravels or conglomerates are similar to those exposed above Pyramid cañon, which I have considered as belonging to the later Tertiary epoch.

Fig. 8.—CASTLE-LIKE CONGLOMERATE BLUFF.

They are exposed in bluffs often one hundred and fifty feet high on both sides of the river, frequently eroded into strange imitative forms.

The strata of these cliffs are usually horizontal, but in many localities are more or less disturbed and metamorphosed, as in the westerly bend of the river between Camps 54 and 55.

Near the entrance to the Black cañon consolidated sands and gravel are seen in detached masses and patches, resting on the amygdaloid-trap, trachyte, &c., which compose the foothills of the Black mountains. Here they have been very extensively eroded—in most places entirely removed—leaving the underlying volcanic rocks exposed.

In the foot-hills of the same mountain, west of the river, the Tertiary rocks are very highly metamorphosed, and have been tossed about in great confusion. They consist of sandstones and shales, usually of deep blood-red color, with beds of conglomerate and white infusorial earth. They are broken through by masses of dark compact basalt, which has been poured over or forced between the strata, changing the protoxide of iron to the peroxide, and giving them, with their vivid colors, a considerable degree of hardness. The degree of metamorphosis which they exhibit is, however, generally so slight as to indicate that the beds of sand, clay, gravel, &c., were saturated, perhaps covered, with water at the time of the volcanic eruption. This is also indicated by the fact that the basalt, at the point of contact with the shale and sandstone, is converted into a highly cellular scoria, as though from steam driven out of the wet mass over which it was poured.

I did not find the Tertiary strata, in any locality, extending more than a few hundred feet up the sides of the mountains.

Fig. 9.—CLIFFS OF TERTIARY CONGLOMERATE, CAMP 54.

Quaternary deposits.—Covering the Tertiary series, sometimes even to the height of three hundred feet above the river, are beds of gravel and sand; similar to those which border the Colorado below. These beds are in some localities partially consolidated, and when resting conformably on the older gravels it is impossible to draw a dividing line between them. The same constituents form both series, and it is only where the influence of erupted masses is visible in the disturbance and consolidation of the older strata that they exhibit distinctive characters. We can only say, then, that at such a stage of the formation of the homogeneous, vertical column, volcanic eruptions occurred, by which the deposits already made were locally affected.

In the trough which the Colorado has excavated in the Tertiary formation, the accumulations of more recent materials are, in many places, very conspicuous, even where they have suffered great degradation, still showing a stratified series, at least one hundred and fifty feet in thickness.

The constituents of these Quaternary deposits are very like those which form the valley-drift below, but in our progress up the river the pebbles of sedimentary rock constantly increased in number and size. Here, near the southern entrance to the Black cañon, where the Colorado issues from the channel it has cut in the first of the volcanic barriers it meets in its course, and but few miles below the mouth of the Great Cañon, so long and so deeply eroded in sedimentary rocks, the pebbles of the gravel beds are as often limestone and chert, derived from the limestone or sandstone, as volcanic materials composing the walls of the adjacent cañon.

In the heaps of boulders, which in many places form the bars or banks of the river, I often noticed large rounded masses of Carboniferous limestone, which had been transported by the stream at least one hundred miles from their place of origin.

One of the best exposures of the Quaternary strata of this vicinity is at "Elephant Hill," between our Camps 56 and 57. This is a conical mound, about one hundred and fifty feet in height, which stands in a bend of the river, and is, at its base, continuous with bluffs composed of the same materials, forming the eastern boundary of the trough, in the bottom of which the present stream flows.

Fig. 10.—SECTION OF TROUGH OF COLORADO AT ELEPHANT HILL.

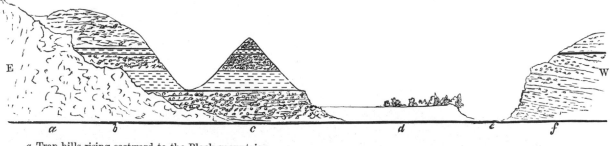

a Trap hills rising eastward to the Black mountains.
b Bluffs of stratified Quaternary, gravel, sand, &c.
c Elephant Hill.
d Alluvial bottom land.
e Bed of river.
f Tertiary conglomerates, inclined and covered with horizontal beds of gravel.

A point of peculiar interest, connected with the structure of Elephant Hill, was the finding of a very large and perfect tooth of *Elephas primigenius* in the bed of coarse gravel and boulders which forms its base.

A section of Elephant Hill from summit to base is as follows:

1. Gravel and sand, twenty feet.
2. Sand and clay, eight feet.
3. Gravel, forty feet.
4. Sandy clay, thirty-five feet.
5. Gravel and boulders with elephant's tooth, fifty feet.

This lower bed is consolidated into a coarse conglomerate by calcareous infiltration. The stratification is entirely parallel with that of the adjacent bluffs, so that there is no room for the supposition that the material of the gravel beds has been re-arranged, as so often occurs in valley-drift, since its deposition. It is evident, therefore, that the elephant's tooth is older than the hundred feet of gravel and sand which overlie it.

As the bed of the Colorado is here constantly deepening, while at its mouth it is rising, and has been for ages moving towards the west, we can only explain the formation of beds of stratified sediment, boulders, &c., of so great thickness, and the occurrence of such a fossil near the base of the series, by supposing that the surface of the water of the Colorado was, at one time, two hundred feet or more above its present level, while in this locality the bottom was nearly as low as it now is. With the great depth of water here recorded, we should hardly expect a velocity adequate to the transportation of the large rounded boulders by which the elephant's tooth is surrounded; but it must be borne in mind that Elephant Hill is scarcely two miles from the stupendous gateway which forms the southern entrance to the Black cañon, of which the walls rise in perpendicular precipices of porphyry from 800 to 1,200 feet in height. When the Colorado began the task of cutting down the gigantic wall at the point where its accumulated waters, in greater volume than now, poured down its southwestern declivity, the cascade which it formed must have surpassed any similar exhibition of Nature's forces of which we have knowledge at the present day. The legitimate and inevitable effect of such a cascade would be to excavate a deep basin or channel at its foot; and subsequently, as the fall was diminished, to fill that excavation with boulders of gravel and sand.

Fig. 11.—ELEPHANT HILL FROM CAMP 55.

I shall refer again to the interesting geological features of the vicinity of the entrance to Black cañon in treating of the surface geology of the country bordering the upper Colorado. In that connexion, the discussion of the erosions to which I have referred, as well as the indications of a diminution of the water flowing in this stream, and the former existence of elephants in a region now too much of a desert to sustain such animals, will find an appropriate place.

BLACK CAÑON.

This magnificent cañon has been so frequently referred to in the preceding pages that but little more need be said of it. It is formed by the passage of the Colorado through the Black mountain range, the most formidable obstacle to its course that we had thus far observed. This chain is here about twenty miles wide, and the cañon, which cuts it diagonally, about twenty-five miles in length; its northern entrance being a short distance below the mouth of the Rio Virgen. Throughout the entire interval between its northern and southern termini the cañon holds the same general character. Nearly perpendicular walls rise on either side to the height of a thousand feet or more, with few interruptions and no open valleys or alluvial land. The structure of the Black mountains is here scarcely different from what it has been described to be below. Masses of granite are exposed at several points in its section, but in magnitude they are far surpassed by the towering heaps of trap, porphyry, trachyte, &c., &c., which make up the bulk of the chain.

Probably nowhere in the world is there a finer display of rocks of volcanic origin than may be seen about the southern entrance to the cañon. The beetling crags which form its massive portals are composed of dark-brown porphyry of hardest and most resistant character. Just within the cañon, on the west side of the river, this porphyry is mingled with huge convoluted masses of light-brown trachyte; tufa, pure white or white veined with crimson, and pale blue obsidian, (pearl-stone); amygdaloids of various kinds, their cavities filled with different zeolites; black and gray basalts, sometimes columnar; scoria, red, orange, green, or black, and of every grade of texture; porphyries in great variety, including some of unequalled beauty; trachytes and tufas of all colors; obsidian in its various forms; all these are abundantly exposed in the immediate vicinity.

Five miles west of the cañon are some hills, composed of soft amygdaloid, everywhere traversed by crevices lined with beautiful specimens of opalescent chalcedony, and rosettes of crystals of quartz which have a stellar arrangement. The soft trap rock having been weathered away, these silicious minerals are left covering the surface and sparkling in the sunshine like so many diamonds.

The view of the western slope of the Black mountains which we obtained from the summits bordering the cañon is scarcely equalled, in its wild savage grandeur, by any I have elsewhere seen. A thousand subordinate pinnacles spring from the mountain side, all displaying the ragged outlines which the materials composing them are so prone to assume, while their colors are as striking and varied as their forms. Not a particle of vegetation is visible in the landscape. Here and there a spiny cactus clings to the rocks, but its color blends with theirs, as its thorny and repulsive nature harmonizes with the forbidding features of the surrounding scenery.

As the eye of the traveller sweeps over this wilderness of sunburnt summits, which stand so stark and still, glittering in the burning sunlight and yet so desolate, he shrinks from the unearthly scene with a feeling of depression which must be felt to be imagined.

Rock salt.—On the banks of a tributary of the Rio Virgen, a few miles from the Colorado, the Indians obtain large quantities of rock salt. Much of it is very pure and beautifully crystallized, and it is said to exist in immense quantities. I regret that I was unable to visit the locality and determine its geological position. Gypsum also occurs in the vicinity in abundance.

I suspect the rocks which contain these minerals are not older than the Tertiary, but it is possible that the Secondary strata, which are so largely developed east of the Little Colorado, and which contain so much salt and gypsum, recur on the Rio Virgen.

CHAPTER V.

GENERAL VIEW OF THE STRUCTURE OF THE GREAT CENTRAL PLATEAU.

Common geological character of all the country between the Mississippi and Colorado —Source and course of the upper Colorado.—Table-lands between Rocky mountains and Cerbats.—Great cañon.—Geological elements of its section.—Basin of the little Colorado —Its outlines and structure.—Ancient granitic barriers which limit it.—High mesa about San Francisco mountain —Valley of the little Colorado.—Structure of mesa bounding it on the north and east.—Cretaceous mesa of the Moquis villages.—Great white mesa resting on the last.—Snowy mesa bordering the Colorado.—Origin of the peculiar topography of the table-lands.—Referred to a vast system of erosion.—All the cañons of western New Mexico due to aqueous action.—Mesa walls, boundaries of broad valleys of erosion.—Area and limits of the palæozoic continent.—Sources of the sediments forming the strata of the table-lands and conditions of their deposition.—Outlines of North American continent approximately defined in the earliest palæozoic ages.

The geology of the country traversed by our party east of the great bend of the Colorado may be conveniently considered in several distinct sections, as there are embraced in this vast region a number of well-marked geographical districts, of which the geological features are, in some respects, peculiar, and are not repeated. And yet these different districts form but parts of the great central plateau of the continent, and the relations which the structure of each part sustains to that of the other portions of the geological arch—if I may use the simile—which spans the interval between the lower Colorado and the Mississippi are such, that it is quite as important it should be studied as a part of a great whole as in its local and minor details.

I shall take the liberty, therefore, of anticipating in some degree my geological narrative, and give very briefly here, as the most convenient and appropriate place, the results of a line of observation carried quite across this great plateau, of which the geological structure is so clearly revealed in the magnificent sections of the banks of the Colorado, not very far distant from the point we had reached at the close of the last chapter.

The Colorado rises in a thousand sources, at an elevation of from ten to twelve thousand feet above the sea, on the western side of the Rocky mountains. Descending from their fountain-heads its tributaries fall upon a high plateau of sedimentary rocks, which forms the western base of these mountains and occupies all the interval between them and the great bend of the Colorado, where the river enters the volcanic district already described. From that point its course trends northeasterly into Utah, where its outline has not been traced. Southward it follows the trend of the Black and Cerbat mountains, which bound it on the southwest, and extends far into Mexico. In the intervals between the ranges of the Rocky mountain system portions of the same "mesa" are seen, often much disturbed, and flanking the axes of the comparatively modern lines of elevation.

East of the mountains it still continues, forming the high prairies which everywhere skirt their bases. Cut into somewhat detached plateaus by the streams flowing from the mountains, a belt of country in that region has been designated by the name of the "high table-lands;" but there is no well-defined geographical area to which that name is strictly applicable, as the most remarkable unity, both of topographical and geological structure, prevails over the entire area of the "plains," which reach from the mountains to the Mississippi. The geological elements which compose the great table-lands of the Colorado here reappear, exhibiting the same harmonious stratification. The strata all dip very greatly eastward, and form the western slope of the great Mississippi valley.

That portion of the central plateau which lies west of the Rocky mountains varies in elevation from 5,000 to 8,000 feet; the smaller number representing the altitude of its surface where deeply eroded. Its average altitude, in the vicinity of our route, may be estimated at 6,000 feet.

Over this plateau the Colorado formerly flowed for at least 500 miles of its course, but, in the lapse of ages, its rapid current has cut its bed down through all the sedimentary strata and several hundred feet into the granite base on which they rest.

For 300 miles the cut edges of the table-lands rise abruptly, often perpendicularly, from the water's edge, forming walls from 3,000 to 6,000 feet in height. This is the "Great Cañon of the Colorado," the most magnificent gorge, as well as the grandest geological section, of which we have any knowledge.

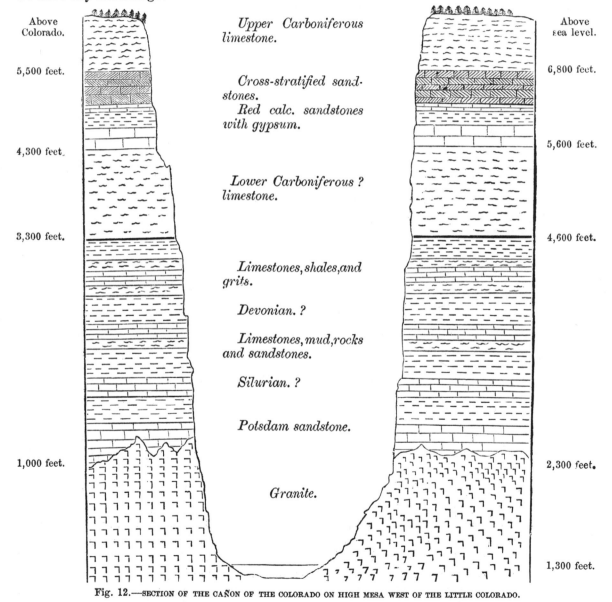

Fig. 12.—SECTION OF THE CAÑON OF THE COLORADO ON HIGH MESA WEST OF THE LITTLE COLORADO.

That portion of the table-lands lying between the mouth of the Virgen and the Little Colorado is composed of over 4,000 feet of sedimentary rocks, representing the Silurian, Devonian, and Carboniferous epochs.

The Silurian and Devonian strata are entirely conformable among themselves and with the

Carboniferous rocks. They lie nearly horizontally upon the granite, forming a series of sandstones, limestones, and shales, about 2,000 feet in thickness. The Carboniferous series consists of over 2,000 feet of limestones, sandstones, and gypsum, apparently all marine, and often highly fossiliferous. The upper members of the latter series form the surface of the mesas west of the Little Colorado, upon which the volcanic group of the San Francisco mountains rest as a base.

North of the Colorado, near the Mormon town of Parawan, it is said that the true coal measures make their appearance, with workable beds of coal, but south of the river an open sea existed during the entire Carboniferous epoch; the "Mountain limestone" appearing, if at all, in the cañon of the Colorado, and the Coal measures being represented here—as is the case further eastward in New Mexico—by massive beds of limestones heretofore considered, as I think erroneously, the equivalents of the Lower Carboniferous or "Mountain limestone."

The strata composing the plateau bordering the Great and Little Colorados by their dip form an elongated basin, of which the greatest diameter extends from the Mogollon mountains northwesterly into Utah. The Great Colorado crosses that line nearly at right angles; the course of the Little Colorado being parallel to and locally coincident with it. Near the western margin of the basin some of the older sedimentary strata are seen dipping eastward, resting on the flanks of the mountain chains which I have described as bounding the plateau in that direction. They here present bold escarpments towards the west, oftener the result of erosion than fracture. They have evidently been elevated by the upheaval of the plutonic rocks upon which they rest, but as they are usually quite unchanged, the igneous rocks could not then have been in a state of fusion, but were themselves the products of anterior eruptions. The oldest Palæozoic rocks are nowhere, on our route, included in the elevated escarpments to which I have referred; and in the Great Cañon the lower members of the series are seen deposited around, and abutting against, pinnacles and ridges of granite, which seem to be spurs from the Cerbat or Aztec mountains. Hence it appears that the mountain chains which bound the plateau on the west existed, at least in embryo, before the dawn of the Palæozoic period, and formed a barrier which, to a great degree, limited the deposition of the Silurian and Devonian strata to the basin-like area lying east of them.

The same phenomena recur on the other side of the plateau, near the Rio Grande, where the Carboniferous strata are upheaved in many places, and are seen to rest directly upon the granite. The absence of the older rock in both instances is doubtless dependent upon a common cause.

As has been mentioned, I am inclined to suspect that some of the strata composing the great plateau recur on the western side of the Black mountains, beneath the Tertiaries of the synclinal trough of the Colorado basin; and that fused, they form some of the porphyries, trachytes, &c., which characterize the mountain chains of that region.

The Silurian and Devonian sandstones are not recognizable in any of the metamorphosed strata of the Peninsular Sierra, (nor are any of the rocks of the table-lands, unless perhaps the Carboniferous limestone,) though they may be represented by the foliated granites and schists. It is quite possible, therefore, that the sediments derived from the erosion of the land during the older Palæozoic periods, did not extend so far into the ocean which bordered it on the west.

In crossing the table-lands in a direction from southwest to northeast, or nearly in the line of the transverse diameter of the trough formed by the strata, I obtained a section, of which the general features are as follows: Leaving the lower Colorado, where its bed is less than 500 feet above the sea level, we crossed three mountain chains, of which the eastern bases are, respectively, many hundred feet higher than the western. When we had passed the third of these ranges, at an elevation of nearly 5,000 feet, we found ourselves on Lower Carboniferous strata, of which the upturned and broken edges form part of the crest of the mountains. They thence extend eastward in a plateau, having a distinct dip in that direction.

This plateau is locally much broken and covered by floods of lava, which have flowed from the mountains we had passed; and yet, from commanding points of view, we could see that it had a distinct existence, stretching far away as a margin to the mountains, in a northwesterly direction. It is bounded on the east by a wall several hundred feet in height—in many places perpendicular, and generally abrupt—formed by the cut edge of a portion of the Middle Carboniferous series. Having ascended this wall, we found our view again limited on the east by the bold escarpments of the edge of another and much higher mesa, which, with its salient angles, stretched away in magnificent perspective, both to the north and south.

The surface of this mesa has an altitude of nearly 7,000 feet, due in part to a line of upheaval, which traverses it with a trend nearly N.NW. and S.SE. It is composed of the Upper Carboniferous strata; the later members of that series forming the surface rock of a broad belt of country extending, from a point southeast of the San Francisco mountain, northwest across the Colorado into Utah.

The great volcanic vent of the last-mentioned mountain has been opened up through this mesa, and has doubtless been an important agent in its elevation. Apparently little disruption has been occasioned by it, but the floods of lava and heaps of ashes which have been thrown out of its many flues cover and conceal the underlying sedimentary strata in its vicinity.

The surface rock of the high mesa dips rapidly toward the northeast, and forms the western slope of the broad valley of erosion through which the drainage of the northern declivities of the Mogollon and San Francisco mountains was formerly carried to the Colorado; and of which the surface is now cut by the profound chasms, in the inaccessible depths of which flow Cascade river, and, through a part of its course, the Little Colorado.

The opposite side of this valley is formed by a third mesa wall, which at the crossing of the Little Colorado is, with the slope at its base, at least 1,000 feet in height. This mesa is composed of deep-red sandstones, shales, and conglomerates, resting conformably on the Upper Carboniferous limestone, over which is a series of variegated marls, with bands of magnesian limestone. The latter series forms the surface of the mesa for many miles towards the northeast, and has an aggregate thickness of perhaps 1,500 feet.

The variegated marls and the underlying red sandstones are all regarded as Triassic by Mr. Marcou; but the marls exhibit a remarkable lithological identity from top to bottom, and the upper portion contain plants of Jurassic affinities. Without more fossils from these formations it seems to me, at least doubtful whether we can draw the lines of classification as sharply as he has done; and it would even be a little surprising if there should ever be found good palæontological evidence for the identification of all the European subdivisions of the Permian, Triassic, Jurassic, and Chalk, of which he claims to have demonstrated the existence in this vicinity.

Upon the mesa of the variegated marls at the Moquis villages rises still another, to the height of 800 or 900 feet, composed of coarse yellow sandstones, green shales, and beds of lignite—a group of strata which has been called Jurassic, but which contain impressions of dicotyledonous leaves, with *Ammonites*, *Gryphœa*, and *Inoceramus* of Cretaceous species. These fossils leave no room for doubt in reference to the age of the strata which contain them, but prove them to be Lower Cretaceous.

This mesa is, geologically and physically, the highest which we actually passed over on our route west of the Rocky mountains. Near Fort Defiance its summit has an altitude of nearly 8,000 feet. It should also be said that basin-shaped depressions on this mesa contain fresh-water Tertiary strata, both east and west of the great "divide." At the Moquis villages the strata forming the table-lands begin to rise toward the east, and near Fort Defiance they plainly show the disturbing influence of the most westerly axis of elevation of the Rocky mountain system. Further east, to and beyond the Rio Grande, they are much dislocated, and finally lose their distinctive character in the intricacies of the mountain ranges.

In the interval between Fort Defiance and the Rio Grande is another great volcanic mountain—Mt. Taylor ("San Mateo")—which, like that of San Francisco, has burst through the sedimentary strata and poured over them floods of lava, which are as fresh as though ejected but yesterday.

I have said that the Lower Cretaceous mesa was the highest of the table-lands which we passed over, and yet another must be added to the series before my description of them will be complete.

On our route across the continent we passed somewhat south of the centre of what we may, perhaps, properly call the basin of the upper Colorado, and did not therefore mount quite to the summit of its geological series. Going north from the Moquis villages, on the Lower Cretaceous mesa, our progress was arrested by a want of water; the surface being everywhere cut by deep cañons, by which it is drained to excess; every rain drop which falls finding its way immediately into the bottom of these ravines, where it is hurried off to the far deeper cañons of the Colorado and its larger tributaries. Before we turned back, however, we had approached nearly to the base of a wall rising abruptly from the mesa in which we stood to the height of more than 1,000 feet. This wall was as white as chalk, and reflected the sunlight like a bank of snow. It is evidently the edge of another and higher plateau, and apparently reaches to the Great Colorado, where it caps the "high mesa," forming part of the stupendous mural faces, presented toward the south and west, which were distinctly visible when we had receded from them to the distance of a hundred miles.

What is the character of this upper mesa I had no means of determining at this time, and even now there may be some question about it; but I have scarcely a doubt that it is composed of the Upper Cretaceous strata, the equivalents of the "white chalk" of Europe.

EROSION OF THE TABLE-LANDS.

The sketch which has been given of the table-lands of the upper Colorado, though brief, will perhaps suffice to convey an idea of the generalities of their structure and relations. But before returning to the details of the local geology of our route, I ought perhaps to refer briefly to two questions of general import, which would naturally suggest themselves to any geologist who should traverse the table-lands west of the Rocky mountains, or should receive an accurate description of them from others.

The first of these questions is: To what cause is due the peculiar topographical features of the surface of the table-lands—where the different formations succeed each other in a series of steps, which generally present abrupt and wall-like edges—the more recent strata occupying the highest portion of the plateau? The other has reference to the place and extent of the dry land, of which the erosion furnished the sediments now composing the table-lands.

The first of these questions belongs appropriately to the subject of surface geology, and will be referred to again. I may say here, however, that, like the great cañons of the Colorado, the broad valleys bounded by high and perpendicular walls *belong to a vast system of erosion, and are wholly due to the action of water*. Probably nowhere in the world has the action of this agent produced results so surprising, both as regards their magnitude and their peculiar character. It is not at all strange that a cause, which has given, to what was once an immense plain, underlaid by thousands of feet of sedimentary rocks, conformable throughout, a topographical character more complicated than that of any mountain chain; which has made much of it absolutely impassable to man, or any animal but the winged bird, should be regarded as something out of the common course of nature. Hence the first and most plausible explanation of the striking surface features of this region will be to refer them to that embodiment of resistless power—the sword that cuts so many geological knots—volcanic force. The Great Cañon of the Colorado would be considered a vast fissure or rent in the earth's crust, and the abrupt termination of the steps of the table-lands as marking lines of displacement. This theory though so plausible, and so entirely adequate to explain all the striking phenomena, lacks a single requisite to acceptance, and that is *truth*.

Aside from the slight local disturbance of the sedimentary rocks about the San Francisco mountain, from the spurs of the Rocky mountains, near Fort Defiance, to those off the Cerbat and Aztec mountains on the west, the strata of the table-lands are as entirely unbroken as when first deposited. Having this question constantly in mind, and examining with all possible care the structure of the great cañons which we entered, I everywhere found evidence of the exclusive action of water in their formation. The opposite sides of the deepest chasm showed perfect correspondence of stratification, conforming to the general dip, and nowhere displacement; and the bottom rock, so often dry and bare, was perhaps deeply eroded, but continuous from side to side, a portion of the yet undivided series lying below.

The mesa walls should be included in the same category with those of the cañons; some times indeed they are but the sides of cañons miles in breadth. The origin of the series of escarpments which are met with in crossing the table-lands from west to east, is I think dependent upon very general but yet appreciable causes, to which I can here however but briefly allude.

From the Cerbat mountains to the base of the high mesa the strata composing the table-lands have a northeasterly dip of about 100 feet to the mile. There they rise, but soon dip again into the valley of the Little Colorado, their strike being nearly at right angles with the course of the great draining stream, the Colorado. By a glance at the map it will be seen that the water shed made up of the San Francisco group the Mogollon, and spurs of the Rocky mountains, which throws the water into the Colorado over the table-lands from the south, southeast, and east, forms a semicircle imperfectly parallel with the course of the Colorado, into which the drainage from the different parts of this semicircle falls nearly at right angles. The flow of water from the mountains has therefore been here, as before, along the strike of the strata, north and northwest from the San Francisco and Mogollon mountains, on the western side of the basin. The legitimate and inevitable effect of this combination of causes has been to erode the softer down to the harder strata, forming broad valleys bounded on the west by the denuded slope of the harder rocks; on the east, by the abrupt wall of the softer strata, most precipitous when capped by harder material. The erosion, for the most part produced by water flowing from a distant source, has taken place only at the bottom of each trough on the harder material, and thus has preserved the abruptness of the wall.—(See Section, p. 77.)

This theory fully explains the erosion of the Carboniferous strata near Diamond and Cascade rivers, and the formation of the mesa wall of the Gypsiferous rocks bordering the valley of the Little Colorado.

The Cretaceous mesas near the Moquis villages are eroded by the drainage from the spurs of the Rocky mountain system north of Fort Defiance; also across the strike of the strata, which here rise toward the southwest.

The absence of these strata from all the interval between the Moquis villages, and the borders of the basin on the southeast, south, southwest, and west, indicate the immense erosion which the region has suffered. It is, however, more than probable that as the basin was partially filled by the older rocks, the area over which the more recent strata were deposited became more and more restricted.

West of Fort Defiance and east of the Moquis villages, in "Cañon Bonita," Navajo valley, &c., we have examples of erosion, similar in all their general features to those already described, produced by streams running nearly north and south, and emptying into the Little Colorado. So near their sources these streams had less volume and power than farther westward, and have not so deeply scoured the plateau.

I use the past participle in speaking of some of the streams whose erosive action has been so marked, from the remarkable fact that many of these eroded valleys are now dry; and in others the present streams are but miniature representatives of those which formerly flowed in their channels.

Everything indicates that the table-lands were formerly much better watered than they now are.

AREA AND LIMITS OF THE PALÆOZOIC CONTINENT.

The question of the origin of the sediments composing the stratified rocks of the table-lands of the Colorado can scarcely be intelligently discussed till we know more than we now do of the geology of a large area lying north of the Colorado, and of the broad and compound belt of mountains, which we have covered by a single name, (Rocky mountains,) but which, when carefully studied, will probably not be found to form a geological unity.

This much, however, we can fairly infer from the observations already made on the geological structure of the far west, viz: That the outlines of the western part of the North American continent were approximately marked out from the earliest Palæozoic times; not simply by areas of shallower water in an almost boundless ocean, but by groups of islands and broad continental surfaces of dry land.

Since the erosion of rocks is always subaerial, or at least never takes place more than forty feet below the ocean surface, it follows that to form the stratified rocks of only that portion of the great central plateau which borders the Colorado, an island 300 miles in diameter, and at least 6,000 feet high, or, what is more probable, a continent of six times that area and 1,000 feet high, was worn down by the action of waves and rains, and in the form of sediments, sand, gravel, clay or lime, deposited on the sea bottom.

When we reflect that, with the exception of narrow wedges of erupted material in the mountains, an area having, on the 36th parallel, the breadth of the entire distance between the great bend of the Colorado and the Mississippi, (1,200 miles,) and a great, though yet unmeasured extension north and south is occupied by several thousand feet of Palæozoic and Secondary strata, we must conclude that these sediments have not been derived from the erosion of emerged surfaces east of the Mississippi, but here formed by the incessant action of the Pacifi waves on shores that perhaps for hundreds of miles succumbed to their power and by broad and rapid rivers which flowed from the mountains and through the fertile valleys of a primeval Atlantis.

I have already alluded to the absence of the Silurian and Devonian rocks from the sections on the flanks of the Rocky mountain axes in New Mexico, while they occur in great thickness in the sections of the ca on of the Colorado, and that they were deposited around, and abutting in horizontal stratification against, the granitic spurs of the mountains bounding the table-lands on the west; and further, that the axes of these mountains are on the east side flanked by Carboniferous strata resting on the granite; the Silurian and Devonian rocks being absent. These facts show that the older Palæozoic strata were deposited in a trough or basin bounded on the east and west by granitic mountains which rose above the ocean's surface.

The Potsdam (?) sand stone which is largely developed in the Great Cañon is a coarse silicious rock that must have been derived from the erosion of land at no great distance.

It is true that the Silurian, Devonian, and Lower Carboniferous limestones are, where I examined them, nearly destitute of fossils, and seem to be deep-sea deposits, but shore lines would doubtless, by proper search, be found, where fossils are abundant, within a few miles of the localities where these strata are exposed on our route.

It would seem that in that vicinity (mouth of Diamond river) the water shoaled by the deposition of the sediments forming the older rocks, as the overlying Carboniferous strata abound in fossils, and one of the members of that series, a sandstone, everywhere affords striking evidence of current action in its cross stratification.

In harmony with this fact is the occurrence of true coal measures with beds of coal, indicating emerged land at that epoch, north of the Colorado, at no great distance from this locality.

Hence the theory generally received that the formation of the continent began in a nucleus about Lake Superior, and that the places of the Rocky and California mountains were, until the Tertiary period, occupied by an open sea is proved untenable.

CHAPTER VI.

GEOLOGY OF THE COUNTRY BETWEEN THE MOJAVE VALLEY AND THE LITTLE COLORADO.

Descending the Colorado to the first pass through the Black mountains, at the upper end of the Mojave valley, thence striking northeast to the mouth of Diamond river, and going thence eastward to Cascade river and to San Francisco mountain, we found the geology of our route to present the following features:

MOJAVE VALLEY.

Quaternary deposits.—From the immediate banks of the Colorado, the trail which we followed led some twelve miles up the gentle slope which I have described as bordering the river on either side in this valley, and extending to the bases of the mountains.

This surface really deserves the name of desert throughout its extent; the narrow bottom-lands being immediately succeeded by bluffs of Quaternary gravel, of which the slopes and summits, though when we passed covered with a most brilliant array of spring flowers, usually sustain no vegetation, except here and there a dwarfed bush of *Larrea* or a clump of prickly *Opuntia*. After the ephemeral influence of the few spring showers has passed, the annual plants are soon burned up by the sun's heat, and perfect sterility prevails throughout the remainder of the season.

Tertiary strata.—The Quaternary gravels, transported by the river or brought down from the neighboring mountains, cover most of this slope, and compose the greater part of its mass near the river. As we approached the bases of the mountains, however, we found a series of Tertiary strata—tufaceous limestone, sand, gravel, &c.—exposed in all the ravines, and forming the first of the foot-hills. These strata closely resemble those occurring at Camp 49, above Pyramid cañon, but are composed of a larger proportion of volcanic materials, some of the beds being little else than stratified volcanic ashes.

They are considerably disturbed, and bear testimony to violent volcanic action both during and subsequent to their deposition. I was not able to detect any traces of fossils in any of the beds examined.

BLACK MOUNTAINS.

Where we crossed them these mountains are composed entirely of erupted rocks—porphyries, amygdaloid, basalt, trachyte, &c.—similar to those so fully represented in my collections from the vicinity of Camp 49. The vivid colors of these rocks, and the picturesque pinnacles and castellated summits which they form, so characteristic of this range, are here quite as conspicuous as in the localities where they have been heretofore described.

On the eastern declivities of the mountains we find large surfaces strewed with concretionary and botryoidal masses of chalcedony, agate, and crystallized quartz of different colors, and frequently of great beauty. Cartloads of specimens, which would be highly prized by mineralogists, might be collected there. These minerals have been formed in the crevices and cavities of a soft and very cellular amygdaloid, which has been much decomposed, and the silicious minerals now strew its surfaces.

The eastern foot-hills of the Black mountains are generally composed of basaltic trap, which is frequently columnar, and they are remarkable for the prevalence of a peculiar form which they exhibit. A number of them are crowned by castle-like summits of columnar trap, having perpendicular faces, from the base of which a glacis, perhaps of several hundred feet, slopes off uniformly on either side.

Tertiary strata.—Among these foot-hills are many masses of sandstone and tufaceous conglomerate, probably of Tertiary age, and very similar to those which skirt the western base of the range.

The sandstones, where unchanged, are yellow and soft, and have been eroded into striking imitative forms. In some localities these strata are much metamorphosed; the tufaceous conglomerate containing great quantities of onyx in nodular masses, which have been infiltrated into its cavities. This rock, under these circumstances, presents almost precisely the appearance of that containing onyx, &c., and metamorphosed by the action of thermal springs on the banks of Warm Chuck river, Des Chutes basin, Oregon.*

LONG VALLEY.

This is an interval of nearly level land some fifteen miles wide, lying between the Black mountains and the next succeeding range on the east. It extends north nearly to the Colorado, and communicates with the Mojave valley at its southern extremity. It is parallel to and somewhat resembles the Mojave valley, but is much higher, (2,000 feet,) and is now traversed by no permanent stream, though there is every indication that a river of some size once flowed through it. It is quite possible that all or a part of the Colorado once found its way southward through this channel.

This plain forms the first step in the ascent to the table-lands; and is probably in part underlaid by the Tertiary sandstones and conglomerates which form the hills on its western margin where we descended from the Black mountains.

CERBAT MOUNTAINS.

Long valley is bordered on the east by hills of trap and coarse gray granite, which form the approaches to a range of mountains having a trend nearly parallel to that of the Black mountains, but rising much higher, at the time of our visit (March 26) its summits being covered with snow. The highest portion of this range—a huge granitic mass, southeast of Camp 62—is visible from a long distance, and is a prominent landmark in all this region. At this point the range, apparently homogeneous southward, increases in breadth and altitude, then falls off to the north and divides into two distinct ranges, our route crossing above the bifurcation.

The western range is principally composed of trap, trachyte, and porphyry, but all having a very different aspect from those of the Black mountains.

With the masses of these rocks, which are the immediate product of fusion, occurs a series of stratified tufas and conglomerates which have been buried beneath floods of molten matter, and to which they are in some places so closely assimilated by metamorphosis as to be with difficulty identified.

These beds are apparently composed of volcanic materials, principally ashes, stratified by

---

* Pacific Railroad Report, Vol. VI, Part 2, page 49.

water. They are probably of Tertiary age, and the equivalents of the sandstones and conglomerates of the opposite side of the valley, from which they differ only from the proximity of volcanic force during the period of deposition. Some of them are strikingly like the stratified tufas of the Des Chutes basin, Oregon, and are evidently the results of the same series of causes.

The pass by which we crossed this range is simply a cañada of erosion, through which the drainage of a portion of the plain bordering it on the east is carried down to the much lower one on the west.

Fig. 13.—CAÑADA OF EROSION THROUGH WESTERN RANGE OF THE CERBAT MOUNTAINS.

At our Camp 63, situated on the eastern base of the western range of the Cerbat mountains, the prevailing rock is a coarse gray, massive granite, which forms the highest summits in the vicinity, and here composes full half the mass of the chain; the remainder being compact and vesicular trap. The granite is in many places intersected by large veins of quartz, containing iron, and perhaps other metallic minerals, though no others were noticed. Many of the trap hills, composed of scoriaceous and decomposable material, have been extensively eroded, and their surfaces are covered with masses of chalcedony and crystallized quartz, formerly contained in the fissures and cavities of that portion of the rock which has been removed. The scanty supply of water which we obtained from this range, though apparently flowing from granitic rocks, is so highly impregnated with salt as to be scarcely drinkable.

YAMPAI VALLEY.

This valley seems to be topographically a basin, there being no outlet by which it is completely drained. A large quantity of water poured into it would find exit by the cañada through which we ascended to it; but the lower portion of its surface is probably annually covered by water, which is removed only by evaporation. Into this area Yampai creek flows from the east; and though dry at the time of our visit, it is evident that its broad and deep bed is at times filled with a volume of water which would speedily submerge and convert into a lake a large portion of the basin described.

The altitude of Yampai valley is 3,600 feet, and 1,200 feet higher than the one which lies between it and the Colorado on the west. On the south it terminates in the conspicuous granitic mass of the Cerbat mountains, to which I have before alluded; and which, with its sheets of snow and forests of pines, unites with the green and grassy surface of its southern portion to form a beautiful landscape. Towards the north it expands to the width of twenty miles, embraced in the diverging ranges of the Cerbat mountains. Its precise length we could not determine; but it extends far northward in a nearly level plain covered with grass and flowers, and completely encircled by mountains, forming one of the most attractive scenes which we looked upon during our journey. The soil is excellent, and with a better supply of water it would be as productive as picturesque.

The cañada, through which we entered Yampai valley at its upper extremity, is cut through a thick stratum of trap, which seems to underlie a large part of the plain. Throughout its southern half the rocks composing its boundaries are exclusively eruptive in character, but the wall which limits its northern portion on the east shows bold perpendicular escarpments of stratified rocks. To these, when in the valley, greatly to my regret, I had no access, but after leaving it and mounting another step in our ascent, I discovered that these mural faces were sections of some of the palæozoic strata of the great table-lands.

THE EASTERN CHAIN, CERBAT MOUNTAINS.

The geology of the northern portion of the eastern wall of the Yampai valley is as interesting and important as that of any other portion of our route; and the inconvenience attending an effort to determine the geology of a district. while connected with a party having another as a main object, was never more keenly felt than when in the vicinity. We had here the line of contact between large areas of which the geological structure is as unlike as possible: the volcanic region of the Colorado basin, and the sedimentary district of the great central plateau. Here was exposed the western edge of the stratified rocks of the table-lands; and the great point of interest was to determine, if possible, from these sections the nature of the causes which limited their extension in this direction; whether their present boundaries had existed *ab initio*, or were comparatively modern. Did these mountain ranges represent the shores which restricted the palæozoic ocean, or were they forced up through the continuous strata of the table-lands long after their deposition? If the latter, what has become of the western prolongation of the table-lands; have they been buried in the deep synclinal trough of the Colorado basin? And do we find them represented in the erupted and metamorphic rocks which prevail over all the region between this line and the Pacific; or have they been swept away by the powerful and incessant action of the waves of the western ocean once rolling so far eastward?

The key to this great problem is doubtless contained in the vertical faces of sedimentary strata before mentioned, but to which we did not gain access. Unfortunately we ascended the mountains bordering Yampai valley just where the line of contact between the granite and stratified rocks is concealed by beds of comparatively recent trap; and when we stood upon the surface of the first step of the plateau, without having seen its edge, knowing nothing of the splendid sections of the table-lands revealed in the cañon of the Colorado, the regret felt for what was supposed to be an irreparable loss was extreme.

That loss I still deplore, though, from the opportunities subsequently enjoyed, it is probably of much less consequence than then supposed. Within ten miles of the escarpment so often referred to, we descended through all the sedimentary rocks which go to make up this part of the table-lands and several hundred feet into the underlying granite.

That experience, with a careful examination of the surface nearly to the brink of the precipice bounding Yampai valley, together with the observations of Mr. Marcou and Mr. A. H. Campbell, who with Captain Whipple crossed the edge of the table-lands a few miles southeast of where we came on to it, have led me to the conclusion that the sedimentary strata covering the eastern flanks of the Cerbat mountains *include only portions of the Carboniferous series*.

I think it will be seen, as we proceed, that there is even reason to suppose that the lower member of that series, the "Mountain limestone," is wanting in all the sections examined by Mr. Marcou west of the San Francisco mountain.

The Carboniferous strata in this region, where all are represented, are at least 2,500 feet in thickness, and consist of three great beds of limestone, separated by red, white, and gray sandstones, beds of gypsum, &c.; the whole forming a series of such magnitude, and of a structure so complex, as almost certainly to confuse the most experienced geologist, unless he chanced to find such a section as that exposed in the cañon of the Colorado.

The mountains which I have called the eastern range of the Cerbats form the last of the ranges which intervene between the "*mesas*" and the lower Colorado. Along the course of the upper Colorado, in the direction pursued by our party, there are no other mountains till that line strikes the first ranges of the Sierra Madre, ("Sierra de Chusca,") east of Fort Defiance; although north of the Colorado isolated mountains are discernible, and opposite them in the south, more than a hundred miles distant, is the similar isolated but more lofty San Francisco group.

Along the 35th parallel the table-lands are not so continuous or well marked—scarcely more than the edge of the basin of the Little Colorado being crossed by it; and the route followed by the party of Captain Whipple, from the San Francisco mountain west, is much broken by effusions of trap, and by lines of upheaval and erosion. Some of the mountain ranges mentioned by Captain Whipple, as that of the "Black Forest," including the Picacho, subsequently visited by us, entirely disappear before reaching the Colorado on the north, and the sedimentary rocks in its line show only slight traces of its disturbing action.

The Aztec and Aquarius mountains, of which interesting though very brief notes have been given by Mr. Marcou, I was not able fully to identify on our route, but have been disposed to regard them as the equivalents of the range under consideration. The Aztec mountains are its precise geological equivalent, and I should not hesitate to consider one the continuation of the other had we not seen a distinct connexion of both the ranges, crossed by us east of the Black mountains, with the principal granitic mass of the Cerbats; and the *Picacho* range disappearing in the north led me to suspect the Aztec mountains had done the same.

Issuing from Yampai valley through the cañada of Yampai creek, we followed this until we came up on to the table-land to which reference has been so frequently made. Throughout its course the cañada, or cañon, of Yampai creek is the effect of erosion. Its lower and broader part is bordered by hills of coarse gray granite, as at Camp 64. Thence to Camp 65 it becomes narrower, running between hills of granite on the west and mesas of trap on the east. The granite is plainly much the older, having once been completely covered and concealed by floods of lava, apparently flowing from the southeast, and doubtless of common origin with those which surround the *Picacho*, and form mesas in Partridge creek.

The drainage from the mesa has followed the line of junction between the granite and trap, leaving walls of the latter rock several hundred feet in height on one side, and on the other granitic masses, from which the trap has been all eroded, or remains in detached capping masses.

From Camp 65 we turned into a branch of the cañada leading down from the east, which, being cut through the trap plateau, has perpendicular walls on either side, and for several miles is a typical cañon.

FIRST PLATEAU OF THE TABLE–LANDS.

Emerging from the cañon of Yampai creek, we found ourselves on a plain extending indefinitely toward the north, and rising gently toward the west, where its broken edge forms the limit of Yampai valley. On the south it is bounded by mountains, of which the relations were not perceptible in the distance. On the east it is partially enclosed by trap hills, north of which our view was limited by the abruptly cut edge of another and higher plateau.

Traversing this plain in a northeast direction we unconsciously passed the edge of the trap, and found ourselves on the somewhat irregular surface of beds of rounded gravel. The drainage of most of this surface is toward the north, and in that direction the arroyos become deeper and expose thick beds of sand, gravel, and boulders; the greater part of the pebbles being of a hard bluish-gray limestone. Ultimately the beds of the draining streams were found to have reached the rocky floor beneath. This they soon begin to erode, forming cañons which lead toward the Colorado. These cañons gradually increase in number and depth till twenty miles north of the point where the denudation commences, the plateau is intersected by a labyrinth of chasms from 2,000 to 3,000 feet deep, of which the nearly perpendicular walls forbid the passage of man or any other wingless animal.

The plain which has just been described is little else than a broad valley of erosion, scooped out of the sedimentary rocks by the flow of water from the mountains south of it.

Its rocky basis is what I have regarded as probably the Lower Carboniferous or "Mountain limestone," though no conclusive evidence of its age has yet been obtained. It extends to the border of Yampai valley, and, I have supposed, forms the greater part of the perpendicular section seen from below.

CAÑON OF DIAMOND RIVER.

Near Camp 66 we descended to the bottom of one of the arroyos I have mentioned, where it has a depth of more than 500 feet. A mile north of this point its sides converge and become perpendicular, forming a cañon of more magnificent proportions than any we had seen, and in geological interest far surpassing anything I had dared to hope for.

This seemed to be our only avenue of approach to the Colorado, and we followed it for fifteen miles, to its junction with the still grander cañon of that stream.

Throughout this distance the dry stream-bed on which we travelled descended at an average rate of about 200 feet to the mile; while the summits of the cliffs on either side held nearly a constant elevation. All the strata here exposed have a strong dip to the northeast. In the direction we travelled we estimated it at fifty feet to the mile.

In traversing this cañon, which joins that of Diamond river just before it reaches the Colorado, I was able to examine each stratum as we came down to the point where it was cut across; and in that way make a very complete and satisfactory analysis of the series of rocks composing this first, and lowest, plateau of the table-lands.

GREAT CAÑON OF THE COLORADO.

The cañon of the Colorado at the mouth of Diamond river is but a portion of the stupendous chasm which its waters have cut in the strata of the table-lands, and of which a general description has already been given. At this point its walls have an altitude of over 3,000 feet above the Colorado, and the bed of that stream is about 1,200 feet above the level of the sea, or 500 feet higher than in the Black cañon. A few miles further east, where the surface of the table-lands has an altitude of nearly 7,000 feet, the dimensions of the cañon become far more imposing, and its cliffs rise to the height of more than a mile above the river.[*]

[*] See section of cañon at this point, Chapter V, p. 42.

J.J.Young from a sketch by H.B.Mollhausen.

Lith.of Sarony, Major & Knapp. 449 Broadway.NY

NEAR HEAD OF DIAMOND CREEK

Near the mouth of Diamond river, by the intersections of the numerous cañons which cut the plateau, portions of it have been left in a series of pinnacles and pyramids, frequently standing entirely isolated, forming some of the most striking and remarkable objects seen on our expedition. Many of these buttes exhibit a singular resemblance to the spires and pyramids which form the architectural ornaments of the cities of civilized nations, except that the scale of magnitude of all these imitative forms is such as to render the grandest monuments of human art insignificant in comparison with them.

The section exposed in the walls of the cañon of the Colorado in this vicinity consists of the following geological elements :

SECTION OF CAÑON OF COLORADO RIVER AT CAMP 67.

	Feet.
1st. Bluish-gray limestone, containing corals, casts of *Euomphalus*, *Spirifer*, &c., with nodules of chert and iron, to summit	1,000
2d. Mottled, red and gray, silicious limestone, interstratified with argillaceous and silicious shales, red, white, and brown, much changed by infiltration of silica; cavities and joints filled with chalcedony	300
3d. Red, green, and yellow shales, with bands of argillaceous iron, and black oxide manganese	100
4th. Red and brown limestone in thin layers, with grits and shales containing imperfect corals	60
5th. Green shales	50
6th. Ferruginous limestones, shales, and mud rocks, the limestones containing corals, (*Chaetetes?*) greenish shales, with mud furrows and carbonaceous particles, closely resembling rocks of Chemung group in New York	75
7th. Mottled, red and blue, thick bedded limestone; red portions having the form of branching corals	25
8th. Soft ochery sandstone	25
9th. Shales with bands of limestone and grits, without fossils	180
10th. Speckled, white or brown, and dark red foliated sandstones with shales	260
11th. Red, gray, and green shales with mud furrows, resembling casts of worm holes	250
12th. Gray coarse silicious sandstones	160
13th. Red quartzose sandstone, often purple, and beautifully striped	150
14th. Conglomerate	3
15th. Massive black and white granite, traversed by veins of quartz and red syenite, and coarse red felspathic granite with large plates of silver mica	600

In the absence of fossils it is impossible to determine the precise geological age of any of the strata composing the preceding section below the limestone which forms the summit of the cliffs. There is some doubt whether this rock is the equivalent of the mountain limestone. The fossils procured from it are few, and not well preserved, but they are apparently quite different from those of the next great calcareous stratum lying several hundred feet above it, which, though hitherto considered by some who have written upon the geology of New Mexico, as the lower carboniferous or Mountain limestone, is doubtless not older than the era of the coal measures. The entire thickness of the upper limestone is, as we shall hereafter see, probably not less than 1,500 feet.

The next 500 feet of the section is made up of shales with bands of limestone and grits, which have been considerably changed by silicious infiltration. They have apparently been much hardened by the process; and their cavities and fissures are filled with masses or plates of chalcedony. Concretions of iron and manganese seem to be characteristic of group No. 3. Fossils have existed in these strata, but only obscure traces are now discernible.

The remains of organisms are somewhat more distinct in No. 6, but even these are too much changed to be satisfactorily determined.

The lithological character of this group is much like that of some of the Chemung rocks; but the corals, as they seem to be, which make up so much of the mass of the limestone bands in their abundance and general appearance, resemble more the intermingled branches of *Chaetetes* which cover the surfaces of some of the Silurian strata, than any fossils of later date.

No. 7 is a very dense and massive limestone, of a light blue or gray color, everywhere penetrated by lines of deep red. This character is common to several bands of limestone in the series, and distinguishes them from any I have ever seen elsewhere. The same appearance would be produced if the stems of corals, sometimes so abundantly distributed through the Devonian and Silurian limestones, were impregnated with oxide of iron. All the limestones below No. 1 contain considerable silica, and have doubtless been affected by the silicious infiltration to which I have already referred.

The foliated sandstones of No. 10 have an indescribable look of antiquity. They are usually fine grained and hard, the lighter ones drab or gray, specked with dark red. The shales above and below these sandstones are very soft, red, or green mudstones, containing great numbers of cylindrical bodies, which resemble the casts of worm holes.

Nos. 12 and 13 are coarse silicious rocks, having the same appearance of extreme age as No. 10, but much coarser and more massive. The lithological characters of these strata are strikingly like those of much of the Potsdam sandstone in the exposures I have examined of that rock on Lake Superior and in Canada.

The color of the upper division is a light yellowish brown, sometimes nearly white; of the lower portion, dark red and purple. In some parts of the sections, especially near the base, the light and dark colors are united in narrow stripes ; and as this portion of the rock is exceedingly compact and fine-grained, it occasionally resembles a striped, purple and white jasper. These sandstones, as will be seen in the specimens collected, are apparently somewhat metamorphosed, portions of them being harder and more crystalline than any unchanged sedimentary rock that I remember to have seen ; but the perfect harmony of stratification everywhere prevailing, as well as the evident antiquity of all the irregularities of the underlying granite, around which the strata of sandstone are now resting just as when so quietly deposited, lead me to infer that their consolidation is not due in any degree to volcanic heat, but rather to molecular changes induced by the long-continued pressure of the immense mass of superincumbent rocks. When it is remembered that every square foot of the basal structure of the table lands has sustained a great and constantly increasing pressure from the earliest palæozoic times, and that since the deposition of the Chalk, that pressure has been at least 500,000 pounds on every square foot, this cause alone will probably be considered quite adequate to produce the degree of metamorphosis exhibited by the strata under consideration.

In the absence of fossils, whatever conclusions may be arrived at in regard to the age of these sandstones must be in some degree conjectural and liable to modification by the discovery of new facts ; yet the evidence is in a good degree satisfactory that they are the equivalent of the Potsdam sandstone of the New York geologists.

The indications of this identity are found in their great relative antiquity and in their lithological characters. From the limestone called Lower Carboniferous by Mr. Marcou, they are separated by over 3,000 feet of sedimentary strata ; and from what I have considered the base of the carboniferous series, by nearly 2,000 feet.

The question of their age, then, resolves itself into this : Are they Devonian or Silurian? They are not so remote from the Carboniferous rocks but that, reasoning from the thickness of the Devonian strata in other parts of the world, we might perhaps include them in that formation; but while in New York the Devonian rocks are several thousand feet in thickness, they thin out rapidly toward the west, and on the Mississippi do not include a thousand feet of strata.

An equally marked change of lithological character is perceptible, following the same line of observation. In New York the "Old Red Sandstone" formation includes thick beds of sandstone of typical character. In Ohio these have disappeared, and the Devonian strata consist of sandy or carbonaceous shales and limestones; further west little but the limestones remain. The structure of the Black Hills, Nebraska, according to Dr. Hayden, (*Proceedings Academy Natural Sciences, Philadelphia, June*, 1858,) seems to afford strong presumptive evidence of the Silurian age of the sandstones in question. Dr. Hayden found the crystalline igneous and metamorphic rocks, forming the core of the Black Hills, overlaid by upheaved sediments, of which the lowest is a coarse deep red sandstone containing *Lingula, Obolus, etc.*, evidently the Potsdam. Above this are, partially metamorphosed, silicious limestones, &c., and then the Carboniferous lime-

GRANITE PINNACLES, CAÑON OF DIAMOND RIVER.

stone. This is the nearest point to the exposures in the cañon of the Colorado, where strata of any considerable thickness have been found below the Carboniferous formation, and the section given by Dr. Hayden exhibits a striking paralellism to that under consideration.

The conglomerate which underlies or rather forms the base of the red sandstones, to any one who has seen the Potsdam of Lake Superior in place, will seem an old acquaintance. It is but a portion of the sandstone which includes pebbles of quartz, jasper, &c., very possibly derived from the attrition of the granite on which it rests. It is much harder than any of the more recent conglomerates met with on our route, resembling more the dense semi-crystalline conglomerate in the vicinity of the trap on Keewanaw Point. The surface of the granite beneath is, in many places, planed off, as though by the action of currents of water flowing over it before the deposition of the stratified rocks.

The granite forming the base of the series is very compact and massive, scarcely showing any tendency to stratification. It is cut by veins of quartz of large size, and contains veins and masses of handsome red syenite and coarse red felspathic granite, with plates of silvery mica. All these seem to have been injected into fissures.

The erosion of the cañon has beautifully displayed the ancient surface of the granite, and shows it to have been extremely irregular; hills several hundred feet high, many of which have precipitous sides, and deserve the name of pinnacles, have been exhumed from the sediments in which they were enveloped. The sandstones and shales are seen to have been deposited quietly around them; their strata, nearly horizontal, abutting against their sides. We have here evidence that at least *these* granite hills are older than any of the stratified rocks of the table-lands.—(See preceding page.)

Retracing our steps, as the only means of exit from the bottom of the Colorado cañon, and reaching the surface of the mesa, a short distance east of Camp 66, we obtained a fine panoramic view of the geological structure of the country for many miles about us.

We stood upon the gray cherty limestone which caps the cliffs on the Colorado, and which forms the surface rock over a large area. It here contains large quantities of iron in nodules, with few fossils, except masses of coral. Below us, on the west, was the broad eroded valley or plain, across which we had approached the Colorado. On the east the bold escarpments of a higher mesa limited our vision in that direction and formed a series of headlands, which diminished in perspective toward the north and south.

From this point the view towards the north was particularly grand; the course of the Colorado was visible for nearly a hundred miles, and the series of Cyclopean walls into which the mesas of different elevations have been cut by that stream and its tributaries formed a scene of which the sublime features deeply impressed each member of our party. Some conception of the character of this scenery may be gathered from the sketches of the artists of the party, Messrs. Egloffstein and Mollhausen.

As we progressed towards the east we found the surface of the Mountain limestone considerably eroded, and in places covered with heavy beds of alluvial gravel; the nodules of chert, which it contains in such abundance, having been left in its decomposition, cover the surface, and with their many angles seriously incommoded our mules.

Approaching the high mesa we ascended rapidly, and for the first time since leaving the Pacific were surrounded by arborescent vegetation sufficient to deserve the name of forest.

There is here apparently a local interruption of the general easterly dip which I have said prevails over all the western portion of the table-lands, and a slight arching of the strata over what seems to be the continuation of the line of upheaval marked further south by the Picacho and other mountains of like character in that vicinity. At one point between our Camps 68 and 69 the stratified rocks have been broken through by the eruptive force and a mass of trap has been protruded. The quantity of erupted material is however small, and, as in many similar cases which came under our notice, it has produced little or no dislocation of the sedimentary strata.

HIGH MESA WEST OF LITTLE COLORADO.

East of that portion of the table-lands which I have described is a belt of country from thirty to fifty miles in width, extending from a point south of the San Francisco mountain northwesterly into Utah, which has a much greater elevation than that on either side of it, and forms a natural water-shed between the tributaries of the Colorado, flowing in a northwesterly direction.

Where we crossed this divide it has the character of an elevated plateau, of which the surface has been considerably modified by erosion, and now presents many broad and shallow excavated valleys. Its geological substrata are everywhere middle or upper Carboniferous rocks, which, though exhibiting local variations from the general eastern dip, nowhere show any disruption or contortion.

Nearly one hundred miles southeast of the line where our route crosses this high mesa it has been burst through by volcanic force, and though much upheaved, is less broken and disturbed than might have been expected. It is there deeply buried under the accumulations of erupted material which compose and surround San Francisco mountain.

The soil of this elevated district is usually fertile; sustaining dense forests of yellow and nut-pine, Douglas's spruce, and cedar, interspersed with large areas covered with a vigorous growth of grama or bunch grass; the contrast which this mesa country presents, in its vegetation and geological structure, to the volcanic and desert region of the lower Colorado, was most agreable to us in many respects. We had all been wearied by the monotonous prevalence of the products of a single destructive force; and the varied and beautiful volcanic minerals so profusely scattered over the Colorado basin, devoid of all traces of organisms, and associated with the death-like sterility now pervading all that area, had ceased to excite a pleasurable scientific interest, and had even produced a positive thirst for *life!* a longing to reach some region where nature's vital fires had not all burned out; where the varied forms of recent animal and vegetable life adorned the earth's surface, and the rocks below contained in their fossils a record of its prevalence on sea and shore from the earliest ages.

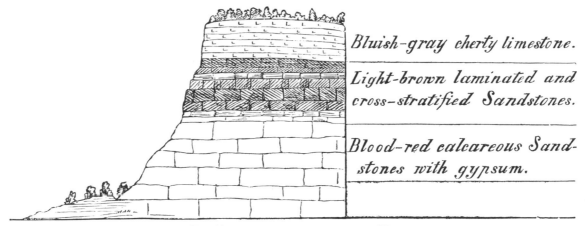

FIG. 14.—SECTION OF MESA WALL AT CAMP 70.

Red calcareous sandstones and shales.—Just before reaching the edge of the high mesa we left the surface of the Mountain (?) limestone, and came upon a series of blood-red calcareous sandstones and shales, which have an aggregate thickness of nearly 500 feet. This series covers a belt several miles in width, bordering the wall of the high mesa and reaching up to form nearly half its height.

Although I examined these red rocks in several localities where fully exposed, I was not able to detect in them any traces of fossils; their mineral constituents are, however, of interest; affording a marked example of the companionship of peroxide of iron with gypsum, which is noticeable in strata of all ages, and to which I shall have occasion again to refer. At our camp 69, interstratified with the red shales and sandstones, is a thin stratum of cream-colored tufaceous limestone, also without fossils.

Brown laminated sandstone.—Overlying the last-mentioned series, and forming the middle portion of the mesa wall, is a group of sandstones of a lighter color, and more purely silicious, having an aggregate thickness of over 200 feet. Like the last, these rocks seem to be entirely destitute of fossils. I subsequently had an opportunity of examining these sandstones in the cañon of Cascade river, fifty miles northeast of the point where I first observed it, and still later, in the valleys of Partridge and Cedar creeks, about the same distance west of the San Francisco mountain. In the cañon of Cascade river they are somewhat more massive and of lighter color; on Partridge and Cedar creeks slightly darker than here; but in all these localities their similarity of character is such as to admit of their immediate identification.   A most striking feature which they exhibit in all the exposures where I observed them is their tendency to cross-stratification, a character which seems to indicate they have been deposited by shallow and rapid currents of water.

Middle carboniferous limestone.—The bluff formed by the cut edge of the high mesa where we ascended it is capped by something more than 200 feet of bluish gray limestone, not very unlike that which covers the lower mesa in its general appearance, but containing larger quantities of fossils.   These consist of crinoidal columns, very abundant, with many species of *Productus, Spirigera, Rhynconella, Orthisina, Spirifer, Archæocidaris,* &c., all of Carboniferous types, and embracing several well known Carboniferous species.

This limestone forms the surface rock over the greater part of the high mesa, and composes the base upon which the San Francisco mountains rest.   With its numerous and well-marked fossils it forms a clearly defined geological horizon; and from its wide distribution it becomes the most convenient and reliable guide to the geologist in the study of all the area lying between the Mississippi and the Colorado.

We shall see as we proceed that in some localities it is separated by an interval of about two hundred feet from another thick calcareous mass, which I have denominated the *Upper Carboniferous* limestone.   It is probable, however, that these two beds should be considered one, as the strata of gypsum and shales which divide them seem to be confined to a comparatively limited area; and the strata of limestone above and below, though exhibiting marked differences in their lithological characters, and each containing some fossils peculiar to itself, have many species in common.   The differences which these limestones exhibit are not greater than those which distinguish the upper from the lower coal measures, and they doubtless represent precisely that geological horizon.   The structure of the "high mesa" will, perhaps, be best understood by the following section:

Section of mesa at Camp 70.

No.	Description.	Thickness.
1	Coarse gray limestone, with nodules of chert, small crinoidal columns, and *Productus semireticulatus*	20
2	Soft, light, dove-colored, massive limestone, with few fossils, but many geodes containing crystals of carb. lime	20
3	Harder and darker limestone, with *Producti* and numerous spines of *Archæocidaris*	15
4	Gray cherty limestone, with many *Producti,* (*P. Ivesi, P. semireticulatus,* &c.,) and large crinoidal columns	27
5	Gray cellular limestone, with great numbers of crinoidal columns, *Productus Ivesi* and *Orthisina pyramidalis*	20
6	Gray silicious limestone; few fossils	42
7	Soft dove-colored limestone, similar to No. 2, with few fossils	30
8	Fine-grained laminated sandstone, light brown, ripple-marked; no fossils	16
9	Massive fine-grained sandstone, nearly white	20
10	Coarse yellow sandstone	16
11	Hard fine-grained sandstone, in thin layers, weathering purple	6
12	Coarse pink sandstone, massive	5
13	Coarse white and pink shelly sandstone	45
14	Coarse pinkish-white sandstone, thicker bedded than last; surfaces of layers as smooth as though polished by art	75
15	Shelly sandstone, weathering reddish brown	55
16	Red calcareous shales and soft, fine-grained crimson calc. sandstones	150
17	Cream-colored tufaceous limestone	10
18	Red calcareous sandstones and shales	250
19	Mountain (?) limestone, with *Euomphalus, Syringapora,* &c	----------

Shales and gypsum.—The crinoidal limestones capping the bluff at the western edge of the high mesa are succeeded in the ascending series by a group of green, white, and pink shales and gypsum, having altogether a thickness of nearly two hundred feet. The materials composing this group are very soft, and, yielding readily to the action of eroding agents, have been removed from all the western portion of the high mesa, with the exception of a few rounded buttes, one of which is situated on the extreme edge of the mesa south of our Camp 70.

For five-and-twenty miles from the point where we ascended the upper mesa wall our route led over the rolling surface and through the pine forests already described. The surface rock is everywhere the crinoidal limestone, which at first rises gently, then falls off, with a rapid and uniform dip, into the valley of the Little Colorado, determining the outline of its eastern slope.

VALLEY OF THE LITTLE COLORADO.

The high mesa does not terminate on its eastern as its western border in a mural escarpment, but following the curve of the underlying rock the surface falls off in a nearly uniform slope of about one hundred feet to the mile for twenty miles. This slope is succeeded by a level plain, having a width varying from twenty to forty miles, and bounded on the east by mesas of different elevations. Towards the southeast, whence the valley has a perceptible descent, its eastern wall, though a marked feature in the landscape, is not more than one thousand feet in height. Near the mouth of the Little Colorado, however, the relative altitude of the mesa is increased by the depression of the surface of the valley, and its absolute altitude enhanced by the addition of two great steps or terraces to its surface. So that the angle of the mesa included between the Great and Little Colorados, on the north side of the latter stream, combining all the formations of the table-lands, and having an absolute altitude of eight thousand feet, overlooks the valley in a nearly perpendicular wall of some four thousand feet in height, of which the base is apparently washed by the waters of both streams at least six thousand feet below its summit.

The valley of the Little Colorado, throughout its entire extent, is destitute of trees, and as we emerged from the dense pine forests of the mesa our eyes swept a hundred miles of its course, and we were able to grasp at a glance all the great features of its structure and relations to the country surrounding it.

On the west the view was everywhere bounded by the forest-covered summit of the high mesa we had crossed, which stretched away in an unbroken line from the Colorado to the point where it was crowned by the snowy peaks of the San Francisco mountain and its subordinates. On the eastern side of the valley the long lines of mesa walls, converging in perspective towards the southeast, filled the horizon and gave to the landscape that linear character so common on the table-lands, but never seen elsewhere. In the northwest the high mesa at the junction of the two Colorados formed a most conspicuous object; though at a distance of forty miles, subtending so large an angle and covered with a glittering sheet of snow, it resembled the line of a lofty and snow-covered sierra.

The area intervening between the objects I have described seemed to us, for the most part, a smooth and grass-covered plain. Such it doubtless was at one time and nothing more; but subsequently, when we attempted to cross to the opposite side of the valley, we found that beneath its modest surface were concealed some of the grandest and most surprising physical features met with on our route, and impediments to our progress more insurmountable than any of the snow-covered mesas or mountains which then engrossed our attention and alone gave us any apprehensions. From the distance we could not see, what we afterwards discovered, that the plain was cut by a series of cañons scarcely less profound than that of Diamond river, forming a labyrinth of difficulties effectually arresting our progress in the line we had hoped to follow.

The theory of the origin and mode of formation of the valley of the Little Colorado has seemed to me to be quite simple, and has been already adverted to. It has evidently been the channel through which the drainage of the northern slopes of the Mogollon and San Francisco mountains found its way to the Colorado since the dawn of the present geological epoch. This flow of water has washed off the variegated marls and red sandstones which, to the depth of more than two thousand feet, once covered the Carboniferous limestone, and the broad valley is the legitimate consequence of the action of such an agent on such materials. When, however, the harder substrata had been reached, and at the same time the precipitation of moisture was, for the most part, restricted to the mountains, the eroding force of the drainage of all that country was expended in deepening the narrow beds of the water-courses. Through countless ages this process has continued until the remarkable results I have described have been effected. What was once a broad and fertile valley, abundantly watered by the streams meandering through it, by the simple process of the deepening of the beds of these streams, and hence its more perfect drainage, has been converted into an arid and sterile plain, rendered absolutely impassable by the profound chasms which cut it in every direction.

CAÑON OF CASCADE RIVER.

In attempting to reach the junction of the Great and Little Colorados we descended to the plain to which I have referred; entered and traversed for some miles a cañon leading in the right direction. This proved to be but a tributary to the greater cañon of Cascade river, in which the progress of our party was arrested by cascades.

In the strata exposed in the walls of these cañons I found a continuation of the geological column to the top of the Carboniferous series. This section is connected with that of Diamond river by the Mountain (?) limestone, which forms the summit of the first and the base of the last. The members of the Carboniferous formation are here all fully exposed; their intimate characters, their thickness, and the order of super-position being as readily determinable as are those of the older palæozoic rocks on Diamond river.

The section here displayed is composed of the following constituents:

Section in cañon of Cascade river.

1. Limestone, varigated, crimson and lemon-yellow, with nodules of chert and iron, to top of hills .... 50 feet.
2. Sandstone, coarse, drab, sometimes pinkish; in places containing many small quartz pebbles and imperfect vegetable impressions .... 20 "
3. Massive cream-colored limestone with geodes, containing calc. spar .... 16 "
4. Chert .... 3 "
5. Cherty limestone .... 25 "
6. Blue limestone, with *Productus semireticulatus*, etc., very abundant .... 4 "
7. Cherty limestone, light-blue, containing *Productus semireticulatus*, *P. occidentalis*, (n. sp.,) *Spirigera subtilita*, *Orthisina umbraculum*, *Rhynconella uta*, etc· 175 "
8. Shales, green, red, and white, with snowy gypsum .... 180 "
9. Hard blue limestone, containing crinoidal columns—spines of *Archæocidaris*, *Producti*, *Spirigera*, etc .... 100 "
10. Soft lemon-yellow limestone, with few *Productus Ivesi*, etc. .... 90 "
11. Drab, cross-stratified sandstones .... 190 "
12. Red calcareous sandstones and shales, with gypsum .... 350 "
13. Bluish gray limestone at base ....

At Camp 74 we found a bed of red shale covering No. 1, which I have supposed to be a portion of the series of red sandstones and shales overlying the yellow limestone at the crossing of the Little Colorado.

No. 1 contains no fossils, as far as my observation extended. It is beautifully mottled; the color being blood-red and yellow, and very bright, rendering it one of the handsomest marbles found on our route. This is doubtless the equivalent of the extreme upper part of the limestone which occupies so much of the surface between the San Francisco mountain and the Little Colorado, called Permian by Mr. Marcou. While it is true that, if the Permian magnesian limestones of Kansas reappear west of the Rocky mountains, this rock is their representative, it must also be said that the evidence of their identity is as yet all to be discovered.

Here the limestone beneath the red shales is separated from that containing Carboniferous fossils by a thin band of sandstone; but as will be hereafter seen, where our party crossed the surface of the limestone west of the Little Colorado, it seemed homogeneous throughout. At Camp 73 this limestone is very different, lithologically, from the Permian limestones of Kansans. It is silicious rather than magnesian, and contains no fossils whatever.

The sandstone (No. 2) beneath the last is a coarse and soft rock, quite unlike any of the sandstones exposed near the crossing of the Little Colorado, which hold a higher place in the series. It is strikingly like the sandstones of the Coal measures in the Mississippi valley, and probably should be regarded as of the same age with them. As has already been stated, the true Coal measures are said to exist north of the Colorado, at no great distance from this locality, and I have regarded this sandstone as an indication that we had here approached near to the shores of the Carboniferous continent, near enough to reach one of the strata formed by the direct erosion of the land. Further north, could we have proceeded in that direction, we should doubtless have found the number and thickness of such beds, intercalated between the strata of the limestone, constantly increasing until we reached seams of coal.

As we went south from this point, we turned our backs upon the ancient land—of which we soon lost all traces—and about the San Francisco mountain had beneath our feet the homogeneous calcareous sediment of the open ocean.

Nos. 3, 4, 5, 6, and 7, of the section, are but subdivisions of what is constantly referred to in my notes on the geology of this region as the " Cherty limestone." With some new species, it contains large numbers of fossils highly characteristic of the coal measures of Kansas, Missouri, Ohio, Pennsylvania, &c. Such as *Productus semireticulatus*, *P. castatus*, *Spirifer lineatus*, *Spirigera subtilita*, *Orthisina umbraculum*, *Rhynconella uta*, etc., etc.

I have supposed the three calcareous beds (Nos. 1, 3 to 7, 9 and 10) of this section were but portions of one great formation, here by the intercalation of strata of sandstone and gypsiferous shales rendered locally distinct.

The shales with gypsum (No. 8) have been noticed as observed in detached hillocks, on the high mesa near Camp 70. They are here fully exposed, in cliffs which would be perpendicular, but that their softness has permitted a portion of the cherty limestone to be undermined and removed, and a broad shoulder formed. The prevailing color of this series is green, but portions of it are gray, white, and red. Like the lower gypsiferous strata these contain no fossils.

Nos. 9 and 10 compose the crinoidal limestone so fully described at Camp 70. It is here, as there, rich in fossils, usually of the same species; but spines of *Archæocidaris* are much less abundant. The upper division is rather darker and harder than at Camp 70, while the lower part is much lighter in color, and softer. It is scarcely distinguishable from the yellow Permian limestone of Kansas.

The cross-stratified sandstones (No. 11) here present nearly the same appearance as at Camp 70, but, perhaps because better protected by the overlying rocks, are much more massive, forming nearly smooth faces in the perpendicular cliff.

The red calcareous sandstones and shales (No. 12,) first noticed on the other side of the high mesa at Camp 69, are here beautifully exposed, forming the most striking features in the wild and peculiar scenery of this and the neighboring cañons.

The bottoms of these chasms and a portion of their bounding walls are colored by them to a deep blood-red, which contrasts strongly with the snowy white of the enclosed gypsum, and the yellow, white, green, &c., of the overlying rocks. As is almost universally the case with gypsiferous rocks, these strata are without fossils.

The companionship of peroxide of iron and sulphate of lime, in the great number of localities, and distinct formations in which they occur together, is, as it seems to me, too marked to be accidental. This conviction has forced itself upon me in the examination of the extensive gypsiferous deposits of different ages which form so marked a feature in the geology of the country traversed by our party; and I have been led to look to the law of that relationship as probably affording a clue to the origin of all the great masses of gypsum which we observed. Without an exception, the *red* sandstones, clays, marls, limestones, &c., of whatever age, so common in New Mexico, contain notable quantities of gypsum, and it is also true that very little of this mineral is found associated with any other materials.

Deferring for the present the discussion of this question in its details, I will only say here that the theory of the formation of gypsum which regards it as the result of the action of sulphurous waters or vapors on coral reefs or other masses of carbonate of lime, however applicable to other countries, is inadequate to explain all the phenomena of the gypsum beds of the Far West, because, 1st. They are too extensive to be the result of an action necessarily local. 2d. The gypsum is more generally and uniformly diffused through the rocks in which it occurs than is accordant with that hypothesis. 3d. The *veins* of gypsum which traverse the different strata present difficulties which, on that supposition, have seemed to me to be insurmountable. They are evidently as much due to segregation as are the crystals of selenite in the clay beds. By their displacement of the enclosing rocks during the process of crystallization they seem to be of comparatively recent origin. 4th. The oxide of iron, so constant in its attendance upon the gypsum, has not only no place in that theory of its origin, but is to some extent incompatible with it.

A more satisfactory explanation of the phenomena, as it seems to me, is afforded by making the iron an important agent in the process. If a blue or gray calcareous rock, containing large quantities of pyrites, were subjected to the peculiar exposure of the strata of the table-lands, profoundly cut by the draining streams, and permeated age after age by meteoric water carrying carbonic acid and oxygen to the pyrites, the result would be precisely what we now find to have taken place. The bisulphuret of iron, taking another equivalent of oxygen, is converted into the protosulphate of iron; then, by double decomposition, from bicarbonate of lime and protosulphate of iron, we should have sulphate of lime (gypsum) and protocarbonate of iron, which last would soon obtain another equivalent of oxygen, and be changed into the peroxide.

This I am disposed to regard as the true theory of the formation of the gypsum disseminated through rocks so deeply colored by peroxide of iron, though there are doubtless many and striking instances of its production by exhalations of sulphuretted hydrogen, or springs containing sulphuric acid, acting on carbonate of lime. Upon the theory suggested the gypsum would be altogether a secondary product, being formed not only after the deposition of the strata containing it, but also in great part subsequent to their elevation above the ocean level. The displacement of strata after their consolidation by masses and veins of gypsum indicates its modern date, whatever its origin may be.

The Carboniferous or Mountain limestone (No. 13) was only seen in the bottoms of the sub-cañons, which are deeply cut in the floors of the greater ones, and in which the streams, where they exist, now flow. No fossils were noticed in it.

CHAPTER VII.

GEOLOGY OF REGION ABOUT SAN FRANCISCO MOUNTAIN.

GENERAL FEATURES.—RELATIONS OF THE SAN FRANCISCO GROUP TO THE MOGOLLON SYSTEM.—GENERAL ASPECT AND ISOLATED CHARACTER OF SAN FRANCISCO MOUNTAIN.—ITS PURELY VOLCANIC ORIGIN.—ISOLATED MOUNTAINS USUALLY COMPOSED OF ERUPTED MATERIALS CHAINS OF METAMORPHOSED ROCKS.—THEORY OF THIS DIFFERENCE.—TRACES OF RECENT ERUPTIONS ABOUT THE SAN FRANCISCO MOUNTAIN.—MODERN VOLCANIC PHENOMENA OF ROCKY MOUNTAIN AND PACIFIC REGION.—OSCILLATIONS OF LEVEL ON THE COAST.—EARTHQUAKES.—CONTINUED AGITATION OF WESTERN HALF OF THE CONTINENT THROUGH ALL GEOLOGICAL AGES.—LOCAL GEOLOGY.—DRIFT OF VALLEY OF LITTLE COLORADO.—TRAP PLATEAUS WEST OF SAN FRANCISCO MOUNTAIN.—ANCIENT SURFACE COVERED BY IT.—SECTION OF STRATA FROM PICACHO TO BILL WILLIAMS'S MOUNTAIN.—PARTRIDGE AND CEDAR CREEKS.—UPPER CARBONIFEROUS LIMESTONE.—CROSS STRATIFIED SANDSTONE.—AGE OF ROCKS DESCRIBED BY MR. MARCOU ON PUEBLO AND CEDAR CREEKS.—NO DEVONIAN OR PERMIAN STRATA IN THIS VICINITY.—BILL WILLIAM'S MOUNTAIN, MOUNT KENDRICK AND MOUNT SITGREAVES.—CARBONIFEROUS LIMESTONE.—MODERN VOLCANIC CONES AT CAMP 44.—MAGNESIAN LIMESTONE WEST OF LITTLE COLORADO.—PROBABLY CARBONIFEROUS.

GENERAL FEATURES.

Allusion has so frequently been made to the San Francisco mountain in the preceding pages, as well as in the report of Mr. Marcou, (*Pacific Railroad Report*, vol. III,) that but little now remains to be said of it; and yet our exploration of this district was so thorough, and our observations have such a bearing on those of the geologist before mentioned, that I have thought it desirable to give a brief notice of them.

The relations which the San Francisco and adjacent mountains sustain to the chains which approach nearest to them are by no means obvious; and it remains yet to be demonstrated that this group is not—what at first sight it seems to be—entirely disconnected with any line of upheaval. It is probable, however, that some light will be thrown upon this subject by an examination of the unexplored region between these mountains and the river Gila.

Such explorations would also result in a valuable contribution to geological science, by giving some intelligible analysis of the structure of the Mogollon mountains in place of the theoretical—and, as it seems to me, erroneous—descriptions which have been published of them. It is possible, and perhaps probable, that the Mogollon mountains will be found to have such a trend and extent as to permit a connexion to be established between them and the San Francisco group; but however this may be, my own convictions, derived from observations—partly my own and partly those of others—completely encircling the mountains in question, are entirely opposed to the theory which gives to their axes a nearly east and west trend, and, disconnecting them from the ranges of the Rocky mountains and Sierra Nevada, establishes upon them a new system of elevation, to which is assigned a distinct and entirely imaginary epoch.

To the casual observer the San Francisco mountain forms a most impressive feature in the scenery which surrounds it, not only from its symmetrical and striking outline but also from its isolation. Rising in solitary grandeur to the altitude of 12,000 feet above the sea, its snowy summit is visible from nearly all parts of a circle drawn around it with a radius of a hundred miles. In all that region it is without a rival or an associate, except its immediate subordinates; and in its relief from the table-land on which it rests it may be compared to some rocky island rising from the surface of the sea.

Its geological structure fully accords with its physical aspects. It is volcanic throughout, and is, in fact, a huge volcano whose fires have been but recently extinguished. Through one great, and several minor vents, opened in the strata of the high mesa, where they have a thickness of at least 5,000 feet, a vast quantity of lava has been poured, covering with a flood of melted matter the country for many miles around, and forming one principal cone with a thousand inferior ones; of which the more conspicuous have received distinct names.

Little disruption of the stratified rocks attended this grand exhibition of volcanic force; and the formation of the mountain mass seems to have been effected entirely by the ejection of matter in a state of complete fusion, through narrow orifices of unfathomable depth.

Comparatively few mountains have been wholly formed in this manner; probably none but those having the same isolated character with that under consideration. All the mountain *chains* which have come under my observation have been composed, in a great measure, of upheaved strata of a decided sedimentary character. Some of them more or less metamorphosed.

Lines of upheaval seem to mark linear fractures in the earth's crust, and bear evidence of the action of lateral pressure as well as of elevatory force. In solitary mountains, on the contrary, I have observed a marked absence of disrupted and metamorphosed sedimentary rocks, and the prevalence of masses of a purely plutonic character. The conspicuous summits which so generally mark the prominent angles in important mountain chains should apparently be included in the same category with isolated cones, as they also, as far as my observation has extended, are principally composed of ejected materials.

The modern date of the later eruptions of the San Francisco mountain is attested by the remarkable freshness of some of the volcanic products which cover its slopes and base. Many of the secondary cones are distinctly crateriform, are composed of black or blood-red scoria, and are entirely destitute of vegetation; showing by all their surroundings that they have been in action, as it were but yesterday, and might be again to-morrow.

Some of the currents of lava which have flowed down the sides of the San Francisco mountain belong so entirely to the present epoch that they have dispossessed still running streams from their beds, and now occupy their places in a congealed flood which seems but just arrested in its flow; as black and ragged, and as little affected by the action of the elements as slag fresh drawn from a furnace.

As will be seen when we come to speak of it, the description given of the San Francisco mountain, its isolated volcanic cone, its recent lava streams, &c., will apply with almost equal force to Mount Taylor; and yet, beyond this similarity, there is perhaps nothing to connect them.

The volcanic phenomena of modern date, exhibited on so grand a scale in the Cascade mountains, and so fully described by the writer, (*Pacific Railroad Report*, vol. VI,) together with those of the San Francisco mountain, Mount Taylor, the Raton, and a multitude of similar peaks scattered throughout the country embraced in the ranges of the Sierra Nevada and Rocky mountains, prove that the forces which have elevated these great systems have, at various points, continued to act even up to the present time. The earthquakes that still prevail upon the Pacific coast, and the recent oscillations of level of which it bears record, are phenomena of similar import. With those before cited, they lead us to infer that the origin of the labyrinth of mountain chains, covering such an immense area in the far west, is not to be referred to one or two remote paroxysms, but to the operation of an incessant and long continued action, commencing anterior to the palaeozoic period, and continuing to the present epoch; and that even now this shaken and everchanging region has not reached a period of repose.

LOCAL GEOLOGY.

Compelled to turn back at the cañon of Cascade river and pass around south of the San Francisco mountain, in order to cross the Little Colorado, we also retraced our geological steps and returned to the strata exposed in the western edge of the high mesa, some fifty miles south of the point where we first struck it. In following southward along the western border of the valley of the Little Colorado we were constantly upon beds of drift, or the Upper Carboniferous limestone, until we reached the edge of the trappean flood already alluded to as covering so large an area about the mountains toward which we were moving.

The limestone is in many places well exposed, being deeply cut by the extreme branches of the cañons which traverse the plain. No change was noticed in its lithological character or fossils from Cascade river to the point where it is covered by the trap; but the sandstone and conglomerate, red shale and clouded limestone disappeared as we progressed southward.

The drift to which I have referred is entirely of local origin, being principally composed of the cherty portions of the carboniferous limestone, and derived from the erosion of that rock. Mingled with these are quantities of pebbles of obsidian, phonolite, basalt, &c. Pebbles of this character are quite numerous in the accumulations of drift high up on the western slope of the valley, where we first entered it; and, as they could have been derived from no other source than the vicinity of the San Francisco mountains, they afford satisfactory evidence that the drainage from that surface flowed in this direction before either the cañons or valleys were excavated to their present depth, and confirm the view that has been taken of the manner in which they were formed.

Fig. 15.—TRAP MESAS NORTH OF SAN FRANCISCO MOUNTAIN.

The edge of the trap overflow was reached near our Camp 75. This material was evidently poured out in immense quantities, and, spreading over the surface of the stratified rocks, conformed entirely to that surface, forming a new table-land at a higher level. In this plateau of trap the draining streams have cut innumerable channels, some of which have passed through, not only its entire thickness, but that of the limestone below, and have exposed the upper surface of the drab sandstone, No. 11, of the Cascade river section. On the borders of the valley of the Little Colorado the trap and the underlying strata have been eroded to such a degree that they form mesa walls of four or five hundred feet in height, of which the upper fifty feet are trap.

Leaving the valley of the Little Colorado at Camp 76, we ascended the mesa, and crossed it in a southwesterly direction, to the headwaters of the Rio Verde. There we struck the trail of Captain Whipple's party, and I was able to connect my observations with those of Mr. Marcou, the geologist who accompanied that officer. The geology of all this region we found to be exceedingly simple, and to include nothing but what had already become quite familiar, from our experience of the preceding month.

A sheet of trap occupies almost without exception the entire surface from the Picacho to the San Francisco mountain. In one or two instances I noticed masses of the underlying sedimentary rocks forming hills not covered by the trap; as that separating Partridge from Cedar creek. These hills had such an altitude that they were not submerged by the lava-flood which covered the lower grounds, and concealed all minor evidences of the erosion previously suffered by the general surface of the country. The sheet of trap has been cut through by most of the streams; exposing the stratification of the underlying rocks, as well as the outline of their upper surfaces. From these exposures it was easy to perceive that the lava had covered a district precisely similar to that nearer the Colorado on the high mesa, where we crossed it; a high plateau of sedimentary rocks, which had been cut into valleys of moderate depth, and on which the landscape exhibited a series of gentle curves, like those of the "rolling country" of the Mississippi valley.

Before the floods of lava covered this region its geological structure was as like that of the high mesa further north, as were its physical features. The hills of sedimentary rock—such as that referred to east of Partridge creek—are composed, above, of the crinoidal limestone, (middle carboniferous,) the same which caps the mesa wall at Camp 70, and forms the surface rock of the high mesa east of that point. Here, as there, it is highly fossiliferous, and contains *Productus semireticulatus*, *P. Ivesi*, *Athyris subtilita*, crinoidal columns, &c., &c., in great numbers. Beneath this is the drab cross stratified sandstone, already so fully described, which holds the same relative position in all the numerous localities on our route where it is exposed.

Fig. 16.—SECTION OF STRATA FROM THE PICACHO TO BILL WILLIAMS'S MOUNTAIN.

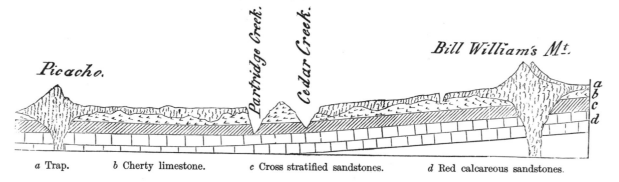

a Trap.   b Cherty limestone.   c Cross stratified sandstones.   d Red calcareous sandstones.

Partridge and Cedar creeks now flow in valleys which had been partially excavated before the period of the trap overflow. The walls of the cañon of Partridge creek are generally composed at base of the cross stratified sandstone—the limestone being in most localities wanting—upon which is a mass of trap, of a thickness varying with the elevation of the surface over which it flowed. In some places the sandstone is entirely wanting; the trap coming down and forming the bed of the stream.

The description of the geology of this vicinity, given by Mr. Marcou, (*Pacific Railroad Report*, vol. III, *Geological Report*, pp. 154, 155 and 156; *Geology of North America*, pp. 23, 24, &c.,) is very brief and not altogether comprehensible. While traversing the region about the San Francisco mountain the party of Captain Whipple were constantly involved in snow storms, and the ground was so generally covered, that the accurate determination of the geological structure was difficult if not impossible.

Mr. Marcou speaks of finding, under the lava in the immediate vicinity of Partridge and Cedar creeks, the "*magnesian limestone*" (Permian) and "*carboniferous sandstones*"—the equivalents of the coal measures; and beneath them the "*mountain limestone*," with *Productus semireticulatus, Terebratula subtilita*, &c. &c. A few miles further west, after passing over surfaces occupied by carboniferous sandstones, and seeing the mountain limestone exposed in many localities, he reached an escarpment composed of granite from base to middle, then red sandstones, which he calls Devonian, "above which are beds of limestone and gray sandstone belonging to the mountain limestone." No fossils were found in the sandstones.

Unfortunately, Mr. Marcou's notice of this interesting section is very brief. This is deeply to be regretted, as the important truths there taught in reference to the original extent and mode of formation of the table-lands are left to the contingency of a visit to that far-off and inhospitable region by some competent geologist, who will make full and accurate observations, and for his conclusions give us satisfactory proofs.

There would be no objection to the acceptance of Mr. Marcou's unqualified assertion that here were exposed the Devonian sandstones and the Mountain or Lower Carboniferous limestone, were it not that the evidences of geological age which induced his decision are of at least questionable value; and there are strong reasons, judging from the exposures examined by us, especially that in the cañon of the Colorado, for suspecting that the strata composing the section described by Mr. Marcou are not older than the Carboniferous epoch. By reference to the sections of the cañon of the Colorado, that of the high mesa at Camp 70, and of the cañon of Cascade river, all of which are given in detail in the preceding chapter, it will be seen that the oldest palæozoic strata, those resting on the granite in the bottom of the basin of the Little Colorado, consist of a series of red sandstones and shales more than a thousand feet in thickness, and that these are deposited around—their strata abutting against—the ridges and pinnacles of the granite. Above these red sandstones, &c., follow another thousand feet of silicious and argillaceous shales, interstratified with thin bands of limestone, clouded red and blue, or yellow. Upon this series we, for the first time, met with a massive, thick-bedded, gray limestone, a very important constituent of the geological column, having a thickness of over a thousand feet. This I have regarded as probably the equivalent of the Mountain limestone. On this limestone rests a series of dark red sandstones and red shales, several hundred feet in thickness; above them, two hundred feet of gray or drab sandstones; then the crinoidal limestone, the surface rock over all the western part of the high mesa.

This latter rock, which is certainly the one exposed on the banks of Partridge and Cedar creeks, is frequently referred to in the journal of Mr. Marcou, and is considered by him the "Lower Carboniferous or Mountain Limestone." Its fossils, however, as will be seen by reference to the chapter on Palæontology, prove it to be the equivalent of the Coal measures of the Mississippi valley, and more recent than the Mountain limestone.

If Mr. Marcou's observations were exact, and if the limestone crowning the cliff, noticed and figured in his journal of January 22, (*Pacific Railroad Report*, vol. III, *Geological Report*, p. 156; *Geology of North America*, p. 24,) is, as he says, identical with that of Partridge creek, it is evident that all the stratified portion of the section in the cliff referred to is composed of Carboniferous rocks, the Middle Carboniferous limestone forming the summit; beneath which, precisely as at Camp 70, &c., are the drab and red sandstones. There is scarcely a doubt that this is the true reading of the facts. The observations made by our party on three sides of the locality in question can scarcely be reconciled with any other conclusion.

Aside from the complete correspondence between the stratified portions of the section given by Mr. Marcou and those of the Middle Carboniferous strata in neighboring localities, there is a striking *discordance* between that section and that of the cañon of the Colorado, which, in a like manner, includes the junction of the granite with the sedimentary rocks.

Mr. Marcou represents the cliffs on Pueblo creek as twelve hundred feet in height, of which six hundred are granite; and from the spacing of his figure we may infer that the thickness of the red sandstones is not greater than two hundred feet, the remaining four hundred being made up of "gray sandstone and carboniferous limestone." Even supposing this limestone to be as he has represented it, the *Mountain limestone*, there is no room between it and the granite for the two thousand feet of strata which should occupy that interval. We can hardly imagine that a group of rocks of such thickness and character as those which underlie the Mountain limestone in the cañon of the Colorado should have been so much reduced in thickness within a distance of fifty miles. From all these considerations I am compelled to ascribe to the "Devonian sandstones" of Mr. Marcou, not only in the locality referred to, but wherever appearing immediately beneath what he considers the *Mountain limestone*, a date not earlier than the Carboniferous era.

The questions involved in the determination of the age of the strata exposed on Pueblo creek have not simply an abstract interest, but are of the highest scientific importance as affecting the mode of formation and original extent of the great central plateau. If, as supposed by Mr. Marcou, we find the granitic masses now forming the natural boundaries of the table-lands crowned with the oldest rocks of the series, we prove that these mountain chains had no existence during the older palaeozoic periods, and that the strata forming the table-lands once extended indefinitely westward. If, on the contrary, we find the Silurian and Devonian strata abutting against, but never covering, the granite ranges, none but Carboniferous rocks crowning their summits, we must conclude that the mountains west of the table-lands, like those bordering the Rio Grande, existed, at least in embryo, anterior to the palaeozoic epoch, and that they limited the area of deposition of the Silurian and Devonian rocks. The evidence which we at present have, bearing on this question, seems to me decidedly in favor of the latter supposition; and while our views of the general geological structure of this portion of the continent are all liable to be changed or modified by the observations which shall be hereafter made in the wide areas yet unexplored, we may safely say that this is one of the generalizations sanctioned by all the knowledge we yet have on the subject.

Magnesian limestone.—Mr. Marcou, in several places in his journal and resumé, speaks of finding, both east and west of the San Francisco mountains, a magnesian limestone, the equivalent of the European Permian rock of the same name. Among other localities of its occurrence, cited by him, is a hill three miles east of Captain Whipple's Camp 96.—*(Pacific Railroad Report*, vol. III, *Geology*, p. 156.)

In his *resumé*, pages 23 and 24, he again refers to this magnesian limestone, and to this among other localities where it is exposed. His words are: "This formation, which is placed between the carboniferous and the trias, corresponds, without doubt, to the magnesian limestone (Permian) of England, and is a new member, which I add to the series of the secondary rocks in "North America."

Of the limestone exposed near the crossing of the Little Colorado—the point where Mr. Marcou supposed he first met with Permian rocks—I shall have occasion to speak again. In reference to that observed by him between Lava and Partridge creeks, I am compelled to say that, on an examination of the same localities, made under the most favorable circumstances, I failed to detect any evidence of the presence of Permian strata. The hill which he describes as formed at summit of magnesian, at base of mountain limestone, was ascended by our party. To me it seemed composed throughout of the crinoidal or Coal measure limestone; exhibiting precisely the same lithological characters and fossils as at our Camps 70, 73, &c. Some of its layers are dolomitic, and some are nearly destitute of fossils. The nodules of chert, mentioned by Mr. Marcou, are abundantly distributed through most parts of it, and are still more characteristic of the Upper Carboniferous limestone; which is, as I have stated, probably only locally separated from this by beds of gypsum. I am very confident that none of the strata exposed west of the San Francisco mountain and east of Partridge creek are more recent than the carboniferous epoch; nor do I believe that the summit of that series is reached in any section there exposed.

From Cedar creek to New Year's Spring the surface is occupied by volcanic materials. A sheet of dark compact or vesicular trap throughout that distance covers the sedimentary rocks, except where cut through in the cañons of the draining streams. As we approached the San Francisco mountain this plateau becomes gradually more and more covered by the products of more recent eruptions poured over, or piled upon its surface. Of these volcanic masses the most conspicuous are Bill Williams's mountain, Mount Kendrick, and Mount Sitgreaves; each of which is a mountain of considerable size, marking the site of a volcanic vent scarcely inferior in magnitude to that of San Francisco. Beside these principal cones there are an infinite number of smaller size, of which many are distinctly crateriform, and all seem to have been the foci of volcanic fires.

The San Francisco mountain has a general conical form, but terminates above in four distinct summits. These seem to surround a central crater; at least, such is the impression we obtained from the best views we had of it. On all sides, and especially towards the north, spurs radiate from it which mark the lines followed by the lava floods of some of its great eruptions.

The soil arising from the decomposition of the lava and ashes ejected from these volcanoes is evidently of excellent quality, sustaining magnificent forests of pine, interspersed with which are prairies covered with luxuriant grass.

Carboniferous limestone.—About New Year's Spring and eastward is an area of considerable size, which, by some chance, has escaped the torrents of lava poured over all the surrounding country. Here the surface of the Carboniferous limestone, forming the summit of the high mesa, is fully exposed; and thence to the Little Colorado, with occasional interruptions, it forms the substratum of all parts of our route. In a number of localities I noticed its characteristic fossils, *Productus semireticulatus*, &c., but in other places it contains no fossils whatever. The geodes of crystallized carbonate of lime, so marked a feature at Camp 70, are usually abundant. The surface of the limestone has been considerably eroded by streams flowing from the San Francisco mountain towards the Little Colorado; and as these streams have no existence at the present day, their dry beds offered us the most agreable line of travel. In the banks of these arroyos the cut edges of the strata show a strong dip towards the northeast, which continues with great general uniformity to the banks of the Little Colorado.

At intervals the sedimentary rock is covered with erupted materials, basaltic trap, scoria or ashes; and at several points are cones, once minor volcanic vents, and the sources from which these igneous rocks were derived. Near our Camp 84 is the most interesting group of these craters met with on our route, (Fig. 17.) Several of them are still very perfect in form, and long sinuous lines of black lava run down their sides—graphic records of their latest eruptions.

Ten miles west of the Little Colorado we entered a region where scarce any soil covers the rock; and thence, to the crossing of the stream, we were travelling almost constantly upon its naked service. Throughout most of this distance we passed over a cream-colored limestone undistinguishable in its lithological characters from that which contains well-known Carboniferous fossils a few miles back, and of which it seems to be the continuation. Fossils are here rare, but not far from the point where we left it I observed a well-marked *Euomphalus*, similar in appearance to *E. rugosus*, which, unfortunately, was imbedded in a block of such size and solidity that I could not remove it by any means at my command.

This limestone forms the walls of the Cañon Diablo, where it was carefully examined by Mr. A. H. Campbell, when attached to Captain Whipple's party. Mr. Campbell found in it crinoidal columns, and regarded it as identical with the limestone which occupies most of the area between San Francisco mountain and that point.

The determination of the age of this rock is a matter of some little consequence from the discussion to which it has given rise. By Mr. Marcou—like that already referred to west of the San Francisco mountain—it is regarded as the equivalent of the English *Magnesian limestone;* and on that identification he bases his claim to have first detected Permian rocks on the North American continent. The evidence which led him to this conclusion will be seen by reference to his journal and resumé.—*(Pacific Railroad Report,* vol. III, pp. 153 and 170,) and *(North American Geology,* pp. 14 and 15.) It is scarcely necessary to say that the fossils, said by Mr. Marcou to have been recognized by him in this rock, if what he supposed them, would prove conclusively that it was not of Permian age; the genus *Nautilus* ranging through all the strata from the older Palaeozoic to the present epoch; the others *(Belemnites and Pteroceras)* being confined to more recent stata than the Permian. The Paleontological evidence, therefore, is rather against than for this conclusion.

Fig. 17.—VOLCANIC CONES EAST OF THE SAN FRANCISCO MOUNTAIN.

The proof furnished by the lithological characters and superposition of this rock will, I think, hardly be regarded by the unprejudiced inquirer as more confirmatory of this theory. It is true that it closely resembles the cream-colored Permian limestones of Kansas; hand specimens, which I have from the banks of Cottonwood creek, Kansas, being scarcely distinguishable from those collected at the crossing of the Little Colorado; but it is also true that the limestone which occupies so much of the space between the Little Colorado and San Francisco mountain exhibits nearly the same lithological characters throughout; and in some localities, where containing quantities of *Productus semireticulatus* and other unmistakable Carboniferous fossils, is, perhaps, a little more like the Permian rock of Kansas than is that nearer the Little Colorado. The same may be said of the cream-colored portions of the crinoidal limestone in the cañon of Cascade river.

The chemical composition of this rock is no proof of its identity with the Magnesian limestone of Europe, as most of the limestones of the far west are more or less dolomitic; and so are many of the limestones of the Coal measures in the valley of the Mississippi. Even if it should be proved that the red sandstones and shales overlying it are Triassic, of which, as yet, we have no satisfactory evidence, it by no means follows that it is of Permian age. In many localities in New Mexico, examined by Mr. Marcou or myself, east of this point, the red sandstones and variegated marls (Trias of Marcou) rest directly upon the Carboniferous limestones. Every geologist knows that the geological column is nowhere complete, but that, in every known locality, either entire formations or important sub-divisions are wanting, though the superior and inferior strata may be fully represented.

Coming, as I did, to the examination of the rock in question from the clear and beautiful exposures of the Carboniferous strata described in the preceding pages, I detected in it no new element, and did not hesitate to consider it a portion of that series. It is possible that when the vicinity comes to be more fully explored there may be found in this rock fossils of Permian character, as in Kansas the Upper Carboniferous strata contain a few prophetic types of the succeeding Permian fauna; but probably then, as now, it would be impossible to draw any line of separation between the strata of limestone immediately underlying the red sandstone, on the Little Colorado, and those a few feet below, which are conformable with and lithologically undistinguishable from them, and which are purely Carboniferous. At present it is not saying too much to assert that we want the first shadow of proof of the Permian age of the rock in question, and, with the knowledge we now have, it is plainly required of us to regard it as an integral portion of the Carboniferous series.

CHAPTER VIII.

GEOLOGY OF REGION BETWEEN THE COLORADO AND FORT DEFIANCE.

VALLEY OF THE LITTLE COLORADO AT CROSSING.

The trough of the Little Colorado, from the cascades to the point where we left it, fifty miles above, is similar in all the general aspects of its structure to what it has been described to be further north, except that the stream has not so deeply eroded the strata here as below, and its bed is formed of a higher member of the geological series; the belt of low and level land which it includes is narrower, and the bluffs or walls bounding it much less imposing in their magnitude.

The river is here scarcely depressed below the plain bordering it; the cañon which it traverses for a hundred miles above its mouth commencing at the falls, fifteen miles below where we struck it. The strata which compose its bed and banks have a distinct dip to the northwest, rising towards the southeast, where they have been upheaved in the elevation of the Mogollon mountains.

Towards the southwest they also rise rapidly, forming the slope descended by our party. On the northeast they are nearly horizontal for a few miles, and then begin to rise toward the western spurs of the Rocky mountain system. From this description it will be seen that the Little Colorado occupies nearly the bottom of a synclinal trough or basin, of which the mountains I have enumerated form the rim of the southern half.

The fall of the river in this part of its course is somewhat more rapid than the dip of the strata, so that, following it towards its sources, we were constantly ascending in the geological series. At the crossing we mounted a distinct step in the scale, formed by the red sandstone group. Fifty miles above this point, as I learn from the members of our party who followed the course of the stream around to Fort Defiance, the variegated marls which overlie the red sandstones close in upon them, and form the substratum of the remainder of their route to the fort. These, to us, new elements in the geological column exhibit the following characters:

Red sandstone formation.—The limestone which forms the surface rock west of the Little Colorado has a dip even more rapid than the descent of the slope of the valley, and three miles from the river it passes beneath a red sandstone and disappears. This rock was first seen in detached outliers, left in the erosion of the general surface, often of most grotesque and remarkable forms. The stratification of these buttes is concordant with that of the limestone, but along our line of observation the two formations are perfectly distinct, and we saw nothing of the interstratification described by Mr. Marcou. This red sandstone forms part of a group of strata several hundred feet in thickness, which, though exhibiting considerable differences among themselves, have certain common characters that serve to form a distinct geological horizon, and one readily recognizable wherever it appears. The group consists of sandstones, shales, and conglomerates, of which the prevailing color is a deep red, deeper than that of the red rocks above or beneath them. To this general rule there are, however, many local exceptions, some members of the series frequently exhibiting a decided green tinge, as in the Navajo country, Fort Defiance, Apache cañon east of Santa Fé, &c. This formation is also characterized by *salt springs* which flow from it in several localities. Though I examined its members in various exposures, I was never able to detect in them a fossil of any kind. In some places the compact red sandstones of this series show a striking lithological resemblance to those of the valley of the Connecticut and New Jersey, so much used for architectural purposes, while the greenish shelly sandstones are scarcely distinguishable from those forming the fish beds at Hadley Falls, Mass., Durham, Conn., &c.

By Mr. Marcou this group is considered the equivalent of the red sandstones of Lake Superior and of that portion of the Trias of Europe called by the Germans *Bunter Sandstein*, by the French *Grés Bigarré.*—(*Geology of North America*, pp. 10, 11.)

No American geologist will need to be informed that the sandstones of Lake Superior are of the age of the Potsdam of New York, and lie at the base of the Silurian series. It is true that there is considerable lithological resemblance between the Potsdam sandstones of Lake Superior and those overlying the Carboniferous series in New Mexico; but that fact serves simply to show how fallacious are the inferences derived alone from lithological characters. There is no evidence opposed to the theory that this group is the equivalent of a portion of the Trias of Europe, but it must also be said we have, as yet, little or no evidence in favor of it. As a conjecture, this classification is perhaps creditable to its author, but all the data for the determination of its truth are yet to be discovered.

Judging from all the facts now in our possession in reference to this group, it seems quite as likely to prove Permian as Triassic. It is, perhaps, still more likely to be both, like the "New red sandstone formation" of the Atlantic States, a series of strata succeeding the Carboniferous rocks, plainly the representatives of the Permian and Triassic formations of the Old World, but showing nothing of the hiatus which separates them in Europe, and being scarcely susceptible of subdivision into exact equivalents of either.

From my journal I extract the following additional observations on these strata, made in the vicinity of the crossing of the Little Colorado:

"*May* 1.—The limestone over which we have passed, descending from the San Francisco mountain, as we approached our present camp, showed a dip to the northeast of at least a hundred feet to the mile; and before reaching the river it passed under beds of red shale and sandstone, which are conformable with it. This sandstone is deep blood-red in color, is soft, and eroded into fantastic blocks and masses, of which the surfaces are most curiously etched and carved by weathering. Above these heavier beds are soft, red, argillaceous shales, with layers of red and green, foliated, ripple-marked, fine grained, micaceous sandstones, all without fossils. Such is the geology of the south bank of the river. On the north bank the red shales appear at intervals, but are usually concealed by alluvial soil, sand, and gravel. About seven miles from the river the valley is bounded by a mesa wall nearly one thousand feet in height, of which the base is formed by the red shales and sandstones before described."

A portion of this series, which is concealed by the alluvium near Camp 85, is more fully exposed further up the river. Near Camp 88 a butte, representing a portion of the upper part, consists of, first, conglomerate, a coarse light-brown sandstone, with white, bluish, red, and black quartz pebbles, varying in size from that of a pea to an egg. It is about twenty feet in thickness, and lithologically, both as regards the paste and the pebbles, quite undistinguishable from much of the Carboniferous conglomerate in Ohio and Pennsylvania. Below this rock is a reddish white, rather shelly, micaceous sandstone, of which over thirty feet are exposed.

At the mouth of Cottonwood Fork the same rocks are still better shown. The banks of the stream are there composed of reddish shaly sandstones, the more solid portions closely resembling the red sandstone of New Jersey. From this rock, about fifty feet below its upper surface, issue copious salt springs, the water of which collects in several natural reservoirs, and is covered with a sheet of salt resembling ice. This salt is very palatable, and apparently quite pure. Above the sandstone is the conglomerate first noticed at Camp 88, here having a thickness of thirty or forty feet, then purplish shales, above which are greenish brown sandstones, which form the summit of this series. Over the sandstones are beds of brown, blue, purple, lilac, red, and cream-colored marls, with bands of magnesian limestone, the base of the series of *variegated marls* hereafter to be described. Thin layers of gypsum occur locally in all the members of the saliferous sandstones, being most noticeable in the middle portion, at the ruined *pueblo* between Camps 88 and 89. I had no means of measuring accurately the aggregate thickness of this group of rocks, but have estimated it, on the Little Colorado, at about seven hundred feet. Further eastward I think it is considerably less.

PAINTED DESERT.

After crossing the Little Colorado at Camp 85, a detachment of our party struck northward, to regain the line of exploration abandoned on account of the impassable cañons of Cascade river. Ascending the mesa wall which bounds the valley north of our crossing place, we entered a region to which the above name was appropriately given, as indicative of its barrenness and desolation, as well as of the peculiar scenery which it exhibits. Although compelled by the want of water to retrace our steps before we had penetrated this district to any great distance, such is the nature of the surface, the atmosphere so clear, our view so entirely unobstructed, that we were able to determine its geological structure at least fifty miles beyond the point where we turned back. Subsequently, when on the high mesa at the Moqui villages, we obtained a nearer view of the region we then saw in the distance north of us, which fully confirmed the impressions we then received, and showed that the peculiar physical aspect and geological structure of the Painted Desert prevail over a wide belt of country bordering the Little Colorado on the east, and extending at least as far northward as our Camp 73.

Fig. 18.—MESA WALLS OF RED SANDSTONE.—PAINTED DESERT.

All this area is occupied by the mesa of which the edge forms the eastern boundary of the valley of the Little Colorado. It is traversed by a series of broad valleys of erosion, which seem to have been formed by a more abundant supply of moisture than now falls upon this surface. These valleys are bounded by abrupt and usually perpendicular walls, composed of the blood-red strata of the saliferous sandstones and the variegated marls which overlie them. In the process of erosion many buttes and pinnacles have been left standing, which, by their forms and colors, closely imitate upon a colossal scale the structures of human art. The geological horizon is here precisely the same as that of much of the country lying between the Mississippi and the Rio Grande, of which the peculiar scenery, so frequently described by travellers, seems also to be very similar to that of the region under consideration.

Variegated marls.—This formation composes the upper portion of the mesa when unbroken throughout the Painted Desert, and usually caps the walls of sandstone already described, to the deep red of which its lighter colors afford a strong contrast. As these marls occupy so large a part of the country traversed by our party between the Little Colorado and Rio Grande, I shall have occasion frequently to refer to them.

On our way to the Moqui villages we passed through a region singularly favorable for accurate geological investigation; where there is no vegetation to impede the view; where the strata are entirely undisturbed, and are cut by valleys of erosion, in the wall-like sides of which every inch of the series may be examined. In this journey we ascended in the geological scale from the summit of the Carboniferous to the base of the Cretaceous series. Of this interval there is no portion of which the exposures are not as complete as could be desired, nor is there any part that was not as carefully examined as seemed necessary to learn all it had to teach. While we had constantly to regret the absence of fossils, which alone can form reliable guides in establishing the subdivision of the great group of rocks occupying this space, the continuity and physical characters of the strata were on that account the more carefully noted. These rocks of themselves form a great mesa; and on this, fifty miles from its southern edge, rises another, which, singularly enough, is composed of the members of a different geological formation, the Cretaceous; and when we had ascended that we could overlook at one view all the space separating us from the carboniferous limestone west of the Little Colorado.*

Fig. 19.—SECTION OF MESA BETWEEN THE LITTLE COLORADO AND MOQUI VILLAGES.

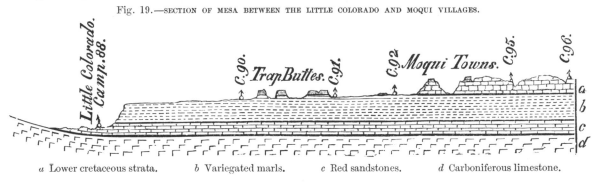

a Lower cretaceous strata.   b Variegated marls.   c Red sandstones.   d Carboniferous limestone.

In the absence of more numerous and characteristic fossils, with all the data in our possession, we were only able to make two or at most three divisions of the strata intervening between the Carboniferous limestone and the Chalk. Of these, the first and lowest is the group of red sandstones already described. The second is that of the variegated marls, a formation which has an aggregate thickness of about fifteen hundred feet, and is remarkably uniform in composition from bottom to top. It consists of red, blue, green, orange, purple, white, brown, lilac, and yellow marls, interstratified with bands of purple, bluish-white, or mottled magnesian limestones, most numerous toward the base. In some localities these marls are sufficiently indurated to deserve the name of soft calcareous sandstones. The only fossils observed in them are silicified trunks of coniferous trees, which are highly characteristic of the lower half of the series, being found abundantly wherever it is exposed. The variegated marls contain gypsum everywhere—near the Colorado in smaller quantities, toward the Rio Grande in immense masses.

Upon the marls, and separating them from the first of the overlying Cretaceous sandstones at the Moquis villages, is a stratum of lignite, or impure coal, which, in its partings of clay, contain an interesting group of fossil plants closely allied to Jurassic species of Europe. This is not a constant member of the series; and whether it should be given a distinct place in the geological scale, or should be regarded as belonging to the Cretaceous group above, or to the variegated marls below, cannot at present be determined, but I am inclined to the latter view, and am disposed to regard it as an index of the geological age of a part at least of that series.

* The geological structure of this region will be comprehended at a glance by reference to the accompanying wood cut.

All the strata of the groups I have described are conformable among themselves as well as to those of the Carboniferous rocks below and the Cretaceous above.

Mr. Marcou fills the interval between the red sandstones of the Little Colorado and the Cretaceous strata of the Rio Grande with a series of rocks of much greater thickness, and presenting diagnostic characters quite different from such as came under our observation. As will be seen hereafter, there is reason to believe that the "Jurassic rocks" of his classification are Cretaceous, and in reference to his subdivisions of the variegated marls I can only say that we failed to recognize them on our route. They may be plainly discernible in the region traversed by him east of the Rio Grande, but certainly are not so in Western New Mexico. His second Triassic group, of which the place is immediately above the red sandstones of the Little Colorado, is, according to his description, (*Geology of North America*, p. 11,) composed of beds of white and red clay, containing immense masses of gypsum, and traversed by veins of selenite, with numerous interposed beds of magnesian limestone, and frequent deposits of rock salt. To this division he assigns a thickness of fifteen hundred feet. In the various exposures of the strata overlying the red sandstones, which we examined in the country between the Little Colorado and Rio Grande, we found them to consist of highly colored marls, containing bands of magnesian limestone, most numerous near the base, but running through nearly the entire series. No beds of rock salt were observed, and the gypsum is most abundant in the upper part of the group, while the silicified wood is confined to the lower half—facts quite at variance with those cited by him as the grounds of his classification. This division Mr. Marcou considers, with perhaps as much reason as the first above the Carboniferous limestone, as the equivalent of a member of the European Trias; in this case of the *Muschelkalk*.

The third division which Mr. Marcou has established he denominates the *Variegated mar's*, and regards it as the equivalent of the *Marnes Irisèes* of France, and of the *Keuper* of Germany. In this division he locates the petrified forest of Lithodendron creek, and considers it characteristic of the formation, whereas the marls containing the silicified wood of Lithodendron creek, and of the north side of the valley of the Little Colorado generally, rest directly upon the red saliferous sandstones, the greater number of fossil trees which they contain occurring within two or three hundred feet of the surface of that group.

The intimate structure of the mesa bordering the Little Colorado on the northeast will be seen from the following sections.

The bluff bounding the valley north of Camp 85, crossed when entering the Painted Desert, is composed of the strata enumerated below.

Variegated Marls.

		Feet.
1.	Ochery sand, very soft; forming summit	25
2.	Bluish white marl	20
3.	Bluish white magnesian limestone	11
4.	Bluish white marl	21
5.	Purple magnesian limestone	4
6.	Purple marl	40
7.	Red shales and sandstone	400

A few miles further east, at the mouth of Cottonwood Fork, a continuation of the same mesa afforded me a somewhat more complete section, reaching higher into the series of variegated marls. It consists of the following elements:

Variegated Marls.

1. Light orange marl .... 15 feet.
2. Green and purple magnesian limestone, containing worm like concretions of
   calcareous spar .... 5 feet.
3. Pinkish purple marl .... 22 feet.
4. Brown shelly sandstone .... 8 inches.
5. Purple marl with silicified wood .... 16 feet.
6. Purplish green cherty magnesian limestone, in several layers, alternating with
   bands of marl .... 8 feet.
7. Purple and cream-colored marls .... 30 feet.
8. Greenish magnesian limestone, in thin layers, with bands of marl .... 12 feet.
9. Yellow, red, and purple marls .... 40 feet.
10. Green limestone, similar to No. 8 .... 3 feet.
11. Red, purple, pink, green, lilac, brown, and blue marls, with silicified wood .. 350 feet.

Red Sandstone Series.

12. Greenish foliated sandstone .... 20 feet.
13. Purple shales with some silicified wood .... 50 feet.
14. Red sandstone and shale .... 45 feet.
15. Conglomerate .... 26 feet.
16. Dark red laminated sandstone, from which issue salt springs, to base.

It will be noticed that in the above section the lower portion of the variegated marls contain no bands of magnesian limestone ; they are, however, here but locally wanting. A few miles west of Cottonwood Fork there are at least six bands of dolomite in the first three hundred feet of the variegated marls.   These marls in this vicinity have so little consistence that they have been even more effected by the action of water, and more extensively and strangely eroded, than are the red sandstones which underlie them.

In our ascent of the mesa between Camps 89 and 90 the trail we followed led through a labyrinth of hills of all conceivable forms and sizes, which had been shaped by the erosion of the lower portion of the marl series.   The colors of the strata are as vivid as would ever be used in the construction of a geological diagram, and the scenery formed by the combination of these brilliant and varied colors, with outlines quite as unusual in natural objects, produced a picture as unlike those presented by most portions of the earth's surface as could well be imagined.

In the denudation of the marls immense quantities of silicified wood have been brought to light.   Fragments of all sizes are thickly strewed over the low lands, and have accumulated in piles of many hundred cords at the bottom of some of the slopes, where they have precisely the appearance of so much drift wood.   These fossil trees are apparently all coniferous, though belonging to several species and probably representing more than one genus.   From the difficulty of having specimens properly sliced for the microscope they have not yet been critically examined.   They exhibit considerable variety in their mode of preservation, but frequently retain, in great beauty and perfection, the details of their anatomical structure.   Some of the trunks are converted into red jasper, and look like huge masses of red sealingwax.   Others are composed of agate or opalescent chalcedony, often showing a variety of bright colors and forming beautiful specimens for the cabinet.   As generally found, these silicified trunks are broken into pieces from one to six feet in length, as though they had been sawed through transversely. These pieces have usually been separated from their fellows and lie scattered about in the greatest confusion, but where the marls containing them have been horizontally wooded I found a number of trunks of which the fragments were all in opposition, and the tree complete from root to summit. Of these, some had a diameter of at least three, and a length of more than forty feet.

I examined these specimens with some care to determine, if possible, whether they had grown on the spot, as those of Lithodendron creek are supposed to have done by the members of Captain Whipple's party, or whether they had been transported to their positions. In all that came under my observation, I failed to find any evidence that they had grown in the vicinity. All the trunks are stripped of their branches and exhibit precisely the appearance of those transported to some distance by the agency of water. In confirmation of this view I should also say I found in the marls, with the entire trunks, rounded and water-worn fragments of wood, in some instances silicified and in others converted into lignite.

I gathered the same impression from all the collections of silicified wood which I observed in this formation in Western New Mexico, viz: that all had been *transported*, but not *far* removed from their place of growth.

Trap buttes.—A few miles north of the point where we ascended the mesa, we approached a series of detached buttes which rose from its surface to the height of several hundred feet, and of which the peculiar outlines had attracted our attention, while we were yet many miles west of the Little Colorado. These buttes we found to consist of masses of trap at top, beneath which was a continuation of the series of variegated marls already given. The trap is, in some cases, partially columnar, the columns being vertical, and evidently once formed part of a basaltic mesa which covered a large area in this vicinity. The source from which this trap was derived seems to have been some point on a line from the crossing of the Little Colorado to Fort Defiance, but east and south of our route, as the trap buttes become broader and more numerous northeast of our Camps 90 and 91, but were not visible on any part of our route from the Moqui villages eastward.

The amount of erosion which this mesa has suffered since the trap was poured over it is measured by the present altitude of the layer of trap (nearly 400 feet) above the general surface. Beneath the trap the marls are still horizontal, and but little changed. The composition of the basis of the different buttes is everywhere the same, showing conclusively that they are but fragments of once continuous strata.

Although the denudation here indicated is surprisingly great, I think we have incontestable proof that the amount of erosion previous to the trap overflow was even greater than what has taken place since. On the north the region occupied by the trap buttes is bounded by the elevated mesa composed of the Cretaceous rocks which once stretched over all this surface, as far as the Little Colorado, and doubtless still further, completely covering the entire series of the variegated marls. From the whole of this area the Lower Cretaceous strata, nearly a thousand feet in thickness, (and we have even reason to suppose an equal thickness of Upper Cretaceous rocks,) were removed by denudation previous to the overflow of the flood of volcanic matter.

This will appear sufficiently obvious to any one who has an opportunity to examine this region, but it was also demonstrated by the discovery in one of these buttes of a patch of Cretaceous sandstone overlying the marls, and interposed between them and the trap. The sections afforded in the bases of the trap buttes supply the continuation of the series of the variegated marls, from the point reached in the section last given to the top of the formation.

A large butte at Camp 91, of which the castellated summit rises to the height of more than five hundred feet above the plain, exhibits fine exposures of the following strata:

		Feet.
1. Trap, partially columnar		160
2. Green, reddish-brown, and drab, soft calcareous sandstones, (indurated marls.)		60
3. Green, purple, red, and yellow marls, and calcareous sandstones		150
4. Magnesian limestone, pinkish, cherty		5

Feet.

5. Thick-bedded, light-brown, pink, purple, and banded calcareous sandstones 50
6. Orange yellow, and red marls 140
   Summit of last section.

In another butte, between Camps 90 and 91, the trap rests upon the magnesian limestone— No. 4 of the last section—and the indurated marls or calcareous sandstones below are pink or pure white. In another, east of Camp 91, the same section as that just given in detail is exposed, with the addition of a stratum of coarse yellow sandstone, the base-rock of the great Cretaceous mesa, which, ten miles further north, completely covers and conceals the variegated marls. In the upper part of the series represented in the buttes, fossil wood, so abundant below, was nowhere observed. The strata contain gypsum in small quantities, and are highly charged with salts of several kinds; such as chloride of sodium, and sulphates of soda and magnesia. The marls are generally more indurated here than below, better deserving the name of calcareous sandstones. The variety of colors which they present is also not as great, the vertical breadth of the color-bands being much greater. These differences are, however, not strongly marked, and are somewhat local.

At Camp 92 we had passed the region of the trap buttes, and found the first outliers of the Cretaceous mesa, which, five miles north of us, rose like a huge wall from the plain. We had here ascended imperceptibly through all the series of the variegated marls, and the summit of a low hill, on which we were encamped, was crowned with the first of the Cretaceous rocks, forming a fit terminus to the fine section of the upper marl beds exposed in its sides. The details of this section are as follows:

Feet.

1. Coarse yellowish sandstone with concretions of oxide of iron, and obscure impressions
    of dicotyledonous leaves 16
2. Impure coal, alternating with bands of bituminous shale and fire clay, containing
    fossil plants—*Clathropteris, Cyclopteris, Sphenopteris, Pecopteris*, &c.—all new
    species 12
3. Fire clay and shale 3
4. Coarse, compact, white, concretionary sandstone 6
5. Green marl 25
6. Bright-red marl 22
7. White, soft, saccharoidal calcareous sandstone—to base.

The summit rock is, for the most part, as indicated above, a coarse yellowish sandstone; but it sometimes contains small quartz pebbles, becoming a conglomerate. It also includes spherical and botryoidal concretions of carb. ox. iron. Many obscure vegetable impressions are visible on its surfaces, of which some are those of dicotyledonous leaves, but so badly preserved in its coarse texture as to be scarcely determinable. The coal seam beneath it is compound in character, consisting of a great number of alternations of coal—some of which is of good quality—with bituminous shale and a pure white clay, closely resembling the finer varieties of fire clay, associated with the coal seams of the Carboniferous epoch. The details of structure of this bed of coal or lignite, are:

Inches.

1. Bituminous shale 6
2. Coal 10
3. Clay 3
4. Bituminous shale 6
5. Coal 12
6. Clay 2
7. Bituminous shale 11
8. Coal 6

	Inches.
9. Clay	3
10. Coal	9
11. Bituminous shale	18
12. Coal	15
13. Clay	2
14. Bituminous shale	12
15. Coal	15
16. Bituminous shale	3

All the fissures in the coal and clays are studded with tufts of fibrous gypsum. The sandstone below the coal is white and coarse, but hard; and is similar to the sandstone found beneath the fire clay of the first coal seam in the Alleghany coal field.

The marls, red and green, which lie below this are precisely like many of those found near the base of the series. As is the case with all the rocks of this region, they contain gypsum and salts which effloresce on exposed surfaces. The sandstone below the shales is pure white, very soft, and looks like white sugar. It contains a large quantity of lime and is curiously eroded by the action of the weather, as shown in the accompanying sketch.

Fig. 20.—ERODED SANDSTONE, NEAR THE MOQUI VILLAGES, (CAMP 92.)

Fossil plants.—The coal seam of Camp 92 varies greatly in thickness even within the limits of the section there exposed. Five miles north I found it occupying the same position, but thin; and in several localities further east, where the exposures included its place in the series, it was not to be found. Wherever it appears it would probably form an important guide in the determination of geological structure, as it contains numbers of fossil plants very beautifully preserved and of peculiar and unmistakable character. I deeply regret that the time I had for the examination of this locality was so short, and the means at command for excavating the strata were so imperfect, that I was able to obtain only a very fragmentary and imperfect series of specimens. Such as they are, however, they give a very appetizing glimpse of the interesting flora there buried. It is to be hoped that before long some one will visit this locality, with ample time and means to make a complete collection of all the species it includes.

The descriptions of the plants procured from this deposit are given in detail in the chapter on palæontology. It will be seen that the *species* represented are all considered new, but are closely allied to some of those most characteristic of the Jura and upper Trias of Europe.

With the amount of material we have as yet procured from this locality, we are hardly prepared to discuss the question whether this bed of lignite belongs to one or other of these formations. The plants of both are very similar, so much so that they are included in one flora by Brongnart—"the flora of the Jurassic epoch."*

While there is so much difficulty in separating the plants of the Keûper from those of the Lias in Europe, the effort to do so here, where they are all specifically different, is nearly hopeless. It is almost certain, also, that when we have collected all the species contained in these strata we shall still be unable to draw this European line clearly and sharply through them. In determining the parallelism of strata in different parts of our own continent it is probable these plants will be of great value, as they enable us to fix the lower limits of the Cretaceous series, and give us palæontological data for detecting the presence of the American Jurassic wherever developed.

Calling this florula Jurassic, as Brongnart would do, the practical bearing of its discovery on the mooted questions of the existence and extent of Jurassic rocks in New Mexico is less important than might have been anticipated, from the fact that they are restricted, as far as at present observed, to an exceedingly unimportant member of the geological series. It seems scarcely possible, however, that this coal seam can be the only representative of a great formation; and there is every reason to believe that we shall ultimately find evidence which will lead to the union with it of some of the associated strata.

The sandstones, shales, and limestones lying above also include many beds of lignite closely resembling this, and on lithological grounds would be appropriately grouped with it. In fact, they have been considered Jurassic, and the only Jurassic rocks in this region, by the geologist who claims to have discovered the representatives of this formation in New Mexico. Unfortunately, however, for that classification, immediately over the thin stratum of yellow sandstone which overlies the coal are beds of clay shale with bands of limestone, in which are unmistakable Cretaceous fossils. It is, therefore, quite evident that the Jurassic formation cannot be extended in this direction, and there is no alternative left but to consider the coal seam, if Jurassic, the sole representative of the Jurassic series, or to combine with it some portion of the underlying variegated marls, which for this purpose must be abstracted from the Trias of Mr. Marcou.

Perhaps future explorations will furnish the means for defining the limits of the formations which fill the interval between the Carboniferous and Cretaceous rock, but it has seemed to me doubtful whether an effort to identify the strata composing the geological series of this far off region, in another hemisphere, with all the subdivisions of the formations found in Europe, would be crowned with entire success. We have everywhere evidence that the diversity of fauna and flora exhibited by the different portions of the earth's surface at the present time, as well as the variety in the physical characters of all mineral deposits now forming, were foreshadowed by similar phenomena during the different geological ages.

MOQUI COUNTRY.

Cretaceous rocks.—At the Moqui villages a mesa rises abruptly from the surface of the variegated marls, presenting a striking contrast, both in physical aspect and geological structure, to

* Tab. des Gen. des Veget., Foss., Dict. de Hist. Nat., vol. XIII, p. 151.

that upon which it rests. Its broken edge has here an altitude of about five hundred feet, composed exclusively of Lower Cretaceous strata. A few miles further north additions are made to it by accessions of other, but similar, members of the same geological series, until a thickness of from seven to eight hundred feet is attained. Preserving such characters, this Lower Cretaceous mesa extends over a large area northwest, north, and east of the point where we ascended it. With the exception of valleys of erosion cut down to the formations below, it stretches continuously to the Great Colorado on the northwest, and to the Rio Grande on the east. How much of the area within this angle is occupied by it is as yet unknown; for a wide territory towards the north is still unexplored, but we traversed enough of this district to see that the Lower Cretaceous strata cover a larger space on our route than those of any other formation.

On the way from Santa Fé to Fort Leavenworth we were for nearly half the distance travelling on a continuation of these rocks; and there seems good reason to suppose that they form the geological substratum of much the greater part of the country bordering the Rocky mountains between the 35th and 40th parallels. They extend, as we know, with more or less interruption, in a broad belt, along the eastern bases of the mountains far northward into the British possessions.

From the fossils collected in the country bordering Grand and Green river by Dr. Schiel, as well as from his description of its geological structure, (*Pacific Railroad Report*, vol. II, p. 101,) it is apparent that the Cretaceous strata, as well as those of the variegated marls, are visible over a considerable area on the route of Captain Beckwith north of the Moqui country; and there is little doubt that the formations passed over by us in this region are continuous to and beyond the mouth of Grand river.

Fig. 21.—AN OUTLIER OF THE CRETACEOUS MESA, MOQUI VILLAGES.

Lower cretaceous mesa wall, Moqui villages.

The cliffs, on the summits of which the Moqui towns are perched, are composed of the following strata:

		Feet.
1.	Soft coarse yellowish sandstone	25
2.	Green shale	12
3.	Blue shale with pinnules of *Neuropteris angulata*	1
4.	Lignite	18
5.	Green shale	2
6.	Cellular sandstone	5
7.	Brown ferruginous shale	4

Feet.

8. Green shales··   28

9. Coarse yellow or white sandstone·······›···   80

10. Green shales with bands of sandstone; in some localities all soft greenish yellow
     sandstones ···   60

11. Coarse light yellow or whitish massive sandstone····························· 120

12. Green shales with bands of ferruginous sandy limestone and beds of lignite. In
     this group, at Oraylee and Camp 96, are *Pinna? lingula* (n. sp.) and *Gryphaea
     Pitcheri;* and over the lignite beds are impressions of leaves of *Platanus, Alnus
     Quercus,* &c., and fossil ferns of the genus *Sphenopteris* ·····················   90

13. Green, blue, and gray argillaceous shales, with bands of brown or yellow silicious
     limestone, containing *Ammonites percarinatus, Inoceramus Crispii?* and *Gryphaea
     Pitcheri,* var. *navia*·· 160

14. Coarse yellowish sandstone, precisely like Nos. 9 and 11, (base of Cretaceous forma-
     tion?) ···   25

15. Lignite, (Jurassic?) better than that above, to base····························   ··

Of these strata the lower two have been already noticed in the description of the section exposed at Camp 92.

It will be seen that there is great lithological similarity among all the strata of this mesa, while they are strikingly different from those of the one below it.

I have no hesitation in including all above the lower lignite bed in one geological group; and this is proved by its fossils to be a subdivision of the great Cretaceous formation, probably representing the lower third of that series.

The palæontological evidence of the age of these rocks is quite conclusive, and of unusual value, as it fixes the place in the geological scale of a well-marked formation in New Mexico, and one which has been the subject of considerable discussion. In the second member of the Cretaceous portion of the section, counting from the base upward, are contained fossils which are characteristic of the Cretaceous formation in Texas and Nebraska. These are *Inoceramus Crispii* and *Gryphaea Pitcheri*—well known Cretaceous fossils, common in Texas and the Indian Territory—and in greater numbers specimens of an ammonite, (*A. percarinatus,*) highly characteristic of Nos. 1 and 2 of Meek and Hayden's section of the Cretaceous rocks on the upper Missouri.

The vegetable impressions contained in No. 12 indicate a more highly organized flora than any which occupied the earth's surface previous to the Cretaceous period, and afford conclusive evidence that the strata containing them are not, as has been supposed, of Jurassic age. Up to the present time no angiosperm dicotyledonous plants have been found in strata older than the Chalk; and yet (though making my collections under the most unfavorable circumstances) I here procured representatives of several genera belonging to this class.

These plants afford another link connecting these strata with those of the upper Missouri. Their general character is quite similar to that of the exceedingly interesting group of plants obtained by Dr. Hayden from the Lower Cretaceous sandstones of Kansas and Nebraska, several of the genera and at least one species being common to the two localities. A somewhat similar flora has been discovered by Mr. Harper in Mississippi, Professor Tuomey in Alabama, and Professor Cook in New Jersey, in strata of the same age.

There is no doubt of the parallelism of this group of sandstones with those of the base of Meek and Hayden's Cretaceous section. It is true that in Kansas and Nebraska they are more often red than yellow or white, yet in some localities they exhibit the same lithological characters as in New Mexico. Going from Santa Fé to Fort Leavenworth, I noticed a progressive change from yellow to a reddish color in these sandstones, which for several hundred miles were almost continually in sight, and of which the continuity is uninterrupted.

In all that portion of New Mexico passed over by our party I saw no other rocks immediately overlying the variegated marls than such as I regarded as the equivalents of those given in the preceding section.   From the Moqui villages to Santa Fé the line of junction of these two formations was visible on almost every part of our route; and while I do not feel at liberty to enter upon the mooted question of the geological age of the superficial strata on the Llano Estacado, a region I have never visited, I am compelled to say that west of the Rio Grande the yellow sandstones overlying the red and white gypsiferous marls and calcareous sandstones (the upper portion of the variegated marls) belong to the Cretaceous series, and are identical with those just described.

As far as we progressed north of the Moqui villages we were travelling upon the strata forming the cliffs on which they are built.   The valleys of erosion which traverse the plateau everywhere expose its structure, permitting the different formations to be readily distinguished, even at a distance of thirty or forty miles.

At Camp 96, the point where we turned back, the view down one of these valleys, which leads toward the Colorado, was particularly interesting.   Its smooth surface, tinged with green by a sparse growth of *Artemisia* and *Ephedra*, was bounded for several miles by the cut edges of the Cretaceous sandstones on which we stood.   The erosion then reached the surface of the Marl series, and thence to the distance of forty or fifty miles we could see walls and pinnacles of red and white rising abruptly from the green plain, producing the peculiar scenery of the Painted Desert.   At a greater distance we could trace the outlines of lower mesas, growing less and less distinct, till eighty miles away the view was bounded by the lofty line of the snowy mesa first seen from Camp 72.   This mesa fills sixty degrees of the horizon from this point, and terminates in the awful precipice overhanging the Little Colorado, sharply defined and grand even at this distance.   Toward the northeast the Cretaceous rocks, after continuing for several miles nearly horizontal, were seen to rise rapidly and cover the flanks of a line of hills—spurs of the first of the Rocky mountain ranges.   Eastward our view covered a large part of the country lying between us and Fort Defiance, and showed everywhere a geological structure similar to that prevailing in our immediate vicinity.   South and southeast we overlooked the entire extent of the Painted Desert and the valley of the Little Colorado, beyond which rose the snowy summit of the San Francisco mountain, still a grand and beautiful object, though separated from us by an interval of a hundred miles.   All that was wanting to fill up that interval to the level of a line drawn from our position to the base of the San Francisco mountain had been removed in the formation of this great valley of erosion—a much grander monument of the power of aqueous action than even the stupendous cañon of the Colorado.

Fig. 22.—DISTANT VIEW OF GREAT WHITE MESA, FROM NEAR CAMP 96.

Upper Cretaceous strata.—Some miles north of Camp 96 a mesa wall rises to a height which we estimated at something like twelve hundred feet.   It occupies 30° of the horizon in that direction, and shows bold, nearly perpendicular faces, both in profile and in front.   These are pure white in color, and reflect the sunlight like snow.   Compelled by the want of water, with extreme regret we turned our backs upon this interesting geological feature, leaving its structure and age to be matters of conjecture until it shall be reached by some more fortunate explorers.

Rising, as it does, so distinctly from the mesa of Lower Cretaceous rocks, but two formations are left in the series of which it could be composed, Upper Cretaceous and Tertiary. The lithological characters of both these groups of rocks are frequently such as to exhibit snow-white sections similar to that described. The upper members of the Cretaceous group, the "White chalk," or *Craie blanche* of European geologists, compose the white cliffs on the southern coast of England, which afford an exact counterpart in appearance to that under consideration. It is also true that the materials composing the strata of the different Tertiary basins in the country bordering the Rocky mountains on the east are frequently nearly as white as chalk.

In the order of succession of the different formations the White chalk or Upper Cretaceous, in the ascending series, immediately follows the group forming the base upon which this white mesa rests; yet this proves nothing, for it happens that the fresh water Tertiaries are not unfrequently found occupying basins in the Lower Cretaceous strata, and such is the case with those passed over on our route. From these facts it will be seen that nothing but an actual examination will clear this subject of all doubt.

There are some reasons, however, why we should suspect this white mesa to be Upper Cretaceous rather than Tertiary, and these are, first, that all the Tertiary rocks of the Rocky mountain country, as far as they have yet been examined, are of fresh water or estuary origin, have been usually deposited in basins of less extent and depth than would be indicated by this great plateau, which has evidently been greatly reduced in dimensions by the erosion it has suffered; second, the materials composing the Tertiary strata found on the great central plateau are generally soft, and yield readily to the action of the elements, presenting rounded and unbroken outlines or pinnacles and deeply channelled surfaces, the results of erosion. On the contrary, the Upper Cretaceous strata, as they appear in several points on our route, holding precisely the relative position of the white mesa to the Lower Cretaceous sandstones, consist of a series of shales and limestones, which, though dark internally, weather to an almost chalky whiteness, and yet are as resistant to atmospheric erosion as any other sedimentary rocks.

Judging from the view we had of it, we regarded the white mesa as continuous with the high mesa bordering the Colorado, which has about the same altitude. If so, the strata composing it must occupy a very large area north and west of our Camp 96, one almost too large to accord with the supposition that it is of Tertiary age.

NAVAJO COUNTRY.

The route from the Moqui villages to Fort Defiance, though leading through a more fertile region than that last traversed, one abounding in picturesque and beautiful scenery, and every-where exhibiting magnificent exposures of its geological structure, added little that was absolutely new to our former experience.

Its general structure may be given in a few words. The Lower Cretaceous mesa occupies the greater part of its surface, but near Fort Defiance we approach the eastern border of the great basin of the Little Colorado, and the strata all begin to rise rapidly on to the first of the lines of upheaval, which complicate the structure of so large an area eastward of this point. A few miles west of Fort Defiance the culminating point in this ascent is reached, and thence all the formations pitch rapidly toward the east. In this vicinity the profound erosion they have suffered has cut through and locally removed the entire mass of Lower Cretaceous rocks, as well as the variegated marls below, and has reached and laid bare the lower and harder portion of the red sandstones. These are here considerably affected by the proximity of the igneous axis of the line of elevation. They have been much hardened and brought to resemble, in color and consistence, the light red sandstones of the carboniferous series west of the Colorado.

Tertiary rocks.--For twenty miles after leaving Walpi, the most eastern of the Moqui villages, we saw none but Cretaceous strata, sandstones, shales, and beds of lignite precisely like those at Moqui. Then, however, we came on to a series of strata very different in character from any seen between this point and the Pacific, and such as I am inclined to believe are not represented in all the region bordering the first half of our route across the continent. These I have supposed to be fresh water Tertiaries, probably of Miocene age, parallel to those of the "Bad Lands" of Nebraska. They fill a depression in the Lower Cretaceous rocks, and occupy a space of several miles on our route, forming a basin, of which the northern and southern limits are not yet determined.

The prevailing color of the beds is white or light ash, and cream color. They possess little consistence, and have been, by atmospheric erosion, cut into pyramids and pinnacles of as varied and peculiar forms as those of the *Mauvaise Terre*. Unfortunately, we were compelled to hasten over this interesting district so rapidly that I was unable to make the search necessary to discover fossils in this formation.

The lithological character of these rocks will be seen from the following section :

1. Reddish brown marl, forming summit of hills.

2. White and light ash-colored marls, with thin layers of sandy, cream-colored limestone, 200 feet.

3. Light brown marls, 100 feet.

4. Coarse reddish yellow sandstone, Cretaceous.

Fig. 23.—MONUMENT IN ERODED VALLEY, NEAR CAMP 100.

Near the eastern portion of this Tertiary basin we descended into an extensive and beautiful valley, eroded in the Cretaceous and underlying rocks. The bottom of the valley is a grassy plain, stretching far away to the north, and bounded in that direction by picturesque mesa walls, which rise above it to the height of eight or nine hundred feet. The sandstones here exposed of the Cretaceous and Marl series are of a chalky white or greenish yellow, and in the erosion of the valley a number of isolated buttes have been left, resembling in their forms churches, castles, gates, and monuments of various kinds.   These are surrounded by a green and level plain, with which their various outlines and colors strongly contrast, the whole picture vividly recalling the ruined structures of the Old World.

Like most of the other phenomena of erosion in the Colorado country, this great valley was principally formed in an epoch in which the annual amount of rain was much greater than at present, for no stream now flows through it.

The strata which compose the cliffs which bound this valley include the lower portion of the Cretaceous formation with a greater thickness of the Marl series.   At the base of the Cretaceous rocks is a group of brown foliated sandstones and beds of lignite, entirely undistinguishable from the upper part of the section exposed north of Oraybe and given on page 84.   It is possible, however, that these beds of lignite form the equivalent of that containing the fossil plants at Camp 92 ; but I was not able to find any fossils to establish that parallelism.   These lignite

Fig. 24.—NATURAL BRIDGE, CAMP 100.

beds are either in the base of the Cretaceous series or immediately beneath it; holding, therefore, the place in the scale of that at Camp 92.   If an identity could be established between these deposits we should here have something more than twice as many feet in thickness of what may be considered Jurassic rocks, as at that locality.   A few miles further east this group entirely disappears, and nothing is there interposed between the base of the Cretaceous and the summit of the Marl series.

In a great number of localities about Camp 100 the lignites have been burned out, giving a decided red color to the strata which enclosed them.   This phenomenon is probably due to spontaneous combustion, being caused by the oxidation of the bisulphuret of iron, which is abundantly contained in all these carbonaceous strata.   The same thing has taken place in the Cretaceous lignites east of Fort Defiance, and on a still grander scale in the same formation on the Upper Missouri.

The upper member of the Marl series at Camp 100 is a soft, fine-grained, nearly pure white calcareous sandstone, very similar to that already noticed in the description of the section at Camp 92.

NAVAJO VALLEY AND CAÑON BONITO.

Ascending the mesa east of Camp 100, we travelled upon its surface, with nothing new in our experience, for twelve miles, when we reached the brink of the wall limiting a larger, richer, and more beautiful valley than that last described. This is one of the favorite grazing grounds of the Navajos, and the green plain below us, as far toward the north as the eye could reach, was dotted with their herds and flocks. The walls bounding Navajo valley are generally abrupt, frequently perpendicular, and exhibit the brilliant and varied colors characteristic of the Marl series composing them. Toward the south they approach each other to form what has been most appropriately named Cañon Bonito.

The strata have here a strong westerly dip, and the Cretaceous rocks have so nearly run out that they only appear capping the western wall of the valley where it is highest. In the first arm of this great valley which we entered the upper and middle portions of the Marl series are fully exposed, while its eastern branch, through which flows a permanent stream, is cut down to the middle of the underlying red sandstones.

Fig. 25.—MASSES OF WHITE CALCAREOUS SANDSTONE SHAPED BY EROSION, NEAR CAMP 100.

The upper portion of the Marl series here, as in the region immediately south of the Moqui villages, is composed of strata of greater individual thickness and more indurated than those below. They consist of soft, thick-bedded, calcareous sandstones, pure white or nearly blood-red. The colors and consistence of this portion of the series are, however, by no means constant. As we have seen, at Camp 92, soft green and red marls overlie white calcareous sandstone, and represent the green and purple calcareous sandstones of Camp 91; while at Fort

Defiance nearly the whole of the upper part of the Marl series is represented by a great stratum of pink, soft, calcareous sandstone.

Below these indurated marls is exposed some four hundred feet of buff, orange, purple, lilac, olive, green, and blue marls, with strata of gypsum and magnesian limestone. This series closely resembles that in the mesa wall bounding the valley of the Little Colorado, between our Camps 89 and 90, and is undoubtedly its exact equivalent. The beds of dolomite are less numerous here than there, but are in the same manner most characteristic of the lower part of the section. Silicified wood also occurs abundantly along the same horizon, and is profusely scattered over denuded surfaces. The Marl series is here susceptible of division into two groups, but, as before remarked, their lithological differences are rather in degree than kind, and are not constant.

Beneath the variegated marls nearly a hundred feet of red and green foliated sandstones and shales are exposed, which form the upper member of the red sandstone group. These strata here exhibit nearly the same characters as on the banks of the Little Colorado, where I first observed them. At Fort Defiance, Bear Spring, Agua Azul, and many other points on our route, the exposures form the same geological horizon as at Navajo valley; and while the correspondence between all its different portions is such as to render the work of identification both easy and sure, the features presented by the last-mentioned group are peculiarly constant wherever it is visible.

From Camp 101 to Fort Defiance we were constantly travelling on the red saliferous sandstones. The general surface gradually rises, but less rapidly than the geological substrata.

The upper part of the valley traversed by the Pueblo Colorado creek is excavated in the upper member of the sandstone group. Going east from this point we saw no more of the variegated marls till we had crossed the valley in which Fort Defiance is located. Gradually descending in the geological scale, we passed through the upper members of the red sandstone group, and, as we approached the crown of the arch formed by the strata, we found the surface rock to be a reddish, compact, cross-stratified sandstone, also belonging to the Saliferous series, but much harder than any portion of that group exposed on the Little Colorado, and doubtless somewhat changed by the proximity of the igneous rocks below. The limit of the rise in the strata was reached near Camp 102, at an elevation of nearly 7,000 feet above the sea level. From this point they pitch to the east at an angle of 10° to 15°, which brings in review within a few miles all the strata above the Carboniferous limestone we had up to that time observed.

CHAPTER IX.

GEOLOGY OF THE ROUTE FROM FORT DEFIANCE TO SANTA FE.

FORT DEFIANCE.

The geology of the region lying between Fort Defiance and the Rio Grande, while including only the rocks that have been so fully described in the preceding chapter, presents many new features in the condition in which they are found. In the Moqui country all the strata intervening between the Carboniferous and the Upper Cretaceous are nearly horizontal, and nowhere dislocated or disturbed, each member of the series in the beautiful exposures which came under our observation holding its proper relative position, and exhibiting its normal aspect. East of Fort Defiance, on the contrary, the table-lands, although continuous with, and once in all respects similar to those we before passed over, have been broken up by various lines of dislocation of the Rocky mountain system, and their strata thrown about in the greatest confusion. The difficulties which geological investigations here present are such that it would be scarcely possible for one who had not studied the formations here represented in some other school to arrive at conclusions of unquestionable accuracy. Coming, as we did, to the examination of the complex structure of this disturbed region from one whose perfect quiet and magnificent sections gave us the best possible preparation for the task, we were, perhaps, able to accomplish as much in the solution of its problems as could be done by a party moving as rapidly as we did.

Fort Defiance is situated in a picturesque valley of erosion not unlike, in its general aspects, to those lying west of it, yet exhibiting some peculiarities, both in the elements composing its geology, and their arrangement. It has been excavated in a north and south direction on the slope of strata dipping rapidly eastward from the summit of the anticlinal axis a few miles west of it. These strata have been cut through nearly to the Garboniferous limestone, while the cliffs bounding the valley on the east include about a thousand feet of Cretaceous rocks. In the midst of the valley several large castellated buttes of basaltic trap rise abruptly from its alluvial surface, the unyielding material of which they are composed having resisted the action of the agent that has removed the sedimentary rocks for miles around them. The structure of this valley will be most readily understood by reference to the accompanying wood-cut, which gives a transverse section of it.

It will be seen from this section that the softer portion of the variegated marls forms the base of the eastern boundary of the valley, and there is little doubt that its excavation has been effected in the same manner as that of the valley of the Little Colorado, viz : by the washing away of the softer strata on which the eroding stream has constantly had its bed, and the gradual descent of that stream along the slope of the surface of the harder rocks below, undermining the more resistant portion of the eastern cliff. This process is indicated by the present outline of the valley, its western slope being formed by the dipping surface of the saliferous sandstones, its eastern by the broken and abrupt edge of the indurated variegated marls and cretaceous sandstones.

The drainage of the western slope has formed tributary valleys of considerable depth, much deeper, indeed, geologically, than the great trough into which they lead. These excavations lay open the Saliferous sandstone series to its base, and afford us the information of the structure of the western side of the valley incorporated in the preceding section.

The most important of these secondary channels—rather a cañon than a valley—known to the occupants of the fort as "Cañoncita Bonita," is the worthy object of their admiration. From its more modest dimensions it has received the diminutive appellation it bears, but in picturesque beauty it is scarcely inferior to its grander namesake, the Cañon Bonito.

Fig. 26.—SECTION OF THE VALLEY AT FORT DEFIANCE.

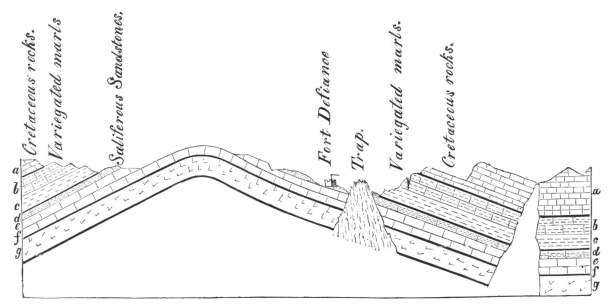

a Sandstones and shales.
b Pink and white soft calc. sandstones.
c Soft variegated marls, with fossil wood.
d Red and green sandstones and shales.
e Conglomerate and red soft sandstones.
f Red or whitish compact sandstone.
g Carboniferous limestone.
x Trap.

Between four and five hundred feet of the saliferous sandstones are exposed in Cañoncita Bonita, and in that over which is thrown the beautiful arch of the natural bridge. As a whole, the sandstones of this group are lighter in color, more massive and compact, than on the Little Colorado. The conglomerate, however, presents precisely the same appearance here as there, specimens from the two localities being undistinguishable.

Garnets and beryls of unusually fine quality are found in considerable abundance in the alluvial soil about Fort Defiance, and in the other portions of the Navajo country. As the region has never been swept by any general drift current, and the mountains of crystalline rocks are so remote, I have thought it probable that they were derived from the decomposition of the conglomerates. I have never been able to discover any of them in this rock where I have examined it, but the gravel in which they occur is composed, almost exclusively, of pebbles once contained in it.   All of the garnets and beryls found here are more or less worn and broken, showing the attrition they have suffered in their transportation from some remote source.

The road leading from Fort Defiance to Albuquerque emerges from the valley through a cañon cut in its eastern wall; of which it affords a remarkably interesting section.   The softer portion of the variegated marls is concealed beneath the alluvial surface, but the silicified wood which they formerly contained is scattered about in the greatest profusion.   The indurated marls or soft calcareous sandstones which overlie them form a great number of detached pinnacles, and the lower portion of the first bluff bordering the great valley.   They here present nearly the same characters as at Camps 91 and 92 and in the Navajo valley, but are somewhat more massive, and their colors less varied.   Their aggregate thickness is from four to five hundred feet, of which the lower two-thirds is of a nearly uniform rose-red color.   The upper third is pinkish-white or greenish.

The summit of the cliff is formed by a stratum of yellow sandstone, precisely like that of Camps 92 and 93, (Moo-sha-na-ve.)   It has a thickness of nearly one hundred feet, and is conformable to the rocks below.   With them, it dips so rapidly to the east that, within less than half a mile, it comes down to the road we travelled.   Before reaching that level, however, it is covered by a second cliff, which rises over it to fully the height of the first.   This is composed exclusively of Lower Cretaceous strata, light yellow sandstones, with green and gray shales, the precise counterparts of those forming the mesa of the Moqui villages.   Like those of the first cliff, these strata are inclined at an angle of 15° with the horizon, and soon disappear beneath the surface.

At this point is a line of fracture running north 26° east; and immediately beyond the place where the highest member of the preceding series sinks from view we entered a group of rounded hills, also composed of Cretaceous strata, a continuation of the section afforded in the cliffs described, but lying nearly horizontal.   These consist of green and dove-colored shales, brown and greenish sandstones, brownish-yellow concretionary limestone containing *Gryphœa Pitcheri*, and beds of lignite.   For several miles the trail winds about among hills of these materials, in which the lignite beds are very conspicuous.   In many places they have been burned out, probably by spontaneous combustion, and have changed the color of the contiguous shales to a bright red.   The strata in immediate contact with them are often converted into red or black scoria, which is scarcely distinguishable from that produced by volcanic action.

The lignite of this vicinity is generally brown in color, less dark and compact than that of Camp 92, but similar to that in the upper part of the Lower Cretaceous series north of the Moqui villages.

This formation extends with little variation to, and beyond, Camp 104; where, after ascending for some miles, we had passed over at least two hundred feet of strata, consisting of a repetition of those I have enumerated, and had reached a higher point in the geological scale than anywhere on the Moqui mesa.   The uppermost member of the series is a brown somewhat concretionary silicious limestone overlying a soft, yellowish, thick-bedded sandstone.   Both these rocks are precisely like many of the strata immediately below them, and equally like those of the upper portion of the Moqui mesa north of Oraybe.

After leaving Camp 104, we descended into a valley through which flows at certain seasons a tributary to the Little Colorado.   At this point we crossed another line of fracture, twenty miles distant from the former one, the strata throughout the interval between them having a slight easterly dip.   Here they have for a short distance a strong reversed dip, and a mesa south of the trail shows an anticlinal axis.   This line of disturbance is, however, soon passed, and the Cretaceous rocks, similar to those about Camp 104, fall back to the position they there held, running for several miles eastward, with a slight dip in that direction.

At Salt Spring we crossed another marked line of fracture and dislocation, which affords one of the most interesting geological sections met with on our route. Travelling from the west upon the Cretaceous strata, for some miles lying nearly horizontal, we came suddenly, and without preparation, to a wall from three to five hundred feet in height, of which the western face, inclined to the horizon at an angle of 70°, is formed by the same stratum as that on which we stood. Passing through an avenue opened in this wall by a stream, we found it to be a huge fragment of the rocky basis of this region, broken up from its connexions, and set nearly at right angles to its former position. All the stratified rocks exposed about Fort Defiance are here represented, parallel among themselves, but nearly vertical; presenting in the sides of the gap through which we passed a very perfect and instructive horizontal section. This wall here runs dam-like across a valley of considerable width, and, strongly relieved from the level surface on either side, it is one of the most impressive examples of dislocation I have ever seen.

Fig. 27.—SECTION OF DISLOCATED STRATA AT SALT SPRING.

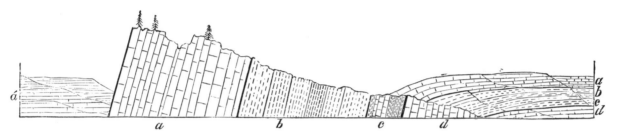

á Upper part of the Lower Cretaceous formation. ⎱
a Lower Cretaceous sandstone shales.   ⎰ Chalk series.
b Variegated marls and red calc. sandstone.   ⎱
c Soft variegated marls with magnesian limestones and silicified wood. ⎰ Variegated marls.
d Green and red sandstones and shales —Salt Group.

The convulsions which have shaken this vicinity are not alone attested by the upturned mass just described, for a different geological horizon is presented on its eastern from that on its western side. In our approach to it, for many miles, nothing had been visible but the upper portion of the Cretaceous series, but, issuing from the passage cut through it, we found ourselves in a broad valley, bounded by bluffs of great height, in which appeared all the strata we had observed in this region. The bottom of this valley is composed of the upper strata of the Saliferous sandstone group, above which are the variegated marls and the red and white calcareous sandstones, the latter presenting mural faces of several hundred feet in height. Upon these, more than a thousand feet above the valley, the Lower Cretaceous sandstones appear, forming a distinct mesa wall. From this description it will be seen that at the same absolute level we were, on the western side of the wall, geologically nearly two thousand feet higher than after passing it.

Where the bluffs approach this transverse barrier on the north side of the valley I could perceive that the strata were bent down towards the corresponding ones in the dismembered portion, while toward the northeast, after rising rapidly for a short distance, they begin to dip in that direction. This would seem to indicate that in the action of the forces by which this displacement of the strata was produced they were raised into an immense arch, of which the curvature became too great for its tenacity, and a double line of fracture was produced. That portion of the arch which was included between these two lines still stands as the wall I have described.

From Salt Spring to and through Campbell's Pass the geology of our route included little or nothing new. We were constantly passing through a broad valley of erosion, bounded by precipitous and most picturesque cliffs of the variegated marls, and the red calcareous sandstones of the same formation.   Above these, generally forming a distinct and more remote wall, are the cream-colored strata of the Lower Cretaceous series.   In places we descended through the red and green shales and sandstones of the Saliferous group, and came upon the coarse sandstones and conglomerates which overlie the Carboniferous limestone.   The dip of these strata is nearly northeast, and our route lay so closely along their strike that they seemed to be almost horizontal.

In all this region a fact was observed, to which our attention was first called on the banks of the Little Colorado, viz: that the lower hills and the bases of the highlands are covered with dead cedar trees, an apparent indication of the increasing dryness of the climate.   The timber in this country is confined to the more elevated surfaces, where the precipitation of moisture is greatest, and the belts of deadened trees, certainly untouched by fire, prove that the conditions favorable to the growth of arborescent vegetation are becoming restricted to narrower limits.   This fact is mentioned merely as being confirmatory of the conclusion drawn from other data, that the amount of rain on the table-lands west of the Rio Grande is now much less than formerly.

CAMPBELL'S PASS.

Here, almost unconsciously, we crossed the divide between the waters of the Pacific and those of the Atlantic.   No mountain chain or line of upheaval marks the summit, and the mesa of the Lower Cretaceous sandstones, and that of the variegated marls, stretch over from one side to the other, without break or interruption, except such as have been produced by erosion.

On reaching the summit we obtained a fine view of Mount Taylor, (or San Mateo,) some forty miles distant.   This mountain has an elevation of 11,000 feet above the level of the sea.   It somewhat resembles, in form, as in all other respects, San Francisco mountain, but its base is broader, and, as a consequence, its apparent altitude is less.   The summit is irregular, and contains a crater.   By the Mexicans it is sometimes called El Tintero, or the Inkstand, from its general form, and the depression which is said to exist in its summit.

After passing the divide our descent was more rapid than had been our ascent on the western slope, and we soon struck a flowing stream, the headwaters of the Rio San José, which we followed from this point to its intersection with the Puerco.   Some ten miles from the summit of the pass we began to meet with fragments of scoria, and then reached masses and streams of lava poured from Mount Taylor, by which all the country adjacent to it has been flooded.   This lava is undistinguishable from that of the San Francisco mountain, and we here had a repetition, in all their details, of the magnificent volcanic phenomena there displayed.

At Agua Azul the stream we were following has cut down through all the red sandstone series, and has exposed, over a considerable area, the Carboniferous limestone, here brought up by an arching of the strata.   This limestone is blue, gray, and pink; portions of it cellular and cherty. It contains many fossils, among which are *Productus, Nautilus, Bellerophon, Allorisma*, etc.   I have regarded it as identical with that holding the same relative position on the Little Colorado, and as representing the summit of the Carboniferous formation.

The series of strata exposed in the descent from the top of the upper mesa at Campbell's Pass to Agua Azul is as follows, the thickness given being estimated, and not measured:

1. Cretaceous sandstones, shales, and lignites, forming first and highest mesa · · · ·   700 feet.
2. Soft red, white, and green calcareous sandstones or indurate marls, Marl series ·   600 feet.
3. Variegated marls, with silicified wood and bands of magnesian limestone, Marl
series · · · · · · · · · ·   150 feet.
4. Red and green foliated sandstones and shales, Salt group · · · · · · · · · · · · · · · · ·   120 feet.
5. Coarse red or drab sandstone and conglomerate, Salt group · · · · · · · · · · · · · · ·   250 feet.
6. Red, blue, and white shales, Salt group ·   150 feet.
7. Limestone, blue, gray, and pink, Carboniferous.

East of Agua Azul the strata dip very rapidly in that direction, and the walls enclosing the valley are composed of the yellow Cretaceous sandstones, on the north side covered with a thick sheet of trap. On the south side the Cretaceous strata form detached mesas, which are without the trap covering, but show in many places fractures and dislocations. For many miles the bottom of the valley is occupied by a lava stream, evidently of more modern date than any of the erosions of the surface. It has dispossessed the watercourse of its bed, and, following all its sinuosities, now lies a congealed flood, as black, bare, and ragged as if just poured out.

These geological features continue without change to Covéro and Laguna—Cretaceous sandstones composing the walls of the valley, which is formed entirely by erosion. The northern wall is capped with trap. At Covéro the greenish shales, enclosed in the yellow sandstones, contain large numbers of *Gryphaea Pitcheri*. The town is built upon a stratum of coarse yellow sandstone, which here forms the bottom of the valley, and is cañoned by the stream.

Laguna is built upon a similar stratum, lower in the series, and separated from that of Covéro by white and bluish shales.

At Laguna the Rio San José cuts through the Cretaceous formation, and for several miles below flows in a picturesque cañon, which it has excavated in the red and white calcareous sandstones, gypsum, &c., of the Marl series.

The section of the strata exposed at Laguna is as follows, the thickness being estimated:

1. Yellow sandstones and greenish shales, Cretaceous · 250 feet.
2. White and bluish shales, Cretaceous · 100 feet.
3. Yellow sandstone, Cretaceous · 50 feet.
4. Soft red and white calcareous sandstones, (in cañon east of Laguna,) variegated Marl series · 150 feet.
5. Gypsum, variegated Marl series · 80 feet.
6. Blue calcareous shale, variegated Marl series · 20 feet.
7. White soft calcareous sandstone, variegated Marl series · · · · · · · · · · · · · · · · · · 40 feet.
8. Red soft calcareous sandstone, Salt group · 120 feet.
9. Red and green foliated sandstones and blood-red shales, Salt group.

From Sheep Spring to the Puerco the strata are very much broken up and displaced. The upper member of the saliferous sandstone group is beautifully exposed at Sheep Spring, and here exhibits precisely the same characters as in the localities where it was noticed in the Navajo country.

This formation soon disappears with an easterly dip, and for a short interval the surface is strewed with silicified wood derived from the lower portion of the variegated marls. Thence eastward nothing is visible but the Cretaceous sandstones and green shales, forming many detached mesas, in which the strata are broken and inclined at various angles.

Between the Puerco and the Rio Grande we were almost constantly crossing hills of loose sand, which entirely conceal the underlying rocks.

On the east bank of the Puerco the green shales, so conspicuous immediately west of it, are visible for a short distance, when they give place to white, soft, concretionary, tufaceous strata, in which I was unable to discover fossils or any indications of their age. In their lithological character these beds differ widely from the Cretaceous rocks on which they rest, as they also do from any strata containing Cretaceous fossils met with on our route. They much more resemble the fresh water Tertiary beds of the Arkansas, White river, &c., and, guided by this similarity, I should be inclined to consider them of that age. Their physical characters are not of great value, however, and it is possible they are Cretaceous. If belonging to the latter formation, I think it will be found that they are more recent than any of the Lower Cretaceous strata described in the preceding pages, and should be placed in the upper division of that series.

VALLEY OF THE RIO GRANDE.

The geological structure of the immediate borders of the Rio Grande presents the same elements, with similar complications, as that of the region lying west of it. From the observations made by our party, and by those who have crossed the continent south of our line, it appears that the same general description will also apply to a belt of country east of the Rio Grande, extending to a great distance north and south, and reaching as far eastward as the disturbing influence of the Rocky mountain ranges is felt. The generalities of the geology of all this great area may be given in few words, but the strata are so much disturbed by numerous and interrupted lines of upheaval that the work of investigating its local features would be one of infinite labor. Considerable time was spent by our party on the Rio Grande, at and above Albuquerque, and the geological observations made then include many local details, which it is scarcely necessary should be given, as they would swell the dimensions of this report without adding, in any material degree, to its value.

This region has been so often visited and fully described that I shall confine myself to a brief synopsis of its geology, presented mainly for the purpose of comparing it with that of the country before passed over, and of noticing some errors which have been promulgated in reference to it.

The valley of the Rio Grande in the vicinity of Albuquerque is for the most part occupied by sandstones and shales of Cretaceous age, continuous with or resting upon those spread over so much of the surface in Western New Mexico.

A little north of Albuquerque, on the west side of the river, a large area is occupied by a mesa, composed of Cretaceous rocks and the underlying red and white indurated marls, precisely like that northeast of Laguna. Like the mesas bordering the Rio San José, this is capped with a thin layer of basaltic trap, and it is quite probable both are but portions of a continuous plateau, wholly covered by a lava flood from Mount Taylor.

Picturesque escarpments, formed by the cut edges of this mesa, border the valley on the west side near the pueblos of San Felipe and San Domingo; thence northward, for many miles on the right bank, the same formation prevails, in some places the trap entirely concealing the sedimentary strata.

On the east side, near Albuquerque, the valley is bounded by the Sandia mountain, of which full descriptions have been given in the report of Captain Whipple. The structure of this mountain is visible even from the river; the escarpment of Carboniferous limestone, that forms its summit and covers its eastern slope, being plainly distinguishable from the underlying granite.

From Albuquerque to Algodones the surface is generally composed of alluvial soil or beds of drift from the Sandia mountains. The only rock seen in place is the red calcareous sandstone, or indurated marl, of the Upper Marl series. This forms low hills back of Manzana and Bernalillo.

Between Algodones and Galisteo creek is a table land principally formed of the white and red indurated marls. In one locality is an exposure of white concretionary tufaceous rock with bands of cream-colored nodular limestone; they are without fossils, as far as observed, and of uncertain date, but the lithological characters lead me to suspect that they are of fresh water origin and Tertiary age.

On Galisteo creek the strata are considerably disturbed, but the exposures are very full and interesting.

The strata visible in the north bank of the stream where we crossed it are—

1. Cretaceous sandstones, yellowish or greenish white, and shales with beds of lignite.
2. Red and white marls, all somewhat indurated with silicified wood.
3. Soft red sandstones and shales of the Salt group.

From a locality north of Galisteo I have specimens of greenish brown calcareous shale, containing many fragments of *Inoceramus* and obscure impressions of *Ammonites*. These fossils are too fragmentary for specific determination, but a precisely similar rock, containing like organic fragments, is exposed on the banks of the Ocaté and Canadian. Its place in the series is at the base of the Upper Cretaceous group, immediately over the coarse yellow or reddish sandstones of the lower division of that formation. It is probable that the strata containing Cretaceous fossils at Poblozon are of the same age with these.

On the north side of Galisteo creek we found the sedimentary rocks just enumerated cut through in many places by trap dikes, having various directions. These dikes, composed of more resistant material than the strata once enclosing them, have been left by the erosion of the softer rocks in walls of most artificial appearance. The trap is columnar, the columns lying horizontally as usual, having been formed with their axes at right angles to the cooling surfaces. Some of these walls were noticed which extend for long distances with a nearly uniform height of four or five feet, closely resembling old field walls. Others are less extensive but higher, and occasionally pierced with holes, resemble the walls of ruined buildings. The ends of the columns are distinctly visible on the surface of these dikes, imitating so perfectly the appearance of masonry that it is not surprising, in the country once exclusively occupied by the Pueblo Indians, they should have been generally regarded by the unlearned as the ruins of human habitations and enclosures.

The valley of Galisteo creek is bounded on the north by high, and in many places perpendicular bluffs of trap, the cut edges of a plateau of that material which occupies a large space in this vicinity. From this mesa rise the volcanic cones of the "Cerrillos," as I have supposed, marking the place of origin of the lava floods which once deluged the surrounding country.

The Cerrillos furnished a great part, if not all, the *chalchuitl*, so much worn for ornament, and so highly prized by the ancient Mexicans. This mineral is a variety of turquoise, and is found in veins running through a light-colored trachyte.* The ancient excavations made in search of it are now distinctly visible, and seem to have been carried to the depth of two hundred feet or more. Several of the Indian tribes of New Mexico—Navajos, Mojaves, &c.— still hold this gem in the highest esteem. The most valued possession of Cairook, a Mojave chief, was a wedge-shaped piece of *chalchuitl*, suspended from his nose. At Romero's we reached the edge of the trap mesa. Thence to Santa Fé the only rock visible in place is a soft red calcareous sandstone of the Marl series, which forms low hills, generally covered by drift from the adjacent mountains.

The Santa Fé mountains are a part of the great Rocky mountain system, and constitute its only important representatives met with on our route. They form a series of high and picturesque chains, connecting on the north with the Raton mountains, the Spanish peaks, and the lofty summits around the "Parks;" while on the south they are represented by the Sandia, Organ, Hueco, and Guadalupe ranges, east of the Rio Grande. The general bearing of the Santa Fé mountains is about north northwest and south southeast, but some of the ranges composing this compound system depart widely from that trend. With their connexions, they include many peaks and sierras covered with perpetual snow, which formed prominent features in the scenery of more than two hundred miles of our route.

From the fact that this group of ranges is not continuous southward, they permit the passage through them of the drainage of the basin of the upper Rio Grande, and therefore are not the divide between the waters of the Atlantic and Pacific in New Mexico, though they are so in Utah. The line of elevation which really forms the divide is, however, in other respects, a much less important topographical feature than that under consideration; for, as has been

---

* To Mr. J. Mercure, of Santa Fé, I am indebted for fine specimens of this, as of many other minerals and ores, found in this part of New Mexico.

stated, at "Campbell's Pass," where we crossed it, no mountains whatever are visible, except the distant and isolated volcanic cone of Mount Taylor.

The great mass of the mountains at Santa Fé is made up of a red coarse granite, traversed by numerous veins of quartz, some of which are metalliferous, containing silver, gold, copper, and lead.

On the flanks of this igneous axis the limestone of the Carboniferous series is frequently seen resting, usually but little metamorphosed. Over the limestone, sometimes in concordant, sometimes in discordant stratification, are such portions of the red sandstones, variegated marls, and Cretaceous rocks, as have been spared by the erosion they have suffered.

The Carboniferous limestone at Santa Fé is dark bluish-brown in color, and very hard. It contains great numbers of fossils, for the most part of species common in the coal measures of the Mississippi valley, though a few are new. The most common are *Productus scabriculus*, *P. Rogersi*, *P. semireticulatus*, *P. nodosus*, (n. sp.,) *Spirigera subtilita*, *Spirifer cameratus*, etc.

At various localities in the vicinity of Santa Fé Carboniferous shales are interstratified with the limestone, and contain fossil plants characteristic of the Coal measures. From these facts, as well as those before cited, it will be seen that the limestone of this region—called Lower Carboniferous or "Mountain" limestone by Mr. Marcou—is the equivalent of the Coal measures. As we approached the Mississippi on our homeward journey, we were able to trace the changes which take place in the lithological character of the Coal measures from the series of the sandstones, shales, limestones, fire clays, coal, &c., forming the productive Coal measures to the massive and nearly homogeneous limestone of the southwest.

Specimens of excellent anthracite coal were given me by Mr. Mercure, obtained at the "Old placer," where it occurs in a stratum of workable thickness. Whether it is of Carboniferous age or not I had no means of determining. I regretted that I was unable to visit a locality of so much economical and scientific interest as that which furnishes it.

The fact which has already been referred to, that the limestone of this vicinity rests directly on the granite, and that it is so little changed by that contact, indicates that these granitic masses had an existence before the Carboniferous epoch; that the limestone was deposited upon them, and that since that period, though greatly elevated, they have not been fused.

The great mass of sedimentary rocks which underlie the Coal measure limestone, in the cañon of the Colorado, is here apparently wanting, for I have seen nothing I could imagine to represent them even in any metamorphic form. This fact seems to teach that some of the ranges of the Rocky mountains had representatives at a very early period, forming limits which restricted the deposition of the older palæozoic rocks, and that their summits were only covered by sediments during the Carboniferous era.

It will be seen that in the preceding sketch of the geology of the country west of the Rio Grande, bordering our route, I have failed to recognize the Jurassic formation in any of the localities where it has been said to occur; and that I have regarded the yellow sandstones, green, gray, and blue shales, &c., called Jurassic by a recent writer, as of Cretaceous age. The evidence of the accuracy of this determination is, I think, incontrovertible. These strata were traced by us almost without interruption from the Moqui country to the Rio Grande, and there is scarcely room for error even if we had no other guide than this continuity, their relations to the associated rocks, and their lithological characters. In addition to these, however, we found at the Moqui villages abundant fossils of unequivocal Cretaceous character in them, and a sufficient number of those called such by our best palæontologists (Messrs. Hall, Shumard, and Meek) at various other points along our route, to furnish all necessary palæontological proof of their identity.

It is not asserted that Jurassic rocks do not exist in this region, for it is possible, and perhaps probable, that they do, but only that those called such on that portion of our route passed over by Mr. Marcou are Cretaceous.

Nor is it claimed that the Trias is not here represented. So far is that from the truth that the writer has little doubt that strata many hundred feet in thickness, intervening between the Carboniferous and Cretaceous formations, are the equivalents of Triassic rocks of Europe, and that at some future day the evidence of identity, which up to the present time has not been discovered, will be supplied. At the same time, that the subdivisions of the European Trias, the "*Bunter Sandstein*," the "*Muschelkalk*," and the "*Keuper*," will ever be fully identified in New Mexico, I regard as doubtful.

The aggregate thickness assigned to the rocks filling the space between the Chalk and the Coal series in the preceding pages is, as will have been noticed, considerably less than the estimates before published. A part of the discrepancy will be accounted for by my bringing down the Cretaceous system so as to include all the Jurassic rocks of Mr. Marcou; but, excluding these, the red sandstones and variegated marls, called Triassic by Mr. Marcou, are said by him to have a thickness of 5,000 to 6,000 feet, (*Geology of North America*, pp. 10, 11, 12,) while in all of our measurements of the splendid sections of these strata, in the Painted Desert and Moqui country, we found an aggregate thickness of about 2,000 feet; and on the Rio Grande the same geological interval is several hundred feet less.

It is true that the eye, in a region where the atmosphere is so pure, and the reach of vision so great, where all the physical features are on so grand a scale, is a very unsafe guide, and will continually lead to under estimates ; but we made constant use of the barometer, and employed the observations on the same strata at different points as checks on each other. I am very sure that in attributing a maximum thickness of 2,500 feet to the Triassic formation of Mr. Marcou its relative importance has not been underrated.

CHAPTER X.

GEOLOGY OF THE ROUTE FROM SANTA FE TO FORT LEAVENWORTH.

General features of the country.—Fertility of the mississippi slope.—Contrasting aspects of the mountain region and sea-like plains.—Analysis of the differences between the plateaus west and east of the rocky mountains.—The causes, both extraneous and structural, climatic and geological.—Geological itinerary.— Granitic axis east of santa fe.—Carboniferous limestones, &c.—Gypsiferous series in apache cañon and the valley of the pecos.—Section at pecos church.—Ojo vernal.— Carb. limestone.—Las vegas.—Upper cretaceous strata.—Las vegas to the cimarron.—Lower cretaceous sandstones.—Trap of the raton region.—Upper cretaceous strata and fossils on red river.—Patches of tertiary limestone.—Tertiary basin of the arkansaw.—"High prairies."—Pawnee fork to council grove.—Cretaceous sandstone.—Jurassic and triassic beds covered.—First true permian strata seen.—Council grove to fort leavenworth.—Permian and carboniferous rocks.— Carboniferous fossils.—Fusilina limestones.—Kansas section of meek and hayden.

The general features of the country traversed between Santa Fé and the Missouri may be very briefly described. For seventy-five miles after leaving Santa Fé we were involved in the spurs of the Rocky mountains, and were passing through a remarkably picturesque and beautiful region, in which the surface is nearly equally shared between rocky, ragged, and pine-covered sierras, and open, grassy valleys, through which flow streams of the purest water, fed by the melting of the snows. In this interval we crossed the rim of the great Mississippi valley, and began to descend its western slope—a period in our experience marked by many agreeable incidents. The soil became more fertile, the vegetation more general and varied; and for the first time in our long eastward march familiar faces began to meet us in home species of trees and flowers. The noisy mountain streams made music to which our ears had long been unaccustomed; and the summer showers by which we were drenched were, for a time, so refreshing a novelty that we scarcely cared to avoid them. By all these and other signs we saw that we were emerging from the vast arid area in which many preceding months had been passed—where sterility is the rule and productiveness the marked exception—and were approaching a region where a flowing stream is not a wonder, and where an unbroken sheet of vegetation covers the soil.

The geological structure of this section of our route is scarcely in any respect different from that of the country immediately west of the Rio Grande. The Coal measure limestone is the lowest stratified rock exposed. This is brought to the surface in several localities, and rests upon the granite. Over the Carboniferous rocks the Red sandstones, the Variegated marls, and the yellow Cretaceous sandstones are shown in many fine sections, among which those of the Apache cañon, at Pecos and Ojo Vernal deserve special mention.

At Las Vegas we for the first time met with unmistakable Upper Cretaceous strata resting upon the yellow sandstone group so often mentioned.

We here stood on what seemed the shore of a boundless sea; behind us the forest-covered hills through which we had passed rose, step by step, till lost in the distant snow-covered mountains; before us a green and grassy plain, rising in gentle undulations, stretched away as far as the eye could reach. North and south a shore line showed many bold and wooded headlands, separating bay-like indentations. In the offing several isolated buttes rose abruptly from the surface like so many rocky islands. This was our first introduction to the "Plains," as they are commonly called, over which our road lay for more than seven hundred miles—the longest, broadest, and smoothest in the world, but almost as monotonous as the path of a ship over the ocean.

The contrast which the smooth and unbroken surface, the long and gentle swells, the uniform coating of grass of the plains, present to the physical aspects of the western half of the great plateau, is most striking; and since the geological structure is nearly the same in both, the origin of this contrast forms an interesting subject of inquiry. I think these differences may be referred to the combined action of several distinct causes, mainly geological, but in part atmospheric. Of these one is to be found in the nearly uniform easterly dip of the rocks, which prevails over so much of this region, forming a grade of sufficient slope to carry off the drainage from the mountains freely but gently, without any such headlong descent as that from the western edge of the table lands into the trough of the lower Colorado. From this gradual descent of the surface the line of summits bounding the valleys runs parallel in elevation with the beds of the draining streams. Hence the valleys scarcely increase in depth though they grow constantly broader, and ultimately, by elimination of the dividing ridges, occupy the greater part of the surface.*

Another and perhaps equally efficient cause of the topographical features of the plains is the more copious and general rain which falls upon them. The legitimate effect of this agent is to widen the valleys by washing down their sides, to round off and wear down the hills, to diminish all irregularities, in short, to accomplish its mission as the greatest of levellers.

Indirectly the same effect is produced by the growth of vegetation formed by the moisture. This also has a tendency, as is known, to round over and soften down all asperities of the surface. It is true that the more elevated portions of the prairies are very dry as compared with the low humid banks of the Mississippi, but none of the area traversed by the Santa Fé road at all deserves the name of desert, or is comparable in dryness and sterility with the cañoned country west of the mountains. A thick mat of grass covers the ground, which could sustain an immense amount of animal life, an accurate index of the quantity of precipitated moisture. It should also be said that in the higher and drier parts of the plains, and there only, the streams traversing them flow through excavated cañons.

It will have been seen in the sketch of the general structure of the table-lands given in Chapter V, that the plateau, now cut by the great cañons of the Colorado and its tributaries, had originally but a moderate descent from the base of the Rocky mountains to the great bend of the Colorado, but near that point was a fall of several thousand feet. The force of a running stream is constantly expended in establishing an equilibrium in all parts of its descent, and producing a uniform grade in its bed from mouth to source, and the Colorado, in the lapse of ages, has done much towards the accomplishment of its task, and has distributed the great fall at the Black mountains along several hundred miles of its course.

---

* There are some other geological facts which have a bearing on this subject, perhaps no less important than those cited above, but they require more minute and extensive observation for their complete anylysis.

These are, first, the indications that the country lying between the Rocky Mountains and the Mississippi has occupied a lower level, and has been oftener and longer submerged during the Tertiary and Post Tertiary ages, than the highest plateau west of the Rio Grande.

Without repeating the facts which teach this, since they have been enumerated in the preceeding pages, we may say that such a conclusion is apparently inevitable from them.

The effect of the submergence of this region by fresh or salt water would necessarily be, not only to forbid all erosion, but to deposit sediments, by which former inequalities would be, to a degree at least, filled up and effaced, and the surface made smooth and even.

The second fact in this category is, that a large part of the prairie country has been swept by drift currents, or drift agents, whatever their nature, and by their action the rocks have been broadly and uniformly planed down, and the depression filled with the *debris*.

West of the Rio Grande the drift action has never been in operation, but the erosion of the surface has been confined to the lines of drainage.

During the Tertiary period that region was, as a whole, elevated above the sea level, and only locally covered by fresh water lakes. Since the Tertiary epoch it has apparently always held its present character: a high plateau, perhaps the highest of equal area in the world; probably the oldest portion of the earth's present surface, at least one that has longest exhibited its present conditions; one that has been longest exposed to the influence of agents now in action, and hence bearing the most deeply inscribed records of their power.

This will account for the profound depth of its excavation, or, in other words, for the great relative height of the sides of its trough. Why those sides are so often perpendicular, presenting mural faces a mile in height, and why they are not the gentle slopes of broad and fertile valleys, has been explained by reference to the facts that very little moisture in the form of rain falls on that surface; almost no vegetation is there to aid in softening the savage scenery, but the flow of water from the distant mountains, constant and copious, ever spends its energy in wearing away the rock beneath it in long and narrow lines. The walls on either side of the deepening beds of the streams, when beyond their influence, suffer little change, but stand as monuments on which are written the history of countless ages.

The picture presented by the "Plains" east of the mountains where we crossed them is quite a contrast to this. The fall from the bases of the Rocky mountains to the sea level is spread over twice the distance, and distributed along a slope so gentle that its descent is invisible to the eye, and it seems in all directions level. All that slope is at least moderately well watered, and near the Mississippi, where the erosive action would have left its most conspicuous marks, copious rains have washed them all away or stripped them of all character.

It should be borne in mind that this description is only applied and is only applicable to that part of the prairies bordering the Santa Fé road. Both north and south of that line, though at considerable distances from it, we might find regions more like, in their physical aspects, geological structure and climate, to the western portion of the table lands.

North of the Platte is a wide area much more dry and sterile than that adjacent to our route. The surface is not as high nor as level as the plateau traversed by the Colorado, and the fall of the stream is less rapid. Great cañons are consequently not found there. Cañons of smaller size are not uncommon, and the banks of the stream generally present more abrupt faces than those on our route.

South of the Santa Fé road the *Llano Estacado* (judging from the descriptions we have of it) seems to reproduce, on a smaller scale, the scenery of the table-lands of the Colorado. The climate of the *Llano* is very dry, and as its surface has an average elevation of nearly 4,000 feet, the fall of its draining streams is very rapid; consequently, their channels are deeply cut and bounded by precipitous banks.

The contrast of physical features presented by the plains east and west of the mountains is not of merely abstract interest. It involves all the economical differences between a nearly uninhabitable desert and perhaps the best agricultural region on the continent. To the geologist, the change from west to east is not so pleasant. Instead of the everywhere abounding exposures of the strata—as frequent and complete as though made expressly to facilitate his investigations—he here finds an unbroken sheet of soil, covering the underlying rocks as completely as the integuments cover the bones of a well-fed animal. The harder strata may occasionally be seen in the banks of the streams, but even there the softer intervals are represented by smooth and grassy slopes. From this cause the determination of the details of the geological structure becomes a matter of extreme difficulty, and on the march one can hardly hope to do more than make a skeleton sketch of the formations over which he passes, and which for many miles may be concealed from his view. Fortunately the rocky foundations of the plains have never been broken up, and the regularity in the succession of the strata gives to the necessarily interrupted observations along a single line of travel a value they would not otherwise have. Made under such circumstances, the subjoined sketch of the geology of the Santa Fé road must be brief and imperfect, leaving much blank space to be filled by future observations, and embracing views in regard to the superficial extent, thickness, and subdivisions of formations which are only provisional, and liable to modification by the discovery of new facts.

SANTA FÉ TO LAS VEGAS.

The altitude of Santa Fé is 6,846* feet; and for some miles after leaving the city we continued to ascend, till we reached the summit of the pass over the first of the lines of elevation intervening between the valley of the Rio Grande and the "Plains." The axis of this range is granitic, and from Santa Fé, to and beyond Rock Corral—our first camp—we had the red granite, already spoken of, constantly in sight.

On the flank of this great granitic mass the stratified rocks of its western slope reappear, much disturbed, but very fully exposed. At the base of the series, as on the Sandia mountain, is the Carboniferous limestone, but here generally covered and concealed by the more recent strata. Above the limestone are the saliferous sandstones and variegated marls, of which splendid sections are exposed in Apache cañon. These strata are much disturbed, but otherwise unchanged.

The base of the cliffs in the cañon is composed of the red and green foliated sandstones and shales, the upper portion of the Saliferous group. They here present precisely the same appearance as at Camp 101, in the Navajo country, Sheep spring, &c. Above these are the white and red calcareous sandstones of the Marl series, of which a thickness of perhaps 500 feet is visible.

These latter strata show marked differences from their equivalents in the country west of the Rio Grande. The variegated marls so conspicuous further west, and which, with bands of magnesian limestone, form the base of the series, are here entirely wanting, or so modified as not to be recognizable. The only representatives of the group of rocks are, in this vicinity, the red and white calcareous sandstones, or indurated marls, which in the Navajo country form its upper half. This change is a progressive one, as will be seen by reference to the preceding pages; and even progressive, both east and west, from a centre on the meridian of the Moqui villages. In the valley of the Little Colorado, in that longitude, the greater part of the interval between the saliferous sandstones and the Cretaceous rocks is filled with thin beds of highly colored marls and bands of magnesian limestone; west of that point, in the Painted Desert, the same interval is filled with thicker and more indurated strata, though otherwise similar. In coming eastward toward the Rio Grande we observed the variegated marls with bands of dolomite and silicified wood, a locally well-marked subdivision of the series, becoming less and less conspicuous, until here in Apache cañon they are entirely wanting. As the aggregate thickness of the Marl series is at the same time considerably lessened, it might be supposed that its lower division was simply thinning out, but a converse change was noticed in the more massive portions of the series running parallel with this. The indurated marls or calcareous sandstones of the Moqui sections (Camps 91 and 92) increase in thickness and solidity toward the east, until at Fort Defiance, Laguna, &c., they quite overshadow the diminishing marls. We may therefore infer that this change is one of conversion as well as elimination; and it presents another difficulty in the way of an attempt to draw, without more fossils, division lines between different portions of the Marl series.

On the banks of the Pecos extensive erosions have laid bare all the strata from the Carboniferous to the Cretaceous formation. The section from the summit of the mesa near Pecos village to the bed of the stream is as follows:

Cretaceous.

1. Yellowish white sandstone.

---

* Emory's reconnaissance, 1848, p. 37.

Marl series.

2. Red, white, and green sandstones, and shales.
3. Soft white calc. sandstone.
4. Soft red calc. sandstone.
5. Red and white sandstones and shales with gypsum.

Saliferous group.

6. Red and green sandstones, conglomerates and shales.

Carboniferous.

7. Limestones with beds of shale and sandstone.

I had no means of measuring the interval between the surface of the Carboniferous limestone and the summit of the Marl series, but judged it to be considerably less than 2,000 feet.   Mr. Marcou estimates the thickness of his Triassic rocks (variegated marls and red sandstones) on the Sandia mountain at from "4,000 to 5,000 feet," a difference at localities but fifty miles apart, which, if it really exists, is quite surprising.

The limestone at Pecos is highly fossiliferous, and has often been referred to in the preceding pages.   Its fossils are nearly all common in the coal measures of Kansas and Missouri, of which this deposit is undoubtedly the geological equivalent.   It is called by Mr. Marcou the Lower Carboniferous or mountain limestone, and it is barely possible some portions of it may represent the period of deposition of the Lower Carboniferous strata of the Mississippi valley, but as yet we have no proof of it.   On the contrary, all the fossils it has yielded, *Productus semireticulatus, P. Rogersi, Spirigera subtilita, Rhynconella Rocky montana*, etc., etc., are in North America characteristic of the coal measures.

Along the Pecos, from Pecos village to San José, the saliferous sandstones and shales form the bottom of the valley over which the road passes, while the adjacent hills are composed of the Marl series and capped with Cretaceous sandstones.

At Ojo Vernal an arch of the strata has brought the Carboniferous limestone within reach of the powerful erosive action which has scooped out the valley, and for a short interval it forms the surface rock.   The overlying strata here form picturesque mesa walls and isolated buttes, of which the height, according to our estimate, is about 1,500 feet.

From Ojo Vernal to Las Vegas we had constantly in view the strata included in the section at Pecos.   They become more and more disturbed, however, and, within five miles of Las Vegas, are broken through by a mass of protruded granite.   Along this line of upheaval the order of succession of the strata is very much obscured, and in passing it we entered an entirely new geological field.   The Carboniferous limestone here sinks below the surface, and does not appear again on our route for more than six hundred miles; with it also sink our old friends the variegated marls and saliferous sandstones, and of these our farewell was final; for, although they were immediately beneath our feet through more than one day's march in Eastern Kansas, they do not rise above the soil and grass, and were not recognized.   Even the Lower Cretaceous sandstones, the summit rock of the highlands bordering our route west of Las Vegas, here for a time disappear, and the surface for many miles is exclusively occupied by Upper Cretaceous rocks.

These were first noticed some ten miles west of Las Vegas; thence to the vicinity of the Moro they appear wherever the surface of the prairies is broken.   They consist of greenish brown or gray shales, and compact, blue, argillaceous limestones.   The shales include thin arenaceous bands, containing fragments of shells of *Inoceramus*, which at first sight resemble fish scales.   The limestone is very homogeneous and compact, but usually in thin layers; though quite dark internally, it weathers white, and exposed surfaces of it in the distance appear as white as chalk.   We found these strata much better displayed further eastward, but even here they exhibit characters sufficient to distinguish them from any rocks we had before met with.

It will be remembered that I have suggested that the high white mesa seen north of the Moqui villages is composed of this series of Upper Cretaceous strata.

LAS VEGAS TO THE CIMARRON.

Throughout the entire interval of two hundred miles between Las Vegas and the crossing of the Cimarron, with the exception of occasional sheets or masses of trap, and a small basin of fresh water Tertiary strata, the only rocks seen belong to the Cretaceous formation. In this region the streams are generally more or less cañoned, and the exposures of the underlying rocks are frequent and full, showing that beneath the more modern materials an unbroken sheet of Cretaceous strata occupies a belt of this width. We shall see hereafter that the crossing of the Cimarron is by no means the eastern limit of this formation, but that, except when covered by Tertiary beds, it extends full two hundred miles further eastward. The exact outlines of the great area occupied by rocks of this age are not yet known, but from the observation of the Canadian geologists on the Assinaboin, Dr. Hayden on the Upper Missouri, Captains Stansbury and Frémont on the Platte, of Drs. Roemer and Shumard in Texas, of myself on the Santa Fé road, &c., &c., it is apparent that they occupy a larger space within the territory of the United States than those of any other firmation, and at least 500,000 square miles of surface. I am aware that Mr. Marcou has represented the greater part of the country lying between the Mississippi and the Rocky mountains as covered with Jurassic and Triassic rocks, and has so colored his map. In regard to the accuracy of this conclusion in other regions than those traversed by our party I will not venture to decide, but in reference to the geology of our route he is certainly far from right. He has divided the country between Las Vegas and the great bend of the Arkansas about equally between the two formations I have mentioned, while in fact not a single outcrop of either exists on our route throughout all that interval, the entire distance (450 miles) being taken up by Cretaceous and Tertiary strata.

On the Moro and about Fort Union the surface rocks are coarse friable sandstones of Lower Cretaceous age, apparently the equivalents of those of the Moqui villages, &c., but here tinged with red; a change already referred to, and which is more marked further east.

Streams, sheets and buttes of trap are conspicuous features in the scenery, not only of this vicinity, but of all the prairie country adjacent to the Raton mountains. These mountains seem to form a great volcanic focus, similar in many respects to those of San Francisco and San Mateo; many of the summits showing the peculiar outlines and colors of trappean rocks, and the long lines of trap mesas filling the horizon in that direction. Like those before described, the Raton volcanoes had innumerable subordinate vents scattered over all the adjacent region, from which the flow of lava was, in part, subsequent to the erosion of the beds of many of the present streams; for, as in instances before cited, the melted lava, obeying the laws that govern the flow of water, has followed the lines of drainage, and dispossessed some of these streams of their beds.

On the banks of the Ocaté the Upper Cretaceous strata again make their appearance and form the hills between the valleys of that stream and the Red Fork of the Canadian.

The banks of the latter, at the crossing and nearer the mouth of the Ocaté, afford the best view of the Upper Cretaceous series obtained on our route. The coarse, reddish-yellow sandstones (Lower Cretaceous) form the trough in which it flows from the crossing and the walls of the cañon below. Upon this rests the series of shales and limestones which I have called Upper Cretaceous, forming precipitous bluffs near the stream and hills which rise toward the east to the height of 500 feet. The exposures of the strata composing the summits of these hills is less satisfactory than at their bases, but it was easy to perceive that no marked change occurs from top to bottom.

The green and gray shales which immediately overlie the sandstones are nearly homogeneous for 30 or 40 feet, when thin bands of bituminous shaly limestone begin to be introduced. Those continue to increase in number and thickness till, about 100 feet above the base, they entirely replace the shales. From this point to the summit of the series alternations of both recur, but the limestones predominate.

The fossils of the shales are very fragmentary and imperfect, but those of the limestones are numerous and well preserved. At the crossing of the Canadian the most abundant fossil is the well known *Inoceramus problematicus*, (*I. mytiloides,*) so common in the Cretaceous rocks of both America and Europe.

This occurs in such numbers that its flattened valves quite cover the surfaces of some of the strata. On the Upper Missouri this species of *Inoceramus* is found in the Middle and Upper Cretaceous rocks, forming Nos. III and IV of Meek and Hayden's Nebraska section. This confirms the conclusion, drawn from their own fossils, in reference to the relative age of the sandstones and shales of the Cretaceous mesa at the Moqui villages, viz: that they are the equivalents of Nos. I and II of Meek and Hayden's section.

In New Mexico I was unable to draw any satisfactory line of separation between the different portions of what I have called *Lower Cretaceous* strata, nor are the upper members of this great formation sufficiently developed on our route to be susceptible of intelligible subdivision. I have, therefore, made of the Cretaceous rocks two great groups, upper and lower, which are readily distinguishable both by their lithological characters and fossils. This classification is not advanced as any substitute for a different one adopted elsewhere, but merely as an expression of the stratigraphical development of the Cretaceous formation along our line of survey. Messrs. Meek and Hayden have apparently found in their subdivisions of the strata of this epoch in Nebraska tangible and distinctive characters, yet, as we have seen, it is probable some of them have only a local value.

Beside the fossils already mentioned, I found in the limestones at the crossing of Red Fork of the Canadian a small *Arca*, a *Gryphœa*, and fish teeth, all too imperfect for accurate determination.

The section here exposed is peculiarly interesting, as it includes so much of both groups of Cretaceous rocks and their point of junction. As it is directly on the line of the great Santa Fé road, it is to be hoped that it will be more carefully examined by those who have more time at command, and a larger collection of fossils made than I obtained.

From Red Fork to Point of Rocks we were constantly upon the Upper Cretaceous formation, here composing high and rounded hills. "Point of Rocks" is a bald headland of trap, the terminus of a lava flood poured from a neighboring cluster of volcanic mountains, apparently belonging to the Raton group. Its perpendicular faces are the result of erosion, and show how much the aspect of this region has been modified by aqueous agency.

From "Point of Rocks" to the Cimarron the surface rock is generally the Lower Cretaceous sandstone, though in some localities a sheet of trap overlies and conceals it.

On the left bank of Cottonwood creek a limited area is occupied by strata of nearly white tufaceous limestones, probably of fresh water origin, and an outlier of the great Tertiary basin of the Arkansas. At the crossing of McNees's creek an exposed surface of soft Cretaceous sandstone is covered with the names of travellers who have stopped there. At Cedar Spring, Cold Spring, Upper Cimarron Spring, "Hole in the Rock," &c., as well as at many intervening points, the same stratum is exposed.

CIMARRON CROSSING TO PAWNEE FORK.

In traversing this interval (200 miles) we followed down the valley of the Cimarron three days, then crossed the "Jornada" to the Arkansas, which we descended to the "Dry Road," and then crossed by way of the Crow creeks to Pawnee Fork. In this part of our route we were constantly passing over rocks which are nearly as soft and homogeneous as the variegated marls of the Painted Desert, but they have been affected by the erosive action they have suffered in a strikingly different manner. Instead of vertical sections of many hundred feet in height never absent from our sight, here were rounded hills and broad valleys, of which the smooth and grassy slopes revealed nothing of their rocky frame-work. Occasionally along the Cimarron the harder Cretaceous rocks break through the monotonous surface; but, aside from that, the views we had of the geological formation are comparatively few and superficial. Wherever seen, however, with the exceptions already made, we found the substrata to have a common character; and our observations would indicate the prevalence of rocks of one geological age over all this interval.

These are soft, white limestones, either tufaceous and concretionary, or fine and chalky. They are generally in their beds, but in some instances are massive and somewhat sandy. So far as observed, these contained no fossils in the localities where we examined them.

Till these strata can be more carefully studied, and fossils found in them, any conclusion in reference to their age must be liable to error. There is, however, little doubt in my own mind that they are Tertiary, and continuous with, or equivalent to, Tertiary strata which have been identified as such at various points north and west of this crossing of the Arkansas. They rest upon the Cretaceous rocks, generally on the Lower Cretaceous sandstones, and may be portions of the same formation; but their aspect is rather that of fresh-water deposits, and unlike any Cretaceous strata which have come under my observation in any country. Their lithological characters are precisely those of the Tertiary rocks of Nebraska, so fully explored by Dr. Hayden, as well as of the strata noticed in the descriptions of the geology of the Moqui country. I am also inclined to class with them the white tufaceous limestones of the Rio Grande valley. The conjecture that they are Tertiary is strengthened by the fact that Tertiary fossils were found by Colonel Emory (op. cit., p. 12) a little higher up the Arkansas than where we crossed it, in strata of somewhat similar character. I think it highly probable that future explorations will not only prove the area between the crossing of the Cimarron and Pawnee Fork to be part of a great Tertiary basin, but show that it stretches far away to the north, approaching, if not joining, the basin of White river. The high table-lands which separate the valleys of the tributaries of the Arkansas are portions of a once continuous plateau which occupied all this region. The soil is good, and they are covered by a thick mat of most nutritious grass, (Buffalo grass, *Sesleria dactyloides;*) but the amount of rain which falls here is too small to admit of cropping the ground. The bottom lands of the Arkansas may, however, be successfully cultivated. Containing these different surfaces, this region is peculiarly adapted to grazing, and will doubtless soon be covered with domesticated flocks and herds in place of the bands of buffalo which now roam over it.

PAWNEE FORK TO COUNCIL GROVE.

Cretaceous formation.—As we descended from the high divide crossed by the "dry road" we left the Tertiary limestones behind us, and on the banks of Pawnee Fork came again into the reddish-yellow Cretaceous sandstones which we had last seen on the Upper Cimarron. They are best exposed on the banks of Pawnee Fork, a few miles further east. We could not determine with accuracy the eastern limits of this formation, as after passing Pawnee rock the underlying strata are entirely concealed for many miles. It is probable, however, that it does not reach beyond Walnut creek, for the consistence of the rock which represents it is such that it would be likely to make its appearance above the surface did it exist there.

The sandstone composing Pawnee rock is reddish-brown in color, soft and coarse, much like that forming the base of the Cretaceous system at Smoky Hill, (sixty miles northeast,) from which Messrs. Meek and Hayden have obtained a very interesting suite of Angiosperm-dicotyledonous leaves, including all the genera, and one or more species found in the cretaceous sand-stones at the Moqui villages.

East of Pawnee rock we saw no rock in place till we approached the Little Arkansas, and even then the exposures are exceedingly meagre and unsatisfactory. The surface is entirely unbroken, and the soil somewhat sandy and red, especially between Walnut and Cow creeks, about Plum buttes. I have supposed that beneath the surface were here concealed the varie-gated marl series, and the equivalents of the red sandstones of the Little Colorado; but in what force and exhibiting what characters can only be conjectured. The impracticability of making a direct comparison between the eastern and western outcrops of these strata was a source of extreme regret to me, but it was impossible to accomplish it without the time and means at command. From the section given by Messrs. Meek and Hayden of the strata intervening between the Cretaceous and Carboniferous formation in parts of Kansas just north of the localities in question, it is evident that there is not a perfect correspondence with those filling that interval in New Mexico.

From the Little Arkansas to Council Grove we were occasionally able to obtain some inti-mation of the nature of the underlying rocks, or, at least, of the harder ones. These are light-yellow, or gray calcareous sandstones, with gypsum, and cream-colored, yellow, and blue magnesian limestones; a group quite different, in many respects, from any rocks found west of the Rio Grande.

They have been carefully studied in this vicinity by Messrs. Meek and Hayden, and have afforded them the first conclusive evidence of the existence on the American continent of representatives of the Permian rocks of Europe. On Turkey creek are exposed a few feet of yellowish arenaceous limestone, containing gypsum and layers of carbonate and sulphate of lime, which were evidently deposited on a surface fissured by a net-work of cracks. These layers are now covered with, or composed of, a series of angular cells, formed by the anasto-mosing plates which once filled the cracks referred to.

On the banks of Cottonwood creek a cream-colored magnesian limestone was noticed, which is known to be Permian, but which yielded me no fossils. From Messrs. Meek and Hayden I learn that it is highly fossiliferous at no great distance from the crossing, containing various Permian fossils, such as *Monotis Hawni, Myalina perattenuata, Bakevellia parva,* &c., &c., good specimens of which I received from these gentlemen, and have placed in the collections of the survey.

At Diamond Spring a limestone is quite fully exposed, having been extensively quarried to form the corral. It is bluish-gray in color and more compact than those noticed on Cotton-wood creek and the Little Arkansas. It contains no fossils, that I could discover, at the spring, but Mr. Meek found a few fossils somewhere in the vicinity, which prove it to lie at the base of the Permian, or summit of the Carboniferous series.

COUNCIL GROVE TO FORT LEAVENWORTH.

Passing Council Grove we left behind us all the undoubted Permian rocks, and after an interval of some miles of debatable ground, occupied by strata of intermediate age, we came upon those of purely Carboniferous character, which continue thence, without interruption, to Fort Leavenworth.

The geological structure of this portion of our route is so simple and so well known that but little need be said of it. The Carboniferous formation, as here developed, when compared with its equivalents east of the Mississippi, shows great lithological differences, though containing in abundance many fossils which are characteristic of the Coal measures in Illinois, Ohio, and Pennsylvania; such as *Productus semireticulatus, Spirifer cameratus, Spirifer lineatus, Spirigera subtilita,* &c., &c. With these, however, are others which I have never met with in the Alleghany coal fields, *Fusilina cylindrica, Productus splendens, Spirifer plano-convexa, Spirifer hemiplicata,* &c. The *Fusilinas* are a very marked feature of the fauna of all parts of the coal measures of Kansas which I examined. They are so abundant in some layers of limestone as to compose the greater part of their substance. The lithological characters which I have referred to as contrasting with those of eastern Coal measure rocks, consist mainly in the substitution of calcareous beds for the shales, sandstones, coal seams, fire clays, &c., which form the productive Coal measures on the Ohio. The coarse and massive sandstones, so conspicuous in the Coal series east of the Mississippi, are here almost entirely wanting, being replaced by alternations of limestone with fine argillaceous shales or indurated clays.

The coal seams are few and thin, and the coal plants, so abundant in the Alleghany coal-fields, are almost entirely absent. Workable beds of coal occur, however, at several points on our route—as near Burlingame and on the Delaware reservation. The Burlingame coal is of fair quality, and is mined to some extent for the supply of the country for many miles around. Like all the coals of Kansas which I saw, it is less hard, bright and pure, than that of Ohio and Pennsylvania.

Though comparatively rare, fossil plants are not entirely wanting in Kansas, as I found near Easton, on the banks of the Stranger, gray shales lying between beds of *Fusilina* limestone, and containing large numbers of fronds of the world-wide coal plant, *Neuropteris flexuosa.* No other genus or species was found with it.

In our progress eastward from Council Grove to St. Louis, Missouri, I noticed a gradual change in the character of the Coal measure rocks—to which reference has before been made—viz: a diminution of the number and thickness of the limestone beds, and a corresponding increase in the relative importance of the arenaceous layers and in the coal strata.

As far as Fort Leavenworth the limestones predominate, showing the prevalence of marine conditions over this region throughout the greater part of the time included in the Carboniferous era. Between the limestone strata there are, however, many beds of carbonaceous matter and transported sediments—shales and clays—which indicate that with the periods of submergence, alternated shorter intervals of emergence, and those in which littoral deposits were made.

Near Santa Fé, in New Mexico, we saw the first evidences of oscillations of level, which brought the sea bottom to the surface. Further west and south the waves of an open ocean rolled without impediment or interruption through all the ages of the Carboniferous epoch—from beginning to end. Near Santa Fé, in Northern Texas, &c., temporary islands projected above the ocean's surface, and gave support to a vigorous growth of land plants. Doubtless contemporaneous with these islands were many others—now buried beneath the later Cretaceous and Tertiary strata—which once dotted the sea bordering the mainland shore.

With the oscillations of level here so plainly indicated, the continental shore line must have advanced and receded, not once, but many times, from northern Iowa, where the palæozoic rocks have never been covered by Carboniferous strata, to and beyond the Arkansas.

Since the preceding pages were written, Messrs. Meek and Hayden have published a synopsis of the observations made on their recent geological excursion into central Kansas. Among their valuable notes is given a section of all the strata observed from the Cretaceous down into the Carboniferous series. This section is principally drawn from exposures near our route, just where, immediately on our line of observation, the geological structure was least apparent and yet most interesting. Hence it will supply in part the deficiencies of my notes for making a comparison between the eastern and western outcrops of the strata filling the interval between the Cretaceous and Carboniferous formations.

The bearing which this section has on all that has been said in this report of the geology of the country between the Little Colorado and Rio Grande is so direct and important that I take the liberty of repeating it here.

General section of the rocks of Kansas valley from the Cretaceous down, so as to include portions of the Upper Coal measures.

Feet.

1. Red, brown, and yellowish, rather coarse-grained sandstone, often obliquely laminated, and containing many ferruginous concretions ; also, fossil wood and many leaves of dicotyledonous trees, some of which belong to existing genera, and others to genera peculiar to the Cretaceous epoch. *Locality, summit of Smoky Hills* 60

2. Whitish, very fine-grained argillaceous sandstone, underlaid by bluish purple and ash-colored clays. *Locality same as preceding* 15

3. Long, gentle slope, with occasional outcrops of ash-colored red, blue, and whitish, more or less laminated clays, with thin beds of sandstone. *Locality same as preceding, and extending down at places nearly or quite to the bluffs of Smoky Hill river*; thickness about 200

4. Red sandstone, with some layers of hard, light gray calcareous ditto, and both containing ferruginous concretions. *Locality, bluffs Smoky Hill river, five or six miles above Grand Saline river.* Probably local, thickness seen about 15

5. Bluish, red, light-yellow, and gray clays, and soft claystones, with sometimes a few thin layers of magnesian limestone. In many places these clays have been traversed in every direction by cracks, into which calcareous and argillaceous matter have found their way, and subsequently become consolidated so as to form thin seams of impure yellowish limestone, which cross and intersect each other at every angle. The red clays are usually less distinctly laminated, contain more arenaceous matter, and often show ripple-marks on the surfaces. *Locality, bluffs along Smoky Hill river, above the mouth of the Grand Saline* 60

6. Light gray, ash-colored, and red clays, sometimes arenaceous, and often traversed by cracks, filled with calcareous matter as in the bed above—alternating with thin layers and seams of gypsum. *Locality, near mouth of Smoky Hill river* 40

7. Rather compact amorphous white gypsum, with near the base disseminated crystals, dark colored ditto. *Locality same as last* .... 4½ to 5

8. Alternations of ash-colored, more or less arenaceous clays, with thin beds and seams of gypsum above; towards lower part, thin layers of claystone, and at some places soft magnesian limestone. *Locality same as last* 50

9. Rough conglomerated mass, composed of fragments magnesian limestone and sandstone, with sometimes a few quartz pebbles, cemented by calcareous and arenaceous matter ; variable in thickness and probably local. *Locality, south side Smoky Hill river, ten or twelve miles below Solomon's Fork.* Seen 18

10. Bluish, light-gray, and red laminated clays, with seams and beds of yellowish magnesian limestone, containing *Monotis Hawni, Myalina perattenuata, Pleurophorus? subcuneata, Edmondia? Calhouni, Pecten* undt. and *Spirigera* near *S. subtilita;* also *Nautilus eccentricus, Bakevellia parva, Leda subscitula, Axinus rotundatus,* and undetermined species of *Bellerophon, Murchisonia, &c. Locality, near Smoky Hill river, on high country south of Fort Riley, as well as on Cottonwood creek* 90

11. Light grayish and yellow magnesian limestone, in layers and beds sometimes alternating with bluish and other colored clays, and containing *Solemya,* a *Myalina,* near *M. squamosa, Pleurophorus? subcuneata, Bakevellia parva, Pecten* undt., and a *Euomphalus* near *E. rugosus;* also, a *Spirigera* allied to *S. subtilita,* but more gibbous, *Orthisina umbraculum? O. Shumardiana, &c. Locality, summit of the hills near Fort Riley, and above there; also seen on Cottonwood creek* .... 25 to 35

Feet.

12. Light-grayish yellow, rather granular magnesian limestone, containing spines and plates of *Archæocidaris;* a few fragments of small *Crinoid* columns, *Spirifer* similar to *S. lineatus,* but perhaps distinct; also same *Spirigera* seen in beds above, *Orthisina Shumardiana, O. umbraculum?* and *Productus Calhounianus. Forms distinct horizon near summit of hills in vicinity of Fort Riley; also seen on Cottonwood creek* · 7 to 8

13. Soft argillo-calcareous bed, apparently local. *Kansas Falls* · · · · · · · · · · · · · · · 5

14. Light-grayish and yellowish magnesian limestone, containing many concretions of flint; also the same *Spirigera* found in beds above, and *Productus Norwoodi, P. Calhounianus,* with *Discina tenuilineata* and an undetermined *Monotis. Fort Riley and below; also at Kansas Falls and on Cottonwood creek* · · · · · · · · · · · · · · 38

15. Alternations of bluish, yellowish and brown clays, with a few thin seams of limestone. *Fort Riley, Kansas Falls; also below Fort Riley, and on Cottonwood creek* · 35

16. Light-yellowish magnesian limestone, containing *fucoidal* markings, fragments of small *Crinoid* columns, *Pecten, Allorisma, Spirigera, Orthisina umbraculum? O. Shumardiana, Discina tenuilineata, &c. Lower quarry at Fort Riley, and at other places above and below Fort Riley, as well as on Cottonwood creek* · · · · · · · · 4 to—

17. Alternations of blue, red, and light-gray clays, with sometimes thin layers and seams of magnesian limestone. *Fort Riley* · 28

18. Light-gray and whitish magnesian limestone, containing *Spirigera, Orthisina umbraculum? O. Shumardiana, Productus Calhounianus, Acanthocladia Americana,* and undt. sp. *Cyathocrinus.* Lower part containing many concretions of flint. *Fort Riley and on Cottonwood creek.* Whole thickness about · · · · · · · · · · 40

19. Brown, green, and very light gray clays, alternating; contains near the upper part fragments of *Crinoid* columns, *Synocladia biserialis, Spirigera, Productus Norwoodi, Chonetes mucronata, Orthisina Shumardiana, Orthisina umbraculum, &c.,* with teeth of *Petalodus Alleghaniensis. Fort Riley* · 14

20. Alternations of rather thin layers light yellowish magnesian limestone, and various colored clays; the limestone layers containing *Monotis, Synocladia biserialis, &c. Locality same as last* · 33

21. Slope; no rocks seen. *Below Fort Riley* · 25

22. Whitish, or very light-gray magnesian limestone, rendered porous by cavities left by the weathering out of numerous *Fusulinæ.* This is the highest horizon at which any remains of *Fusulina* were met with. *Some four miles below Fort Riley, along a creek on the south side of the Kansas, and apparently not more than ten feet above it* · 2

23. Bluish, light-gray, and brown clays, with occasional layers of magnesian limestone. *Chonetes mucronata, Orthisina umbraculum? Monotis, Fusulina, &c. Ten miles below Fort Riley* · 35

24. Hard, very light yellowish-gray magnesian limestone, with *Fusulina,* and spines of *Archæocidaris.* Forms a marked horizon near the *same locality as last* · · · · · 6

25. Slope, with occasional exposures, thin layers of *Fusulina* limestone, and seams of gray limestone containing *Myalina, Monotis, Pecten* and fragments of *Synocladia biserialis. Near same locality as last* · 36

26. Light-gray argillaceous limestone, showing on weathered surfaces a somewhat laminated structure; contains large spines of *Archæcidaris. Near Ogden's Ferry and Manhattan* · 9

27. Gray limestone, often fragmentary, with much clay above; lower part hard, and more or less cellular in middle. *Locality same as last.* · · · · · · · · · · · · · · · 5

Feet.

28. Whitish clays and claystones, with a thin layer of hard compact gray limestone near the middle. *Locality same as last* ·   10

29. Light-greenish indurated clays. *Same locality* ·   3

30. Hard, heavy bedded, white argillaceous limestone, containing *Monotis* and *Avicula*. *Ogden Ferry, and below there* ·   5

31. Very thinly laminated dark-green shale. *Three miles nearly east of Ogden Ferry, on McDowell's creek; also at Manhattan, on the Kansas* · · · · · · · · · · · · · · ·   1

32. Light-greenish and flesh-colored hard argillaceous limestone, with *Spirifer cameratus*. This is the highest horizon at which we found this species. *Same localities* ·   3

33. Alternations of bluish, green, and red more or less calcareous laminated clays, light gray limestones and claystones, with *Pecten, Monotis* and fragments of *Crinoid* columns. *Same localities* ·   30

34. Alternations of bluish, purple, and ash-colored calcareous clays, passing at places into claystones, and containing in a thin bed, near the middle, *Spirifer planoconvexa, Spirigera subtilita, Productus splendens? Rhynconella uta, &c. Locality same as preceding* ·   12

35. Blue, light-gray, and greenish clays, with occasional harder seams and layers of claystone and limestone. *Same locality* ·   33

36. Somewhat laminated claystone of light-gray color, with more or less calc spar near lower part. *Manhattan* ·   19

37. Alternations of dark-gray and blue, soft decomposing argillaceous limestone, with dark laminated clays, or soft shale, containing great quantities of *Fusulina cylindrica, F. cglindrica*, var. *ventricosa, Discina Manhattanensis, Chœtetes*, and fragments *Crinoids*; also, *Chonetes Verneuiliana, C. mucronata, Productus splendens? Retzia Mormonii, Rhynconella uta, Spirigera subtilita, Spirifer cameratus, S. plano-convexa, Euomphalus*, near *E. rugosus* and *Synocladia biserialis;* also *Cladodus occidentalis. Locality same as last* ·   18

38. Soft bluish shale, with yellow laminated arenaceous seams below, containing Fucoidal markings. *Same locality* ·   25

39. Two layers gray argillo-calcareous rock, separated by two feet of dark green and ash-colored clays. The calcareous beds contain fragments of Crinoids, Chonetes, and *Myalina* of undt. species. *Same locality as last* · · · · · · · · · · · · ·   4½

40. Light-greenish, yellow, and gray clays and claystones, extending down nearly to high-water mark of the Kansas, *opposite the mouth of Blue river* · · · · · · · · · · ·   27

By comparing this section with those which I have before given of the rocks intermediate in age, between the Carboniferous and Cretaceous formations in New Mexico, particularly those exposed on the Little Colorado*, it will be seen that the differences are very marked, and that from lithological characters it is impossible to work out the parallelism with any certainty.

The sections given of the strata between the base of the Cretaceous mesa at the Moqui villages and the Carboniferous limestone west of the crossing of the Little Colorado, p. ———; that at Fort Defiance, p. ———; at Agua Azul, p. ———; at Pecos village, p. ———, and at Ojo Vernal, all represent the same geological horizon, and yet how different in all subdivisions and details !

These facts will illustrate the uncertainty of deductions made from lithological characters, and show the necessity for waiting the discovery of fossils in the almost fossilless rocks occupying the place of the Permian, Triassic, and Jurassic formations west of the Rio Grande, before a

---

*Chapter VIII of this Report.

parallelism can be established between them and the subdivisions of the group of strata to which they are *generally* equivalent on other parts of this continent.

If their mineral composition is a wholly unreliable guide in going from this side to the other of the Rio Grande, how much more questionable are inferences drawn from it on opposite sides of the Atlantic!

In the foregoing section of Messrs. Meek and Hayden it will be observed that the Carboniferous fossils of the lower members extend up, mingling with Permian forms, to the base of No. 10. Here the last traces of that formation disappear; and No. 10 contains only fossils which are regarded in Europe as characteristic of the Permian rocks. Above No. 10 no fossils have been found below the sandstone (No. 1) which forms the base of the Cretaceous series.

The intermingling of Permian and Carboniferous in the strata of this section is an interesting fact which has been remarked upon by Messrs. M. & H. It shows plainly that no line of demarcation can be drawn between these formations in the west; that the periods of deposition of all these rocks were but parts of one great epoch during which the same general physical conditions prevailed. There were, doubtless, marked local peculiarities in the physical geography of different districts on the continent—peculiarities recorded in the discrepancies I have referred to between the synchronous deposits of the banks of the Kansas and Little Colorado—but the strata are entirely conformable both with the older rocks below and the Cretaceous beds above.

Throughout this interval the general lithological uniformity, in the many repetitions of the strata, evince greater stability, a longer period of geological rest, than has been indicated by the rocks of any other portion of the globe which has yet been examined.

Such being the case, we shall probably look in vain for data which will permit us here to draw the lines which separate formations in other countries—or rather in books—sharply through the geological column.

Geological classification is everywhere to some extent a conventionality, being without precise counterpart in nature; but on the great plateau west of the Mississippi lines of division between the different formations elsewhere (see p. 69) are not to be discovered; and the effort to apply rigidly to the rocks of that region the classification adopted in other countries will be but partially successful; this difficulty is felt by Meek and Hayden in attempting to define the limit between the Carboniferous and Permian rocks of Kansas.

In Europe the line of demarcation is not very apparent; in Kansas it does not exist. If compelled to draw that line, however, it should doubtless be done, as they suggest, at the base of No. 10, where the last vestige of the fauna of the lower and more important formations disappear.

CHAPTER XI.

PALÆONTOLOGY.

ARCHÆOCIDARIS. McCoy.

ARCHÆOCIDARIS LONGISPINUS, (n. sp.)

Plate I, figs. 1 and 1a.

Interambulacral plates unknown. Spines elongate, fusiform, $2\frac{1}{2}$ to $3\frac{1}{2}$ inches in length, acute, with a cylindrical section at all points; surface smooth, or very finely and longitudinally striated. The ring at the base of the spine is small, slightly crenulated, and in my specimens encircles it at right angles to its axis; a character which, however, probably varies with the position of the spine. Below the ring the diameter of the base rapidly contracts, forming the frustum of a cone, of which the surface is concave. At the lower extremity of the spine a shoulder is cut in this cone, by which the diameter of the articulating surface is reduced to $\frac{1}{4}$ that of the ring. Spine straight throughout, with the exception of a very slight curve just above the ring, the greatest diameter exceeding that of the ring.

The interambulacral plates of this species have generally not been preserved with the spines, as, in localities where the spines were abundant, I was unable to find traces of them. The spines are beautifully preserved, and present characters which separate this species from any heretofore known. Its smooth surfaces, entirely devoid of tubercles, and its circular section, distinguish it from those described by Prof. Swallow* and Prof. Hall.† As indicated above, there is great difference in the length of the spines; the shorter ones are much the more robust. The surface markings are, however, the same in all, and the variation in size and form is less than that exhibited in the spines of a single individual of any living species of *Cidaris*.

Locality and formation.—These fossils occur in great numbers in the crinoidal limestone in the upper part of the Carboniferous series on the banks of the Colorado river. They are so numerous in some localities that a dozen or more are visible on a square foot of the weathered surface of the rock. They seem to be strictly confined to this horizon, as I found none in the upper or lower of three Carboniferous limestones which are found in that region.

ARCHÆOCIDARIS ORNATUS, (n. sp.)

Plate I, figs. 2, 3, and 3a.

Body unknown. Primary spines fusiform, robust, 2.50 inches long by 0.36 inch in diameter, thickly set with secondary spines .08 inch in length, arranged in imperfectly spiral lines; the points slightly inclined toward the remote end of the spine. Ring at the base of moderate size, crenulated.

The spines of this species, in size and general form, resemble those of *A. longispinus*, but are strikingly different in bearing a number of relatively large secondary spines which are separated from each other by intervals usually less than the diameter of their bases.

From *A. megastylis*, Shumard, it is distinguished by the proximity and size of the secondary spines, which are both much larger and more closely approximated than in that species.

---

* Proc. Acad. Nat. Sc., St. Louis. † Geological Report of Iowa, Vol. 2, p. 698, &c.

Locality and formation.—Occurs abundantly with *A. longispinus* in the crinoidal limestone near junction of the two Colorados, and in the same rock, sixty miles west of that point, near the Great Cañon of the Colorado.

ARCHÆOCIDARIS GRACILIS, (n. sp.)

Plate I, figs. 4 and 4*a*.

Form of interambulacral plates unknown. A fragment bearing the central boss shows that the circle surrounding the articulating tubercle is ornamented with a single row of small tubercles, and that the articulating tubercle is deeply perforated.

Spines straight or curved, slender, elongate, conical, scarcely fusiform, with a circular section throughout; diameter of all parts much less than that of the ring. Surface thickly set with fine granulations, toward the base separated by spaces scarcely greater than their diameters; nearer the summit they are more scattered. Ring prominent, crenulate (?) in my specimens encircling the spine at right angles to its axis.

This delicate and beautiful species is scarcely likely to be confounded with any other known. Its slender, conical form and fine and numerous granulations separate it widely from its associates, as well as from other described species of which I have any knowledge.

Locality and formation.—Occurs with the last.

AMMONITES. Brug.

AMMONITES PERCARINATUS, Hall & Meek. *Memoirs Amer. Acad. Arts & Sciences*, 1856, *p.* 396. *Pl. IV, figs.* 2 *and* 2*a*.

This beautiful species, so characteristic of the Lower Cretaceous strata of the country bordering the Upper Missouri, was first described from young specimens collected by Mr. Meek and Dr. Hayden at the mouth of Vermillion river, in No. II of their section of the Cretaceous rocks.

Subsequently Dr. Hayden brought from the same region a large series of specimens, exhibiting its more mature forms, and in a beautiful state of preservation.

The younger specimens are accurately represented in the figures given by Hall and Meek, (loc. cit.,) and are thus described by them: "Discoidal depressed; umbilicus wide and shallow; volutions four or five, scarcely one-fourth of each embraced in the succeeding one; shell thin; surface marked by thirty-eight to forty-five prominent, flexuous, sharp ribs, some of which originate in the umbilicus, and others upon the latero-ventral margin, and all extend to the dorso-lateral edge, where they bend abruptly forward and terminate before reaching the dorsal line, which is marked by a thin, sharp carina extending to the aperture. Ribs thickened and sometimes nodose toward the periphery."

The nodes which ornament the ribs are, as is usual with other species, not developed in the very young, and become obsolete on the outer whorls of the very old specimens.

This shell attained much greater dimensions than would be inferred from the specimens figured by Hall and Meek. Some which I obtained are as much as eight or ten inches in diameter. On these larger specimens the development of the nodes may be very distinctly traced. Until the disk of the shell has reached a diameter of nearly an inch, no nodes are observable on the ribs; then a single row begins to appear; and when the disk is two inches in diameter, two rows of nodes are developed, in some specimens more conspicuous than in others. Sometimes a sudden expansion of the ribs near their ventral ends produces even a third row of nodes.

The carination of the dorsal surface, which is continuous in the younger specimens, becomes in older ones interrupted, presenting a series of semi-circular lobes, separated by sinuses of similar form.

Specimens in the beautiful collections of Dr. Hayden, which I have been kindly permitted to examine, exhibit these different phases of growth more distinctly than do mine, and show the species to have attained a large size.

Locality and formation.—The specimens of *A. percarinatus*, which are in my collection, are possessed of no ordinary interest, as they afford the best of evidence as to the age of a series of strata which have been subjects of considerable difference of opinion.   I obtained them from bands of limestone traversing the green shales, underlying and interstratified with the yellow sandstones which overlie the variegated marls, red and white calcareous sandstones, and gypsum, called by D'Shumard the "Gypsum formation."   By Mr. Marcou the series of variegated marls is regarded as Triassic, and the overlying yellow sandstones as Jurassic.

Most of my specimens were obtained from the base of the yellow sandstone series, a few feet above a bed of coal containing plants having a general resemblance to those of the Jurassic of Europe.   The fossils associated with *A. percarinatus* are *Gryphœa Pitcheri*, both forms, and *Inoceramus Crispii* (?)

In the same group of rocks which contain these molluscous fossils, both above and below them, I found impressions of leaves of several species of dicotyledonous trees, the whole affording conclusive evidence of the Cretaceous age of the formation.   The lithological character of the strata, as well as their superposition and observed continuity, contribute to the same conclusion, and assist to establish an identity of geological age between the yellow sandstones and shales of western New Mexico, the reddish yellow sandstones of eastern New Mexico and western Kansas, the Lower Cretaceous strata of the Upper Missouri, (Nos. I and II of Messrs. Meek and Hayden's Cretaceous section,) and the red sandstone with impressions of leaves of New Jersey.

NAUTILUS.   Breynius.

NAUTILUS, Sp.

A fragment of a large *Nautilus* was obtained from the limestone which underlies the red sandstones and variegated marls at Agua Azul, near the base of Mount Taylor.   It is too imperfect for satisfactory description, exhibiting a portion only of the external whorl.

It evidently comes near *N. planovolvis*, Shumard, having similar flattened sides, rounded angles, and slightly arched dorsum, but the septa are nearly straight on the dorsum, while in the species to which I have compared it they are much curved.

This fossil is associated with *Productus, Allorisma* and *Bellerophon*, but unfortunately all are badly preserved, and scarcely susceptible of specific determination.

The rock containing them is a cherty limestone, much like that which contains *Productus semireticulatus, Spirigera subtilita,* &c., at the top of the section on Cataract creek, (p. —.)   It holds the same position in relation to the overlying sandstones and marls as the limestone at the crossing of the Little Colorado, that at Ojo Vernal, and Pecos, &c.

It is probably Upper Carboniferous; its surface limiting that series, and perhaps containing a mingling of Permian and Carboniferous forms.

BELLEROPHON.   Montfort.

I obtained a cast of a species of this genus from the limestone at Agua Azul.   The specimen was too imperfect for specific determination, but it has the aspect of *B. Urii*, and is, probably, a Carboniferous species.

INOCERAMUS. Sowerby.

INOCERAMUS PROBLEMATICUS.—D. Orb. *Palæont.* 3, *p.* 510, *Pl.* 406.

Inoceramus mytiloides.—Mantell. *Geol. Sussex, p.* 215, *Pl.* 28.

Roemer, *Kreide V. Texas, p.* 60, *Pl. VII.*

Inoceramus pseudomytiloides.—Schiel. *Beckwith's Report.* (*P. R. R. R., Vol. II, p.* 108, *pl.* 3, *fig.* 8.)

This species occurs abundantly in the limestone overlying the Cretaceous sandstone at the crossing of Red Fork of the Canadian, on the Santa Fé road. It is readily recognized by its elongated form and thin and finely undulate shell.

It is widely distributed in Europe, and has been found in most parts of North America west of the Mississippi, where the Cretaceous strata are exposed. In Nebraska the place of the fossil is in the base of formation No. III and summit of No. II of Meek and Hayden's Cretaceous section.

This corresponds well with the position it holds on the banks of Red river, where I obtained it from the limestones which overlie the yellow sandstones of New Mexico; which last are the equivalents of Nos. I and II of the Cretaceous strata of Nebraska.

The shell described by Dr. Schiel (loc. cit.) seems to be only one of the many phases presented by this Protean species.

INOCERAMUS CRISPII (?)—Mantell. *Foss. of South Downs, p.* 133, *Pl. XXVII, fig.* 11.

In the Lower Cretaceous strata at the Moqui villages I found specimens of an *Inoceramus* which I refer to this species.

As our means of transportation were then quite exhausted I was compelled to content myself with few specimens of a kind, and it was only by abandoning a portion of our medicines that I could find room for even these.

Unfortunately the only large and perfect specimen of the *Inoceramus*, to which I have referred, was crushed and nearly ruined on the way home; some small specimens were, however, preserved entire.

A sketch which, as a matter of precaution, I took of the larger one when collected, shows the form of the shell to have been broad and rounded, the hinge-line comparatively long, the cardinal border joining the anterior margin almost at a right angle, and marked by a row of distinct teeth. The shell is thin, fibrous throughout—as in most of the *Lower* Cretaceous species—strongly undulate; the concentric undulations widely separated and finely striated. In young specimens the form is rather more elongate, the beak more acute, and the shell exceedingly thin and delicate.*

PINNA. Linn.

PINNA (?) LINGULA, (n. sp.)

Shell elongate, arcuate, compressed, strap-shaped, narrow throughout; anal extremity slightly rounded; beak pointed, strong; external surface without longitudinal costæ; internal surface without medial furrow; length, 6–7 inches; greatest breadth, 1.25 inch.

I have referred this fossil to *Pinna* with much doubt, as some of the characters of that genus are wanting in it. The general form, plain surface, and the absence of an internal furrow assimilate it to *Mytilus*, with which it also accords in its gregarious habit, but the shell is apparently open at the anal extremity, and is composed of both lamellar and fibrous layers.

I have not been able to discover in my specimens, which are very imperfect, any indication of the existence of the peculiar hinge of *Gervillia.*

---

*The smaller ones may not be the young of the larger; if not, they may be found to be identical with *I. fragilis*, Hall and Meek.

Locality and formation. This fossil occurs in immense numbers in a coarse brown calcareous sandstone in the Lower Cretaceous strata at Oraybe, one of the Moqui villages. The number of the shells is so great as to make up a large part of a stratum three feet in thickness, their very abundance rendering it difficult to obtain good specimens. The general appearance is so striking that I have thought it best to call attention to it, that it may be hereafter recognized, and serve as a means for the identification of strata.

It is associated with *Ammonites percarinatus* and a small *Gryphœa*, probably identical with *G. Pitcheri*, but too imperfect for determination. *G. Pitcheri*, var. *navia*, occurs in the same strata within two or three miles of Oraybe.

GRYPHÆA. Lamarck.

GRYPHÆA PITCHERI, Morton, *Synopsis, p.* 55, *Pl. XV, fig.* 9.

This characteristic fossil occurs in bands of brown concretionary limestone interstratified with green shales, yellow sandstones and lignite beds, a few miles east of Fort Defiance. Still further eastward, near Covero, it is found in the same strata, and in Cretaceous limestones on the banks of the Pecos, east of Albuquerque. In Texas it occurs in great abundance in many localities. The Cretaceous strata of Nebraska do not contain it. It is generally found in the lower part of the Cretaceous series in Western New Mexico, in the equivalents of Nos. I and II of Messrs. Meek and Hayden's Cretaceous section. This is the typical form of the species as given by Morton.

GRYPHÆA PITCHERI, *var.* NAVIA. Hall, *P. R. R. Repts., vol. III; Geol. Rept., p.* 500, *Pl.* I, *figs.* 7–10.

I found the narrower form of *G. Pitcheri* at the Moqui villages associated with *Ammonites percarinatus*; subsequently, in the same formation east of Fort Defiance, and I have specimens collected on the Pecos.

This shell should perhaps be considered specifically distinct from the preceding, as the differences which it exhibits from the typical form of *G. Pitcheri* are as striking and constant as those that serve to distinguish several species of *Gryphœa*. It is true, however, that the specific determination of all the oysters is peculiarly difficult and unsatisfactory, from their great variation in size and form, and the absence of sharp lines, numerical parts, and geometric proportions, which so much facilitate the diagnoses of species in many families of mollusks. As a consequence, these shells should be carefully scrutinized when used as palæontolog l evidence, and deductions made from them should be given their proper subordinate value.

ALLORISMA. King.

ALLORISMA CAPAX, (n. sp.)

Plate I, figs. 9 and 9*a*.

Shell large, sub-elliptical, somewhat arcuate, thick, marked exteriorly with parallel lines of growth by which it is somewhat undulated; very inequilateral; anterior end thick, abruptly rounded from the beaks; posterior end flattened and slightly narrowed; beaks nearly terminal, prominent; hinge-line following the curve of the opposite margin, lowest in the centre; impression of anterior adductor muscles large, rounded, placed near the anterior margin, projecting by nearly the entire diameter above a line drawn horizontally through the shell; greatest transverse diameter posterior to the beaks and above the middle; pallial impressions not visible. Length of cast, 4.42 inches; transverse diameter, 1.54 inch; vertical diameter, 2.25 inches.

The only specimen I have of this fossil is a cast which retains but a small portion of the shell. This gives the general form satisfactorily, but, for the most part, leaves the external markings to be conjectured. The size and form are, however, such, that these alone are sufficient to distinguish it from other known species, and will enable collectors to recognize it wherever it may hereafter be found.

The rock from which I obtained it is of peculiar geological interest, and it is therefore desirable that its fossils should be as fully made known as possible.

I have placed it in *Allorisma* with some hesitation, as Prof. King, in his definition of the genus, describes the position of the posterior adductor muscles as generally much lower than they occur in this specimen. In other respects it harmonizes with his description.

The determination of the generic limits of fossils allied to the one in question seems to have given the palæontologists of Europe no little trouble. The genus *Allorisma* is generally accepted by American palæontologists, but it is rejected by Morris, who includes the species in *Myacites*, Brown; while Pictet puts them into *Pholadomya*, Sowerby, and McCoy places them in his genus *Sanguinolites*.

Locality and formation.—The limestone underlying the red and white sandstones, shales, and gypsum, at Agua Azul, near the base of Mount Taylor; the equivalent of that exposed at the crossing of the Little Colorado, considered by Mr. Marcou as Permian.

It also contains *Productus, Bellerophon, Nautilus*, crinoidal columns, &c., and doubtless represents the top of the Carboniferous series, though it may here, as do the equivalent rocks in Kansas, include some Permian forms.

PRODUCTUS ROGERSI. Norwood & Pratten. *Jour. Acad. Nat. Sci., Philadelphia, vol. III,* *p. 9, pl. I, fig.* 3.

The various species of *Productus* which I obtained from the limestones on the banks of the Colorado, at Santa Fé, Pecos, and other parts of New Mexico, probably include most of the species obtained by Mr. Marcou from the same region, but I have found it exceedingly difficult to establish an identity between my specimens and his figures and descriptions. The specimens obtained by him, so far as they are represented in his collections deposited in the Smithsonian Institution, do not present the same difficulties of identification with mine, but are equally different from his figures. Unfortunately, none of his specimens bear names given to them by himself, and the most interesting species to which he refers, as collected by the party of Lieutenant Whipple, are not included in his collections in the Smithsonian.

I have from New Mexico a species of *Productus* undistinguishable from one in Mr. Marcou's collection procured at the Pecos village, and considered by Prof. Hall, when studying that collection, identical with *P. Rogersi* of Norwood & Pratten. Mr. Marcou fails to recognize *P. Rogersi* among those obtained by him in New Mexico; referring all his *Producti*, with one exception, (*P. Delawarii*,) to European species. Which of his figures are taken from the specimens of this shell, what he considers it, or whether he figures it at all, are questions not easily answered.

The figure of what he calls *P. scabriculus* approaches nearest it in form and markings; nearer indeed, it seems to us, than to the true *Scabriculus*.

P. Rogersi is characterized by a high and narrow form, ears slightly developed, cardinal border less than greatest breadth, &c.; entire surface occupied by fine striations, annular folds and tubercles; tubercles most numerous on anterior surface; annular folds obtuse, rounded, &c., &c.

It has been found in several localities in the Coal measures of Missouri, Illinois, &c. My specimens are from Pecos village and from the Coal measures of Kansas.

PRODUCTUS IVESI, (n. sp.)

Plate II, figs. 1–8.

Shell large, transverse; width ¼ greater than extreme length, strongly revolute; beaks projecting beyond the cardinal border. *Ventral valve:* sinus strongly marked, extending from near the beak to the anterior border; ears broadly expanded, lateral angles acute; visceral region somewhat reticulated and tuberculated; anterior surface striated; striæ coarse, nearly uniform, and crowned with tubercles; ears covered with rows of tubular spines radiating in different directions, of which those on the cardinal border exceed two inches in length. *Dorsal valve:* strongly concave; surface thickly set with spines scarcely exhibiting a determinate arrangement. *Interior:* cardinal tooth ob-conical, narrow, trifid; from it a distinct but slightly elevated median ridge extends to the centre of the dorsal valve; hepatic impressions somewhat elongated; impressions of the adductor muscles semicircular, with nearly uniform outline; interior of ventral valve marked with a strong ridge corresponding with the external sinus, of which the surface is striated; muscular impressions quadrate, deep.

In its general form, and in the magnitude of its spines, this shell resembles *P. horridus*, but in that species the mesial sinus is more profound, the surface much smoother, the tubular spines of the wings much less numerous. In the striation and reticulation of the ventral valve it approaches *P. semireticulatus*, but the striæ are much coarser, and the tubercles more distinct and numerous. There is no species with which I am familiar for which it is liable to be mistaken.

Locality and formation.—Middle Carboniferous limestone, banks of the Colorado, near mouth of Diamond river.

I have dedicated this fine species to Lieut. J. C. Ives, U. S. T. E., the commander of the Colorado exploring party, as a slight acknowledgment of the unremitting kindness and consideration received by the members of the scientific corps at his hands.

PRODUCTUS OCCIDENTALIS, (n. sp.)

Plate II, figs. 9 and 10.

Shell small or medium size, transverse, strongly revolute, antero-posterior diameter about ¾ the length of the cardinal border. *Ventral valve:* mesial sinus distinct on anterior surface, scarcely reaching the beak; visceral disk somewhat flattened, covered with distinct and rather strong tubercles, which toward the anterior border coalesce, to form continuous costæ; costæ 18–20; in the sinus 5 or 6 finer than the others; those bordering the sinus remarkably strong, broad, and prominent, increasing in width toward the anterior border. The costæ of the sides of the valve converging toward the beak unite with those of the sinus on the borders of the visceral disk, while the most prominent ones bordering the sinus on either side become earlier obsolete in the angle formed by the costæ of the sinus and those of the sides of the valve; giving to the shell a peculiar appearance, perceptible at a glance. The wings are broad and inflated, with waved edges; the angles slightly rounded; they are separated from the umbo of the valve by a distinct sinus. The costæ of the anterior surface are tuberculated and bear scattered spines.

This shell is nearly related to *P. costatus;* more resembling the specimens figured by Sowerby, (*Min. Conch. t.* 560) than the American variety given by De Koninck, (*Monographie t.* VIII, *figs.* 3*a*, 3*b*, 3*c*,) but the costæ bordering the mesial sinus in our shell, so much stronger and more prominent than the others, and crowded out by the approach of the lateral and central costæ, give it a character distinguishing it from that and other species.

Locality and formation.—The cherty limestone, near the top of the Carboniferous series, (C. 73,) banks of Cascade river, near junction of Great and Little Colorados.

PRODUCTUS CALHOUNIANUS. Swallow.

This large species was found on no part of our route until we reached the vicinity of the Missouri, in Kansas. The specimens there obtained exhibit a striking resemblance, in size and general form, to the most robust individuals of *P. semireticulatus* procured on the banks of the Colorado. The striæ are, however, finer, and the tubercles more numerous in the Kansas specimens. The fossils presenting these variations from the common form of *P. semireticulatus* might be considered as representing but one of the many phases of this variable species, but Prof. Swallow remarks that, in addition to its external character, the markings of the interior of the shell of *P. Calhounianus* are peculiar, and such as serve to distinguish it from all others.

PRODUCTUS COSTATUS. Sowerby.

I obtained imperfect specimens of a strongly costate *Productus* from the cherty limestone (Upper Carboniferous) on the banks of the Colorado, which approach more nearly to *P. costatus* than any other described species. The shell is, however, narrower, the wings are less expanded, the costæ broader, and the sulci separating them narrower than in any of the forms of *P. costatus* given in the figures of European palæontologists.

From the Coal measures of Nebraska I have other specimens which correspond with *P. costatus*, as recognized by our best authorities in Carboniferous mollusca, (Messrs. Norwood and Pratten, Shumard and Swallow,) closely resembling the form of that species figured in De Konninck's Monograph of the genus *Productus, pl. VIII*, figs. 3, 3*a*, 3*b*, but the spines of the cardinal border are smaller, those of the anterior surface much larger, and the striæ more irregular than De Konninck represents them. There can be no doubt, however, that they represent the same shell figured by De Konninck, (*Monograph, plates VIII and XVIII,*) as that came from the vicinity of St. Louis, Missouri.

It is perhaps possible that the marked differences which the American shells exhibit from those figured by Sowerby (*Min. Conch. t.* 560,) have a specific value, but as yet no one has been so well qualified to make this comparison as De Konninck, and he regards them as mere varieties of a common species.

PRODUCTUS COSTATOIDES. Swallow. *Trans. Acad. Nat. Sci. St. Louis*, No. 2, *p.* 23, *pl. I, figs.* 8–8*c*.

From the cherty limestone on the banks of the Colorado (near Camp 73) I procured specimens of a *Productus* apparently identical with that described by Prof. Swallow under the above name. From the smaller forms of *P. costatus* and other allied species, it is distinguished by the conspicuous pits which mark the smaller valve. For its more ready identification I transcribe the excellent description of Prof. S.

"Shell small, transverse, subrectangular; cardinal longer than the width of the shell; beak small, recurved scarcely beyond the cardinal border; ears large, thin vaulted and reflexed; dorsal valve, (ventral of Davidson) somewhat regularly arched, slightly flattened on the visceral region, and toward the anterior border marked with broad depressed irregular longitudinal costæ; of these, four on each side of the mesial sinus are much larger, and extend from the visceral region to the anterior border; the whole surface ornamented with large tubular spines, arranged somewhat regularly in diagonal lines; mesial sinus deep and broad, ventral valve, (dorsal, Davidson) strongly arched, slightly flattened on the visceral region, and toward the anterior margin; marked with longitudinal depressions corresponding to the costæ of the opposite valve; mesial ridge conspicuous on the anterior prolongation, the whole marked with deep pits, almost as numerous as the spines of the opposite valve; visceral regions of both valves have indistinct irregular transverse rugæ.''

PRODUCTUS SEMIRETICULATUS. Martin. De Konninck. *Monographie, p.* 83.

This widely-distributed species occurs at several points on our route. In the cherty limestone at Camp 73, near the junction of the Great and Little Colorados, it is found in the greatest abundance, associated with *Spirigera subtilita,* &c. It here attains a large size, fully equalling in this respect any specimens of this species which have been figured. In all those from this locality the form of the shell is strongly revolute, the striae coarse, and the annular folds upon the wings, and over the visceral region very conspicuous. This is the largest and most strongly marked variety which I met with, and seems to correspond with Marcou's figure, *Geol. N. Amer. Pl. VI, fig.* 6. From Pecos village I have a more delicate form, smaller in size, with markings all finer than the last.

The limestone at Camp 73 contains considerable numbers of a smaller Productus, of which the form is strongly revolute, the antero-posterior diameter being much less than the transverse; the visceral disk reticulated, and the anterior surface marked with beautifully regular and parallel striæ, on which are set numerous delicate but long tubular spines. In many respects this resembles *P. semireticulatus* var. *sulcatus,* but the spines crowning the costæ between the wings and the umbo of the ventral valve do not exist in my specimens, and the spines of the anterior surface are much more conspicuous. It has seemed to me best to consider it a variety of *P. semireticulatus,* but further examination may prove it to be new.

The same shell has been collected in Kansas by Messrs. Meek and Hayden.

PRODUCTUS NODOSUS, (n. sp.)

Plate I, figs. 7, 7b.

Shell of medium size, strongly revolute; antero-posterior diameter less than its breadth; beak pointed, extending slightly beyond the cardinal border; wings very small, much plaited, like the entire surface of the ventral valve, covered with numerous fine, distinct and uniform thread-like striæ; ventral valve without sinus, but the mesial line is marked by a row of large and remote nodes, which extend from the beak to the anterior margin, and toward which the contiguous striæ converge. The striæ are scarcely more numerous on the anterior border than on the beak; a few are introduced without bifurcation, but the increased space is covered by a gradual enlargement of the striæ and a widening of the space between them. Visceral region arched and without reticulation; entire surface spineless, unless the nodes of the mesial line are the bases of large spines. Dorsal valve striated like the ventral, often without nodes or spines. Antero-posterior diameter 1.08; breadth 1.50.

This beautiful species has some resemblance in form and markings to *P. Cora,* to *P. Altonensis,* N. & P., and to *P. Hildrethianus,* N. & P., and may be grouped with them; but by the entire absence of spines, the parallel and uniform striæ, and particularly by the row of nodes along the mesial line, it is distinctly separated from all known species.

Locality and formation.—Limestone of Carboniferous age; Santa Fé, New Mexico.

PRODUCTUS SPLENDENS? Norwood & Pratten. *Jour. Acad. Sci. Phila., May,* 1855, *p.* 11, *pl. I, fig.* 5.

In the limestone of the Coal measures on the Santa Fé road, ten miles west of Burlingame, Kansas, I collected specimens of what appears to be this species, though of smaller size, more revolute, and less distinctly striated than that described by Norwood and Pratten.

The tendency to exfoliation which my specimens exhibit renders accurate determination of their surface markings difficult. The visceral region is scarcely flattened, but in other respects the shell corresponds well with the description of *P. splendens*.

The wings are very prominent and distinctly arched, and the surface of the shell occupied by the bases of relatively large, scattered spines.

A larger amount of material from the locality may show this to be a distinct species, but the number and preservation of my specimens do not warrant me in considering it new. In size it resembles *P. Wabashensis*, N. & P., but it is more revolute. the mesial sinus deeper, the wings more inflated, and it apparently lacks the striations which *P. Wabashensis* usually exhibit, even when not in good preservation.

PRODUCTUS SCABRICULUS. Martin. *Animaux Foss. dans le Terrain Carbonifère de Belgique,* p. 190.

Among the *Producti* which I collected about Santa Fé are several which seem undistinguishable from the European *scabriculus:* a broadly expanded shell, with rounded outlines and the peculiar surface markings described by De Konninck ; the striæ interrupted and terminating in tubercles, which are set in quincunx ; annulations broken and inconspicuous, &c.

The correspondence is so complete that it is difficult to resist the conviction that if Martin's *scabriculus* exists in America the shell to which I have referred is of that species. There is little resemblance between my specimens and Marcou's figures of what he calls *P. scabriculus,* (*Op. cit., pl. V, figs. 6 and 6a,*) which represent a much narrower shell and one distinctly annulated, without tubercles, except near the beak. His description agrees better with the true *scabriculus,* and it may be that there is an error in lettering the plate.

In Europe the station of *P. scabriculus* is Lower Carboniferous and Upper Devonian, as is true of many of the fossils associated with it in the limestones of New Mexico. Notwithstanding that fact, we must regard this limestone as Upper Carboniferous, as the fossils which characterize it are all found in the Coal measures of the Mississippi valley and in the coal fields of Kansas and Missouri, where the entire Carboniferous series approaches nearest to the exposures of the rock in question.

This discrepancy of station in what have been regarded as the European and American representatives of the same species suggests the probability that a revision of the matter of the identification of this species, accompanied by a careful comparison of a sufficient number of specimens, will show specific differences, which will relieve the subject of many of its difficulties. This is, however, not a necessary result ; for, as has been shown,[*] the local faunæ of parallel formations in palæozoic times exhibited, in some degree, the diversity which is so conspicuous in those of the present epoch.

I am not aware that *P. scabriculus* has been recognized in America elsewhere than in New Mexico.

STREPTORHYNCUS. King.

STREPTORHYNCUS UMBRACULUM.
Orthis umbraculum. V. Buch. *Ueber Delthyris, &c.*

This shell is very widely distributed through the Carboniferous strata of the west, its range, vertical and geographical, being perhaps equal to that of any other species.

If palæontologists have not been mistaken in their identifications, it is not only common to Europe, America and Asia, but runs through all the Carboniferous series from the Permian down, and is found in the Devonian strata of the Eifel and in the fine-grained sandstones, the equivalents of the Chemung group, in Ohio and Kentucky.

---

[*] Prof. J. Hall, in Report of Foster & Whitney, &c.

In Europe it is a Lower Carboniferous and Devonian fossil. In this country it extends from the Devonian up through all the Carboniferous strata, and is found in Kansas in what Prof. Swallow calls "Lower Permian rocks," but which this fossil, with the many others we have cited as associated with it, indicate should rather be regarded as Upper Carboniferous.

Large and strongly marked specimens of *S. umbraculum* were found by the writer in the cherty limestone, the highest member of the series, in the cañon of Cascade river, near the junction of the Colorado Chiquito (Flax river) with the Colorado. This rock is continuous with that forming the high mesa about the San Francisco mountain, extending to the crossing of the Little Colorado, where its upper portion is regarded as Permian by Mr. Marcou.

At Agua Azul, east of Fort Defiance, at Santa Fé, at Ojo Vernal, and again on Cottonwood creek, Kansas, this limestone is exposed; at each place containing this fossil, associated with Upper Carboniferous species.

Mr. Marcou, in *The Geology of North America*, *p.* 45, describing his *Productus Delawari*, pronounces the *Orthis umbraculum* figured by Hall (*Stansbury's Report*) as not an *Orthis*, but a *Productus* and *P. Delawari*. In this he is evidently in error, as the original specimens, which he never saw, are clearly *Orthis*, as the genus was then limited, and undistinguishable from *O. umbraculum*.

STREPTORHYNCUS PYRAMIDALIS, (n. sp.)

Plate II, figs. 11–13.

Shell nearly orbicular in outline; elevated, sub-globose; cardinal border somewhat rounded; ventral valve high, rising to a height greater than half the antero-posterior diameter; beak prominent, often much produced and laterally distorted; sometimes nearly equidistant from the cardinal and anterior borders, when this valve has a pyramidal form; foramen forming a triangle of which the base is usually about one-third the altitude; dorsal valve gently arched, highest toward the cardinal edge; surface marked with about twelve strong radiating costæ, which are finely but sharply striated longitudinally. This shell is distinguishable from *S. occidentalis*, which it somewhat resembles in the character of its surface markings, by its stronger costæ, more strongly arched valves, broader area, and narrower foramen.

Locality and formation.—Carboniferous limestone over red cross-stratified sandstone at Camp 70, on high mesa west of Little Colorado.

STREPTORHYNCUS OCCIDENTALIS, (n. sp.)

Plate I, figs. 5, 5a.

Shell depressed, broadly rounded; cardinal border nearly equal to greatest diameter; ventral valve flattened and slightly concave toward the anterior margin; beak produced and generally twisted laterally. Cardinal area twice as broad as high; cardinal notch forming a triangle of which the base is half the height; dorsal valve slightly arched throughout; surface bearing 11 to 13 strong radiating costæ, which are striated near the anterior margin.

This shell is nearly twice the horizontal diameter of *S. pyramidalis;* being broader, flatter, and less strongly ribbed and striated than that species. With any other described it is scarcely likely to be confounded.

Locality and formation.—Cherty limestone, top of Carboniferous series, Camp 73, in cañon of Cascade river.

ATHYRIS.

ATHYRIS SUBTILITA.
Terebratula subtilita. Hall. *Stansbury's Report, p.* 409, *t.* 4, *figs.* 1–2.

This fossil occurs in large numbers in the cherty limestone on the banks of the Colorado, between the Little Colorado and Diamond river. It is also common in the limestone at Pecos village, east of Santa Fé, and is equally abundant in the Coal measures of Kansas, Missouri, and Ohio. Wherever found it is indicative of the presence of the Coal measures or their equivalents, and, with the other evidence which has been cited, proves conclusively that the limestone at Pecos and neighboring localities is not the equivalent of that which underlies the Coal measures throughout the southern portions of the coal basins of Nova Scotia and the Mississippi valley, usually considered identical with the Mountain limestone of Europe. It also constitutes one of the indices of the Upper Carboniferous date of the limestone occupying so large a surface west of the Little Colorado, of which the exposures at Camp 70, Cascade river, Partridge and Cedar creeks, and east of the San Francisco mountains, are fully described in the preceding chapters. This shell, so widely distributed, both geographically and vertically, affords conclusive proof that throughout the greater part of New Mexico an open sea prevailed during the entire continuance of the Carboniferous epoch. The Upper Carboniferous limestones, in their great thickness and uniformity of character, indicate the uninterrupted prevalence in this region of the physical conditions represented by the numerous, but thin and widely separated, calcareous bands which are a constant feature in the structure of the productive Coal measures in the Mississippi valley. Specimens collected by the writer on the banks of the Colorado exhibit the spiral cones of the interior with great distinctness.

SPIRIFER. Sowerby.

SPIRIFER CAMERATUS. Mort. *Amer. Jour. Science, vol. 29, p. 150, pl. II, fig. 3.*

This fossil, so characteristic of the Coal measures of the Mississippi valley, occurs abundantly in the limestones about Santa Fé and Pecos village, New Mexico, and in the limestones of the Carboniferous series in Kansas and Missouri.

I have collected the same fossil in various parts of eastern Ohio and western Pennsylvania. It is liable to considerable variation in size, and also, to a less degree, in the size and arrangement of its plications. It is not, however, so like other species as to be easily confounded with them; and from its abundance in most of the localities where it is found, and its wide distribution, it is one of the most valuable guides in the identification of strata.

We did not find it in the Carboniferous limestones west of the Rio Grande, although its associates, *Spirifer lineatus, Spirigera subtilita, &c.,* are abundant.

This is the shell figured by Mr. Marcou, *(Op. cit. p. 49, pl. VII, fig. 3,)* under the name of *S. striatus,* var. *triplicatus.* Both forms given by him are presented in many localities where this fossil exists. Such is especially the case in the series which I have collected in Ohio.

The largest, most inflated, and least angular specimens resemble *S. striatus,* but by far the greater number depart very widely from it. Even when most like *S. striatus,* the form is more angular and the number of plications less. In *S. striatus* these vary from 80 to 100 in each valve, while in all the specimens which I have the number is from 60 to 70. Roemer and Hall, who describe this species under different names, regard it as distinct from *S. striatus.*

SPIRIFER ROCKYMONTANI. Marcou. *Geol. N. Amer., p. 50, pl. VII, figs. 4–4e.*

This is a distinct and beautiful species, of not uncommon occurrence in the Carboniferous limestones of New Mexico. Dr. Hayden has also found it in the Black Hills, Nebraska.

SPIRIFER LINEATUS. De Konninck.

This species is even more widely distributed than *S. cameratus,* being common to Europe and America, and found over all parts of our continent, wherever the Carboniferous series is developed. It is quite common in the cherty limestone west of the Little Colorado, occurs again on our route in the limestones of the vicinity of Santa Fé, and in Kansas and Missouri.

I have also collected great numbers of specimens of it in the Coal measures of Ohio.

Like many other fossils common to both sides of the Atlantic, this species has a lower range in the Old World than in America.

De Konninck reports it as occurring in the Mountain limestone in many parts of Europe, and in the Devonian rocks of the Eifel and Wales. I have never known it to be found in strata older than the Carboniferous in this country, and it generally occurs in the Coal measures.

The surface markings of this shell are so delicate that they are frequently not observable; and imperfectly preserved specimens, having the general form and appearance of *Terebratula Royssii*, are liable to be mistaken for that fossil.

CHONETES. Fisher.

CHONETES VERNEUILIANA. Norwood & Pratten. *Jour. Acad. Nat. Sci., Phil.; new series, vol. III, part 1, page* 26.

Plate II, fig. 6.

Some portions of the cherty limestone on the banks of the Colorado, one hundred miles northwest of the San Francisco mountain, are charged with specimens of a *Chonetes* which approaches more nearly to *C. Verneuiliana* than to any other described species.

The figure and description of *C. Verneuiliana* given by Norwood & Pratten represent it as "small, transverse, having its greatest breadth on the cardinal border; beak much larger and higher than in any other known American species. An extremely deep sinus extends from the beak to the anterior border, which is emarginated by it as seen from above. This sinus is bordered by high ridges, between which and the ears another sinus occurs. Cardinal border furnished with four tubes on each side of the beak," &c.

From this description the specimens found on the banks of the Colorado in some respects depart; the outline of the shell being more oblong; *i. e.*, the breadth near the anterior border approaching that of the cardinal edge; the mesial sinus being less deep, sometimes scarcely perceptible, and, in the same degree, the carinations bordering it being less conspicuous; the lateral sinuses not generally visible; the tubes of the cardinal border varying from three to five on each side of the beak, but usually four; the beak scarcely projecting beyond the cardinal border, &c.

In other respects no differences are perceptible, and I have supposed this to be a form of the above species.

Specimens precisely agreeing with mine were collected by Messrs. Meek and Hayden, at Manhattan, in Kansas, in the upper Coal measures.

RHYNCONELLA. Fisher.

RHYNCONELLA UTA.

Terebratula uta. Marcou. *Geol. N. Amer., p.* 51, *pl. VI, figs.* 12–12e.

Common in the middle and upper limestones near the mouth of the Little Colorado; also in the limestones of the Coal measures of Kansas and Missouri.

The specimens on which the description of this species was founded were obtained in Utah, near Salt Lake City.

PECTEN. Linn.

PECTEN OCCIDENTALIS. Shumard.

I obtained an imperfect specimen of this species from coal shale on the banks of the Stranger, above Easton, Kansas.

PECTEN (MONOTIS?) COLORADENSIS, (n. sp.)

Plate I, fig. 6 and 6a.

Shell of moderate size, (two inches in diameter,) sub-orbicular, oblique; slightly lobed on posterior side; anterior ear rounded? small? posterior ear prominent, with a straight hinge-line and flexuous lateral margin; apicial angle, 85°; surface bearing 18–19 radiating costæ, which are straight and strongly marked on the anterior and middle portions, and become slightly curved and gradually smaller as they approach the posterior side, on the lobed expansion of the shell becoming entirely obsolete. These carinations are crowned at intervals somewhat greater than their breadth by prominent arched lamellæ, by which the surface is highly ornamented and roughened.

This is a beautiful fossil, apparently quite distinct from any species of *Pecten* or *Monotis* hitherto described.

The details of structure are not sufficiently well preserved in my specimens to enable me to determine certainly to which of these genera it should be attached, the characters which it exhibits being such as are shared by both.

The posterior ear is flat, broad, and apparently angular, bordered by a straight line on one side; the other flexuous and pecten-like. The anterior ear is partially wanting, but is evidently narrow, and probably rounded. The straight hinge-line of the opposite wing is not continued beyond the beak.

FUSILINA. Fisher.

FUSILINA CYLINDRICA. Fisher.

This fossil, which is found in the Carboniferous or Mountain limestone in different parts of Europe, though, so far as I am aware, not yet discovered in the Alleghany coal-field, is exceedingly abundant in the Carboniferous rocks of the western part of the Mississippi valley, where it ranges from the "Carboniferous limestone" to the Coal measures.

I did not find it in the limestones on the Colorado nor about Santa Fé, though it has been found at no great distance east of that point.

After leaving the Cretaceous and Permian rocks of western Kansas, and coming into the Coal measures, I found it occurring in such abundance as to form the greatest part of the mass of some of the beds of limestone.

The strata which contain it are interstratified with the shales and coal seams of the productive Coal measures, and it seems to run through the entire series.

FOSSIL PLANTS.

CYCLOPTERIS. Brong.

CYCLOPTERIS MOQUENSIS, (n. sp.)

Plate III, figs. 1 and 2.

C. fronde simplici, stipitata, orbiculata vel ovata, cordata, saepe basi latere uno obliqua; nervo medio basi valido medio evanescenti; nervis secundariis tenuibus creberrimus dichotomis, furcatis aequalibus. Fructificatio marginalis?

I have included this beautiful form in *Cyclopteris* with some hesitation, as by its strong median nerve it differs strikingly from any known species of that genus, and is clearly excluded from it by the definitions of Brongniart, Gœppert, Unger, and all other writers on fossil botany.   As, however, the limits of the genera of fossil plants when first established are in a great degree provisional, and each discovery of new species is liable to modify the previous grouping, and necessitate a revision of generic definitions, it would tend to retard rather than advance scientific progress to insist upon the establishment of new genera for species which, however closely allied to those before described and generically grouped, should present some characters incompatible with former generic descriptions.

The genus *Cyclopteris* has been the conventional receptacle of a large number of plants which have in common a general flabelliform, orbicular, or heart-shaped outline; are without a median nerve; their fine and crowded nervules radiating from the base to the margins, and dichotomously forked. Among these are some species which, if we had the living plants before us in fructification, we should probably find to be somewhat widely separated.   Some of them are doubtless the basal and abnormal fronds of highly decompound ferns like those of *Allosorus sagittatus.** Others were the cauline pinnules of *Neuropteris;* and still others were simple stipitate species like the common living *Camptosorus rhizophyllus* and various other simple-fronded ferns.   Brongniart has separated from the others those which he supposes to have been attached to the stipes of *Neuropteris*—such as *C. obliqua, C. orbiculata, C. dilitata*— under the name of *Nephropteris,* and leaves as types of his genus *Cyclopteris, C. reniformis, C. trichomanoides, C. digitata, C. Huttoni,* &c.[†]   My observations in the different species of *Cyclopteris* found in the Coal measures have led me to the same conclusions, and to infer that nearly all the large solitary orbicular, cordate or auricled fern fronds should be regarded as the basilar or rachidian folioles of *Neuropteris.*   I have found several species of that genus so generally accompanied by particular species of *Cyclopteris* that I have been compelled to regard them as portions of the same plant.   So marked is this companionship that I have been inclined to doubt whether any of the simple leaved species of *Cyclopteris* of the Coal measures should be retained in that genus.

Locality and formation.—Bands of clay in beds of lignite between the base of the Cretaceous series and the summit of the variegated marls near the Moqui villages.

PECOPTERIS.   Brong.

Pecopteris cycloloba, (n. sp.)

Plate III, figs. 3, 4 and 4*a*.

P. fronde bipinnatifida v. tripinnatifida; pinnis longis linearibusque, pinnatifidis; pinnulis brevissimis semirotundis v. suborbiculatis vel oblongis, obstusisimis, contiguis, sæpe inequalibus, superioribus majoribus; nervis pinnatis valde notatis (3 utrinque lateris) simplicibus vel rarius furcatis.

This is an exceedingly pretty species, of which the details of structure are well shown in my specimens, though they are small.   The size and form of the frond, as well as its range of variation, will require a greater amount of material for their elucidation.

The pinnæ are very long and slender, as shown in the figure given of a portion of the upper parts of the frond; the pinnules are usually semicircular, or forming more than a half circle; when, as sometimes happens, they are opposite, the pinnæ have a peculiar beaded appearance. The upper pinnules are frequently largest.

Although this plant is new, it is not without value in the determination of the geological position of the rock in which it occurs.   It is most nearly allied to the *Pecopterides* of the Oolite of Europe, such as *P. acutifolia* and *P. obtusifolia,* Lind. and Hutt; *P. arguta,* Brong; and among American fossil plants to *P. undulata,* Hall.[‡]

---

* Gœppert Gatt. Foss. Pflantz. p. 89, pl. VIII and IX, fig. 1.
† Dict. Hist. Nat. vol. XIII, p. 65.
‡ Fremont's Report, Expedition of 1842 and 1848.

The extremely long and slender pinnæ, in which the upper pinnules are frequently largest, give it a character quite different from that of any species of this genus from the coal formation, and connect it closely with the group mentioned above.

Associated with *Clathropteris* of Jurassic affinities, and with the first appearing species of the dicotyledonous plants of the Cretaceous epoch, this *Pecopteris* confirms the inference derived from other sources that the lignite bed containing it lies just at the point of junction between the Cretaceous and older rocks, and showing a mingling of forms belonging to the two formations, proving the impossibility of drawing sharply the lines of division.

NEUROPTERIS, Brong.

NEUROPTERIS ANGULATA, (n. sp.)

Plate III, fig. 5.

N. fronde pinnata v. bipinnata; pinnulis orbiculato-ovatis, basi cordatis vel rotundatis, apice sub 5 angulatis; nervis raris validisque, in angulis marginis terminantibus.

Scattered pinnules only of this plant were found in Cretaceous shales lying upon a bed of lignite north of Oraybe in the Moqui country. Better specimens may require some modification of the description now given, but the angles of the remote margin of the pinnules distinguish it from any species hitherto described.

SPHENOPTERIS, Brong.

SPHENOPTERIS, species.

Fragments of the frond of a very pretty and distinctly new species of this genus were found in the clay bands of the lignite bed at Camp 92, (Moqui villages.) It is most like *Sphenopteris dichotoma*, Alth. from the Zechstein (*Neue Pflanz. aus dem Keupershiefer, Palæontographica* 1, 1846, *t.* 4, *fig.* 1,) but the pinnules are less abruptly truncated, the upper ones being almost spatulate. More material is necessary before a satisfactory description can be made of it.

Another and larger species was detected in the shales overlying another bed of lignite in the Cretaceous formation two hundred feet above the last, but the specimens obtained were too imperfect for determination.

PHYLLITES. Sterub.

PHYLLITES VENOSISSIMUS, (n. sp.)

Plate III, fig. 6.

Ph. folio lineari-lanceolato acuto integerrimo nervo primario valido, nervis secundariis paucis, vix conspicuis, arcuatis, apice confluentibus, nervis tertiariis, creberrimis confluentibus.

The specimens of this leaf which I obtained are too imperfect to form the basis of a satisfactory specific description, or to enable us to determine with any certainty its botanical affinities. Like the next, however, it is highly characteristic of the formation in which it is found, and may have a certain value in tracing the parallelism of strata upon this continent. It is only in consideration of this fact that a name and description have been given to it by which its identification may be possible. It is from the lignite bed lying just at the base of the Cretaceous series at Camp 92, in the Moqui country. It is undoubtedly the leaf of an Angiospermous plant, and perhaps of a *Salix*.

PHYLLITES CORIACEOUS, (n. sp.)

Plate III, figs. 7 and 7a.

Ph. folio lanceolato, utrinque acuto, integerrimo, lævissimo, crasso; nervo medio crassissimo striato; nervis secundaris tenuibus, sæpe obsoletis, simplicibus? e nervo primario sub angulo acuto egredientibus.

A thick coriaceous leaf, with a very strong mid rib, in which the lateral veins are scarcely discernible. The margins are quite entire, the summit acute, the base decurrent on to the petiole. It is apparently generically identical with some leaves from the Cretaceous rocks of Blankenburgh, &c., compared by Gœppert to those of *Dellenia*. They are from the Lower Cretaceous strata of the Moqui villages.

As I am about to revisit the locality where these plants are found, I will defer all discussion of their botanical relations till more and better materials have been obtained.

CLATHROPTERIS.   Brong.

A large number of fragments of a species of this genus were obtained in the lignite bed at Camp 92, (Moqui country,) but too imperfect for description.

CATALOGUE OF THE GEOLOGICAL COLLECTION.

I.—MINERALS AND FOSSILS FROM THE COAST OF CALIFORNIA.

No.	Name.	Locality.
1	Infusorial earth	Coast near San Francisco, California.
2	Lignite	.... do .... do ....
3	Conglomerate with shells and shark's teeth	.... do .... do ....
4	*Scutella interlineata*	.... do .... do ....
5	....do	.... do .... do ....
6	....do	.... do .... do ....
7	*Dendraster excentricus*	.... do .... do ....
8	....do	Point Lobos
9	....do	.... do
10	Metamorphic clay	St. Luis Obispo
11	Infusorial rock	.... do
12	Infusorial rock with *Pholas*	.... do
13	Shale impregnated with asphaltum	.... do
14	Impure asphaltum	.... do
15	Pure asphaltum exuding by sun's heat	.... do
16	Metaphoric clay with asphaltum	.... do
17	Shale with Entomostraca and *Pholas*	Monterey
18	Limestone with fossils	.... do
19	*Tamiosoma gregaria*	.... do
20	*Ostrea Titan*	.... do
21	Shale impregnated with bitumen	.... do
22	Fossilliferous limestone	.... do
23	Infusorial clays	.... do
24	Infusorial clays bored by *Pholas*	Raised sea bottom. Monterey
25	Shell conglomerate	St. Luis Obispo
26	Infusorial clay bored by *Pholas*	Eighty feet above sea. San Pedro.
27	Shells from ancient sea beach	San Pedro
28	Infusorial earth	San Diego
29	Cetacean bones	....do
30	Shells from raised beach	Point Loma, San Diego
31	Tertiary fossils	....do.......... do
32	....do	....do.......... do
33	....do	....do....... ....do
34	....do	....do.......... do
35	....do	....do....... ....do
36	....do	Mission of San Diego
37	....do	....do....... do
38	....do	....do....... do
39	....do	....do....... do

CATALOGUE—Continued.

No.	Name.	Locality.
40	Tertiary fossils	Mission of San Diego
41	....do	....do.........do
42	....do	....do.........do
43	....do	....do.........do
44	....do	....do.........do
45	....do	....do.........do
46	....do	....do.........do
47	....do	....do.........do
48	....do	....do.........do
49	....do	....do.........do
50	....do	....do.........do
51	....do	....do.........do
52	....do	....do.........do
53	....do	....do.........do
54	....do	....do.........do
55	Lignite	Point Loma, San Diego

II.—FROM PENINSULAR MOUNTAINS AND COLORADO DESERT.

No.	Name.	Locality.
56	*Ostrea Vespertina*	Carriso creek
57	*Ostrea* in limestone	....do
58	*Ostreas*	....do
59	*Anomia subcostata*	....do
60	*Ostrea Titan*	....do
61	Feldspar	Vallecito
62	Micaceous granite	San Felipe
63	Granite	Top of Santa Amedia mountain, Fort Tejon.
64	Sandstone	San Fernando
65	Shells	Bed of dry lake, Colorado Desert
66	Fossil wood	Colorado Desert
67	Etched limestone	Desert surface
68	....do	....do
69	Quartzite	....do
70	Hornblende	Vallecito
71	Granite	Fort Yuma
72	Etched pebbles	Desert surface—banks of Colorado
73	Blackened and polished pebbles	....do.........do
74	Trachyte, transported	Fort Yuma
75	....do	....do
76	Pottery	Banks of New river, Colorado Desert
77	Limestone eroded in bed of Colorado by current	Great cañon
78		

CATALOGUE—Continued.

III.—ERUPTED ROCKS—LOWER COLORADO.

No.	Name.	Locality.
79	Brecciated porphyry	Purple Hills
80	Porphyry, (lilac)	....do
81	Brecciated porphyry, (red)	Chocolate mountains
82	Porphyrytic trachyte, enclosing jasper	Purple Hills
83	Trachyte, (drab)	Purple Hill cañon
84	Trachyte, (lilac)	Purple Hills
85	Trachyte, (white)	....do
86	Porphyry with drusy quartz	....do
87	Porphyry, (purple)	....do
88	Quartz crystals in trachyte	....do
89	Quartz vein in mica slate	....do
90	....do........ ....do	....do
91	Trachyte	....do
92	Trap	....do
93	Trachyte	....do
94	Hornblende rock veins in mica slate	....do
95	Mica slate	Hills opposite Chimney Peak
96	Talcose slate	....do........do
97	Trachyte	Chocolate mountains
98	Trachyte, (red)	...do
99	Drusy quartz, lining cavities in trachyte	Purple Hills
100	Basalt	Chocolate mountains
101	Porphyry	....do
102	Trachyte	....do
103	Porphyry, (dark red)	....do
104	Trachyte	Purple Hills
105	Granite	Chocolate mountains
106	Mica slate	Near Chimney Peak
107	Trachyte	Barrier rocks
108	Tufaceous trachyte	Light-house rock
109	Metamorphic sandstone	....do
110	Trachyte	Porphyry Gate
111	Trachyte, (veined)	....do
112	Mica slate, containing veins of copper	Near Chimney Peak
113	Quartz, containing iron	Riverside mountain
114	Hornblendic granite	Purple Hills
115	Quartz, with carbonate of copper	Riverside mountain
116	Eroded metamorphic limestone	....do
117	Weathered limestone with silicious bands	....do
118	Weathered mica slate	....do
119	Weathered metamorphic limestone	....do
120	Tufaceous limestone	....do
121	Metamorphic limestone	....do
122	Red trachyte	....do
123	Mica slate	....do
124	Augitic trap	....do
125	Fibrous talc	....do

CATALOGUE—Continued.

No.	Name..	Locality.
126	Talcose slate	Riverside mountain
127	Basaltic trap	Chocolate mountains
128	Quartzite	Riverside mountain
129	Trachyte	Purple Hills
130	....do	Light-house rock
131	....do	Purple Hills
132	Jasper, (red)	Monument mountains
133	Porphry, (green)	Chocolate mountains
134	Hornblende rock	Purple Hills
135	Green porphyry, with large crystals of feldspar	Chocolate mountains
136	Jasper, (striped)	....do
137	Porphyry, (red)	....do
138	Trachyte, with scales of mica	Chimney Peak
139	Porphyry, (mottled)	Purple Hills
140	Trachyte, (purple)	....do
141	Porphyrytic trachyte	....do
142	Trachytic porphyry	....do
143	Quartzite	Riverside mountain
144	Gneiss	Monument mountain
145	Quartzite	Riverside mountain
146	Cinnabar	Purple Hills
147	Porphyry, (blue)	Monument mountain.
148	Brecciated porphyry	Purple Hills
149	Quartzite, with iron veins in granite	Monument cañon
150	Quartzite, (green)	Monument mountain
151	Auriferous quartz veins in mica slate	Near Chimney Peak
152	Quartzite, (orange)	Monument cañon
153	Fossilliferous limestone	Desert surface, Beaver island
154	Granite, containing veins of copper and iron	Monument cañon
155	Copper and iron veins in granite	....do
156	Volcanic conglomerate	....do
157	Quartz veins in granite	....do
158	Quartzite, masses and veins in granite	Mouth of Bill Williams's Fork
159	Hornblende rock, masses in granite	Monument cañon
160	Syenite, (red and green)	Mountains opposite mouth of Bill Williams's Fork.
161	Crystals—carbonate of lime, iron and copper in granite	Monument cañon
162	Carb. lime, veinstone of Galena	....do
163	Porphyry, (purple)	Above mouth of Bill Williams's Fork.
164	Carb. lime, iron and copper veins in granite	Monument cañon
165	Gneiss	Chocolate mountains east of Colorado.
166	Brecciated porphyry	Monument cañon
167	Gneiss	Chocolate mountains
168	Metamorphic limestone	Monument cañon
169	....do........do.... (Tertiary ?)	Camp 36
170	Basaltic trap in syenite	....do
171	Metamorphic limestone	....do

CATALOGUE—Continued.

No.	Name.	Locality.
172	Trap with zeolites	Camp 36
173	....do	....do.
174	....do	....do.
175	Dog tooth spar lining cavities in metamorphic limestone	....do.
176	....do........do........do	....do.
177	Stalactitic lava	....do.
178	Trachyte	....do.
179	Metamorphic limestone	Mouth of Bill Williams's Fork
180	Carb. iron, veins in granite	Monument cañon.
181	Metamorphic limestone	Camp 36
182	Porphyry, (purple)	Mojave cañon
183	Trachyte	....do.
184	....do	....do.
185	Porphyry, (purple)	....do.
186	Amygdaloid trap	....do.
187	Brecciated porphyry	Chocolate mountains
188	Carb. lime, with manganese veins in granite	Monument cañon.
189	Trachyte, (white)	....do.
190	Porphyry, (purple)	Mojave cañon
191	Trachyte with manganese	....do.
192	Basaltic trap	....do.
193	Porphyry, (pink and white)	Mojave mountains.
194	Granite, (white)	Spirit mountain
195	Porphyry	Mojave mountains.
196	Granite	....do.
197	Jasper, (red)	....do.
198	Porphyry, (green)	....do
199	Scoria	Hills at base of Mojave mountains.
200	Porphyry, (dove-colored)	Mojave mountains.
201	....do.... (pale pink)	....do.
202	....do.... (light green)	....do.
203	....do.... (purple)	....do.
204	....do.... (drab)	....do.
205	....do.... (pale pink)	....do.
206	Azoic slate in gneiss	Mountains west of Mojave valley
207	Hornblendic syenite	....do........do.
208	Porphyry	....do........do.
209	Purple quartz	Mojave valley
210	Porphyry	....do.
211	....do	....do.
212	Quartzite veins in granite	....do.
213	Granite	Spirit mountain
214	Scoria, (black)	Pyramid cañon.
215	Porphyry, (purple)	....do.
216	Porphyry	....do.
217	....do	....do.
218	....do	....do.
219	Granite	....do.

CATALOGUE—Continued.

No.	Name.	Locality.
220	Granite, (white)	Spirit mountain
221	....do...(coarse) with plates of mica	....do.
222	Porphyry	Pyramid cañon
223	....do....(rose-colored)	....do.
224	....do....(pink)	....do.
225	Basaltic porphyry	....do.
226	Hornblendic syenite	Mojave mountains
227	Porphyry	Pyramid cañon
228	....do.	....do.
229	....do....(pink)	....do.
230	....do....(purple)	....do.
231	Hornblende rock	....do.
232	Porphyry, brecciated	....do.
233	....do..... (pale purple)	....do.
234	....do.	....do.
235	....do.	....do.
236	Calc. spar. in porphyry	....do.
237	Basaltic porphyry	Black mountains
238	Scoria, (red)	....do.
239	Trachytic porphyry	....do.
240	Quartzose porphyry	....do.
241	Trachytic porphyry	....do.
242	Porphyry	....do.
243	Trachytic porphyry	....do.
244	Porphyry	Pyramid cañon
245	....do.	....do.
246	Carb. copper in quartz	Spirit mountain
247	Quartzose porphyry	Black mountains
248	Syenetic porphyry	......do.
249	Porphyry	......do.
250	Trachyte, containing crystals of quartz	......do.
251	Porphyry, (lilac)	......do.
252	Trachyte, (crimson)	......do.
253	....do....(porphyritic)	......do.
254	....do.	......do.
255	Granular obsidian	......do.
256	Porphyry, (purple)	......do.
257	Trachyte, (pink and white)	......do.
258	....do.....(red)	......do.
259	Trachytic porphyry	......do.
260	Porphyry, (gray)	......do.
261	....do.	......do.
262	....do.	......do.
263	Trachytic porphyry	......do.
264	Porphyry	......do.
265	Trachytic, (rose-colored)	......do.
266	Porphyry, (purple)	......do.
267	Scoria, (green and white)	......do.

CATALOGUE—Continued.

No.	Name.	Locality.
268	Jaspery porphyry	Black mountains
269	Porphyry	do.
270	Porphyritic scoria	do.
271	Trachytic porphyry	do.
272	Porphyry, white, with crystals of limpid quartz	do.
273	Banded porphyry	do.
274	Trachyte, (purple)	do.
275	Porphyry...do	do.
276	Trachyte	do.
277	Scoriaceous basalt	do. ....Camp 48
278	Porphyry	do. .... do.
279	Porphyritic trachyte	do. .... do.
280	Volcanic conglomerate	do. .... do.
281	Silicified wood from Tertiary strata	Jesup rapids
282	Porphyry	Black mountains, Camp 49
283	....do....(mottled white and red)	do. .... do.
284	Trachyte with Jasper	do. .... do.
285	Brecciated trachyte	do. ....Camp 57
286	Porphyry	do. ....Camp 49
287	Tufaceous trachyte, (white, veined with red)	Mouth of Black cañon
288	Porphyry	do.
289	Trachytic porphyry	Black mountains, Camp 50
290	....do.......do	do. ....Camp 49
291	Porphyry, (white)	do. ....do.
292	....do	do. .... do.
293	....do.... (pinkish white)	do. .... do.
294	Obsidian, containing crystals of red feldspar and scales of mica	do.
295	Trachyte	do. ...... mouth of Black cañon.
296	....do...(white)	do. ....Camp 49
297	Porphyry, (purplish)	do. ....Camp 57
298	....do.... (lilac)	Mouth of Black cañon
299	....do.... (purple)	do.
300	Silicious porphyry, (purple)	Black mountains, Camp 49
301	Hornblende slate	do. .... do.
302	Porphyritic scoria	do. .... do.
303	Trachytic porphyry, (dark red)	do. ....Camp 57
304	Porphyry, white, with crystals of hornblende	do. .... do.
305	....do.... (pink and banded)	do. ....Camp 50
306	....do.... (brown)	do. ....Camp 49
307	Scoriaceous basalt	Walls of cañon...Camp 57
308	Trachyte, (pale red)	Black cañon
309	Porphyry, (purple)	Black mountains, Camp 49
310	Jasper, (striped)	do. .... do.
311	Porphyry, (brownish and mottled)	Walls·of cañon...Camp 57
312	Basalt (black) overlying Tertiary sandstones	Mouth of Black cañon
313	Porphyry, (light yellow, veined)	Black mountains, Camp 49
314	Trachyte, (gray)	do. .... do.
315	Porphyry, (black and red mottled)	do. ....Camp 57

CATALOGUE—Continued.

No.	Name.	Locality.
316	Porphyry, (reddish brown,) with scales of mica	Black mountains, Camp 49
317	Porphyry	do. Camp 57
318	Obsidian veins and masses in porphyry	Mouth of Black cañon
319	Porphyry	Black cañon Camp 57
320	Porphyry, (pale green, with tufa)	Black mountains, Camp 49
321	do. (greenish yellow)	do. do.
322	Trachytic porphyry	do. Camp 55
323	Amygdaloid trap cavities filled with carb. lime	Entrance to Black cañon, Camp 57
324	Porphyry	Black mountains, Camp 49
325	Red jaspery rock	do. do.
326	Massive quartz veins in granite	Cañon below Virgen river
327	Amygdaloid trap	Black mountains, Camp 55
328	Black basalt	Chocolate mountains
329	Trachyte, (red and yellow)	Black mountains, Camp 49
330	Tufaceous trachyte, (pure white)	do. do.
331	Porphyry, (dark red, with yellow spots)	do. do.
332	Trachyte, (lilac, spotted with white)	do. do.
333	Trachytic porphyry	do. Camp 57
334	do. do. (deep red)	do. Camp 49
335	Syenite, (dark green)	do. Camp 48
336	Trachyte (yellowish gray) with transparent crystals	do. Camp 49
337	Porphyry brecciated	do. do.
338	Trachyte	do. do.
339	Scoria	do. do.
340	Porphyry (light blue) with scales of mica	do. do.
341	do. (gray) with red and white crystals of feldspar	do. do.
342	Trachyte, (grayish red)	do. do.
343	do. (purple)	do. do.
344	do. brecciated, (yellow, with red spots)	do. do.
345	Volcanic tufa, (white, veined with pale pink)	do. do.
346	Black scoria	do. do.
347	Porphyry, (dove-colored, veined with red)	do. do.
348	Trachyte (rose-color) arenaceous	do. do.
349	Porphyry, (bluish white)	do. do.
350	Red syenite	Black cañon, below mouth of Virgen.
351	Trachyte	Black mountains, Camp 49
352	Metamorphic conglomerate	do. do.
353	Porphyry, (red and green)	do. do.
354	Amygdaloid trap, cavities lined with crystals of carb. lime	do. do.
355	Basalt, (dark blue,) section of column	do. Camp 50
356	Trachytic porphyry, (green, with white and purple spots)	do. Camp 49
357	Striped porphyry	do. do.
358	Cellular silicious porphyry	do. do.
359	Porphyry, (pink and white)	do. do.
360	do. (pale yellow)	do. do.
361	Tufa, (grayish white)	do. Camp 50
362	Trachytic porphyry (purplish) brecciated	do. Camp 49

CATALOGUE—Continued.

No.	Name.	Locality.
363	Black basalt	Black mountains, Camp 48
364	Porphyry, (yellow,) with deep red veins and spots	......do........Camp 49
365	....do....flinty, (clouded)	......do............do
366	Trachytic porphyry, (rose-colored,) with large crystals of glassy feldspar	......do............do
367	Syenitic porphyry, (green base,) with crystals of white feldspar and green hornblende	......do........Camp 57
368	Porphyry, (pale purple)	......do........Camp 50
369	....do....(deep purple, with orange spots)	......do........Camp 57
370	Pitch stone, cellular	......do........Camp 49
371	Porphyry, (grayish white)	......do............do
372	Trachytic porphyry	......do............do
373	Silicious porphyry, (purple banded)	......do............do
374	Porphyry, (deep red)	......do......... Camp 54
375	Cal. travertine in trachyte	Mojave cañon
376	Trachyte	Black mountains, Camp 50
377	Porphyry, (clouded, purple, and yellow)	......do............ do
378	Tufaceous trachyte, (pinkish white)	......do............ do
379	Trachytic porphyry, (dark red)	......do. ....Camp 49
380	Porphyry, (dull, purplish brown)	......do. ....Camp 50
381	Scoria, (red)	......do. ....Camp 48
382	Porphyry, (reddish gray)	......do. ....Camp 50
383	....do.....(grayish white,) with black crystals of hornblende	......do. ....Camp 48
384	Trachytic porphyry, (gray)	......do. ....Camp 50
385	Porphyry, (brown, lined with white)	......do............ do
386	....do.... (red)	......do............ do
387	....do.... (light purple, variegated)	......do......... Camp 54
388	....do.... (red and bluish white, banded)	......do......... Camp 57
389	....do.... (light red, with crystals of white feldspa)	......do......... Camp 49
390	....do.... (purplish brown, with scales of mica)	......do......... Camp 50
391	Trachytic porphyry, (dull red, with large crystals of feldspar)	......do............ do
392	Porphyry, (dark brown)	......do............ do
393	Trachytic porphyry, (red and white)	......do............ do
394	Porphyry, (light purple)	......do......... Camp 48
395	....do.... (bluish white)	......do............do
396	....do.... (pale rose color)	......do......... Camp 49
397	Basaltic trap, (dark gray)	......do......... Camp 48
398	Porphyry, (rose-colored)	......do......... Camp 57
399	Tufaceous trachyte, (dove-colored)	......do......... Camp 49
400	Trachyte, (brownish yellow)	......do......... Camp 50
401	Porphyry, (dark brown)	......do............ do
402	Trachytic porphyry, (purple, with scales of mica)	......do......... Camp 48
403	....do............ (red and white)	......do......... Camp 50
404	Trachyte, (dove-colored, with yellow spots)	......do......... Camp 48
405	Trachytic porphyry, (brecciated)	......do......... Camp 50
406	Porphyritic syenite	......do............ do
407	Porphyry, (gray and purple crowded)	......do............ do
408	Brecciated porphyry, (red and yellow)	......do............ do
409	Trachyte shading into porphyry	Walls of Black cañon, Camp 57

CATALOGUE—Continued.

No.	Name.	Locality.
410	Porphyry, (mottled,) containing masses of red jasper	Black mountains, Camp 50
411	Obsidian, (pearl stone)	Walls of cañon, Camp 57
412	....do........do......(dove color)	......do............ do
413	Jasper, (red and yellow)	......do............ do
414	Dog tooth spar lining cavities in trap	......do............ do
415	Silicious porphyry, (pink)	...... do......... Camp 49
416	Tufaceous trachyte, (greenish yellow, enclosing cobalt bloom?)	......do......... Camp 48
417	Porphyry	......do......... Camp 54
418	Trachyte, (green)	......do......... Camp 50
419	....do....(red and yellow)	......do......... Camp 57
420	....do....(cream-colored, veined with red)	......do......... Camp 49
421	....do....(dark red, arenaceous)	......do......... Camp 57
422	....do....(pinkish yellow)	......do......... do
423	Trachytic tufa	......do......... do
424	Gray porphyritic basalt with olivine	......do......... Camp 49
425	Porphyry, (dull red, with white spots)	......do......... Camp 54
426	Coarse feldspathic granite	Mountains west of Camp 57
427	Jasper, (yellow and red mottled)	Black mountains, Camp 57
428	Porphyry, (rose-colored, veined with yellow)	Black cañon above Camp 57
429	Trachytic porphyry	Black mountains, Camp 54
430	Tufaceous rock, (white, veined with purple)	......do......... Camp 57
431	Granular obsidian in trachyte	......do......... do
432	Trachyte, (coarse bluish gray)	......do...... Camp 48
433	Trachyte porphyry	......do......... Camp 57
434	....do......do....with numerous decomposing crystals of white feldspar	......do...... Camp 49
435	Trachyte, with large cavities set with crystals of quartz	Walls of Black cañon, Camp 57
436	Silicious porphyry, (dark purple)	Black mountains, Camp 57
437	Trachyte, (white)	......do............ do
438	Jasper, (yellow)	......do......... Camp 54
439	Basaltic trap overlying Tertiary sandstones	......do......... Camp 57
440	Porphyry, (purple,) with crystals of red feldspar	......do......... Camp 54
441	Silicious brecciated porphyry, (base liver color, with red and white spots)	......do......... Camp 49
442	Porphyry, (brown, speckled with white)	......do......... Camp 54
443	Red syenite, containing specular iron	Cañon below mouth of Rio Virgen
444	Porphyry, (purplish gray,) with scales of mica	Black mountains, Camp 48
445	Brecciated porphyry, base yellowish red, with angular fragments of quartz	......do......... Camp 54
446	Carnelians	......do......... Camp 57
447	Porphyry, (white and crimson clouded)	......do............ do
448	Feldspathic tufa, (white)	Walls of cañon, Camp 57
449	Porphyry, (dark red, with circular cream-colored spots)	Black mountains, Camp 57
450	Syenite, (very compact and fine grained)	Walls of cañon below Virgen
451	Feldspathic granite	......do............ do
452	Amygdaloid trap, (porphyritic)	Black mountains, Camp 54
453	....do......do	......do......... Camp 55
454	....do......do	......do......... Camp 54
455	....do......do	......do......... Camp 55
456	....do......do	......do......... Camp 57
457	....do......do	......do......... do

CATALOGUE—Continued.

No.	Name.	Locality.
458	Amygdaloid trap, scoriaceous	Black mountains, Camp 49
459	....do...... .do	......do......... Camp 54
460	Chalcedony, (lemon yellow)	......do......... do
461	Trap containing veins of jasper	......do......... Camp 61
462	Amygdaloid trap	......do......... Camp 57
463	Trachytic porphyry, (red purple)	......do......... do
464	Quartzite (pink) veins in granite	......do......... Camp 63
465	Porphyritic trachyte, partially columnar, overlying 481 and 483	......do......... Camp 62
466	Serpentinoid porphyry	......do......... Camp 57
467	Stratified prophyry	......do......... do
468	Scoria	......do......... Camp 48
469	Pitch stone, (brown)	......do......... Camp 57
470	Porphyry, (purple monochrone)	......do......... do
471	....do.... (purple,) with large crystals of feldspar	......do......... Camp 54
472	Trachyte, (pale purple)	......do......... Camp 48
473	Obsidian, with crystals of red feldspar	......do......... Camp 57
474	Quartz pebble, valley drift	......do......... Camp 54
475	Porphyry, (purple and white)	......do......... Camp 57
476	Granular obsidian	......do......... do
477	Pearl stone, containing garnet in spherical masses	......do......... do
478	Tufaceous trachyte, (yellow, veined with red)	......do......... Camp 48
479	Trachyte	Leroux's Spring, San Francisco mountain.
480	Lava	Mount Taylor, Hay Camp, N. Mexico.
481	Volcanic tufa	Black mountains, Camp 62
482	Obsidian, (gray)	San Francisco mountain
483	Stratified tufa	Black mountains, Camp 62
484	Tufaceous conglomerate	Mouth of Rio Virgen
485	Volcanic tufa, containing onyx	Black mountains, Camp 61
486	Carnelian rolled pebble, valley drift	......do......... do
487	Black basalt.....do......... do	......do......... do
488	Carb. lime, masses in tufa	......do......... Camp 55

IV.—TERTIARY ROCKS, BANKS OF COLORADO.

No.	Name.	Locality.
489	Silicified wood	Desert surface, Camp 14
490	Infusorial rock	Beaver Island
491	....do	......do
492	....do	White rock, Camp 35
493	....do	......do....... do
494	Red sandstone associated with No. 493	......do....... do
495	Infusorial rock	......do....... do
496	....do	......do....... do
497	....do	......do....... do
498	Sandstone incrusted with carb. lime	Monument cañon
100	Sandstone, (drab, coarse)	......do
500	Metamorphic conglomerate	......do

CATALOGUE—Continued.

No.	Name.	Locality.
501	Red sandstone, (fine)	Monument cañon
502	Tufaceous sandstone	do
503	Red conglomerate	Red Rock Monument cañon
504	Coarse red sandstone	Monument mountain
505	Metamorphic Tertiary (?) limestone, containing iron	Camp 36
506	Infusorial rock	Chemehuevis valley, Camp 38
507	Red sandstone	Base of Black mountains, Camp 49
508	Conglomerate, containing silicified trunks	do do
509	Silicified wood from 508	do do
510	Limestone capping conglomerate bluff	do do
511	do do	do do
512	Red sandstone under trap	Camp 57
513	Red shale under trap	do
514	Red sandstone under trap	do
515	do do	do
516	Infusorial rock	do
517	Silicified wood	Desert surface, Camp 50
518	Carb. lime filling veins in White Rock	Camp 35
519	Infusorial rock, (pisolitic)	White Rock, Camp 35
520	Tooth of *Elephas primigenius*	Valley drift, Camp 35

V.—ROCKS FORMING TABLE-LANDS OF THE UPPER COLORADO.

	a. Azoic.	
521	Granite, (gray,) base of series	Mouth of Diamond river, Camp 67
522	Granite (red coarse) veins and masses in 521	do do
523	Red syenite, veins and masses in 521	do do
	b. Silurian and Devonian.	
524	Conglomerate, base of stratified series	Cañon of Colorado Camp 67
525	Quartzose sand rock, (striped, purple, and white,) lying over 524	do do
526	Dark red sandstone, overlying 525	do do
527	Light brown sandstone, over 526	do do
528	Red shale mud rock, with casts of fucoids (?) over 527, and interstratified with 529	do do
529	Red shaly sandstone over last, and interstratified with 530	do do
530	Green shale, similar to 528	do do
531	Red speckled sandstone, interstratified with last	do do
532	White speckled sandstone, interstratified with last	do do
533	Pebble of 525	Valley drift of Lower Colorado, Camp 48.
534	Thin banded sand rock, with mud furrows, interstratified with shales under thick bedded standstone	Cañon Diamond river, Camp 48
535	Thin banded sand rock, with mud furrows, interstratified with shales under thick bedded sandstone	do do
536	Limestone with corals (?) over last	do do
537	Silicious clouded limestone over last	do do

CATALOGUE—Continued.

No.	Name.	Locality.
538	Green shale	Cañon, Diamond river, Camp 48
539	Shelly limestone, like 535	do do
540	Indurated shale with hard manganese	do do
541	Foliated sandstone, over last	do do
542	Silicious shale	do do
543	Argillaceous indurated shale, with mud furrows	do do
544	Silicious limestone, (pale pink,) metamorphosed by silica in solution	do do
545	do (purple) do do	do do
546	do containing manganese	do do
547	do (clouded purple and gray,) similar to 537	do do
548	do (pale pink,) similar to 544	do do
549	Silicious clouded limestone, containing corals? replaced by peroxide of iron	do do
550	do (pale yellow,) highly crystalline	do do
551	do (light gray, banded)	do do
552	Indurated argillo calcareous marl, with hard manganese	do do
553	Red arenaceous limestone	do do
554	Metamorphosed argillaceous shale with scales of chalcedony in joints	do do
555	Indurated argillaceous shale, (buff,) cavities lined with chalcedony	do do
556	do (clouded yellow and gray)	do do
557	do (banded red and yellow)	do do
558	Chalcedony coating surfaces of joints of last	do do
559	Indurated clay, (whitish)	do do
560	Cellular argillaceous rock, filled with silicious infiltrations	do do
561	do do	do do
562	Chalcedony from joints of 554	do do
563	Silicious limestone interstratified with preceding series of metamorphic marls	do do

c. Carboniferous.

No.	Name.	Locality.
564	Dense, bluish gray limestone over preceding series	Cañon, Diamond river, Camp 48
565	Higher part of last, containing imperfect fossils, *Euomphalus*, corals, &c	do do
566	Hematite iron ore in 565	do do
567	Jaspery chert in 565	
568	Coral from iron ore in 565	Camp 66
569	*Spirifer* from iron ore in 565	do
570	Red calcareous sandstone, containing gypsum, over 569	Camp 69
571	do with red shale and gypsum	Camp 73
572	White gypsum, with last	do
573	Light tufaceous magnesian limestone, overlying 571	Camp 69
574	Drab thick-bedded sandstone, over 573	Camp 70
575	Drab thin-bedded sandstone, same as 574	do
576	Pebble of last, valley drift	Camp 54
577	Crinoidal limestone, over 575	Camp 79
578	Pebble of 557, valley drift	Camp 48
579	do containing crinoidal columns	Camp 55
580	do do	Camp 31
581	do containing *Fenestella*	do

CATALOGUE—Continued.

No.	Name.	Locality.
582	Pebble of 557	Camp 55
583	......do	Camp 48
584	Limestone same as 577, containing *Productus Ivesii*, showing external surface	Camp 67
585	......do......do......do.	....do.
586	......do......showing ventral surface	....do.
587	......do......do.	....do.
588	......do......do.	....do.
589	......do......showing exterior of dorsal valve	....do.
590	......do......showing interior of dorsal valve	....do.
591	......do......with spines of *P. Ivesii*	....do.
592	......do......with crinoidal columns	Camp 69
593	......do......with *Fenestella*	Camp 70
594	......do......with *Dictyonema*	....do.
595	......do?......with coral, valley drift	Camp 48
596	......do......with *Orthisina*	Camp 70
597	......do......with corals	....do.
598	......do......with *Orthisina pyramidalis avicula*	....do.
599	......do......Crinoids and *Orthisina pyramidalis*	....do.
600	......do......with spines of *Archaeocidaris longispinus*	....do.
601	......do......with *Orthisina*	....do.
602	......do......with spines of *Archaeocidaris gracilis*, Newb	....do.
603	......do......do......do	....do.
604	......do......do......do	....do.
605	......do......with spines of *Archaeocidaris ornatus*, Newb	....do.
606	Coral from same	....do.
607	*Productus Ivesii*......do	....do.
608	*Productus*......do	....do.
609	Coral......do	....do
610	Crinoidal column	....do
611	Spines of Archaeocidaris gracelis, Newberry	Cañon, Diamond river, Camp 70
612	Crinoidal column, very large	......do......do
613	Section of *Dictyonema*	......do......do
614	*Rhynconella, Rocky Montana*	......do......Camp 73
615	....do......do....and Spirifer lineatus	......do......do
616	Geodes of calc. spar. in 577	......do......Camp 70
617	....do......do......do	......do......do
618	....do......do......do	......do......do
619	....do......do......do	......do......do
620	....do......do......do	......do......do
621	....do......do......do	......do......do
622	Gypsiferous shale, overlying 577	......do......Camp 73
623	Snowy gypsum, interstratified with last	......do......do
624	....do......do......do	......do......do
625	*Orthisina umbraculum*, cherty limestone, overlying 624	......do......do
626	....do......do......do	......do......do
627	....do......do......do	......do......do
628	Orthisina occidentalis, Newberry, cherty limestone, overlying 624	......do......do

CATALOGUE—Continued.

No.	Name.	Locality.
629	Orthisina Occidentalis, Newberry, cherty limestone, overlying 624	Cañon, Diamond river, Camp 70
630	Spirigera subtilita, (cast)	do do
631	do do	do do
632	do do	do do
633	Rhynconella, Rocky Montana	do do
634	Productus occidentalis	do do
635	do do	do do
636	do costaloides	do do
636½	do mucronatus? N. & P.	Manhattan, K. T.
637	Spirifer lineatus	Cherty limestone, mouth of Little Colorado, Camp 73.
638	do do	do do
639	Productus semireticulatus, var. Sulcatus	do do
640	Chonetes Verneuiliana?	do do
641	Pecten (Monotis?) Coloradensis	do do
642	do do in pebble val. drift	Cherty limestone mouth of Little Colorado, Camp 49.
643	do in cherty limestone	do do
644	Spirifer lineatus, in cherty limestone	Cherty limestone, mouth of Little Colorado, Camp 73.
645	Productus Ivesii, (cast,) in cherty limestone	Banks of Cedar creek
646	do do do	do
647	do do do	do Camp 73
648	Fenestella do do	do do
649	Productus do do	do do
650	Crinoidal limestone	do Camp 70
651	Cherty limestone	do Camp 73
652	Red shale, over 651	do Camp 74
653	Conglomerate	do Camp 73
654	Sandstone, (reddish white,) 653	do do
655	Limestone over last, (yellow)	do do
656	do 655 and 656 (red)	do do
657	do 655 and 656, (red and yellow)	do do
658	do arenaceous, (red,) = 657	do do
659	Cast of Productus	do Camp 70
660	Nautilus from carb. limestone	Agua Azul
661	Allorisma, (cast,) do	do
662	Bellerophon. do do	do
663	Productus do do	do
664	Carboniferous limestone, with Producti, &c.	Santa Fé
665	Productus, from 664	do
666	Productus modusus, Newberry	do
667	do do do	do
668	do Rogersi	Pecos
669	do Semireticulatus	do
670	Spirigera subtilita	do
671	Spirifer cameratus	do

CATALOGUE—Continued.

No.	Name.	Locality.
672	*Productus scabriculus*	Santa Fé
673	Coal, (semi-bituminous)	Near Parawan, Utah
674	Coal, (bituminous)	do do
675	Coke of 673	do do
676	Coal, (anthracite)	Gold Placers, New Mexico
677	Coal, (bituminous)	Burlingame, Kansas
678	*Productus splendens*, Coal measures	Near Burlingame, Kansas
678½	*Productus Colhounianus*, Coal measures	Manhattan, K. T
679	*Fusilina cylindrica*, Coal measures	Western Kansas
680	Carb. limestone with *Fusilinas*	Big Spring, K T
681	do *Productus splendens*	Near Burlingame, K. T
682	Shale with *Neuropteris flexuosa*	Easton, K. T
683	do do	do
684	do do	do
685	*Peten occidentalis*, from carboniferous shale	do
686	Chert, containing *Fusilina*	do
687	Carb limestone with *Productus*	Near Burlingame, K. T
688	*Rhynconella esta*, (*Terebratula esta*, Marcou,) Upper C. M	Manhattan, K. T
689	*Productus*	Council Bluffs
690	*Spirifer Cameratus*	do
690½	*Spirifer, Rocky Montana Marcou*	Fort Laramie
691	*Chonetes Granulifera*, (?) Owen	Lexington, Missouri
692	*Productus*	Bellevue, Nebraska
693	do *Rogersi*	do do
694	do *costatus* (Sowerby)	do do
695	*Chonetes mucronata*, (Meek and Hayden,) Upper Carboniferous	Diamond Spring, K. T
695½	*Chonetes Verneuiliana*, (N. and P)	Manhattan, K. T
696	*Productus punctatus*, under valve Upper Coal measures	Bellevue, Nebraska
697	*Spirigera subtilita*	Council Bluffs
698	*Dicina*, Upper C. M	Manhattan, Kansas
699	*Retzia Mormoni*, (*Terebratula*, Marcou,) C. M	Fort Leavenworth
700	Limestone, (magnesian)	Cañon Diablo, near crossing of Little Colorado.

d. Permian, Triassic, (?) and Jurassic. (?)

No.	Name.	Locality.
701	Red sandstone resting conformably on carb. limestone, (646, 660. and 661.)	Crossing of Little Colorado
702	Conglomerate, overlying 701	Little Colorado, Camp 88
703	do do	Fort Defiance
704	Red, foliated, ripple-marked sandstone, with red shale, over 702	Navajo Country, Camp 102
705	Greenish ditto over 703	do do
706	Shelly, gray sandstone interstratified with 704	do do
707	Conglomerate over 705	Apache Cañon
708	Silicified wood, red, &c., from variegated marls over 707	Banks of Little Colorado
709	do do (red and green)	do do
710	do do (jasperized)	do do
711	do do do	do do
712	do do	do do
713	do do (whitish)	do do

CATALOGUE—Continued.

No.	Name.	Locality.
714	Silicified wood, red, &c , from variegated marls over 707, coniferous...........	Banks of Little Colorado ....
715	Purple limestone interstratified with variegated marls............................	......do.........do ....
716	Bluish white limestone..do.............do......................................	......do.........do ....
717	Silicified wood from marls over 716	......do.........do ....
718	Blue and purple magnesian limestone over marls containing 717........	......do.........do..Camp 90....
719	Silicified wood from variegated marls.......	Fort Defiance......................
720	Red marl over 718..	Mesa, Camp 90.....................
721	Purplish magnesian limestone over 720..............................	Camp 91...........................
722	Purple indurated marl over 721.......................................	....do ....
723	Red calc. sandstone = 722, below cretaceous rocks....................	Laguna..........................
724	Whitish calc sandstone, alternating with 722.........................	Camp 91..........................
725	White sandstone = 724...	Camp 92..........................
726	Pure, white calc. sandstone = 725	Navajo valley, Camp 101...........
727	Purple indurated marl over 725.......................................	Camp 91..........................
728	Green.........do.........727.....................................	....do ....
729	Snowy gypsum under red sandstone	East of Laguna....................
730	Magnesian limestone with *Fenestella*, Permian.....................	Council Grove....................
731	...do................. ....do..... (cream-colored)	Little Arkansas...................
732	Fibrous carb. lime, Permian..	Turkey creek ....
733	Magnesian limestone, Permian......................................	Cottonwood creek ....
734	Avicula...	......do ....
735	Red sandstone under 723	Laguna..........................
736	White sandstone = 724......................	....do ....
737	Saline stratum in red marl..............	Camp 90...........................
738	*Pecopteris* from clays in lignite..................................	Moqui country, Camp 92...........
739	...do............do	......do.........do ....
740	*Sphenopteris*...	......do.........do ....
741	*Pecopteris cyclotoba*, Newb...................................	Camp 92..........................
742	....do.............do	....do ....
743	....do.............do	....do ....
744	*Camptopteris*......... do......................................	....do ....
745	....do.............do......................................	....do ....
746	....do.............do......................................	....do ....
747	*Phyllites venosissimus*, do...................................	....do ....
748	....do.............do......................................	....do ....,............
749	*Cyclopteris moquensis*, Newb	....do ....
750	....do.............do......................................	....do ....
751	....do.............do......................................	....do ....
752	....do.............do......................................	....do ....
753	....do.............do......................................	....do ....
754	...do.............do......................................	....do ....
755	Clay containing plants in coal..................................	....do ....
756	Coal ....do	....do ....
757	Coal .... do	....do ....
758	Magnesian limestone with *myalina perattenuata*, Permian............	Cottonwood creek ....
759	*Monotis Hawni*, (M. & H,)......................do.............	......do ....
760	*Pleurophorus subcuneata*, (M. H.)..............................	......do ....

CATALOGUE—Continued.

No.	Name.	Locality.
761	*Orthisina umbracula*, permo-carboniferous	Turkey creek, Kansas
762	*Myalina perattenuata*, (M. & H.)	Cottonwood creek
	c. Cretaceous.	
763	Yellow sandstone with impressions of dycotyledonous leaves over 787	Camp 92
764	*Inoceramus crispii* (?) from bands of limestone in green shale over 763	Moqui villages
765	*Ammonites percarinatus*, with last	......do
766	....do............do	......do
767	....do............do	......do
768	....do............do	......do
769	....do............do	......do
770	*Gryphaea pitcheri*, var. *Navia*	......do
770½	*Gryphaea*, iu yellow sandstone	Covero
771	Ferruginous concretions from yellow sandstone	Moqui villages
772	*Pinna? lingula*, Newb	Oryabe
773	....do........do	...do
774	*Phyllites coriaceus*, Newb	Moqui country, Camp 92
775	*Quercus?*	......do........ Camp 95
776	*Phyllites coriaceous*, N	......do............do
777	....do	......do........-do
778	....do	......do........do
779	*Quercus?*	......do........do
780	....do	......do........do
781	*Cornus?*	......do........do
782	*Phyllites coriaceus*, Newb	......do........do
783	*Platanus*	......do........do
784	....do	......do........do
785	....do	......do........do
786	....do	......do........do
787	Rvt shale with leaves of *Neuropteris angulata*, Newb	......do........do
788	*Neuropteris angulata*, Newb	......do........do
789	....do............do	
790	....do............do	
791	....do............do	
792	....do............do	
793	....do............do	
794	Lignite	Camps 95 and 96
795	....do	Camp 96
796	Cretaceous shale	Banks of Ocaté
797	Blue cret. limestone	Red fork of Canadian
798	*Inoceramus problematicus*	......do
799	Fish tooth	......do
800	*Inoceramus problematicus*	......do
801	....do........do	......do
802	Sandstone (white) dycot. leaves	Blackbird Hill, Neb
803	....do.... (red)........do	......do
804	....do.................do	......do

CATALOGUE—Continued.

No.	Name.	Locality.
	f. Tertiary.	
805	Light gray arenaceous limestone resting on cretaceous sandstones	Navajo country, Camps 99–100
806	White tufaceous limestone over 806	......do............do. ....

VI.—ORES AND MINERALS.

No.	Name.	Locality.
807	Red oxide with native copper	San Gorgonio Pass, Cal.
808	Cinnabar	Monterey, Cal.
809	Specular iron	San Diego, Cal.
810	Magnetic iron	......do............do. ....
811	Malachite	San Antonio, Lower California
812	Red oxide of copper	......do............do. ....
813	Malachite	Buena Vista, San Diego county, Cal.
814	....do.....from surface	......do............do. ....
815	Argentiferous gray copper ore	......do............do. ....
816	Malachite	......do............do. ....
817	Carbonate and red oxide of copper	......do............do. ....
818	Malachite	San Antonio, California
819	Red oxide copper, near surface	La Grulla, Lower California
820	Veinstone of copper ore	......do............do. ....
821	Quartz, with silicate and carbonate of copper and gold	Buena Vista, Lower California
822	Black manganese	San Diego, California
823	Red oxide and blue and green carbonates of copper with silver	Santa Tomas, Lower California
824	Variegated copper pyrites	"Arizona Mines" on Gila
825	Copper pyrites, (yellow)	......do............do. ....
826	Red oxide and green carb. copper	......do............do. ....
827	Black oxide and green carb. copper	25 miles east of Fort Yuma
828	Black oxide of copper	On Colorado, near Chimney Peak
829	Malachite, surface	......do............do. ....
830	Sulphurets of lead and silver in carb. lime	On Colorado, 20 miles above Fort Yuma.
831	......do............do.	On Colorado, 20 miles above Fort Yuma.
832	Metallic lead from 830	On Colorado, 20 miles above Fort Yuma.
833	Sulphuret of silver?	On Colorado, 20 miles above Fort Yuma.
834	......do........in carb. lime	Monument cañon
835	Argentiferous galena, crystalline	Trinidad, Sonora
836	......do............massive	......do. ....
837	Sulphuret of silver	Monument cañon
838	Copper, iron, and manganese	
839	Ore of copper and iron, veins in granite	Monument cañon
840	Specular iron	......do. ....
841	......do	......do. ....
842	......do	Mojave cañon
843	Magnetic oxide iron	Near Parawan, Utah

CATALOGUE—Continued.

No.	Name.	Locality.
844	Specular iron	Near Parawan, Utah
845	Hard manganese	Southern Utah
846	Argentiferous galena	New Mexico
847	..... do	Stevenson's Mine, Las Cruces
848	Specular iron, crystallized	Camp 73
849	Sulphuret of silver	Sopori, (Douglas's) Mine, near Teuson, Arizona.
850	Chloride of silver	.... do.
851	Silicate of copper	New Placer, near Santa Fé. Mexico.
852	Blue carbonate of copper	......do..........do......
853	Native gold	Cunningham mine, Old Placer, 26 miles from Santa Fé
854	Chloride of silver?	Cerrillos, 15 miles from Santa Fé
855	Litharge	Jornada del Muerto, New Mexico
856	Carb and oxide copper	Jemez, New Mexico
857	Gypsum	Mouth of Virgen river
858	Rock salt	Banks of Virgen river
859	....do....in transparent crystals	......do..........do....
860	Tabular quartz	Black mountains, C. C
861	Onyx, large	......do........Camp 62
862	Snowy quartz with jasper	......do........Camp 49
863	Striped chert	......do..........do....
864	Black garnets in granite	Black cañon, Camp 58
865	Red.........do	......do..........do......
866	Red jasper in limestone	Valley drift, Camp 48
867	Rock salt	Salt Lake
868	Schorl in granite	Near mouth of Rio Virgen
869	Garnet? spherical concretions in pearl stone	Black cañon, Camp 57
870	Arsenate of cobalt? in volcanic tufa	Camp 48
871	Onyx in tufaceous trap	Camp 61
872	Garnet? spherical concretions in trachyte	Camp 57
873	Plates of selenite	Carisso creek
874	Plumbago, (metamorph. lignite?)	Near San Francisco mountain
875	Gadolinite? in trap	Camp 91
876	....do.......do....in large crystals	......do
877	Turquoise, "Chalchuitt"	Cerrillos, near Santa Fé
878	Crystals of rock salt	Near Los Vegas, Utah
879	Crystallized quartz, lining fissures in trap	Black mountains near Camp 57
880	....do..........do........stellate groups	......do..........do....
881	....do..........do..............do......	......do..........do....
882	....do..........do........with opalescent chalcedony	......do..........do....
883	....do..........do..............do......	......do..........do....
884	....do..........do..............do......	......do..........do....
885	Chalcedony	......do........Camp 61
886	Crystallized quartz	......do..........do....
887	....do	......do..........do....
888	....do	......do..........do....

CATALOGUE—Continued.

No.	Name.	Locality.
889	Crystallized quartz	Black mountains, near Camp 61
890	Dark chalcedony with crystallized quartz	do do
891	Crystallized quartz	do Camp 57
892	do	do do
893	do	do do
894	do	do do
895	do	do do
896	Dark blue chalcedony	do Camp 61
897	Pale blue chalcedony	do do
898	do do	do do
899	Chalcedony	do do
900	do	do do
901	do (brown,) botryoidal concretions	do do
902	do (yellow,) botryoidal concretions	do do
903	do (red) with crystals quartz	do do
904	do opalescent	do do
905	do do with crystallized surface	do Camp 57
906	do (pinkish white) in mammillary masses	do Camp 61
907	do (dark blue) with crystallized quartz	do do
908	do colored red by oxide of iron	do do
909	Opalescent chalcedony lining fissures trap	do Camp 57
910	do do	do do
911	Rosettes of crystals of quartz	do do

VII.—FOSSILS AND MISCELLANEOUS.

No.	Name.	Locality.
912	Shell limestone, Pliocene (?)	Adair bay, Sonora, collected by C. P. Stone.
913	Natica	do do
914	Cast of Murex	do do
915	Venus	do do
916	do	do do
917	Pecten	do do
918	Murex	do do
919	Cast of Mactra	do do
920	Mactra	do do
921	Natica	do do
922	Cast of Mactra	do do
923	do	do do
924	Murex	do do
925	Scutella	do do
926	do	do do
927	do	do do
928	Turitella	do do
929	Natica	do do
930	Anomia	do do
931	do	do do

CATALOGUE—Continued.

No.	Name.	Locality.
932	*Cardium*	Adair bay, Sonora, collected by C. P. Stone.
933	....do	......do............do...... ......
934	....do	......do............do............
935	*Oliva*	......do............do............
936	Soil from dry lake	Colorado Desert...................
937	Saline efflorescence on soil	San Felipe......................
938	Alluvial soil, (best)	Mojave valley.....................
939	....do........ do.	Cottonwood valley.................
940	....do....... (sandy)	......do........................
941	Saline efflorescence	Mouth of Bill Williams's Fork.....
942	Calcareous tufa formed by spring	Fort Tejon, Cal...................
943	Crystallized salt from salt plain	Near southern boundary of Kansas.
944	Pottery from surface	North of San Francisco mountains.
945	....do	......do............do............
946	Cinnabar	New Almaden mine, near San José, Cal.
947	Gold in quartz, (rich)	Mariposa county, Cal..............
948	....do..........do	......do........................
949	....do........ (meagre)	......do........................
950	Gryphæa pitcheri, var. *Navia*	Banks of Pecos river..............

EXPLANATION OF PLATE I.

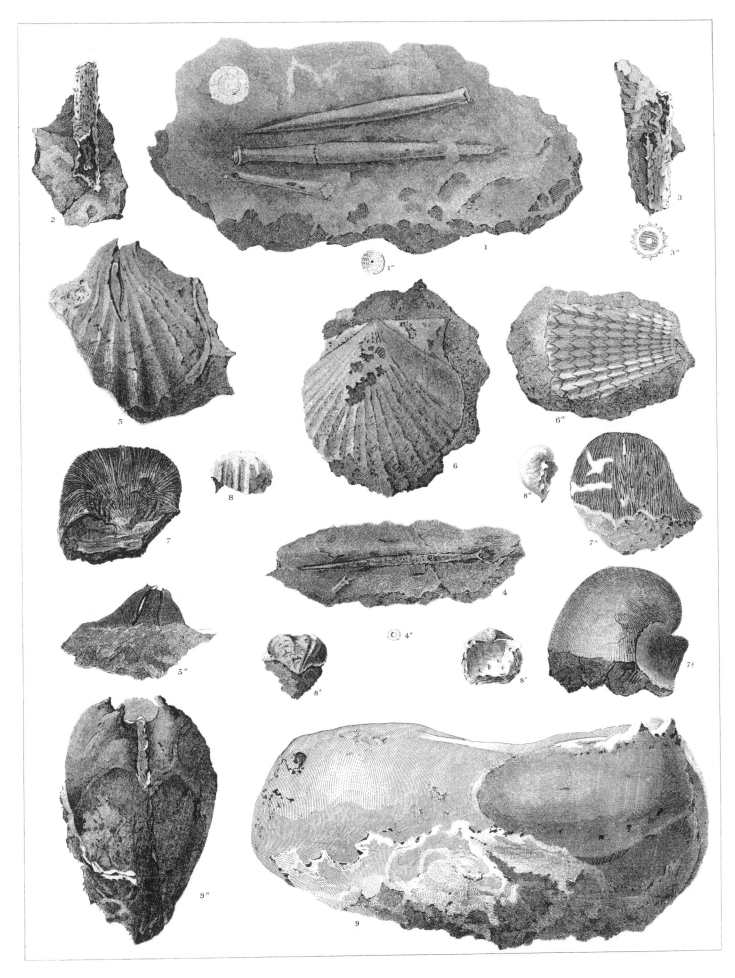

EXPLANATION OF PLATE II.

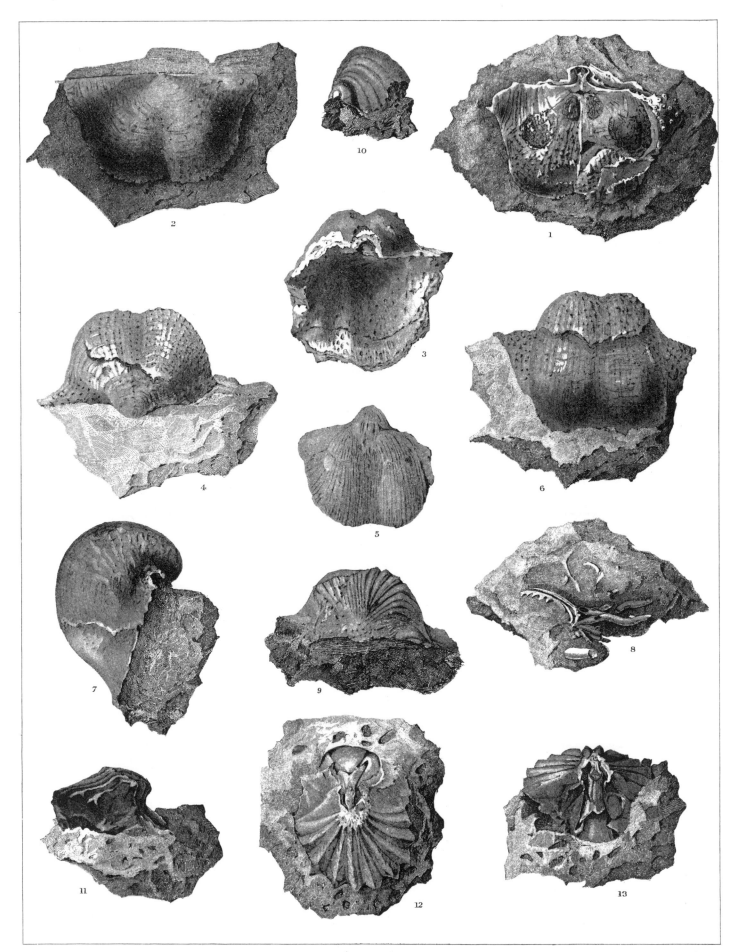

EXPLANATION OF PLATE III.

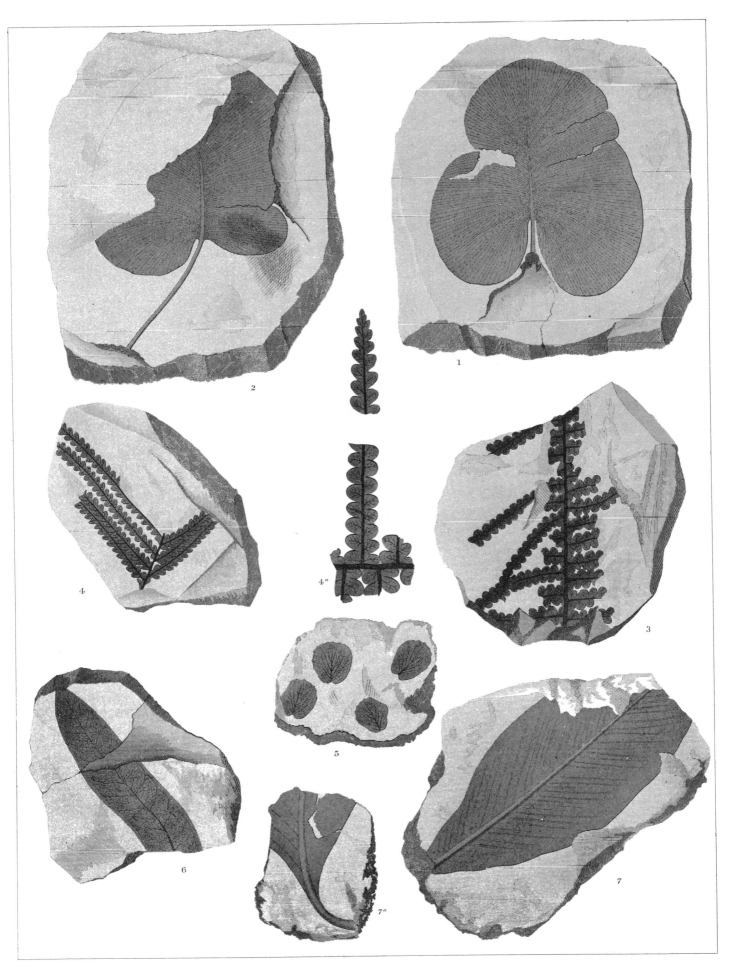

PART IV.

EXPLORATIONS AND SURVEYS.   WAR DEPARTMENT.

COLORADO EXPLORING EXPEDITION, LIEUTENANT J. C. IVES, TOPOGRAPHICAL ENGINEERS.

BOTANY.

BY Professors GRAY, TORREY, THURBER, AND DR. ENGELMANN.

WASHINGTON, D. C.
1860.

CATALOGUE

OF

THE PLANTS COLLECTED UPON THE EXPEDITION.

RANUNCULACEÆ.*

ANEMONE DECAPETALA, *Linn. Mant. p.* 79; *DC. Prodr.* 1, *p.* 19; *Hook. & Arn. Bot. Beech. p.* 3, *t.* 1. A. trilobata, *Juss. in Ann. Mus. Par.* 3, *p.* 247, *t.* 21. A. Caroliniana, *Walt. Fl. Car. p.* 157. A. heterophylla, *Nutt. in Torr. & Gray. Fl.* 1, *p.* 12. A. Berlandieri, *Pretzel, Revis. t.* 6. "Rocky hill-sides. Sitgreaves's Pass and high table-lands; March. Flower reddish purple, pale pink, greenish pink, and white." The identity of A. Caroliniana with the South American A. decapetala was long ago asserted in the Flora of North America. Indeed, the larger western forms of the North American plant perfectly accord with Chilian specimens. But I can by no means follow Dr. Hooker in uniting the northern A. multifida (A. Hudsoniana of Richardson) to this species.

MYOSURUS ARISTATUS, *Benth. in Lind Jour. Bot.* 6, *p.* 469. M. apetalus. Gray. "Cedar creek. . . . April 25." Also a Chilian species.

DELPHINIUM PATENS, *Benth. Pl. Hartw. p.* 296. Camp 67. Partridge creek; April 24.

DELPHINIUM DECORUM, *Fisch. & Meg.; Torr. in Whipple's Rep. &c.* Moqui villages; May 13.

BERBERIDACEÆ.

BERBERIS AQUIFOLIUM, *Pursh. Fl.* 1, *p.* 219, *t.* 4. "Camp 70. High table-lands north of the San Francisco mountain; in flower April 10. Santa Fé ; June 1. Highlands of New Mexico generally."

BERBERIS FREMONTI, *Torr. Bot. Mex. Bound vol.* 4, *p.* 31. B. trifoliata, Torr. Bot. Whipple's Rep. p. 63. Banks of Little Colorado; April. Moqui country; May. Shrub 10–15 ft. high; berries blue.

PAPAVERACEÆ.

ESCHSCHOLTZIA CALIFORNICA, *Cham.* Yampai valley; March 25. Common along banks of Colorado.

ESCHSCHOLTZIA DOUGLASII, *Hook & Arn.;* var. *tenuifolia* and var. *hypecoides.* E. tenuifolia and E. hypecoides, *Benth.* Southeastern California and Sitgreaves's Pass; March 24. Some of the specimens with very small flowers.

FUMARIACEÆ.

CORYDALIS AUREA, *Willd.; DC. Prodr.* 1, *p.* 128. Camp 64, to Rio Grande. Common over all the table-lands of New Mexico.

* The plants enumerated in this catalogue, in all the orders preceding *Verbenaceæ*, were examined by Prof. Gray, with the exception of the *Cactaceæ* and *Euphorbiaceæ*, elaborated by Dr. Geo. Engelmann. The remainder of the catalogue was made out by Prof. Torrey, with the exception of that of the grasses, prepared by Prof. Thurber.

CRUCIFERÆ.

Nasturtium sinuatum, *Nutt. in Torr. & Gray, Fl.* 1, *p.* 73. Banks of Colorado Chiquito, near crossing. Camp 88.

Turritis patula, *Graham; Gray, Pl. Wright.* 2, *p.* 10. Long valley; March 25.

Streptanthus cordatus, *Nutt. in Torr. and Gray, Fl.* 1, *p.* 77. High table-lands. Camp 75. Flowers purple and orange.

Streptanthus sagittatus, *Nutt. in Torr. and Gray, l. c.?* Long valley; March 27. A large plant. Calyx (only 3 lines long) and the broadly ovate limb of the petals deep purple.

Streptanthus: a doubtful species, of the Euclisia section; too incomplete to characterize; near the two following. Sitgreaves's Pass. Black mountains; March 23.

Streptanthus longifolius, *Benth.; Gray, Pl. Fendl., p.* 6. Colorado Chiquito; May 5.

Sisymbrium deflexum, *Harv.; Torr. in Whipple's Rep., p.* 66, and a smooth form of the same. Jessup rapids; February 23 and March 22.

Sisymbrium canescens, *Nutt.* Sitgreaves's Pass, Black mountains, and high table-lands; March.

Erysimum asperum, *DC.* Cheiranthus asper, *Nutt.* Mesa, near Partridge creek; April 25.

Draba platycarpa, *Torr. & Gray, Fl.* 1, *p.* 108. Everywhere on the Upper Colorado. Camp 49; March 22.

Draba cuneifolia, *Nutt. in Torr. & Gray, l. c.* Sitgreaves's Pass and Yampai valley; March 23–25.

Vesicaria angustifolia, *Nutt. in Torr. & Gray, Fl.* 1, *p.* 101; *Gray, Pl. Wright.* 2, *p.* 13. Yampai valley, coloring large surfaces yellow; March 27.

Vesicaria Fendleri, *Gray, Pl. Fendl. and Pl. Wright.?* Long valley; March 25. An imperfect fragment.

Vesicaria purpurea, *Gray, Pl. Wright.* 2, *p.* 14; var. albiflora. High table lands. Camp 68–70; "flowers white." Thurber gathered the same thing, with nearly white and with lilac flowers.

Vesicaria Fendleri, *Gray, Pl. Fendl., p.* 9. Banks of Little Colorado; May 1; in flower only.

Physaria newberryi, (sp. nov.;) pube stellata apprerrissima argentea; foliis radicalibus obovato-spathulatis acutis angulato-dentatis, in petiolum attenuatis caulibus floridis brevioribus, caulinis lineari-spathulatis; racemo sparsifloro; petalis linearibus patentibus calyce laxo duplo longioribus; silicula globoso-didyma basi haud emarginata; stylo e sinu angusto leviter exserto. "Near Tegua, (Moqui village,) May 14; in tufts, on rocks. A singular plant; flowers irregular in form, and appearing ragged and past prime when in full anthesis." Stems numerous in a tuft, from a perennial root, three inches high, erect or ascending. Radical leaves, an inch or an inch and a half long, including the petiole, three to five lines broad, generally with one or two angulate teeth on each margin; the cauline ones two to four, much smaller and narrower, entire or nearly so, often linear. Pedicels four to six lines long in fruit, ascending, sepals linear. Petals yellow; almost half an inch long, scarcely a line and a half wide, with no marked distinction of blade and claw, but of nearly the same breadth from the base to the very obtuse apex. Filaments slender; anthers linear oblong. Style as long as the ovary; stigma subcapitate. Silicle (not yet mature) three lines in length and breadth, circular in general outline, obcordate didymus, but with a narrow sinus, (the lobes not at all diverging, but rather the contrary,) membranaceous in texture, but not very thin or bladdery, minutely canescent; the cells 1–2-seeded; the persistent style not exceeding a line and a half in length.

An interesting addition to this small genus, and a very distinct species; in the silicle intermediate between P. didymo carpa (but less inflated and didymous) and P. Geyeri—nearest the latter, but the silicle more inflated, and of quite a different outline. As flattened in the dried specimens, the dorsal part of each carpel is inflexed into the cell; but probably it is not so in the living plant.

THLASPI FENDLERI, *Gray, Pl. Wright.* 2, *p.* 14. San Francisco prairie; Camp 81; April 27.

DITHYREA CALIFORNICA, *Harv. in Hook. Lond. Jour. Bot.* 4, *p.* 77, *t.* 5; *Torr. in Whipp. Rep., p.* 66. Cottonwood valley and Black mountains; March; "flowers greenish white."

DITHYREA WISLIZENI, *Engelm. in Wisl. Mem. N. Mex., p.* 11; *Torr. in Marcy's Rep. t.* 11, *and Whipple's Rep., p.* 66. Banks of Little Colorado; May 1.

LEPIDIUM ALYSSOIDES, *Gray, Pl. Fendl., p.* 10, *&c.* Colorado Chiquito and on the Great Colorado; March to May.

LEPIDIUM WRIGHTII, *Gray, Pl. Wright.* 2, *p.* 15. Yampai valley and Upper Colorado; March.

STANLEYA PINNATIFIDA, *Nutt.*; *Gray, Gen. Hl. t.* 65. Diamond river, Moqui country, &c. Some specimens are said to have the "flowers white changing to yellow."

THYSANOCARPUS LACINIATUS, *Nutt., in Torr. & Gray, Fl.* 1, *p.* 118. Sitgreaves's Pass; March 24.

CAPPARIDACEÆ.

ISOMERIS ARBOREA, *Nutt., in Torr. & Gray, Fl.* 1, *p.* 134. San Diego, California; November 1.

RESEDACEÆ.

OLIGOMERIS GLAUCESCENS, *Cambess, Gray, Pl. Wright.* 2, *p.* 16. Alluvial bottoms of the Colorado; head of Mojave valley; Camp 49; February 18.

CISTACEÆ.

HELIANTHEMUM SCOPARIUM, *Nutt. in Torr. & Gray, Fl.* 1, *p.* 152. San Pasqual, California; November 11.

VIOLACEÆ.

VIOLA PEDUNCULATA, *Torr. & Gray, l. c.; Torr. Bot. Whippl., p.* 68. Partridge creek; April 20. A shorter peduncled form; to be united with V. Nuttallii, *Pursh. &c.*

FRANKENIACEÆ.

FRANKENIA GRANDIFOLIA, *Cham. & Schlecht.; Torr. & Gray, l. c.* San Diego, California; November 6.

CARYOPHYLLACEÆ.

SILENE DRUMMONDII, *Hook, Fl. Bor.-Amer.* 1, *p.* 89. Sitgreaves's Pass; March 24.

ARENARIA FENDLERI, *Gray, Pl. Fendl., p.* 13; *Torr. Bot. Whippl., p.* 69. Oraybe; May 13.

ARENARIA NURDIFOLIA, *Ledeb. Fl. Alt., Hook. Fl. Bor.-Amer.* 1, *t.* 32. Cedar creek; Camp 79; April 24.

PORTULACACEÆ.

PORTULACCA RETUSA, *Engelm. Plant. Lindh. in Bost. Jour. Nat. Hist. VI., p.* 154. Mojave valley and Colorado region; March, in flower and fruit; small specimens with stems two inches long.

CLAYTONIA PERFOLIATA, *Donn.* San Diego, California; Long valley; Camp 62; March 25; very widely distributed.

CLAYTONIA LANCEOLATA, *Pursh. Fl.* 1, *p.* 175, *t.* 3. Cedar creek; Camp 79; April 24. The imperfect specimen, like others from the Rocky mountains, has the appearance of C. Caroliniana, and probably belongs to that species.

CALYPTRIDIUM MONANDRUM, *Nutt. in Torr. & Gray, Fl.* 1, *p.* 198. Camp 62; Long valley; March 26. Accords throughout with Nuttall's character of the plant. Calindrinia monandra DC. is not a congener of it.

SESUVIUM PORTULACCASTRUM, *Linn.;* var. SESSILE. Explorer's Pass; Lower Colorado; January 13.

LEWISIA REDIVIVA, *Pursh, Torr. & Gray, Flor.* 1, *p.* 677. Partridge creek; April 24. Flowers white, veined with pink, beautiful.

MALVACEÆ.

MALVASTRUM EXILE, (sp. nov.;) stellato-puberulum, viride; caulibus e radice annua diffusis, 2–6-pollicaribus, lateralibus inferne nudis; foliis rotundatis 5-lobis semipollicaribus, lobis obtusissimis parce crenato-incisis; floribus axillaribus parvis bibracteolatis; sepalis lanceolato-subulatis corollam albam subæquantibus; carpellis muticis reniformi-circinatis evalvibus dorso transversim grosse rugosis ad ventrem tenuem demum ruptis.

On sandy surfaces of the Colorado desert, near the river; Pyramid cañon; March 15. A small inconspicuous but well-marked species; a winter annual, flowering from the crown or the axils of the subradical leaves, and also along the upper part of the ascending stems or branches; the earlier peduncles about an inch long in fruit, the upper ones much shorter. Bractlets linear setaceous, opposite, just below the flower. Calyx deeply 5 parted. Corolla "white," about 3 lines long. Anthers not very numerous, on a short column. Styles about 12 or 15; stigmas capitate. Carpels in fruit of a cellular chartaceous texture, glabrous, rugose on the back with 10 or 12 salient and narrow transverse lines or ridges, not dehiscent, but the more delicate and fragile ventral portion gives way for the escape of the seed. The seed is that of the genus, the radicle inferior.

MALVASTRUM MONROANUM, *Gray, Pl. Fendl.,* p. 21.

Malva Monroana, *Dougl. in Bot. Reg.,* t. 1306.

M. fasciculata, *Nutt. in Torr. & Gray, Flor.* 1, *p.* 225.

Malvastrum Thurberi, *Gray, Pl. Thurb.*

M. Marrubioides, *Durand, Pl. Heerm.* Sitgreaves's Pass; March 24.

SIDA HEDERACEA, *Torr. in Pl. Fendl. l. c.* Fort Yuma to Big Cañon; January to March.

SPHÆRALCEA EMORYI, *Torr. l. c., Gray, Pl. Wright.* 1, *p.* 21. Big Cañon of the Colorado; March 7.

SPHÆRALCEA INCANA, *Torr. l. c.,* Purple Hills; January 15.

Also var. OBLONGIFOLIA, *Gray, Pl. Wright.* Riverside mountain; February 28.

LINACEÆ.

LINUM PERENNE, *Linn.; Torr. & Gray, Flor.* 1, *p.* 204. Common on the Colorado and on the table-lands of New Mexico.

LINUM ARISTATUM, *Englm. in Mem. Wisl. & Pl. Wright.* 1, *p.* 25. Sand hills of the Colorado; May 4, just coming into flower. Covero, May 29.

GERANIACEÆ.

ERODIUM CICUTARIUM, *L'Herit.* Sitgreaves's Pass; March 24. Very abundant over all the region east of the Colorado.

ERODIUM MACROPHYLLUM, *Hook. & Arn. Bot. Beech.,* p. 227. Yampai valley and alluvial bottoms of the Colorado; March 1.

All with small leaves. The name is not very appropriate; and the species must include E. Texanum, *Gray, Gen. Hl. t.* 150.

ZYGOPHYLLACEÆ.

LARREA MEXICANA, *Morie; Gray, Pl. Wright.* 1, *p.* 28. Colorado Desert. "Petals twisted so as to stand vertically."

FAGONIA CALIFORNICA, *Benth. Voy. Sulph., p.* 10. Barrier Islands, &c.; January 16.

RUTACEÆ.

THAMNOSMA MONTANA, *Torr. in Frem. Rep. & in Bot. Whippl., p.* 27, *t.* 3. Cañon of Diamond river; shrubby, in tufts.

ANACARDIACEÆ.

STYPHONIA INTEGRIFOLIA, *Nutt. in Torr. & Gray, Fl.* 1, *p.* 220. San Diego to the eastern slope of the mountains. A spreading shrub, 10 feet high, with very tough wood and pinkish-white, rather pretty flowers.

RHUS TRILOBATA, *Nutt. l. c.* Camp 66 and Peach Orchard Spring, Moqui country; May 16. Common on table-lands of New Mexico.

VITACEÆ.

VITIS RUPESTRIS, *Scheele; Gray, Pl. Wright.* 2, *p.* 27. Hay Camp, west of Covero, New Mexico; May 28.

RHAMNACEÆ.

CEANOTHUS CUNEATUS, *Nutt. in Torr. & Gray, l. c.; Torr. Bot. Whippl., p.* 75. Yampai valley; March 28.

POLYGALACEÆ.

POLYGALA ALBA, *Nutt.; Gray, Pl. Wright.* 1, *p.* 28. Rio Puerco, New Mexico; May 29.

LEGUMINOSÆ.

LUPINUS CONCINNUS, *Agardh.; Torr. & Gray, Fl.* 1, *p.* 372. Hill sides, Yampai valley; March 28.

LUPINUS PUSILLUS, *Pursh.; Torr. & Gray, l. c.* Crossing of Little Colorado; May 3.

LUPINUS HIRSUTISSIMUS, *Benth.; Torr. & Gray, l. c.* Conglomerate Bluffs to Black Cañon, Colorado; January 15 to March 7.

LUPINUS SPARSIFLORUS, *Benth. Pl. Hartw., p.* 303. Sandy hills, Pyramid Cañon, on Colorado; February 17.

PSORALEA LANCEOLATA, *Pursh.; Torr. & Gray, Fl.* 1, *p.* 299. Alluvial banks of the Little Colorado; May 5.

HOSACKIA SCOPARIA, *Nutt. in Torr. & Gray, Fl.* 1, *p.* 325. Only a form of H. juncea. San Luis Obispo, California; November 1.

HOSACKIA ARGOPHYLLA, *Gray, Pl. Thurb., p.* 316. Laguna, California. Without flowers or fruit; November 15.

HOSACKIA PUBERULA, *Benth. Pl. Hartw., p.* 305; *Torr. Bot. Whippl., p.* 79. Sitgreaves's Pass; March 24. A form of the species which had already been gathered in the same region by Mr. Thurber and Dr. Bigelow.

HOSACKIA MARITIMA, *Nutt. in Torr. & Gray, l. c.* Mouth of the Colorado to Black Cañon.

TRIFOLIUM LONGIPES, *Nutt.*; var. pygmæum: digitate; pedunculo folia nunc longe nunc vix superante; foliolis ovalibus oblongisve $\frac{1}{4}$–$\frac{1}{2}$-pollicaribus. Base of Bill Williams's mountain; April 25.

TRIFOLIUM SUBCAULESCENS, (sp. nov.;) caespitosum, nanum, cinereo pubescens, foliorum pagina superiore excepta; stipulis ovatis dentatis; foliolis obovatis oblongiusve rigidulis striato-venosis rigido-denticulatis sæpius mucronatis nec retusis pedunculis petiolos radicales haud superantibus; capitulo nudo pluri floro; calycis villosi, dentibus lanceolato subulatis tubo sub-longioribus corolla alba dimidio brevioribus.

In pine forests of high table-lands near Fort Defiance; May 22. Flowering stems or scapes 2 or 3 inches high, usually 1–2-leaved below, perhaps elongating and more leafy later in the season. Radical stipules scarious or membranaceous; the cauline ones smaller and more foliaceous, or rigid, like the leaflets. The latter are half an inch or an inch in length. very strongly veined on both surfaces, the upper quite glabrous. Head 12–15-flowered; the flowers half an inch long, resembling those of T. longipes, except as to the calyx, the teeth of which are much broader and shorter.

DALEA SPINOSA, *Gray, Pl. Thurb.*, p. 315. On the Colorado, Carisso creek, &c. "Tree sometimes 20 feet high." Young plants bear some thick phyllodia-like leaves, an inch or two in length.

DALEA EMORYI, *Gray, l. c.* Colorado desert, forming low tufts, 2 or 3 feet high.

DALEA FORMOSA, *Torr. in Ann. Lyc. N. Y.* 2, *p.* 78, *and in Emory, Rep. t.* 1. Banks of the Puerco, New Mexico; May 30.

DALEA MOLLIS, *Benth.;* var. NEO MEXICANA, *Gray, Pl. Wright.* 1, *p.* 47. Sandy arroyos along Colorado; January 25.

ASTRAGALUS NUTTALLIANUS, *DC.; Torr. & Gray, Fl.* 1, *p.* 334. Jesup Rapids; February 20. Further west than this species has been found before, but it is common in New Mexico.

ASTRAGALUS MISSOURIENSIS, *Nutt,; Torr. & Gray, l. c.* Yampai valley to Little Colorado; April.

ASTRAGALUS DIPHYSUS, *Gray, Pl. Fendl.*, *p.* 34. Banks of Little Colorado; May 5. And var. ALBIFLORUS, *Gray, l. c.* Peach Orchard Spring, Moqui country, flowers yellowish-white.

ASTRAGALUS SUCCUMBENS, *Dougl. in Hook. Fl. Bor.-Amer.* 1, *p.* 151? Leroux's Spring; April 28. In flower only.

ASTRAGALUS (PHACA) FILIFOLIUS, *Gray in Stevens's Pacific R. R. incd. cum. i. e.*
Phaca longifolia, *Nutt. in Torr. & Gray. Fl.* 1, *p.* 346.
Psoralea longifolia, *Pursh.* Orobus longifolius, *Nutt. Gen.* Sandy hills, Moqui villages, New Mexico; May 14. "Flowers greenish-yellow, or greenish-purple, becoming yellow. Pod mottled crimson and yellow."

ASTRAGALUS (PHACA) TRIFLORUS, *Gray. Pl. Wright.* 2, *p.* 45. Phaca triflora, *DC.* Banks of Little Colorado. Peduncles often many-flowered.

ASTRAGALUS (PHACA) FENDLERI, *Gray, Pl. Fendl.*, *p.* 36, *and Pl. Wright.* 2, *p.* 44. Fort Defiance; May 23. A small form.

ASTRAGALUS (PHACA) CHAMÆLEUCE.
Phaca pygmæa, *Nutt. in Torr. & Gray, Fl.* 1, *p.* 349. Common on high table-lands from Colorado to Rio Grande. In flower only. There is a prior A. pygmæus.

LATHYRUS POLYMORPHUS, *Nutt.; Torr & Gray, Fl.* 1, *p.* 277. Banks of Colorado Chiquito, New Mexico; May 1. Also a narrow leaved variety at The Oaks, California.

SOPHORA STENOPHYLLA, (sp. nov.;) herbacea, nana, pube villoso sericea undique incana; caulibus e radice perenni ramosis; foliis impari pinnatis sessilibus, foliolis 5–9 linearibus vachi brevi paullo latioribus, parvi infimo cauli adproximato stipulas mentionte; racemo spicato pluri-floro; calycis dentibus subulatis tubo campanulato subdimidio brevioribus; corolla læte cærulea, vexillo integro, carinæ petalis obtusissimis; staminibus omnino liberis. Oryabe, (Moqui village;) May 13. On sandy hills.

An evident and interesting congener of SOPHORA (PSEUDO-SOPHORA) SERICEA, *Nutt.;* a span high, the short leaves with crowded leaflets, and the raceme of showy blue flowers. giving the plant somewhat the appearance of a dwarf lupine. Leaflets about half an inch in length. Pedicels shorter than the calyx. Flowers almost an inch long, crowded. Ovary silky, many ovuled. Fruit not seen.

SOPHORA SERICEA, *Nutt.; Torr. & Gray, Fl.* 1, *p.* 390. Banks of Colorado Chiquito, New Mexico; May 1.

THERMOPSIS FABACEA, *DC.; Gray in Mem. Amer. Acad.* 6, *p.* . Leroux's Spring; April 27. In bloom.

OLNEYA TESOTA, *Gray, Pl. Thurb.*, *p.* 328; *Torr. Bot. Whippl.*, *p.* 82. Dry arroyos of the Colorado. A spreading tree 20–25 feet high.

HOFFMANSEGGIA JAMESII, *Torr. & Gray, Fl.* 1, *p.* 393; *Gray, Pl. Wright.* 1, *p.* 54. Rio Grande, New Mexico; June 1.

PARKINSONIA MICROPHYLLA, *Torr. in Bot. Whippl.*, *p.* 82, *and in Mex. Bound. Surv.*, *p.* . Purple Hill Pass to Big Cañon, Colorado, on rocky hills. Shrub 5 to 10 feet high, with sparse foliage, and no flowers nor fruit in January.

CERCIDIUM FLORIDUM, *Benth. in Pl. Wright.* 1, *p.* 58. Fort Yuma and Bill Williams's Fork ; common on Lower Colorado; a small handsome tree with very green bark, called *palo verde.*

ALGAROBIA GLANDERLORA, *Torr. & Gray, Fl. l. c. &c.* Riverside mountain on the Colorado; common everywhere below Black Cañon; ' *Mezquite.''*

ACACIA GREGGII, or COULTERI, *Gray, Pl. Wright.* Common on the Colorado; up as far as the Mojave valley.

STROMBOCARPA PUBESCENS, *Gray, Pl. Wright.*, *p.* 60, *Torr. P. R. R., Vol.* 5, *p.* 360, *t.* 4; with the last called *tornilla* or screwbean.

ROSACEÆ.

SPIRÆA CÆSPITOSA, *Nutt. in Torr. & Gray, Fl.* 1, *p.* 418. In mats on rocks; high table-lands; Camp 70; April 10.

COLEOGYNE RAMOSISSIMA, *Torr. Pl. Fremont.*, *p.* 8, *t.* 4. Sitgreaves's Pass; March 24. A stiff-branched, almost spiny shrub. 3 feet high, with little foliage and few flowers; flowers yellow. The scanty specimens of this remarkable plant furnish nothing to add to the excellent published description and figure.

EMPLECTROCLADUS FASCICULATUS, *Torr. l. c.*, *p.* 10, *t.* 5. Long Valley; Camp 62; March 26. Good specimens, confirming the character and figure; the fruit still unknown.

POTENTILLA RIVALIS, *Nutt. in Torr. & Gray, Fl.* 1, *p.* 437. Jesup Rapids; February 20.

COWANIA MEXICANA, *Don; Gray, Pl. Wright.* 2, *p.* 55. Common from Yampai creek to the Rio Grande, New Mexico; in flower April 5; flower and fruit May 25.

PURSHIA TRIDENTATA *DC.; Hook. Fl. Bor.-Am.* 1, *p.* 170, *t.* 58. Moqui villages; May 15.

GEUM (SIEVERSIA) TRIFLORUM, *Pursh.; Torr. & Gray, Fl.* 1, *p.* 423. Base of Bill Williams's mountain; April 28. "A very pretty plant when growing; flowers pendulous, rose color."

AMELANCHIER CANADENSIS, var. ALNIFOLIA, *Torr. & Gray, Fl.* 1, *p.* 473. Peach Orchard Spring, New Mexico; May 18.

ONAGARACEÆ.

ŒNOTHERA BIENNIS, *Linn.* San Diego, California, to Laguna, New Mexico.

ŒNOTHERA ALBICAULIS *Nutt.; Gray, Pl. Wright.* 1, *p.* 69. Sandy banks of the Colorado generally; May 1–20. The smooth, entire-leaved form. R. pallida, *Dougl.*

ŒNOTHERA (PACHYLOPHIS) EXIMIA, *Gray, Pl. Fendl.*, *p.* 45. Yampai valley; and from Yampai valley to Santa Fé; flowers 3 in. in diameter, pure white; no fruit.

ŒNOTHERA PRIMIVERIS, *Gray, Pl. Wright.* 2, *p.* 58. Yampai valley to Little Colorado; April. Various forms with entire and pinnately-parted leaves.

ŒNOTHERA (CHYLISMA) BREVIPES, *Gray in Torr. Bot. Whippl.*, *p.* 86. Common all along the Colorado in February and March.

ŒNOTHERA (CHYLISMA) CLAVÆFORMIS, *Torr. in Frem. Rep. & Bot. Whippl. l. c.* Common on gravel hills, &c., upper part of the Colorado, in February and March.

ŒNOTHERA (SPHÆROSTIGMA) GAURÆFLORA, *Torr. & Gray, Fl.* 1, *p.* 510. Riverside mountain, on Colorado.

These specimens, like one of Schott's from the Gila, are complete, and allow the cauline leaves, &c., to be described. The petals are pale yellow, tinged with pink outside.

ŒNOTHERA DENTATA, *Cav.; Torr. & Gray, Fl.* 1, *p.* 510. Riverside mountain, on Colorado, January 28.

ŒNOTHERA CHAMÆNERIOIDES, *Gray, Pl. Wright.* 2, *p.* 58. Fort Defiance, New Mexico; May 23. Early; small specimens.

ŒNOTHERA CHEIRANTHIFOLIA, *Horvem.; Torr. & Gray, l. c.* San Diego, California; November 10.

ZAUSCHNERIA CALIFORNICA, *Presl. Rel. Hoenk.* 2, *t.* 52. San Diego and San Luis Obispo; November.

LOASACEÆ.

EUCNIDE BARTONIOIDES, *Zucc.; Gray, Pl. Lindh.* 2, *p.* 192. On ledges of rocks, head of Mojave valley. "Setæ irritating the skin like nettles."

MENTZELIA ALBICAULIS, *Torr. & Gray, Fl.* 1, *p.* 534. On gravelly surfaces, &c., along the Colorado. Common. Mojave valley; March 23.

MENTZELIA (BARTONIA) LÆVICAULIS, *Torr. & Gray, l. c.* Bartonia lævicaulis, *Dougl. in Hook. Fl., t.* 69. Riverside mountain; January 25.

CUCURBITACEÆ.

MEGARHIRA CALIFORNICA, *Torr. in* . Riverside mountain, and on the Colorado, to Black Cañon; March; in flower.

CUCURBITA PERENNIS, *Gray, Pl. Lind.* 2, *p.* 193. On Colorado everywhere, and thence to Rio Grande.

CUCURBITA DIGITATA, *Gray, Pl. Wright.* 2, *p.* 60. Along Lower Colorado.

CACTACEÆ. By Dr. Geo. Engelmann.

MAMILLARIA GRAHAMI, *Engelm. in Mex. Bound. Rep. II, p.* 7, *tab.* 6, *figs.* 1–8 ; *Synops. Cact. in Proc. Americ. Acad. Arts and Sciences, III, p.* 6. Common along the Colorado; in flower April 7; fruit of last year just ripe. In the M. B. Rep. the fruit is erroneously called a *small oval berry, probably green.* The specimens then at command had shrivelled and discolored fruit. Those now before me show that the berry is elongated, clavate, scarlet, three-quarters or even one inch long, with or without the remains of the flower. The seeds are absolutely the same as those of the El Paso plant.

MAMILLARIA PHELLOSPERMA, *Englm. l. c., p.* 6, *t.* 7; *Syn. Cact. p.* 6. Common with the last, and easily confounded with it by the casual observer; apparently more abundant westward, while the former prevails more eastward; generally simple, sometimes many-headed. Some of Dr. Newberry's specimens closely resemble the figure in M. B. R.; others have fewer, (30–35,) shorter, and stiffer spines, almost in three series, the 8–12 interior ones stout and purplish brown. One of the specimens before me has, in each bunch, three divergent, hooked, central spines.

ECHINOCACTUS WHIPPLEI, *Engelm. & Bigelow in Pacif. R. R. Rep. IV, Cactaceæ of Lieut. Whipple's Exped., p.* 28, *t.* 1 ; *Syn. Cact., p.* 15. In sandy soil on the Little Colorado, often half buried in sand, in the same region where Dr. Bigelow discovered this pretty species in 1853; in flower in the middle of May.

The specimens have thirteen compressed, interrupted ribs; the floriferous is contiguous to the spiniferous areola, not separated from it by the cylindric glands present in several allied species. After flowering the floriferous areola forms a groove two-thirds down the upper side of the tubercle, (or prominent part of the rib,) or even almost to its base. Number of radial spines, 7 to 11. The description of the flower, wanting heretofore, may be given thus:

Floribus versus apicem congestis virescenti, flavis pollicaribus; ovaris sepalis squamiformibus paucis (2–5) orbiculatis seu reniformibus munito; sepalis tubi 10–15 inferioribus ovatis, superioribus oblongis obtusis; petalis sub 8 oblongis mucronatis; infimo tubi parte intus nudo; filamentis tenuissimis numerosis; stylo exerto sursum clavato apice infundi buliformi in stigmata 5 brevissima erecta sue conniventia diviso.

The flowers are one inch long, greenish red, externally tinged with brown red; stigma green. The fruit remains unknown as yet; the large seed has been figured in the work mentioned.

ECHINOCACTUS LECONTEI, *Engelm. in M. B. R. II, p.* 23, *t.* 27, *& P. R. R. l. c., p.* 28, *t.* 2, *f.* 3–5 ; *Syn. Cact., p.* 18. In the Colorado valley; in flower in April. Specimens of 3–5 inches diameter have below eight, and upwards thirteen ribs; those of 9–12 inches show 19–21 ribs. The lowest bunches (those developed probably in the 3d or 4th year) have eight radial and one central spine, all annulated. The central one is curved, not hooked; one, or even three, of the lower radial ones are often hooked. The fully developed bunches consist of four central spines, the upper and lower one of which is quite flat, five or seven lower radial ones, never hooked, three upper ones, and 6–12 slender, bristly, radial spines. The ovary is covered with about thirty sepaloid scales, in the specimens examined, in $\frac{4}{11}$ or $\frac{5}{13}$ arrangement.

ECHINOCACTUS ? Young specimens, 3–5 inches high, of another evidently large species, were collected, with thirteen ribs—four central and five lower, stouter, and 3–6 upper slender radial spines, all annulated and curved. The plants, showing no indication of floriferous areolæ, must be undeveloped; they may possibly be young ones of *E. polycephalus*, or belong to species yet unknown to us.

ECHINOCACTUS VIRIDESCENS, *Nutt. in Torr. and Gray, Fl. I, p.* 554. *Engelm. in M. B. R. II, p.* 24, *t.* 29; *Syn. Cact., p.* 19. San Diego, California. 25–30 scales on yellow fruit. Seed as described in M. B. R., but the pits are much closer together than in fig. 6. c! The hooked acute cotyledons are bent over a rather copious albumen; similar to those of *E. Wislizeni*, t. 25, f. 4. e.

CEREUS FENDLERI, *Engelm. in Plant. Fendl. in Mem. Am. Acad.* 1848, *p.* 51, *M. B. R. II, p.* 33, *t.* 51–53; *Syn. Cact., p.* 25. Coveras, New Mexico, and from Laguna to Santa Fé; fl. April.

CEREUS PHOENICEUS.—*Engelm. P. R. R. l. c., p.* 34, *t.* 4, *f.* 1; *Syn. Cact., p.* 28; *Echinocereus coccineus, Engelm. in Wisliz. Rep. N. Mex. note* 9.

This is *Mamillaria aggregata*, Emory's Report, 1848, and the "*Aggregated Cactus*" of the explorers of the western parts of New Mexico and the Gila regions. It grows in large dense masses, often 100 or 200 heads from a single base, the whole often of the shape and size of a bushel basket, generally on apparently naked rocks; in the proper season densely covered with beautiful crimson flowers. It was found from Camp 64 to Camp 78 (Yampai valley to Partridge creek) in flower in April. The flowers collected are less than 2 inches long, much more densely covered with bristle-bearing sepals than the next species, and with only 5 stigmata; the naked space in the base of the tube is nearly four lines long. The fruit and seed of this common plant, which has now been known to science for twelve years, still remains unknown, and living plants are as yet extremely scarce.

CEREUS CONOIDEUS, *Engelm. & Bigelow, l. c., p.* 35, *t.* 4, *f.* 4–5; *Syn. Cact., p.* 28. Camp 96. (Oryabe gardens, Moqui country.)

Flowering in May.   So nearly allied to the last that we considered it a form or sub-species of it. Dr. Newberry has now obtained the flowers.   His specimen has fewer spines than Dr. Bigelow's original ones; 8 or 9 radial ones, about 1 inch long, and 1 or 2 central angulate ones, 1½–2 inches long; all whitish and somewhat translucent. They resemble the spines of *C. enneacanthus*, but the flowers are vastly different, being open day and night, and not diurnal, as those of the species just mentioned.

Floribus magnis diametro transversali duplo longioribus coccineis; ovario parvo squamis sepaloideis 8–12 triangulatis in axilla lanam albam et aculeolos 3–5 graciles gerentibus munito; tubo sensim ampliato sepalis fere 20 lanceolatis aculeigeris instructo; sepalis superioribus sub 8 oblongis obtusis; petalis 10–13 spatulatis obtusis; stamnibus numerosissimus et stigmatibus sub 9 vix exertis petala subacquantibus.

The flowers are 3½–4 inches long and 1½–2 inches in diameter; the slender spines in the axills of the upper sepals are 6–8 lines in length, the stigmas, as in the whole subgenus *Echinocereus*, velvety green.

OPUNTIA BASILARIS, *Engelm. & Bigelow, l. c., p.* 43, *t.* 13, *f.* 1–5, *t.* 23, *f.* 14; *Syn. Cact.*, *p.* 42.

Abundant on the Colorado from Fort Yuma to the Great cañon, and one of the most common species in the Colorado valley and desert.   Dr. Newberry confirms the description before given of the peculiar growth of this species; a large number ot joints of different shape obovate, obcordate, emarginate, or elongate, and almost oblanceolate, issue from nearly the same base, and are covered in spring (March and April) with a profusion of rose-colored or purplish flowers, often 150 on one plant.   The ovary is described as somewhat tuberculate but sometimes almost smooth.   The fruit is dry when ripe; seed large and thick, as in the figure above cited.

OPUNTIA HYSTRICINA, *E. & B. l. c., p.* 54, *t.* 15, *f.* 5–7, *t.* 23, *p.* 15; *Syn. Cact., p.* 43. Common from the Colorado to the Rio Grande.   The form collected by Dr. Newberry, and named in his notes "*hairy-spined Opuntia,*" has fewer, shorter, and usually straighter spines than the specimens figured and described in Lieut. Whipple's report; the larger ones are also angular and erect, and by these characters distinguished from the nearly allied *Opuntia Missouriensis*.   However, Mr. Fendler's specimens from Santa Fé, (the flowers of which were inadvertently distributed with No. 276, *O. phœacantha*, but are easily distinguished by the spinulose ovary,) seem to be intermediate between the two, and may make it necessary to unite them.

Dr. Newberry's specimens have 1–5 larger spines, 1–1¾ inches long, nearly erect, and about 5 smaller deflexed ones below, with a few very small ones above.   Flower nearly two inches in diameter, ovary with 20–25 tomentose pulvilli, each with a short slender leaf, (sepal,) less than one line long, and 5–12 bristly spines of very different lengths : the interior sepals are obovate cuspidate petals, obcordate, orange yellow; 5 erect green stigmata, forming a compact head.

OPUNTIA ECHINOCARPA, *E. & B. l. c., p.* 40, *t.* 18, *f.* 5–10, *t.* 24, *f.* 8; *M. B. Rep. II, p.* 56. *Syn. Cact., p.* 49.   In the Mojave valley, and common on the Colorado; begins to flower end of March.   The specimens obtained are low, with many short branches, much of the habit of the clavate *Opuntiæ*, but distinguished from them by the sheathed spines and the reticulated wood peculiar to the cylindroid *Opuntiæ*.   The ovary is 6–8 lines long, with about 20 pulvilli bearing thick ovate leaves, abruptly narrowed into a subulate point, 1–2 lines long, and in their axils in a white tomentum, 6 or 8 sheathed spines, the large ones 6–8 lines long.   The greenish yellow flower when fully open is 1½ inches wide; petals spatulate, rounded or emarginate, denticulate, the exterior ones mucronate ; stigmata 5–6, large and thick, and apparently yellow.

OPUNTIA ARBORESCENS, *Engelm. in Wislezen. Rep. N. Mex. note 5, M. B. Rep. II, p.* 58, *t.* 75, *f.* 16–17; *P. R. Rep. IV., t.* 17, *f.* 5–6, *t.* 18, *f.* 4, *t.* 24, *f.* 12; *Syn. Cact., p.* 51. Common in Western New Mexico.

CROSSULACEÆ.

RIBES CEREUM. *Dougl.; Torr. & Gray, Fl.* 1, *p.* 551. Banks of Yampai creek, (Camp 65,) April 5; Peach Orchard Spring, and Western New Mexico generally.

RIBES AUREUM, *Pursh.; Torr. & Gray, l. c.*

SAXIFRAGACEÆ.

LITHOPHRAGMA (LITHOPHRAGMELLA) CYMBALARIA, *Torr. & Gray, Fl.* 1, *p.* 585. Saxifraga Californica. *Nutt.* San Diego, California; Nov. 10. Without the radical leaf; petals white, veined with purple.

LITHOPHRAGMA PARVIFLORA, *Nutt. in Torr. & Gray, l. c.* Cedar creek; April 24. Petals pale pink.

FENDLERA RUPICOLA, *Engelm. & Gray, Pl. Wright.* 1, *p.* 77, *t.* 5. Moqui country, Western New Mexico, May 18, in blossom. "Flowers in appearance and fragrance not unlike Philadelphus."

CANOTIA HOLACANTHA, *Torr. in Bot. Whippl., p.* 68. Cerbat mountains; shrub or small tree 15 feet in height; April 1. The specimens exhibit only the fruit of the former year. The flowers of this remarkable shrub are still unknown. The fruit plainly exhibits a thin sarcocarp.

UMBELLIFERÆ.

BOWLESIA LOBATA, *Ruiz. & Pav.* Black Mountains, Sitgreaves's Pass; March 23.

LEPTOTÆNIA DISSECTA, *Nutt. in Torr. & Gray Fl.* 1, *p.* 630? Yampai valley; March 25. Too young and poor for determination.

PENCEDANUM FŒNICULACEUM, *Nutt. l. c., p.* 627. Yampai valley; March 29; in flower.

THASPIUM MONTANUM, *Gray, Pl. Fendl., p.* 57. Fort Defiance, New Mexico; May 23; in flower.

CYMOPTERUS GLOMERATUS, *DC.; Torr. & Gray, Fl.* 1, *p.* 623. Cedar creek; April 24. Petals white; stamens purple. Young fruit oblong; several of the wings more or less abortive.

CYMOPTERUS MONTANUS, *Nutt. in Torr. & Gray, l. c.; Gray, Pl. Fendl., p.* 56, *and var.* PURPURASCEUS. Stony hill-sides. Yampai valley (Camp 64; March 28) to San Francisco mountain, New Mexico. Ivolucre rather obsolete or short and truncate; involucels and flowers deep purple or the former greenish tinged with purple. Oryabe, New Mexico. Involucre like the involucels; both white as if petaloid, with green midribs. Flowers either white or pink in the same specimen.

CYMOPTERUS TEREBINTHINUS, *Torr. & Gray, l. c.* Seseli terebinthinum, *Hook. Fl. Bor.-Amer.* 1., *p.* 266, *t.* 95. Moqui country; May 8; in flower; petals white.

CAPRIFOLIACEÆ.

SAMBUCUS GLAUCA, *Nutt. in Torr. & Gray, Fl.* 2, *p.* 13. San Diego, California; November 10; often 20 feet high.

RUBIACEÆ.

GALIUM APARINE, *Linn?* Specimens too young, from Sitgreaves's Pass. Black mountains; March 24.

GALIUM FENDLERI? *Gray, Pl. Fendl., p.* 60? Yampai basin; April 3; too imperfect for determination.

COMPOSITÆ.

HOFMEISTERIA PLURISETA, *Gray in Torr., Pl. Whippl., p.* 96, *t.* 9. Cañons of the Colorado; February and April.

CARPHEPHORUS JUNCEUS, *Benth. Bot. Voy. Sulph.*, *p.* 21. Purple Hills; January 14.

PEUCEPHYLLUM SCHOTTII, *Gray in Bot. Mex. Bound.* 2, *p.* 74. Purple Hills; January 15; shrub three feet high. Too poor to determine properly.

BRICKELLIA CALIFORNICA, *Gray, Pl. Fendl.*, *p.* 64, *and Pl. Wright.* 1, *p.* 85. "The Oaks," near San Felipe, California.

CORETHROGYNE FILAGINIFOLIA, *Nutt. in Torr. & Gray, Fl.; Gray in Bot. Mex. Bound. Surv.* 2, *p.* 76. Santa Isabel to San Felipe, California. Includes C. tomentella, &c.

ASTER CHILENSIS, *Nees.* var. *Torr. & Gray, l. c.*, *p.* 112. San Luis Obispo, California; November 1.

DIPLOPAPPUS ERICOIDES, *Torr. & Gray, l. c.*, *p.* 182. Banks of Little Colorado; May 1.

ERIGERON DIVERGENS, *Torr. & Gray, l. c.;* and var. CINEREUM, *Gray, Pl. Wright.* 1, *p.* 91. Black mountains to Little Colorado; April.

EREMIASTRUM BELLIDOIDES, *Gray, Pl. Thurb.*, *p.* 320, *and in Bot. Whippl.*, *p.* 98. *Gray in Pacific Railroad Exped.* 5, *p.* 361, *t.* 6. Riverside mountain on the Colorado; January 25. Flowers white, handsome. Fruit is still a desideratum.

TOWNSENDIA SERICEA, *Hook. Fl. Bor. Nu.* 2, *p.* 16, *t.* 119. In meadows at the base of Bill Williams's mountain; April 28.

TOWNSENDIA STRIGOSA, *Nutt.; Torr. & Gray, Fl.* 2, *p.* 186; *Gray, Pl. Fendl.*, *p.* 70; May 8. Banks of Little Colorado, near crossing.

TOWNSENDIA (MEGALASTRUM) TORTIFOLIA, Aplopappus tortifolius, *Gray in Jour. Bost. Soc. Nat. Hist.* 1845. Sitgreaves's Pass; March 24: "In tufts, with yucca and cacti. Stems woody at the base. Flowers pale purple, handsome." So this plant, rediscovered by Dr. Newberry, proves not to have yellow rays, and is therefore no aplopappus. It has a closely related congener in TOWNSENDIA (MEGALASTRUM) WRIGHTII, *Gray in Bot. Mex. Bound. Surv.*, *p.* 78, which was doubtfully appended to Aster in *Pl. Wright.* 2, *p.* 75.

GUTIERREZIA EUTHAMIÆ, *Torr. & Gray, Fl.* 2, *p.* 123. Warner's Ranch, California; November. Same as the plant on the eastern side of the Rocky mountains.

APLOPAPPUS SPINULOSUS, *DC.; Torr. & Gray, l. c.* Yampai valley, &c. Also mouth of Diamond river. The latter very large-flowered.

APLOPAPPUS GRACILE, var. DENUDATUS, *Gray, Pl. Wright.* 1, *p.* 98. Bill Williams's Fork; February 1.

APLOPAPPUS (STENOTUS, *Nutt.*) ARMERIOIDES. Stenotus armerioides, *Nutt.; Torr. & Gray, l. c.* Oryabe, New Mexico, on rocky hills in tufts; May 13. Fine specimens, in flower, of this interesting plant; the same as Nuttall's. Involucre half an inch in length, the broad and coriaceous scales terminated by abrubt and obtuse greenish tips, as in Gutierrezia.

LINOSYRIS (APLODISCUS) MENZIESII, *Gray, Pl. Wright.* 1, *p.* 97, *adn.* Aplopappus (aplodiscus) Menziesii, Torr. and Gray. San Felipe, California; November 17. A slender variety.

SOLIDAGO CALIFORNICA, *Nutt.; Torr. & Gray, l. c.*, *p.* 203. Santa Isabel, California; November 16.

CHRYSOPSIS VILLOSA, *Nutt.* var. C. echioides, *Benth. Bot. Voy. Sulph.* San Diego, California; November 10.

PERITYLE NUDA, *Torr. in Bot. Whipple*, *p.* 100, *and Mex. Bound. Survey*, *p.* 82. On the banks of the Colorado; January 27, &c. "The earliest spring flowers. Rays white, disk yellow."

BACCHARIS CŒRULESCENS, *DC. Prodr.* 5, *p.* 402; *Gray in Mex. Bound. Surv.*, *p.* 83. San Diego, California, to Black cañon. A narrow-leaved variety.

BACCHARIS SALICINNA, *Torr. & Gray, Fl.* 2, *p.* 258. Carisso creek, Colorado, &c.; forming thickets. Runs, perhaps, into B. pilularis.

TESSARIA BOREALIS, *Gray, Pl. Fendl.*, *p.* 75, *and Pl. Wright.* 1, *p.* 102. Vallecito, and along banks of Colorado for 500 miles from mouth.

STYLOCLINE MICROPOIDES, *Gray, Pl. Wright.* 2, *p.* 84. Riverside mountains, Colorado of California; January 25.

HYMENOCLEA SALSOLA, *Torr. & Gray in Bost. Jour. Nat. Hist.* 1845, *and Pl. Fendl., p.* 79; *Torr. Pl. Frém., t.* 8. Fort Yuma to Black Cañon in desert arroyos; February and March. Scanty specimens of this interesting plant, but sufficient to confirm the characters of the species. It is said to be a shrub, two to four feet high, with yellow flowers.

HYMENOCLEA MONOGYRA, *Torr. & Gray, l. c.* Near San Diego, California; November 10. Further west than this species was before known to occur.

FRANSERIA DUMOSA, *Gray in Frém.* 2d *Rep., p.* 316. Desert surfaces along the Colorado; Jesup rapids; March 20.

FRANSERIA DELTOIDEA, *Torr. in Pl. Frém., and Bot. Mex. Bound. Surv., p.* 87. Long valley and Yampai basin; March 24–28. A fragment apparently of this species. There are also fragments of another species, the flowers undeveloped—perhaps of *F. artemisioïdes.*

ZINNIA (DIPLOTHRIX) GRANDIFLORA, *Nutt.; Gray, Pl. Wright.* 1, *p.* 105. A form with the lower leaves more elongated and soft tomentose. Yampai basin; March 29.

EUCELIA CALIFORNICA, *Nutt.; Torr. & Gray, Fl.* 2, *p.* 217. San Diego, California; November. Spreading, suffruticose, three or four feet high.

EUCELIA NIVEA, *Benth. Bot. Voy. Sulph., p.* 27. Mountains and desert places from San Diego to the Colorado, Riverside mountain, &c. A variable species, mostly with alternate leaves, and probably embracing E. conspersa, *Benth.,* and E. farinosa, *Gray.*

SIRUSIA (GERŒA) CANESCENS, *Gray, Pl. Fendl., p.* 85, *and Bot. Mex. Bound. Surv., p.* 89. Along the Colorado and eastward.

SIRUSIA (GERŒA) FRUTESCENS, *Gray in Bot. Mex. Bound. Surv., p.* 89. Jesup rapids; February 18. Two of the specimens are furnished with rather large, yellow rays. "The plant is a shrub, three feet high."

VIGUIERA LACINIATA, *Gray, l. c., p.* —. Near San Diego, California; in tufts a foot or more in height.

LIPTOSYNE DOUGLASII, *DC.; Torr. & Gray, Fl.* 2, *p.* 355. Sitgreaves's Pass; March 24. The (immature) achenia have a thin and broad wing.

POROPHYLLUM GREGGII, *Gray, Pl. Wright.* 1, *p.* 120, *and in Mex. Bound. Surv., p.* 94. Rocky arroyos along the Colorado.

HYMENOTHERUM (ACIPHYLLŒA) ACEROSUM, *Gray, Pl. Wright.* 1, *p.* 115. Hay Camp, New Mexico; May 27.

GAILLARDIA PINNATIFIDA, *Torr. in Ann. Lyc. New York,* 2, *p.* 214. Banks of Little Colorado, New Mexico; May 1.

GAILLARDIA PULCHELLA, *Fong.; Torr. & Gray, Fl.* 2, *p.* 366. Rio Grande, near Albuquerque, New Mexico.

PALAFOXIA LINEARIS, *Lag.; DC. Prodr.* 5, *p.* 124; *Gray in Mex. Bound. Survey, p.* 94. Sand-hills and beaches of the Colorado. A somewhat hispid form of the species.

HYMENOPAPPUS LUTEUS, *Nutt.; Torr. & Gray, Fl.* 2, *p.* 373. Banks of Colorado Chiquito, &c.; May 3–8.

CHŒNACTIS STEVIOIDES, *Hook. & Arn.; Torr. & Gray, Fl.* 2, *p.* 371; *Gray, Pl. Wright.* 2, *p.* 94. Desert arroyos on the Colorado, and eastward into New Mexico. Flowers white. Foliage, &c., variable.

CHŒNACTIS DOUGLASII, *Hook. & Arn.;* var. ACHILLEŒFOLIA. C. achilleœfolia, *Hook. & Arn., &c.* Yampai valley; March 27. Flowers white. The two species of Hooker and Arnott are evidently to be combined.

BAHIA (ERIOPHYLLUM) LANATA, *Nutt.; Torr. & Gray, l. c.* Long valley; March 26.

BURRIELLIA (DICHŒTA) LANOSA, *Gray in Bot. Whippl., p.* 107. Sitgreaves's Pass; March 24.

SYNTRICHOPAPPUS FREMONTII, *Gray in Bot. Whippl.*, *p.* 106, *t.* 15. Sitgreaves's Pass; March 24. An interesting re-discovery.

TRICHOPTILIUM INCISUM, *Gray in Bot. Mex. Bound. Surv.*, *p.* 97. On rocks. Jesup rapids; February 18. "Only one specimen found."

ACTINELLA SCAPOSA, *Nutt.; Torr. & Gray, Fl.* 2, *p.* 382. High mesa west of Little Colorado. Camp 70; April 10.

ACTINELLA TORREYANA, *Nutt., l. c.;* var. of A. acaulis? Cedar creek, New Mexico; April 26. Also a caulescent form, the flowering stems occasionally branched below. Tufts; on rocks. Moqui villages; May 14.

ACTINELLA BIGELOVII, *Gray, Pl. Wright.* 2, *p.* 96. Pine forests on high mesa west of Fort Defiance; May 20.

LAYIA NEO-MEXICANA, *Gray, Pl. Wright.* 2, *p.* 98. Sitgreaves's Pass, and on Colorado; March. This has a rudimentary pappus to the ray-flowers; otherwise it is not different, apparently, from L. glandulosa and L. heterotricha. Rays pure white.

HEMIZONIA RAMORISSIMA, *Benth. Bot. Voy. Sulph.*, *p.* 30. San Luis Obispo, California; November 1.

BAILEYA MULTIRADIATA, *Harv. & Gray, Pl. Fendl.*, *p.* 106; *Torr. in Emory, Rep.*, *p.* 144, *t.* 6. Yampai valley to Rio Puerco, New Mexico; April and May.

ARTEMISIA CANADENSIS, *Michx.; Gray, Pl. Wright.* 2, *p.* 98. Cedar creek, New Mexico; April and May.

ARTEMISIA DRACUNCULOIDES, *Pursh.; Torr. & Gray, Fl.* 2, *p.* 416? Santa Isabel, California; November 15. Apparently same as the plant of Missouri and New Mexico.

SENECIO LONGILOBUS, *Benth.; Gray, Pl. Wright., l. c.* Glabrous form. San Felipe, California; November 17.

SENECIO EXALTATUS, *Nutt.* Pine forests about Fort Defiance, New Mexico; May 20. A low form approaching some states of S. aureus. Another form from Leroux's Spring; April 27.

ANTENNARIA DIOICA, *Gœrtn.* Pine forests. Fort Defiance, New Mexico; May 20.

TRIXIS ANGUSTIFOLIA, *DC.? Gray, Pl. Wright.* 2, *p.* 102. Diamond river cañon; April 2.

ANISACOMA ACAULIS, *Gray in Jour. Bost. Soc. Nat. Hist.* 5, (1845,) *p. t.* 13. Long valley; March 28. This was known only from the specimen gathered long ago by Frémont near the same region. Dr. Newberry has now obtained one or two more specimens, in too early a state, but according well with the published character, except that the setæ of the pappus are plumose almost to the base.

RAFINESQUIA NEO-MEXICANA, *Gray, Pl. Wright.* 2, *p.* 103. Grand valley, on Colorado; January 20. "Flowers white."

CALAIS LINEARIFOLIA, *DC.; Gray, Pl. Wright.* 2, *p.* 102. Yampai basin; March 27.

CALYCOSERIS WRIGHTII, *Gray, Pl. Wright.* 2, *p.* 104, *t.* 14. Jesup rapids; February 18 and March 20. Some specimens nearly want the stipitate glands.

STEPHANOMERIA PANICULATA, *Benth. Bot. Voy. Sulph.*, *p.* . San Luis Obispo, California; November 1.

STEPHANOMERIA EXIGUA, *Nutt.; Torr. & Gray, l. c.* San Diego, California; November.

MALACOTHRIX FENDLERI, *Gray, Pl. Wright.* 2, *p.* 104. Sitgreaves's Pass; March 24. Moqui villages; May 14.

MALACOTHRIX (MALACOLEPIS) COULTERI, *Gray, Pl. Fendl.*, *p.* 113. Sitgreaves's Pass; March 24. "Flowers yellowish-white. Involucre silvery."

MACRORHYNCHUS TROXIMOIDES, *Torr. & Gray, Fl.* 2, *p.* 491. Fort Defiance, New Mexico; May 53.

PRIMULACEÆ.

ANDROSACE OCCIDENTALIS, *Nutt.* Cedar creek, New Mexico; March 24.

PLANTAGINACEÆ.

PLANTAGO PATAGONICA, var. GUAPHALIOIDES, *Gray in Bot. Whippl.*, *p.* 117. Desert surfaces on the Colorado generally.

PLUMBAGINACEÆ.

STATICE LIMONIUM, var. CALIFORNICA,
Statice Californica, *Briss. in DC. Prodr.* San Diego.

SCROPHULARIACEÆ.

MOHAVEA VISCIDA, *Gray in Bot. Whippl.*, *p.* 122. Riverside mountain; January 25. "Flowers handsome, straw-colored, specked with red." Very scantily gathered, and in blossom only, so as to throw no new light upon this rare and interesting plant, except that the limb of the expanded corolla appears as if nearly regular, the throat open, the lobes erose-denticulate at the obtuse summit, and abruptly cuspidate-pointed. But I have the good fortune to possess the fruit, from a specimen gathered long ago by Coulter (Calif. coll. No. 616.) The ovate capsule has thin membranaceous walls, and is two-celled, with a thick axile placenta, covered with closely packed, slightly ascending seeds. The dehiscence, though not by regular pores, is essentially that of the *Antirrhineæ*, so are the seeds, which resemble those of Antirrhinum cyathiferum, *Benth.*; only more oval, and the incurved wing larger. The internal structure is the same. So the genus belongs to Scrophulariaceæ Antirrhineæ.

MAURADNIA ANTIRRHINIFLORA, *Willd.; Benth. in DC. Prodr.* 10., *p.* 296. Cañon of Diamond river; April 6.

COLLINSIA PARVIFLORA, *Dougl. Benth.*, *l. c.* Cedar creek, New Mexico; April 24.

PENTSTEMON WRIGHTII, *Hook. Bot. Mag.*, *t.* 4601; *Gray in Mex. Bound. Surv.*, *p.* 113. Sandy hills, Moqui villages, New Mexico; May 15.

PENTSTEMON AMBIGUUS, *Torr.; Gray, l. c.* Banks of the Puerco, New Mexico; May 29.

PENTSTEMON SPECTABILIS, *Thurber in Bot. Whippl.*, *p.* 119. Yampai creek; March 31. In fruit.

PENTSTEMON CENTRANTHIFOLIUS *Benth. in DC. Prodr.* 10, *p.* 323. Warner's Rancho, to the Colorado Desert.

PENTSTEMON DOUGLASII, *Hook.; Benth. l. c.*, *p.* 321. Yampai creek, (Camp 65;) March 31. On rocky hills; in fruit only.

MIMULUS LUTEUS, *Linn.*; var. Foot of Sitgreaves's Pass, (Camp 61;) March 25.

MIMULUS (DIPLACUS) GLUTINOSUS, *Thurb.; Gray in Mex. Bound. Surv.*, *p.* 116. San Luis Obispo, California; November 5.

VERONICA PEREGRINA, *Linn.* Colorado Chiquito, New Mexico; May 1.

CASTILLEJA HISPIDA, *Benth. in Hook. Fl. and DC. Prodr.* 10, *p.* 532. Camp 61; Long valley to San Francisco mountain; April.

CASTILLEJA CANDENS, *Durand Pl. Heerm. in Pacif. R. R. Expl. Bot.*, *p.* 12, *pl.* xiii. Common about San Francisco mountain, &c. Very showy. Bracts crimson. Flower yellow.

PEDICULARIS CENTRANTHERA, *Gray in Mex. Bound. Surv.*, *p.* —. High mesa west of Little Colorado and near Fort Defiance. April and May. "Flowers purple and yellow." Younger and smaller specimens than those collected by Dr. Bigelow.

ANTIRRHINUM ? FILIPES, (sp. nov.:) diffusum ramorissimum, basi villosum, cæt, glaberrimum; foliis oblongis lanceolatisne subintegerimis teneribus in petiolum attenuatis; pedicellis sparsis longissimis cum ramulis floribus filiformibus tortuosis; floribus (ut videtur) minimis; capsula globosa. Desert arroyos. "Flowers white." The corolla in the specimens scarcely larger than the calyx, its structure hardly to be made out in the spent specimens. Pedicels capillary, tortuous, from one to three inches long. Capsule 1½ line in diameter.

EUNANUS BIGELOVII, *Gray in Bot. Whippl. Exped.*, *p.* 121. Camp 49; February 18.

ACANTHACEÆ.

SERICOGRAPHIS CALIFORNICA, *Nées in DC. Prodr.* Beloperone Californica, *Benth. Bot. Voy. Sulph.*, *p.* 38. Sandy desert bordering Carisso Creek, interior California. A twining shrub, with inconspicuous leaves and crimson flowers.

VERBENACEÆ, (By John Torrey.*)

VERBENA AUTLEBIA, *Linn.; Schauer in DC. Prodr.* 11, *p.* 554; *Torr. in Bot., Mex. Bound. Surv.*, *p.* 128. V. bipinnatifida, *Schauer, l. c.* Camp 60–65. April 25–31, and Partridge Creek, April 24.

VERBENA PROSTRATA, *R. Brown, Hort. Kees,* (ed. 2,) 4, *p.* 51; *Schauer, l. c.* Near San Diego, California; November 9.

LABIATÆ.

Hyptis Emoryi: fruticosa divaricato-ramosa ramis cinerascente-puberulis; foliis petiolatis ovatis dentato-serratis crassiusculis rugosis utrinque cinereo-pubescentibus; cymis pedunculatis axillaribus folio vix longioribus; calycibus pedicello æqualibus turbinato-campanalatis cinereo pubescentibus, dentibus æqualibus lanceolatis tubo subduplo brevioribus. "In rocky arroyos; common on the Upper Colorado; January 14. A fragrant shrub, 5 feet high, with numerous slender spreading branches which are at length nearly smooth." Leaves from one-half to three-fourths of an inch long, obtuse, strongly reticulate-rugose; the petiole about one-third the length of the lamina. Cymes few flowered in loose umbels. Pedicels 2 lines long, naked. Teeth of the calyx acuminate. Corolla purple, about twice as long as the calyx. This plant was first detected on the Lower Gila, by Major Emory, while accompanying the military expedition of General Kearney to California in 1846. It was afterwards found in the same region by Col. Frémont. In the Botany of the Mexican Boundary Survey it was erroneously referred to H. laniflora, *Benth.*, (by a double mistake, printed H. lanata,) which, though nearly allied, differs in the smooth leaves and extremely woolly calyces.

DRACOCEPHALUM PARVIFLORUM, *Nutt. Gen.* 2, *p.* 25; *Torr. Fl. New York*, 2, *p.* 75. Mesa, near Camp 70 and Cedar Creek, April 24. Peach Orchard Spring; May 18.

HEDEOMA INCANA, *Torr. Bot. Mex. Bound. Surv.*, *p.* 130. Oryabe; May 13—17. A handsome shrub with aspect and odor of sage, growing in tufts two to three feet high. Flowers pale purple.

SALVIA COLUMBARIÆ, *Benth. Lab.*, *p.* 302. Sitgreaves's Pass; March 25. This is the *chia* of the native Californians.

BORAGINACEÆ.

AMSINCKIA LYCOPSOIDES, *Lehm.; DC. Prodr.* 10, *p.* 117. Sitgreaves's Pass; March 25. A foot and a half high.

AMSINCKIA INTERMEDIA, *Fisch. & Mey.; DC. l. c.; Torr. Bot. Mex. Bound.*, *p.* 140. Riverside mountain; January 25, and Camp No. 61—62; March 26.

LITHOSPERMUM LONGIFLORUM, *Spreng. Lyst.* 1, *p.* 554; *Torr. l. c.* L. incisum, *Lehm. Asp.* 2, *p.* 305. Cañon of Partridge Creek and Fort Defiance; April 16 to May 22. Grows in tufts with a thick ligneous root.

ERITRICHIUM CHORISIANUM, *DC. Prodr.* 10, *p.* 30; *Torr. Bot. Mex. Bound.*, *p.* 141. Yampai valley; March 27. The whole plant gives out a deep purple stain to the paper in which the specimens are laid.

---

*The orders preceding *verbenaceæ* have been elaborated by Prof. Gray, with the exception of the *cactaceæ* studied by Dr. Geo. Englemann. The orders following were all examined by Prof. Torrey, excepting the grasses, which were worked up by Prof. Geo. Thurber.--J. S. N.

Eritrichium angustifolium, *Torr. in Pacif. R. Road Expl. 5, p.* 363, *and in Bot. Mex. Bound.*, *p.* 141. Riverside mountains; January 25. Sitgreaves's Pass; March 26.

Eritrichium glomeratum, *DC. Prodr.* 10, *p.* 131; *Torr. Bot. Mex. Bound., p.* 140. Myosotis glomerate, *Nutt. Gen.* 1, *p.* 112; *Hook. H. Bor.-Amer.* 2, *p.* 182, *t.* 162. Sandy Hills, Camps 85–86; May 3. Flowers pale yellow.

Eritrichium pterocaryum, *Torr. in Bot. U. S. Expl. Exped., t.* 13, *fig. B, (ined.) and Bot. Mex. Bound., p.* 142. Camp 62; March 26. Plant annual, about a foot and a half high. Flowers white.

Eritrichium. — ? An apparently new species was found at Sitgreaves's Pass, March 25. It is an annual, a foot or more in height, and paniculately branched. The leaves are lanceolate linear, scabrous, with short stiff hairs, many of which have a white elevated tubercular base. The flowers are in compound ebracteate spikes, which are at first short and circinate-capitate, but at length unfolded. Pedicels almost wanting. Segments of the calyx lanceolate, densely clothed with short rather soft hairs. Corolla white; the tubes scarcely longer than the calyx; the orifice closed with five protuberances, which alternate with the stamens; limb widely expanding; the lobes nearly orbicular. Stamens included, inserted in the throat of the corolla just below the protuberances. Style as long as the ovary; stigma capitate, somewhat 2-lobed. Nublets narrowly oblong, only one of them fertile, minutely bispid. This is allied to E. floribundum, *Torr.*, which differs in being a considerably larger plant, with an apparently perennial root, broadly ovate nutlets.

Pectocarya linearis, *DC. Prodr.* 20, *p.* 120. Partridge Creek; April 25.

Echinospermum paulum, *Lehm. Asper. No.* 95. Moqui villages; May 10.

Echinospermum strictum, *Nees in Maximill. Trav. App.; Torr. in Bot. Mex. Bound., p.* 142. Crossing of the Little Colorado; May 1. "Flowers white."

Tiquelia brevifolia, *Nutt. ness. Torr. in Bot. Mex. Bound., p.* 136, *and in Bot. U. S. Expl. Exped. ined.* 2–12, *A.*

Heliotropium Curassavicum, *Linn. DC. Prodr.* 10, *p.* 538. Banks of the Colorado; March 20.

HYDROPHYLLACEÆ.

Phacelia (Eutoca) micrantha, *Torr. Bot. Mex. Bound., p.* 144. Riverside mountain; January 25. Camp 29; March 1. Sitgreaves's Pass; March 25.

Var.? bipinnatifida: patenti-pilosa; caule debili prostrato; foliis bipinnatifidis; pedunculis calyce subtriprolongioribus. Camp 61. Yampai valley. In the flowers this plant entirely resembles P. micrantha. The more divided leaves and longer pedicels may be owing to a more shady and fertile situation. "The plant is very fragrant; the odor being much like that of the apple geranium."

Phacelia (Coreanthus) Ivesiana, (n. sp.:) annua erecta, vel diffusa, viscido-pubescens; foliis oblongo-linearibus, pinnatifidis, lobis utrinque 5–7 obovatis obtusis integris vel 1–2-dentatis, petiolatis basi nudis; racemis simplicibus paucifloris, floribus brevissimi, pedicillatis calycis lacimis spathulatis, corolla tubuloro-campanulata calyce vix excedente; placentis 8–9 ovulatis. Diamond river; April 3. Sandy hills, Oraybe; May 13. Banks of the Colorado; March 20. Camp 49. Plant 6–10 inches high, apparently diffuse when old. Leaves $\frac{1}{2}$ to $1\frac{1}{4}$ inch long and $\frac{1}{4}$ of an inch wide; the lobes scarcely 2 lines long. Racemes 5–10 flowered; pedicels about half a line long. Corolla white or very pale purple, about two lines long, the tube three times as long as the rounded lobes of the limb; appendages very narrow. Stamens included. Anthers broader than long. Capsule oblong. Seeds strongly rugose transversely. In the corolla this species resembles P. infundibuliformis, but differs in the few flowers, the few-flowered loose racemes, and in the very small lobes of the leaves.

Phacelia (Coreanthus) Fremontii, (n. sp.:) annua erecta vel diffusa; foliis oblongo-linearibus pinnitifidis, lobis utrinque 5–8 obovatis obtusis integris vel 1–2-dentatis, petiolis basi nudis; ramis simplicibus 8–12 floris pedicillis brevibus calycis lacemis spathulatis, corollæ tuba infundibuliformis calyce subduplo longiore; limbo patulo placentis 8-ovulatis. Yampai valley; March 26. This was collected by Colonel Frémont in his journey to California in 1843–'44, probably in the interior of that State, or in Western New Mexico. It is nearly allied to the last species, but differs in the much larger flowers, the corolla of which is purple, with the lower part of the tube yellow and much exceeding the calyx. The appendages of the tube are also dilated in the middle. The seeds are strongly corrugated transversely.

PHACELIA (COREANTHUS) ARETIOIDES, *Hook. & Arn. Bot. Beech.*, p. 374; *Hook. Ic. t.* 355. Alluvial bottoms of the Little Colorado; May 9. Camp 88. The specimens are in the earliest flowering state, corresponding with the var. PERPUSILLA, *Hook. & Arn. l. c.*

PHACELIA CILIATA, *Benth. in Trans. Lin. Soc.* 17, p. 280. Riverside mountain; January. Camp 49; February 20, and Sitgreaves's Pass, March 25, to Little Colorado.

PHACELIA TANACETIFOLIA, *Benth. l. c.* Sitgreaves's Pass; March 24.

EMMENANTHE PENDULIFLORA, *Benth. l. c. Alph. DC. Prodr.* 9, p. 301. Sitgreaves's Pass; March 25. Eucrypta, *Nuttall, Pl. Gamb.*, p. 158, seems to be hardly distinct from this genus, but it has fewer seeds.

NAMA JAMAICENCIS, *Linn. Choisy in DC. Prodr.* 10, p. 182. Riverside mountain; January 25. Also at Sitgreaves's Pass; March 25. It forms mats in dry sandy arroyos.

POLEMONIACEÆ.

PHLOX SPECIOSA, *Pursh. Fl.* 1, p. 149. Var. STANSBURY, *Torr. in Bot. Mex. Bound. Surv.*, p. 145. Camp 64; March 29.

PHLOX DOUGLASII, *Benth.* Grows in tufts on rocks. March 31, (Camp 65.) Also Camp 91. "The color of the corolla varies from nearly white to pale purple."

COLLOMIA GRACILIS, *Dougl. Benth. in DC. Prodr.* 9, p. 308. Cedar creek, Camp 79; April 24.

NAVARRETIA SCHOTTII, *Torr. Bot. Mex. Bound.*, p. 145. Banks of the Colorado, Camp 49; March 20.

NAVARRETIA SETOSISSIMA, *(Torr. & Gray, Fl. N. Am. ined.:)* humilis, foliis apice dilatatis grosse tridentatis, basi longe liniari cuneatis margine pinnato-setosis inherdium utrinque unidentatis dentibus apice setiferis; capitulis paucifloris; corolla tuba calyce longiore; staminibus exsertis; ovarii loculis 8–10 ovulibis. Rocky hill-sides, Camp 67; April 3. This well-marked species (which is nearly related to N. Schottii) was first collected by Colonel Frémont in 1844, near the Rio Virgen, towards the great Californian desert, and again in 1848.

GILIA DACTYLOPHYLLUM, (n. sp.?) Mouth of Diamond river; April 3. The specimens are scarcely sufficient for description. A slender plant, about 3 inches high. Corolla twice as long as the calyx, white; ovules about 7 in each cell.

GILIA AUREA, *Nutt. Pl. Gamb. in Jour. Acad. Phil. (n. ser.)* 1, p. 155, t. 32. Camp 62; March 26. Also Camps 80 and 86.

GILIA PUNGENS, *Benth. in DC. Prodr.* 9, p. 316. Cantue pungens, *Torr. in Ann. Lyc. N. York*, 2, p. 220. Camps 98, 99; May 19. Flowers greenish yellow.

GILIA LONGIFLORA, *G. Dou.; Benth. l. c.* Canbua longiflora, *Torr. l. c.* Camp 66.

GILIA DICHOTOMA, *Benth. l. c.*, p. 314. Camp 61; March 25; flowers white, (rose colored in bud.) Camp 64; March 4.

GILIA DICHOTOMA, var. PARVIFLORA, *Torr. in Mex. Bound. Surv.*, p. 147. Camp 61; March 25.

GILIA INCONSPICUA, *Dougl. in Bos. Mag., t.* 2883; *Benth.* Sitgreaves's Pass, &c. A variable plant. Some of the forms that I refer to it may belong to another species.

GILIA VIRGATA, *Steud. Nomencl.; Benth. in DC. Prod.* 9, p. 311. Foliis integris vel adbasim utrinque unidentatis corollis purpureis tubo laceniis breviore anthevis linearibus; ovarii loculis 5–6 ovulabis. "The Oaks," San Felipe, California; November 17. G. Gunnisoni differs in the leaves being all entire, (perhaps not a constant character;) the corolla white, (or nearly so,) with the tube almost twice as long as the lobes and the ovate anthers.

ENODYCTION CALIFORNICUM, *Benth. Bot. Sulph.*, p. 35; *Choisy in DC. Prod.* 10, p. 185. Wigandia Californica, *Hook. & Arn. Bot. Beech.*, p. 364, t. 88. Hills northeast of San Diego, California; November 10.

ENODYCTION TOMENTOSUM, *Benth. l. c.; Torr. Bot. Mex. Bound.* 2, p. 148. Table-lands back of San Diego, California; a bush 8–10 feet high.

FOUQUERIACEÆ.

FOUQUIERIA SPLENDENS, *Engelm. in Wisliz. Rep.*, p. 98; *G ay, Pl. Wright.* 1, p. 85, *and* 2, p. 63. Gravelly and rocky surfaces from Colorado to Rio Grande. Peninsula mountains; November, in flower.

CONVOLVULACEÆ. By G. Engelmann.

CUSCUTA CALIFORNICA, *Hook. & Arn. Bot. Beech.*, p. 346; *Choisy, DC. Prod. IX*, p. 457; *C. acuminata, Nutt. in Herb. Acad. Philad.* A well-marked though somewhat variable species. The tube of the corolla is generally longer than the calyx, and the lacinæ of the corolla longer than the tube. The scales are always wanting, but are sometimes indicated by semilunar entire or denticulate folds in the base of the corolla, corresponding with its lobes, which folds we find in many of our *Cuscutæ* connecting the bases of the scales. The ovary is depressed, the styles capillary, as long, or often much longer, than the ovary. This species is very nearly allied to the East Indian *C. hyalina*, Roth., which, according to original specimens in the herbarium of the Botanical Garden of St. Petersburg, I find to be identical with *C. oxypetala*, Boissier, and not with *C. chinensis*, Lam., as is usually supposed.

SOLANACEÆ.

SOLANUM ELÆAGNIFOLIUM, *Cav. Ic.*, t. 243; *Torr. in Bot. Mex. Bound. Surv.*, p. 152. Oryabe, May 13; and Laguna. May 25.

PHYSALIS CARDIOPHYLLA, *Torr. Bot. Mex. Bound. Surv.*, p. 153. Riverside mountain; January 25. Specimens of what appear to be a variety of this species were found at the Barrier islands, January 25. They differ in the leaves being smaller and less decidedly cordate than in the ordinary form of the plant.

LYCIUM PALLIDUM, *Miers, Ill. S. Amer.*, Pl. 2, p. 108, t. 67, C. ; *Torr. Bot. Mex. Bound. Surv.*, p. 154. Oryabe; May 13.

LYCIUM STOLIDUM, *Miers, l. c.*, p. 126, t. 71, C. ? Monument cañon; February 8. A spreading shrub, five feet high; flowers pale purple; berries crimson. This differs from the plant described by Miers, in the more slender habit, pale branches, and shorter pedicels. An undetermined species of this genus, perhaps new, was found near San Diego, California. It is a spreading shrub, about three feet high, with very small farciculate spatulate-oblong leaves, and small white flowers on short pedicels; the tube of the corolla scarcely exserted from the four-toothed calyx. As Mr. Miers, who has written so ably on the Solanaceæ, and is about publishing many new species of this genus, may have received this from some other source, I therefore refrain from describing it more particularly in this report.

NICOTIANA. Species uncertain. Riverside mountain; January 25.

DATURA METELOIDES, *DC. MSS; Dunal. in DC. Prod.* 13, par. 1, p. 521. San Diego, California, to Rio Grande.

ASCLEPIADACEÆ.

ASCLEPIAS SUBULATA, *Decaisne in DC. Prodr.* 8, p. 571; *Torr. in Pacif. Railroad Expl.* 6, p. 362, t. 7. "Colorado desert, in the most dry and sterile soil near Alamo Mucho; November 28. Grows in tufts three feet high, in company with Larrea, Ephedra, &c.; often leafless."

ASCLEPIAS BRACHYSTEPHANA, *Engelm. MSS.; Torr. Bot. Mex. Bound. Surv.*, p. 163. Oryabe; May 10.

Sarcostemma heterophyllum, *Engelm. MSS.; Torr. l. c., p.* 161. Common along banks of Colorado to Black cañon. In fruit. The stem is sometimes 10 or 15 feet long.

Amsonia tomentosa, *Torr. & Frém. in Frém. 2d Rep., p.* 316; *Torr. Mex. Bound. Surv., p.* 158. Yampai valley, near water; growing in tufts 1–2 feet high; March 25.

OLEACEÆ.

Forestiera ligustrina, *Poir. Enc. Suppl.* 2, *p.* 264; *Torr. Bot. Mex. Bound., p.* 167. Adelia ligustrina, Mieb. Fl. 2, p. 224. Camp 62; May 28. With ferbile flowers and young leaves. A shrub eight feet high.

NYCTAGINACEÆ.

Mirabilis multiflora, *Gray in Bot. Mex. Bound. Surv., t.* 169. Nyctaginea Torreyana: *Choisy in DC. Prodr.* 13, *par.* 2, *p.* 429. About rancherias. "The Oaks;" November 17.

Mirabilis Californica, *Gray, l. c. t.* 46. From San Diego to Santa Isabel, California; November. Sitgreaves's Pass; March 25. Riverside mountain and cañon of Diamond river; April. Flowers white and purple.

Allionia incarnata, *Linn, Choisy, l. c.* Mouth of Diamond river; April 3.

Abronia fragrans, *Nutt.; Torr. & Gray, Bot. Beckwith Rep.* 14, *t.* 10. Mouth of Diamond river and Camp 66; April, in flower.

Abronia mellifera, *Dougl. in Hook. Bot. Mag., t.* 2879. Sandy hills, Camp 49. Flowers, pale rose color, fragrant; March 1 to 25.

POLYGONACEÆ.

Eriogonum fasciculatum, *Benth. in Linn. Trans.* 17, *p.* 411. San Diego, California. A shrub 2–5 feet high, with white and purple flowers; November.

Eriogonum polifolium, *Benth. in DC. Prodr.* 14, *sect.* 1, *p.* 12. Jesup's rapid, on rocks, Camp 48; February.

Eriogonum parvifolium, *Smith in Rees's Cycl. Benth., l. c.* San Luis Obispo; November. A shrub 2–3 feet high. Flowers white, veined with purple.

Eriogonum heleanthemifolium (E. Wrightii) var. heleanthemifolium, *Torr. in Bot. Mex. Bound, p.* 176; *E. Benth., l. c., p.* 15. San Felipe, California; November.

Eriogonum virgatum, *Benth. in DC. Prodr., l. c., p.* 16. San Diego, California; November. E. elongatum, *Benth.* at least, Frémont's plant, quoted by Bentham, seems to be hardly distinct.

Eriogonum polycladon, *Benth., l. c.,* Santa Isabel and "The Oaks;" November.

Eriogonum inflatum, *Torr. in Frémont 2d Rep.; Benth., l. c.* Gravelly and rocky hills on the Upper Colorado, common, March. The branches are more or less inflated below the divisions; flowers greenish yellow; radical leaves mostly waved on the margin. Sometimes there are small lanceolate leaves at the first division of the stem.

Eriogonum Thomasii, *Torr. in Pacif. R. Road Surv.* 5, *p.* 364. Riverside mountains and Sitgreaves's Pass, Upper Colorado; January, March.

Eriogonum deflexum, (n. sp.:) annuum; caule nudo ramosisimo glabro ramulis rigidis foliis radicalibus ovato-orbiculatis, hirutis pedicellis brevissimis deflexis; involucris campanulatis obtuse–5-dentatis; perigonii laciniis late ovatis obtusissimis basi cordatis interioribus multominoribus ovate lanceolatis acutiusculis. Three Point Bend; January 19; allied to E. cernuum, *Nutt.,* but that is much more slender, the peduncles considerably longer than the involucre, and the form of the sepals is very different. We have this plant also from the collections of Mr. Schott collected on the Lower Gila.

Chorizanthe brevicornu, *Torr. in Bot. Mex. Bound., p.* 177. Desert arroyos, banks of the Colorado; March 1–20; flowers greenish.

ACANTHOGONUM RIGIDUM, *Torr. in Bot. Whippl. Rep.*, *p.* 133, *and in Pacif. R. Road Expl.*, 7, *p.* 362, *t.* 8. Banks of the Colorado and in the desert; March 20.

PTEROSTEGIA DRYMARIORIDES, *Fisch. & May, Benth. l. c.* Under rocks, Sitgreaves's Pass; March.

RUMEX SALICIFOLIUS, *Weinm.; Meisn. in DC. Prodr. l. c.*, *p.* 47. Santa Isabel and San Felipe, California; November.

RUMEX VENOSUS, *Pursh. Fl.* 2, *p.* 732, *Hook, Fl. Bor.-Amer.* 2, *p.* 130, *t.* 174. Yampai valley March 29.

RUMEX. Leaves and flowers, but no fruit of undetermined species; cultivated by the Mojaves. Camp 52.

AMARANTACEÆ.

ALTERNANTHERA LANUGINOSA, *Torr. in Emory's Rep. and in Bot. Mex. Bound.*, *p.* 180. Achyranthes lanuginosa, *Nutt.* Banks of the Colorado, near Chimney Peak; January 16.

SARRATIA BERLANDIERI, *Moq. in DC. Prodr.* 13, *par* 2, *p.* 240, var. FIMBRIATA, *Torr. in Bot. Mex. Bound.*, *p.* 79. "The Oaks;" Nov. 17.

CHENOPODIACEÆ.

OBIONE HYMENELYTRA, *Torr. in Bot. Whippl. Exped.*, *p.* 129, *t.* 20, *and in Bot. Mex. Bound.*, *p.* 182. On rocky hills, growing in tufts; Explorer's Pass and above; January. The male plant only was found.

OBIONE BARCLAYANA, *Benth.; Durand and Hilgard, Pacif. R. Road Expl.* Vallecito; very common in many parts of the Colorado desert, &c.; often 10 feet high, forming large clumps and masses. This is pretty clearly the plant described by Durand & Hilgard, l. c., but may not be that of Bentham ; perhaps it is only a form of O. acanthocarpa, *Torr.*

OBIONE CANESCENS, *Magin in DC. l. c.* From San Felipe to the Colorado river; most common on table-lands; November. A form with broadly-winged fruit. It is one of the shrubs called artemisia by travellers.

OBIONE POLYCARPA, *Torr. in Emory's Report*, *p.* 119, *and in Bot. Whippl. Exped.*, *p.* 130. Colorado desert, growing in tufts; November.

OBIONE CONFERTIFOLIA, *Torr. & Frém. in Frém. 2d Rep.*, *p.* 318. At the crossing of the Little Colorado; May 1. Only the male plant was found; the female (as in several other species of this genus) is rarely seen in collections.

OBIONE ARENARIA, *Moq. Chenop.*, *p.* 71.? San Diego, California; November 17. Differs from the eastern plant in being erect, with smaller and somewhat toothed leaves, and smaller fruit. The specimens are very imperfect.

CORISPERMUM HYSSOPIFOLIUM, *Linn.; Moq. in DC. Prodr. l. c.*, *p.* 141. Camp 15; January 15. In dry sandy places. " It is often uprooted and driven about by the wind; its curved branches forming a kind of ball, which rolls far from its place of growth, and thus distributes the seed."

MONOLEPIS CHENOPODIOIDES, B. TRIFIDA, *Moq. in DC. Prodr.* 13, *par.* 2, *p.* 26. Camp 89; March 7.

SUÆDA FRUTICOSA, var. MULTIFLORA, *Torr. Bot. Whippl. Exp.*, *p.* 130. Saline soils; January 16. A shrub, 4–5 feet high.

ARTHEOCNEMUM MACROSTACHYNUM, *A. Bunge; Torr. in Bot. Mex. Bound. Rep.*, *p.* 184. "On the Colorado, from the Gulf of California to the Great Cañon, in saline soils; January 19. It is called 'salt bush,' and is a shrub, usually about two feet high, but sometimes attaining the height of seven feet."

LORANTHACEÆ.

PHORADENDRON FLAVESCENS, *Nutt. in Jour. Acad. Phil. (n. ser.)* 1, *p.* 185. Santa Isabel, California; November 15, (in fruit.) Parasitic on Quercus agrifolia.

PHORADENDRON CALIFORNICUM, *Nutt., l. c.* Vallecito. Parasitic on Larrea Mexicana; November 18, (immature fruit.) "Banks of New river and on the Colorados; Camp 40; February. On Algarobia glandulosa (mesquit.) Berries pinkish white. It often destroys the trees upon which it grows."

PHORADENDRON JUNIPERINUM, *Engelm. in Gray, Pl. Fendl., p. 59.* "Parasite on Juniperus tetragona. Camp 63; March 27."

SANTALACEÆ.

COMANDRA UMBELLATA, *Nutt. Gen.* 1, *p.* 157, var. ANGUSTIFOLIA, *Torr. Bot. Mex. Bound., p.* 185. "Partridge creek, April 24, and Camp 63, March 28."

EUPHORBIACEÆ. By Dr. George Engelmann.

APHORA SERRATA, *Torr. Bot. Mex. Bound. Surv., p.* 197. Gravelly places on the Upper Colorado; January 25 to April 1. Flowers greenish white.

CROTON (HENDECANDRA) PROCUMBENS, *Eschsch.; Torr. l. c., p.* 195. On the bottom lands of the San Diego river, California; November 9. Grows in tufts two and three feet high.

EUPHORBIA INÆQUILATERA, *Sonder Linnœa; Engelm. in Mex. B. Rep., vol. II, ined.* Mojave valley. This is the same as Plant Fendl., No. 803; an almost prostrate form, with small narrow leaves, which are only towards the end very slightly denticulate; seeds scarcely undulate or nibbed. This species has a very wide extension; it is found in Florida and the West India islands, in the west from Nebraska to Texas and to California and Oregon, (in India, E. Nilagirica; in South Africa, E. inæquilatera and E. setigera,) and in New Holland.

EUPHORBIS MELANADENIA, *Torr. in Bot. Whipple P. R. Rep. IV, p.* 135; E. cinerascens, B.; *Engelm. in Mex. B. Rep. II, ined.* In sandy arroyos, Camp 15, forming mats; January 15, in flower, but without fruit. Many prostrate stems, a foot and more in height, from a ligneous root. The specimens before me are distinguished from those obtained by Dr. Bigelow by having unequal glands to the involucrum, those behind being much longer than those in front; and especially by their petaloid rose-colored appendages. The seeds are not opaque, as Prof. says, but reddish gray.

EUPHORBIA POLYCARPA, *Benth. Bot. Sulph., p.* 49; *Engelm. in Mex. B. Rep. II, ined.* This is one of the most variable species of North America, if I understand it correctly. A form with narrow hispid pubescent leaves and very small appendages was collected with the last, and in the Purple hills, forming dense mats on the sand of dry arroyos. Another, and the most showy form—the same that was found by Mr. Schott and Dr. Parry at San Diego, and of which a specimen from the same locality is in Dr. Hooker's herbarium, labelled by Nuttall *E. ocellata*— was collected at Laguna, and was seen from Los Angelos to the Colorado. This showy form has almost smooth uniform leaves, and very large white appendages to the dark glands.

EUPHORBIA SETILOBA, *Engelm. in P. R. Rep., vol.* 5, *p.* 364. Gravelly beds of arroyos at Purple hills. Also in flower in January, and probably the whole year round. Nearly allied to the last, with the same rough pubescence, but readily distinguished, not only by the deep laciniate appendages, but also by the almost naked inside of the involucres. I find them in Dr. Newberry's specimens generally triandrous, as Prof. Torrey has already noticed in the original specimen sent from Fort Yuma by Major Thomas.

EUPHORBIA (TITHYMALUS?) LURIDA, *nov. spec.:* e basi perennante multicaulis glaberrima junior tota rubro lurida; foliis oblanceolatis acutis basi angustatis subsessilibus patulis; umbellæ quinquifidæ bracteis cuspidatis inferioribus obovatis seu oblanceolatis, superioribus suborbiculatis; involucri parvi intus pubenscentis glandulis transversis crenatis lovis ovatis membranaceis pubescentibus stylis ovario lævi multo brevioribus vix basi connatis bilobis. Camps 81–82, San Francisco mountain; commencing to bloom at the end of April. I introduce thiʋ plant as a new species with a good deal of hesitation, as the specimens are scarcely enough advanced;

but though the fruit is as yet unknown, the plant seems to be well distinguished from any of the known North American or Mexican species. From the very similar *E. esulæformis* and its allies it differs by the absence of horns on the glands, and by the very short styles.

Stems of the young specimens just coming into flower. Six inches high, with the leaves brownish red; upper side of leaves greenish red; leaves 5–8 lines long, and 1½–2 lines wide; involucre 1 line long; linear bracts of the male flowers numerous, hairy, so that it is more nearly allied with Tithymalus than with *Esula*.

EUPHORBIA (ESULA?) INCISA, nov. spec.: perennis e basi ramosa erecta ascenderisve glaberrima glaucescens; foliis brevibus ovatis brevissimi . cuspidatis in petiolum brevem attenuatis; umbellæ trifidæ bractis cuspidatis inferioribus rhormbeis, superioribus basi truncata transversis; involucri majusculi intus subnudi glandulis stipitatis transversis truncatis crenatis seu irregulariter incisis nec cornutis; lobis involucri apice truncatis, glanduloso incrassatis profunde emarginatis seu irregulariter bilobis stylis ovario lævi longe exerto, longioribus basi connatis bilobis. Camp 62, Long valley. Stems 8–12 inches high; leaves 5–7 lines long and 3 or 4 lines wide; involucrum about two lines long, and, with the conspicuous glands, more than that in diameter; flower, end of March; very nearly allied to *Euphorbia montana, Engelm. in Bot. Mex. B. Expedition*, with similar habits, leaves, umbells, but amply distinguished from this and all other peploid Euphorbias by the large involucrum, the absence of horns, and the incised, nearly naked lobes. In all the allied species the lobes are membranaceous, ovate, obtuse, and on the inside villous. The bracts at the base of the male flowers are almost wanting, and the few occasionally found are nearly naked, while in most species they are pubescent or villous. The styles, much longer than the ovary, are united at the lower third and biped at the upper third. Stigmas clavate; fruit and seed unknown. This species is too nearly allied to some of our peploid *Esulæ* to be separated from them, though the glands are hornless.

URTICACEÆ.

PARIETORIA DEBILIS, *Forst.* β FLORIDIANA, *Weddell, Mon. Urt.,* p. 316; *Torr. Bot. Mex. Bound.,* p. 202. P. Floridana, *Nutt.* Rocky arroyos, Colorado Desert; Camp 49; February 22.

PLATANACEÆ.

PLATANUS RACEMOSA, *Nutt. Audub. Birds,* 1, t. 362, *and Sylv. t.,* p. 47, t. 15. San Luis Obispo, California; November.

SAUSURACEÆ.

ANEMOPSIS CALIFORNICA, *Nutt. Hook. & Arn. Bot. Beech.,* p. 390, t. 92. Alluvial lands; San Diego and Los Angelos; November 9, in fruit. Rio Grande; May, in flower.

SALICACEÆ.

SALIX. Several undetermined species.

POPULUS MONILIFERA, *Ait. Michx. Sylva.* 1, p. 116, t. 96, f. 2. Banks of Colorado everywhere; Mojave valley; in flower, February 15.

POPULUS TREMULOIDES, *Michx. Fl.* 2, p. 143, *Sylv.* 1, p. 125, t. 99. High table-lands about San Francisco mountain.

POPULUS ANGUSTIFOLIA, *James, Torr. Ann. Lyc. N. York,* 2, p. 249; *Nutt. Sylv.* 1, p. 52, t. 16. Cañon of Cascade river.

JUGLANDACEÆ.

JUGLANS RUPESTRIS, *Engelm. Torr. Bot. Sitgreaves's Rep.,* p. 171, t. 15. J. pyriformis, *Liebm. Vidensk. Meddel. Kijobenh. for* 1850, p. 80? Banks of Cedar creek, west of San Francisco mountain.

CUPULIFERÆ.

QUERCUS TINCTORIA, *var.*? CALIFORNICA, *Torr. Bot. Whipple's Rep.*, *p.* 138; Q. rubra, *Leibm. in Benth.*, *Pl. Hartwig.*, *p.* 337. Santa Isabel; November, in fruit.

QUERCUS EMORYI, *Torr. in Emory's Rep.*, *p.* 152, *t.* 9. Yampai valley and eastward; common.

QUERCUS AGRIFOLIA, *Nées in Ann. de Scien. Nat.* 3, *p.* 281; *Hook. Ic.* 3, *t.* 377. Coast of California and Peninsular mountains.

QUERCUS OBLONGIFOLIA, *Torr. in Sitgreaves's Rep.*, *p.* 173, *t.* 19. Peninsular mountains, South California.

QUERCUS DUMOSA? *Nutt. Sylv.* 1, *p.* 72. San Diego, California.

CONIFERÆ.

EPHEDRA ANTISIPHILITICA, *Berland.*, *Myer, Ephedra*, 101. Banks of Colorado to Rio Grande.

PINUS EDULIS, *Engelm. in Wisliz. Rep.*, *p.* 88; *Torr. in Bot. Sitgreaves's Rep.*, *p.* 173, *t.* 20. P. Fremontiana, *Gord. in Jour. Hist. Soc. Lond.* 4, *p.* 293. Common in all the higher portions of New Mexico. *Var.* MONOPHYLLUS, *Torr.* Cerbat mountains.

PINUS PONDEROSA, *Dougl. Lond. Arborit*, *p.* 2243; *Newberry, Bot. Williamson's Rep.*, *p.* 36. Mountains at Santa Isabel, San Francisco mountain, and high lands about Fort Defiance, and Santa Fé.

PINUS INSIGNIS, *Dougl. in Lond. Arborit*, 4, *p.* 2265, *figs.* 2170–2172. Monterey, California.

PINUS COULTERI, *Dou. Linn. Trans. vol.* 17, *p.* 440. Coast mountains, back of Monterey, California.

PINUS SABINIANA, *Dougl. Lamb. Pinus* (ed 2d.) 2, *p.* 146, *t.* 80. Mountains south of San Francisco.

PINUS LAMBERTIANA, *Dougl. in Linn. Trans.* 15, *p.* 50. With the last.

ABIES DOUGLASII, *Lina. Nutt. Sylv.*, *p.* 131, *t.* 117. High table-lands west of Little Colorado and Rocky mountains. *Var.* MACROCARPA. Mountains near San Felipe.

SEQUOIA SEMPERVIRENS, *Endl. Syst. conif.*, *p.* 198. Coast mountains, south of San Francisco.

JUNIPERUS TETRAGONA, *Schlecht, Var.* OSTEOSPERMA, *Torr. in Bot. Whipple's Rep.*, *p.* 141. San Felipe, California.

JUNIPERUS PACHYPHLŒA, *Torr. l. c.* Cedar creek and about San Francisco mountain.

JUNIPERUS VIRGINIANA, *Linn. Michx. Sylv.* 2, *p.* 353, *t.* 156. Rocky mountains, east of Fort Defiance.

SYPHACEÆ.

SYPHA LATIFOLIA, *Linn.* Explorer's Pass and along the Colorado generally.

LILIACEÆ.

CALOCHORTUS LUTEUS, *Dougl. Lind. Bot. Reg.*, *t.* 1661. Navajo country; Camp 101; May 18.

CALOCHORTUS SPLENDENS, *Benth. Hort. Trans.*, *p.* 411, *t.* 15, *fig.* 1. Mouth of Diamond river; April 3; Moqui country; May 8. Crossing of the Colorado Chiquito; March 2.

ALLIUM MUTABILE, *Michx. Fl.* 1, *p.* 195; *Kth. Enum.* 4, *p.* 451. Mesa north of the Colorado Chiquito; May 3. The plant not more than half the usual height, and the pedicels (fructiferous) are considerably stouter than in the common form of this species.

ALLIUM ACUMINATUM, *Hook. Fl. Bor.-Amer.* 2, *p.* 185, *t.* 196. Fort Defiance; May 22.

BRODIÆA (DICHELOSTEMMA) CAPITATA, *Benth. Pl. Hartw.*, *p.* 339. Mouth of Diamond river; April 3; Sitgreaves's Pass; March 23; Cedar creek, April 24.

YUCCA ANGUSTIFOLIA, *Pursh. Fl.* 1, *p.* 227; *Nutt. Gen.* 1, *p.* 218. Camp 70 and Camp 65; Hay Camp and Santa Fé. One of the plants called Amolé, or *Soap plant*, by the Mexicans.

YUCCA BACCATA, *Torr. in Bot. Mex. Bound. Survey*, 2, *p.* Sitgreaves's Pass; March 25. Stem, 3–10 feet high. Leaves, 15 inches long. Panicle, two feet long. Flowers more than two inches in diameter, the segments ovate-oblong, straw color internally, brownish-purple externally. The fruit was not collected; the specimens agree so well in other respects with Y. baccata that they must belong to that species.

YUCCA WHIPPLEI, *Torr. in Bot. Mex. Bound. Surv.*, *p.* 222. Y. aloifolia, *Linn. Sp.*, *p.* 457.? *Torr. Bot. Whipple's Rep.*, *p.* 147. Mouth of Diamond river; April 3; growing in tufts, on rocks. Only the leaves were obtained. These so strongly resemble those of Yucca, found at Cajon Pass, by Dr. Bigelow, in Whipple's Expedition, and by Mr. Schott, near San Pasqual, that I think they must belong to the same species.

AMARYLLIDACEÆ.

AGAVE, n. sp.? Camp 65; March 31. The specimens consist of only a single leaf, and a portion of the scape. A sketch of the plant was taken by Dr. Newberry. The leaves form a tuft, close to the ground. They are from eight to ten inches long, and taper from a base three-fourths of an inch long to a narrow thorny point; the margin is entire, of a thick cartilaginous texture. The scape is eight feet high, (including the flowery portion.) Flowers in a long raceme, or rather narrow panicle. Peduncles or branches remote, 6–10 lines long, 2–5 flowered; pedicels very short. Segments of the perianth about six lines long, ovate lanceolate, rather obtuse. Stamens longer than the perianth. Anthers linear, the filaments inserted, versatile. Ovary obtusely triangular, adhering to the tube of the perianth only partially; ovules very numerous in a double series; style as long as the stamen, angular, rather short; stigma small capitate. Fruit not collected. This species seems not to be described. It is nearly allied to A. parviflora, *Torr. in Bot. Whipple's Exped.*, *p.* 214, but the margin is neither filamentous nor denticulate.

BROMELIACEÆ.

DASYLIRRON ERUMPENS, *Torr. Bot. Whippl. Exped.*, *p.* 216. Camp 65. Yampai creek; March 30.

MELANTHACEÆ.

ANTICLEA NUTTALII, *Torr. Bot. Whippl. Exped*, *p.* 144.

JUNCACEÆ.

JUNCUS EFFUSUS, *Linn.* Santa Isabel; November 16. (In fruit.)

CYPERACEÆ.

CYPERUS MICHAUXIANUS. Riverside mountain; January 25.

CYPERUS ERYTHRORHIZOS, *Muhl. Gram.*, *p.* 20; *Torr. Cyp.*, *p.* 280. Fort Yuma to Mojave valley; January 14. This species has not been found before west of St. Louis.

CAREX UMBELLATA. San Francisco mountain; April 26. The specimens are immature.

SCIRPUS PUNGENS, *Vahl. Enum.* 2, *p.* 255; *Gray, Man. ed.* 2, *p.* 499. Near springs, Moqui country; May 9. (Camp 92.)

GRAMINIÆ, (By George Thurber.)

PANICUM (ECHINOCHLOA) CRUS-GALLI, *Linn.*
Oplismenus Crus-galli, *Kunth. Emm.* 1, *p.* 143. Banks of the Colorado generally.

SETARIA CAUDATA, *Roem. & Shultz; Kunth. Emm.* 1, *p.* 153. Long valley and Yampai basin; March 31. A very common species, occurring in all the collections from the regions west of the Rio Grande. The inflorescence varies greatly; the spike being dense and strict and very loose and flexuose in the same stock of specimens.

ERIOCOMA CUSPIDATA, *Nutt. Gen.* 1, *p.* 40.

Stipa membranacea, *Pursh. Hook. Fl. Bor.-Am.*

Fendleria eynchelytroides, *Steud. Lyn. Pl. Glum.* 2, *p.* 419.   Moqui country; May 8.

MUHLENBERGIA VIRESCENS, *Trin. Agrostid.* 2, *p.* 57.   San Francisco Prairie and Leroux's Spring; April 26.

MUHLENBERGIA DEBILIS, *Trin. Agrostid.* 2, *p.* 49.

M. purpurea, *Nutt. Pl. Gamb., p.* 186.   Riverside mountain; January 25; also January 13.

SPOROBOLUS CRYPTANDRUS, *Gray. Man. ed.* 2, *p.* 542.

Agrostis cryptandrus, *Torr. Ann. Lyc. N. Y.* 1, *p.* 151.   Camp 17; January 17.

PHRAGMITES COMMUNIS, *Trin. Fund.* 134.

Arundo phragmites, *Lin.*   Reedy Bend; January 15.   "Grows as far north as mouth of Little Colorado, but smaller northward."

CHLORIS ALBA, *Presl.; Rel. Haluk.* 1, p. 289.   Growing in tufts near the water's edge, on the abrupt sandy banks of the Colorado; November 25; also at Riverside mountain; July 24.

BOUTELONA POLYSTACHYA, *Torr. in Williamson's Rep., p.* 336, *tab.* X.   Chondrosium polysta-chyum, *Benth. Bot. Sulph., p.* 56.   Camp 17; January 17.

BOUTELONA OLIGOSTUCHYA, *Torr.; Gray, Man. ed.* 2, p. 553.   Banks of Little Colorado; May 1. "Large grama grass."

BOUTELONA ERIOPODA, *Torr. in Emory's Rep., p.* 154.   (sub Chondrosium.)   Little Colorado; May 1.   "Small grama grass."

BOUTELONA CURTIPENDULA, *Gray, Man. ed.* 2, *p.* 553.   On rocks; March 31.   Yampai creek.

LEPTOCHLOA FASCICULARIS, *Gray, l. c., p.* 550.   Purple Hills; January 13.   This seems to be quite common along the Colorado.   All of our specimens from there have the panicle more densely flowered than in the ordinary state of the species.

TRICUSPIS PULCHELLA, *Torr. in Whip. Rep., p.* 156.

Uralepis pulchella, *Kunth. Gram.* 1, *p.* 108.   Bill Williams's Fork; Feb. 1.   "Growing in tufts on desert surfaces and hill tops all along the Colorado."

ERAGROSTIS PURSHII, *Schrad. Gray, l. c., p.* 564.   Long Valley, Camp 62.

MELICA IMPERFECTA, *Trin.; Torr. in Whip. Rep., p.* 157.   Laguna, California; November 17. Fragmentary specimens of what appear to be this species, to which M. panicoides, *Nutt. Pl. Gamb.,* probably belongs.

SCLEROCHLOA CALIFORNICA, *Munroe in Pl. Hartweg., p.* 342.   Yampai creek, Camp 65, and April 23.   This seems to be a very common grass in the country between the Rio Grande and the Colorado.

FESTUCA TENELLA, var. ARISTULATA, *Torr. in Whip. Rep., p.* 156.   Yampai valley and Moqui country; March and May.

BRIZOPYRUM SPICATUM, *Hook. & Arn. Bot. Beechy, p.* 403.

Uniola stricta, *Torr. in Ann. Lyc. N. Y.* 1, *p.* 155.   Very abundant in the saline soils of the far west, and in exceedingly variable species.   The Uniola stricta of Torrey was founded upon a very rigid form, with elongated many-flowered, shining spikelets; our very full suite of specimens connect this with the ordinary form.   The wiry foliage of this species is, in many localities, the only pasturage.

BROMUS.   A specimen collected at Sitgreaves's Pass may be a new species, but we do not care to add names in a family where they are far too numerous, without further comparison.

HORDEUM JUBATUM, *Lin.; Kunth. Enum.* 1, *p.* 457.   Moqui country; May 8.   All over the Colorado country.

IMPERATA ARUNDINACEA, *Cyrill, Kunth., l. c., p.* 477.   Along the Colorado generally.   This widely distributed grass was collected on the Rio Grande by Dr. Bigelow and Mr. Wright, and occurs also in Drummond's Texan collections.

PART V.

EXPLORATIONS AND SURVEYS. WAR DEPARTMENT.

COLORADO EXPLORING EXPEDITION, LIEUTENANT J. C. IVES, TOPOGRAPHICAL ENGINEERS, 1857–'58.

ZOOLOGY.

BY Professor S. F. BAIRD, SMITHSONIAN INSTITUTION.

WASHINGTON, D. C.
1860.

LIST OF BIRDS

COLLECTED

ON THE COLORADO EXPEDITION.

The collections in Zoology made by Mr. Möllhausen, zoologist of the expedition, consisted chiefly of birds. The mammals, reptiles, and fishes were like those previously obtained in the same regions by the naturalists connected with the expeditions of Captain Sitgreaves, Captain Whipple, and Lieutenant Parke. Some points of special interest, however, will be found in the indications of geographical distribution afforded by the list of birds.

All the species mentioned in the list of birds are fully described in the General Report on Birds in volume IX of the Pacific Railroad Report, at the pages respectively indicated by the figures in parenthesis immediately following the scientific names. All the specimens collected on Lieutenant Ives's expedition will be found enumerated in the tables at the end of the articles on the several species.

Picus harrisii, Aud., (87.) Harris's woodpecker. Fort Defiance.

Picus scalaris, Wagl., (94.) Fort Yuma.

Centurus uropygialis, Baird, (111.) Gila woodpecker. Fort Yuma. This species appears to extend from the valley of the Lower Gila to Cape St. Lucas.

Colaptes Mexicanus, Sw., (120.) Red-shafted flicker. Mojave valley.

Atthis costæ, Reich., (138.) Coste's humming bird. Colorado river.

Antrostomus nuttalli, Cassen, (149.) Nuttall's whippoorwill. Fort Defiance and the Moqui villages.

Myiarchus Mexicanus, Baird, (179.) Ash-throated flycatcher. Fort Yuma and the Colorado.

Sayornis sayus, Baird, (185.) Say's flycatcher. Fort Yuma.

Empidonax obscurus, Baird, (200.) Wright's flycatcher. Fort Yuma and the Colorado.

Pyrocephalus rubineus, Gray, (201.) Red flycatcher. Fort Yuma.

Turdus migratorius, L., (155.) Robin. Fort Yuma and the Colorado.

Turdus nævius, Gm., (219.) Oregon robin. Colorado river.

Sialia mexicana, Sw., (223.) Western blue bird. Fort Yuma.

Sialia arctica, Sw., (224.) Mountain blue bird. Fort Defiance, Fort Yuma.

Regulus calendula, Licht., (226.) Ruby-crowned wren. Fort Yuma and the Colorado.

Anthus ludoviceanus, Licht., (232.) Titlark. Fort Yuma.

Helminthophaga celata, Baird, (257.) Orange-crowned warbler. Fort Defiance.

Dendroica nigrescens, Baird, (270.) Black-throated gray warbler. Fort Defiance.

Dendroica audubonis, Baird, (273.) Audubon's warbler. Fort Tejon, Fort Yuma, and the Colorado.

Hirundo thalassina, Sw., (311.) Violet-green swallow. Fort Defiance.

Phainopepla nitens, Sclater, (320.) Black flycatcher. Fort Yuma and the Colorado desert.

Collyrio excubitoroides, Baird, (327.) White-rumped shrike. Partridge creek.

Merinus polyglottus, Bore, (344.) Mocking bird. Big Cañon of Colorado.

Oreoscoptes montanus, Baird, (347.) Mountain mocking bird. Little Colorado.

Harporrynchus crissales, Henry, (351.) Mocking thrush. Fort Yuma. This is the second specimen ever collected of the species.

Salpinctes obsoletus, Cab., (357.) Rock wren. Fort Defiance and 120 miles above Fort Yuma.

Troglodytes parkmanni, Aud., (367.) Parkmann's wren. Fort Yuma.

Sitta canadensis, L., (376.) Red-bellied nuthatch. Fort Yuma.

Sitta pygmœa, Vigors., (378.) California nuthatch. Colorado region.

Polioptila cœrulea, Sclat., (380.) Blue-gray flycatcher. Fort Yuma.

Polioptila plumbea, Baird, (382.) Fort Yuma.

Tophophanes inornatus, Cassen, (386.) Gray titmouse. Fort Defiance.

Parus montanus, Gambel, (394.) Mountain titmouse. San Francisco mountains.

Paroides flaviceps, Baird, (400.) Yellow-headed tit. Fort Yuma.

Carpodacus frontalis, Gray, (415.) House finch. Sitgreaves's Pass.

Chondestes grammaca, Bon., (456.) Lark finch. Fort Defiance.

Zonotrichia gambelii, Gambel, (460.) Gambel's finch. Above Fort Yuma.

Junco oregonus, Sclat., (467.) Oregon snow bird. Fort Yuma.

Poospiza bilineata, Sclat., (470.) Black-throated sparrow. Big Cañon.

Poospiza belli, Sclat., (470.) Bell's finch. Mojave village.

Spizella socialis, Bon., (473.) Chipping sparrow. Colorado river and Fort Defiance.

Spizella breweri, Cass, (475.) Brewer's finch. Sitgreaves's Pass.

Pipilo abertis, Baird, (516.) Abert's finch. Fort Yuma.

Molothrus peeoris, Sw., (524.) Cow bird. Fort Yuma.

Agelaius phoeniceus, Vieill, (526.) Red wing blackbird. Fort Yuma.

Xanthocephalus icterocephalus, Baird, (531.) Yellow-headed blackbird. Colorado creek.

Picicorous columbranus, Bon., (573.) Clark's crow. San Francisco mountains.

Cyanocetta woodhousii, Baird, (585.) Woodhouse's jay. Colorado river.

Zenaidura carolinensis, Bon., (604.) Carolina dove. Fort Defiance.

Tophortyx gambelii, Nutt., (645.) Gambel's partridge. Fort Yuma, the Colorado, and Cottonwood valley.

Grus canadensis, L., (655.) Sandhill crane. Colorado.

Tantalus loculator, L., (682.) Wood ibis, Colorado turkey. Colorado river.

Ægralites montanus, Cassin, (693.) Mountain plover. On road to Fort Tejon.

Recurvirostra americana, Gr., (703.) American avoset. Colorado river.

Gallinago wilsonii, Bon., (710.) Wilson's snipe. Colorado river.

APPENDICES.

APPENDIX A.

---

1. REMARKS UPON THE ASTRONOMICAL OBSERVATIONS.

At Camp 1, near the mouth of the Colorado, the longitude was determined with a transit, and by observing occultations. Transit observations for longitude were also made at Camp 61, near the place where the land explorations from the Colorado were commenced. The longitudes of the other positions were determined by taking a mean of the results obtained from three chronometers. The chronometers were new, and furnished by Messrs. Bond & Sons, of Boston. They were carried, during the river survey, upon the steamboat, and, during the land explorations, by hand. The results of each day accorded very closely with the results of the compass survey. All the observations for latitude were made with a sextant.

The observations were computed under the direction of Prof. G. P. Bond, of the Cambridge Observatory. The following communication was received from him in regard to the computations and the values of the results:

CAMBRIDGE OBSERVATORY, *January* 14, 1859.

SIR: In reducing the latitude observations of the survey of the Colorado, the results of which have been already communicated, I have used, in the first instance, approximate errors of the chronometer deduced from your own computations made in the field. The new latitudes were then used to compute the hour angles of the time stars, giving more exact chronometer errors, with which the latitudes were again corrected, and lastly, the hour angles also, to accord with the latitudes as finally adopted.

The tables of the Berliner Jahrbuch have been used, in addition to those of the Nautical Almanac, as a security against mistakes. Corrections for the barometer and thermometer have been applied to the refractions. * * * * * * *

On the dates when transits were obtained, the latter have been used in preference to the sextant observations. * * * Among the observations of time stars, whenever a difference exceeding 5s. between results by east and west stars has been found to exist, the work has been revised, and the single observed altitudes compared together to detect errors in the original record. In this way the corrections made in the note-books have been ascertained. Considering the disadvantages under which such observations are made, I think you have reason to be gratified that so few discrepancies remain unaccounted for. * *

The transit observations at Camp 1, from December 10 to 28, afford data for an accurate rating of the chronometers. Corresponding observations were obtained at Cambridge for each of your four moon culminations, two at Camp 1 and two at Camp 61, (in Sitgreaves's Pass,) and also for the occultation of the Pleiades, December 27. These have afforded the following results for longitudes:

		h.	m.	s.
1857, Dec. 27. Transit ☾ L, longitude of Camp 1		7	39	19.9
28. Do............do		7	39	20.6
27. Immersion of Calaeno		7	39	25.5
27. Immersion of Anon. *, No. 4 of Bessel		7	39	25.1
Adopted longitude of Camp 1		7	39	25.0
1858, Mar. 24. Transit ☾ L, longitude of Camp 61		7	37	06.4
25. Do............do		7	37	13.6
Adopted longitude of Camp 61		7	37	10.0

The determination for Camp 1 must be very exact. The situation of the stars in the moon's path was favorable; the places of the stars are well known; and the corrections of the lunar ephemeris in right ascension and declination were derived from our observations at Cambridge. I presume that as yet the position of few stations on the west coast has been better determined. Besides the above, the following has been used as a zero point for the chronometric longitudes:

Camp 12. Longitude, 7h. 38m. 21s.,

assuming the junction of Gila and Colorado to be in longitude 7h. 38m. 25s.   *   *

Before concluding I would again call your attention to the importance of the transit observations. Their value and precision you seem to have greatly underrated, to judge from the remarks in your letter of October 21.

Respectfully yours,

G. P. BOND.

Lieutenant J. C. Ives,
United States Topographical Engineers.

---

2. REMARKS UPON THE BAROMETRIC OBSERVATIONS.

The barometric observations were computed in pursuance of the system described by Lieutenant Abbot, topographical engineers, in Vol. VI, Pacific Railroad Reports.

These readings of the barometers were first reduced to what they would have been at 32° Fahrenheit, and then corrected for instrumental error. The series of hourly observations taken at Camp 1, after being corrected as above, were used to form a table for the correction of the *horary oscillation*. The observations for each day were plotted in a curve, and by these curves one or two manifest errors of observation were corrected. The mean of all the observations for each hour was then found, thus forming a *mean day*, which was also plotted. The mean of all the hourly readings of this *mean day* was then found, and the difference between it and each of the hourly readings of the *mean day* taken; affecting this difference with the sign + when the grand mean was the greater, and with the sign — when this mean was the less. The corrections for the respective hours, thus found, were applied to all the observations used.

The series of three hourly observations taken at Fort Yuma were used to form a table of corrections for *abnormal oscillations*, the observations being all plotted in a curve. The interval between January 5 and January 12, during which there were no observations, was filled up by drawing the curve as correctly as possible from the general direction of the curve preceding and following the interval. The record for this period was then made up from the curve as thus interpolated.

The mean of all the readings, observed and interpolated, as thus corrected by the curve, was then found, and the difference taken between it and each of the readings; affecting these differences with the sign $+$ when the mean was the greater, and with the sign $-$ when it was the less.

The corrections from this table (corresponding in date and hour to that of the observation to be computed) were applied to all observations taken during the period of time covered by the table. The observations were then ready for computation, for which purpose the tables of Prof. Guyot, in the Smithsonian collection of meteorological and physical tables, were used. The mean of all the observed temperatures at each station was used in making the computations.

In order further to correct the results of the observations made at camps upon the Colorado, a profile of the river, as determined by the computed altitudes, was plotted, the distances from camp to camp being laid off on a scale of five miles to the inch, and the altitudes on a scale of 100 feet to the inch. The profile exhibiting considerable irregularities, a mean line was drawn to represent the slope of the stream, and the tabulated altitudes of the camps increased or diminished by the amount that the corresponding point upon the profile fell below or above the mean line. The final results are given in the column of altitudes in *Appendix B.*

APPENDIX B.

LIST OF CAMPS, WITH DISTANCES, ALTITUDES, LATITUDES, AND LONGITUDES, ETC.

From mouth of river to head of navigation.

Camp	Locality.	Distance by river from—		Altitude above sea.	Latitude.	Longitude.	Remarks.
		Preceding camp.	Mouth of river.				
		Miles.	Miles.	Feet.	° ′ ″	° ′ ″	
1	Robinson's Landing....................	....	10.0	......	31 49 21.8	114 51 15.0	Observations at Camp 1 taken 20
2	Cocopa Village	38.0	48.0	54	32 04 17.2	115 00 15.0	feet above low water mark,
3	......do. ...	16 0	64 0	77	32 11 22 2	115 01 25.5	and reduced to that level.
4	......do.	14.0	78.0	97	32 17 49.2	114 56 22.5	
5	......do.	11.5	89.5	112	32 24 03.6	114 53 40.5	
6	......do.	9.5	99.0	128	....	....	
7	....,. do.	9.5	108.5	140	....	....	
8	......do.	10.5	119.0	155	....	....	
9	......do.	12.5	131.5	172	....	....	
10	......do.	5.0	136.5	180	....	....	
11	Fort Yuma..........................	13.5	150.0	200	32 43 32.3	114 36 09.9	The latitude and longitude of
12	Yuma Shoals........................	3.0	153.0	204	32 45 37.7	114 35 12.0	Fort Yuma are from the deter-
13	Explorer's Pass.....................	13 0	166 0	222	32 50 01.2	114 29 37.5	minations of the Mexican
14	Purple Hill Pass....................	9.0	175.0	234	....	....	Boundary Commission.
15	Purple Hills	7.0	182.0	243	33 00 12.6	114 28 25.5	
16	Canebrake Cañon....................	6 5	188.5	252	....	....	
17	North Bend.............	8.5	197.0	264	....	....	
18	Foot of Great Colorado Valley	13.0	210.0	282	33 10 26.7	114 40 49.5	
19	Long Bend	14.0	224.0	301	33 19 42.5	114 43 13.5	
20	......do.	15.0	239.0	322	....	....	
21	Long Shoals........................	9.0	248.0	334	....	....	
22	......do.	6 0	254.0	342	33 35 12 4	114 32 36.0	
23	......do.	6.0	260.0	350	33 38 11.8	114 30 42.0	
24	Half-way Bend	19.0	279.0	378	33 48 14.9	114 29 04.5	
25	Half-way Mountain..................	5.0	284.0	386	....	....	
26	Sand Island Shoals....................	8.0	292.0	396	33 57 24 8	114 30 16.5	
27	.. ...do.	2.0	294.0	399	33 58 17.0	114 29 09.0	
28	Riverside Mountain	3.5	297.5	404	33 59 58.3	114 26 58.5	
29	......do.	4.5	302.0	409	....	....	
30	Gravel Hill Bend	10.0	312.0	426	34 06 57.1	114 22 51.0	
31	......do.	6.5	318.5	433	....	....	
32	Beaver Island.......................	3.5	322.0	440	34 10 14.8	114 16 15.0	
33	Mouth of Bill Williams's Fork..........	18.0	340.0	465	34 18 16 9	114 06 45.0	
34	Chemehuevis Valley	1.0	341.0	467	....	....	
35	......do.	3.0	344.0	470	....	....	
36	......do.	12.5	356.5	488	34 26 07.6	114 17 18.0	
37	......do.	1.5	358.0	491	... .	....	
38	......do.	6.5	364.5	500	34 27 49.4	114 23 01 5	
39	......do.	4.0	368.5	506	....	....	
40	Mojave Cañon......................	14 0	382.5	524	....	....	

APPENDIX B—Continued.

Camp.	Locality.	Distance by river from—		Altitude above sea.	Latitude.	Longitude.	Remarks.
		Preceding camp.	Mouth of river.				
		Miles.	Miles.	Feet.	° ′ ″	° ′ ″	
41	Mojave Valley..................	9.0	391.5	537	....	....	
42	......do................................	8.0	399.5	548	....	....	
43	......do................................	9 5	409.0	561	34 53 46.1	114 33 15.0	
44	......do.	2.0	411.0	565	....	....	
45	......do............	9.5	420.5	580	34 58 44.5	114 38 18.0	
46	......do.	11.5	432.0	601	....	....	
47	......do................................	8.0	440.0	618	35 07 14.1	114 34 07.5	
48	Deep Rapid...........................	16.0	456.0	656	35 18 31.0	114 33 42.0	
49	Shallow Rapid........................	2.5	458 5	662	35 19 33.9	114 34 22.5	
50	......do................................	3 5	462.0	675	35 21 54.0	114 34 49.5	
51	......do................................	4.5	466.5	694	35 24 03.1	114 37 01.5	
52	......do................................	3.0	469.5	704	....	....	
53	......do................................	9.0	478.5	743	35 32 08.1	114 38 50.0	
54	......do................................	10.0	488.5	790	35 37 50.5	114 39 48.0	
55	......do...........	5.0	493.5	819	....	....	
56	......do................................	1.5	495.0	828	35 41 43.2	114 41 04.5	
57	......do.......................	5.0	500.0	860	35 44 57.1	114 42 13.5	
58	......do................................	13.0	513.0	....	....	....	
59	......do................................	17.0	530.0	....	36 03 02.2	....	
59 ′	......do................................	....	....	....	35 02 50.4	114 35 00.0	

All of the above positions are on the bank of the Colorado. The barometric observations, excepting at Camp 1, were taken from a fixed position on the steamboat, 3 feet above water, and the results are reduced to water level.

APPENDIX B—Continued.

From Mojave Valley to Fort Defiance.

Camp.	Locality.	Distance by trail from—		Altitude above sea.	Latitude.	Longitude.	Remarks.
		Preceding camp.	River at Mojave Valley.				
		Miles.	*Miles.*	*Feet.*	° ′ ″	° ′ ″	
60	Sitgreaves's Pass.......................	13.0	13.0	2,093	35 04 33.9	114 23 15.0	
	Summit of Sitgreaves's Pass.............	....	....	3,652	....	....	
61	Meadow Creek	7.5	20.5	2,992	35 02 17.6	114 17 30.0	
	Valley west of Meadow Creek	....	....	2,506	....	....	
62	Railroad Pass..........................	17.0	37.5	3,346	35 09 51.4	114 04 45.0	
	Summit Railroad Pass...................	3.0	....	3,764			
63	Bitter Spring	14.0	51.5	....	....	....	
64	Rim of Cerbat Basin....................	18.0	69.5	....	35 24 04.7	113 47 22.5	
65	Peacock's Spring	13.0	82.5	4,151	35 25 12.3	113 38 40.5	
66	New Creek............................	16.5	99.0	4,466	....	....	
67	Big Cañon, mouth of Diamond river.....	12.0	111.0	1,426	35 45 41.1	113 24 15.0	
68	Hualpais Spring........................	12.0	123.0	4,258	35 38 50.6	113 25 43.5	
69	Cedar Forest..........................	16.0	139.0	5,868	35 37 06.1	113 13 15.0	
70	Snow Spring	5.0	144.0	6,396	.. ..	....	
71	Pine Forest...........................	16.0	160 0	6,703	35 52 15.3	113 03 37.5	
72	......do.	16.0	176.0	5,802	36 00 52 7	....	
	Cataract Creek	18.0	....	2,602	....	....	
73	Head of Cataract Cañon	8.0	184.0	5,935	36 05 57.9	112 48 00.0	
74	Forest Lagoons........................	14.0	198.0	6,580	....	....	
75	Colorado Plateau	19.0	217.0	5,673	35 43 21.8	112 49 46.5	
76	......do.	21.0	238.0	5,618	....	....	
77	Partridge Ravine......................	4.0	242.0	5,732	35 25 56.2	112 46 58.5	
78	......do.	12.0	254.0	5,245	35 19 46.2	112 39 36.0	
79	Cedar Creek..........................	9.0	263.0	5,889	35 18 48.0	112 30 58.5	
80	Bill Williams's Mountain	13.0	276.0	6,620	35 15 35.1	112 19 24.0	
81	Aspen Spring.........................	18 0	294.0	7,381	35 17 31.1	112 02 24.0	
82	Leroux's Spring.......................	14.0	308.0	7,644	....	....	
83	Lagoons..............................	26.0	334.0	....	....	....	
84	Ruins	14.0	348.0	....	....	....	
85	Flax River............................	21.0	369 0	....	35 17 51.4	110 58 55 5	
86	Painted Desert........................	20 0	389.0	....	35 27 07.5	110 47 58.5	
87	Flax River............................	14 0	403.0	....	....	....	
88	......do.	19.0	422 0	....	35 04 09.0	110 44 25.5	
89	......do.	10.0	432 0	....	....	....	
90	Edge of Blue Mesa	26.0	458.0	5,418	35 17 52 7	....	
91	Pottery Hill..........................	14.0	472.0	5,722	35 28 47.8	110 28 50.0	
92	Limestone Spring......................	16.0	488.0	5,680	35 41 34.8	110 28 16.5	
93	Mooshanch............................	10.0	498.0	5,890	35 47 27.1	....	
94	Oraybe....................	13.0	511.0	5,816	....	....	
95	Oraybe Gardens	7.0	518.0	6,395	....	....	
96	Moquis Desert........................	14.0	532.0	6,281	....	....	
97	Northern Oraybe Gardens	11 0	543.0	....	35 55 39.4	110 42 40.5	
98	Near Tegua	16.0	559 0	....	35 50 27.3	110 29 09.0	
99	Peach Orchard Spring..........	14.0	573.0	6,268	35 47 15.9	110 17 00.0	
100	White Rock Spring	25.0	598.0	6,516	35 44 55.1	109 54 00.0	
101	Pueblo Creek..........................	18.0	616.0	6,329	35 42 22.3	109 36 43.9	
102	Navajo Forest.........................	25.0	641.0	....	....	....	
103	Fort Defiance Valley...................	6 0	647.0	....	35 41 57.1	109 09 49.5	
	Fort Defiance	3.0	....	....	35 44 33.7	109 08 30.0	

APPENDIX C.

BAROMETRIC AND METEOROLOGICAL OBSERVATIONS.

Station.	Date.	Hour.	Number of barometer.	Reading of barometer. Upper vernier	Reading of barometer. Lower vernier	Attached thermometer.	Detached thermometer. Wet bulb.	Detached thermometer. Dry bulb.	Wind. Direction.	Wind. Force.	Clouds.	Remarks.
	1857.			*Inches.*	*Inches.*	°	•	°				
Water edge 8' 11" above mean tide at San Pedro Landing.	Nov. 6	9 a. m.	1096	30.664	0.580	63	59	63	S. 85 W.	3	3 c.	
	6	9.15 a. m.	1096	30.665	0.582	64	56	64	S. 30 W.	1	3 c.	
	6	9.25 a. m.	1096	30.681	0.558	64	57	64	S. 15 W.	0	1 c.	
	6	9.35 a. m.	1096	30.680	0.568	64	57	64	S.	0	1 c.	
	6	9.40 a. m.	1096	30.682	0.558	64	57	65	S.	0	1 c.	
	6	9.45 a. m.	1096	30.680	0.569	65	57	65	S.	1	1 c.	
	6	9.50 a. m.	1096	30.680	0.568	65	57	64	S. 40 W.	2	1 c.	
	6	9.55 a. m.	1096	30.682	0.564	64	56	64	S. 70 W.	2	1 c.	
	6	10 a. m.	1095	30.660	0.566	64	56	61	S. 80 W.	3	1 c.	
	6	10.10 a. m.	1096	30.657	0.582	64	55	64	S. 60 W.	2	1 c.	
	6	10.20 a. m.	1096	30.680	0.568	65	55	65	S. 70 W.	2	1 c.	
Los Angeles	6	9 p. m.	1096	30.484	0.741	68	55	66	S.	3	10 N.	
	7	7 a. m.	1096	30.565	0.677	62	52	61	E.	0	0 W., c.	
	7	9 a. m.	1096	30.565	0.630	63	53	63	S.	0	0 W., c.	
	7	10 a. m.	1096	30.554	0.684	65	54	65	S.	0	1 S.	
	7	2 p. m.	1096	30.551	0.696	70	58	68	S.	0	0 W., c.	
	7	9 p. m.	1096	30.541	0.696	66	51	66	S.	0	0 W., c.	
	8	7 a. m.	1096	30.613	0.628	69	53	59	N. 20 W.	0	0 W., c.	
	8	2 p. m.	1096	30.600	0.644	65	54	66	S.	1	0 W., clear	
	8	9 p. m.	1096	30.591	0.649	62	57	63	S. 40 W.	0	0 W., cl.	
	9	7 a. m.	1096	30.546	0.656	59	51	59	NE.	1	3 c.	
	9	10 p. m.	1096	30.457	0.772	66	59	65	N. 15 W.	0	0 W., c.	
	10	7 p. m.	1096	30.396	0.296	60	60	61	N. 20 W.	1	2 c.	
	10	10 p. m.	1096	30.362	0.829	65	60	66	S.	0	0 W., c.	
	11	7 p. m.	1096	30.376	0.812	61	58	61	N. 15 E.	1	1 c.	
Mission	11	9.45 a. m.	1096	30.376	1.025	52	58	49	N. 30 W.	2	9 N.	
Summit of pass	11	11 a. m.	1096	29.556	1.396	45	58	44	N. 30 W.	3	10 N.	
Foot of San Francisco cañon	12	7 a. m.	1096	29.818	1.212	45	58	45	N. 40 E.	2	W., cl.	
Camp 13—14	13	7.30 p. m.	1096	29.054	1.787	42	58	41	N. 10 W.	1	W., cl.	
	14	6.30 a. m.	1096	29.100	1.751	41	58	44	N. 15 W.	1	W., cl.	
Summit of mountains	14	7.45 a. m.	1096	28.604	2.125	46	58	36	0.	0	W., cl.	
Foot of mountain	14	12.30 p. m.	1096	28.992	1.852	55	58	52	0.	0	W., cl.	
Camp 14—15	14	8.45 p. m.	1096	28.906	1.894	41	58	59	N. 10 W.	2	W., cl.	
	15	7.30 a. m.	1096	28.946	1.900	42	58	34	S. 40 E.	1	W., cl.	

APPENDIX C—Continued.

Station	Date	Hour	Number of barometer	Reading of barometer Upper vernier	Lower vernier	Attached thermometer	Wet bulb	Dry bulb	Wind Direction	Force	Clouds	Remarks
Summit of Sierra Nevada, (cut off) road	1857. Nov. 15	12 m	1096	28.162	2.160	54	58	51	S. 40 E.	2	W., cl.	
Fort Tejon	15	4 p.m	1096	28.966	1.900	47	58	47	S. 40 W	2	W., cl.	
	16	7 a.m	1095	28.978	1.838	44	58	46	E.	3	W., cl.	
	16	12 m	1096	29.253	2.120	59	58	59	E. 10 S	3	0 W., cl.	
	16	3.15 p.m	1096	29.242	2.120	57	58	57	E.	3	W., cl.	
	17	7.30 a.m	1096	29.250	2.150	50	58	51	NE.	2	W., cl.	
	17	12 m	1096	29.243	2.042	61	58	62	SE.	2	W., cl.	
	17	3 p.m	1096	29.210	2.150	60	53	62	E.	1	W., cl.	
	18	7 a.m	1096	29.180	2.164	55	58	55		0	W., cl.	
	18	12 m	1096	29.184	2.162	63	58	64	SE.	1	W., cl.	
	18	3 p.m	1096	29.178	2.168	64	58	65	SE.	1	W., cl.	
	19	9 a.m	1096	29.158	2.184	59	58	60	E.	1	W., cl.	
	19	12 m	1096	29.160	2.192	65	58	66	E.	1	W., cl.	
	19	3 p.m	1096	29.150	2.194	65	58	65		0	W., cl.	
	20	7.30 a.m	1096	29.142	2.189	53	58	55		0	W., cl.	
	20	9 a.m	1095	29.150	2.176	58	58	58		0	W., cl.	
	20	12 m	1096	29.172	2.183	67	58	67	NE.	1	W., cl.	
	20	6 p.m	1096	29.160	2.184	63	58	62	NE.	1	W., cl.	
	21	9 a.m	1096	29.124	2.178	48	58	47		0	1 cir.	
	21	12 m	1096	29.164	2.176	64	58	65	E.	1	2 cir.	
	21	3 p.m	1096	23.166	2.190	66	53	63		0	3 cir.	
	22	7 a.m	1096	29.136	2.184	51	58	49		0	4 cir. str	
	23	12 m	1096	29.104	2.216	56	58	53	S. 40 W.	1	9 cir. str.	
	23	2.16½ p.m	1096	29.100	2.226	60	58	53	S. 40 W.	1	9 cir. str.	Earthquake at 2 o'clock and 16½ minutes during the reading of barometer. The direction of the shock apparently SE. to NW.
	23	10 p.m	1036	29.026	2.224	55	58	40	N. 20 W.	1	W., cl.	
	24	7 a.m	1096	29.081	2.228	55	58	41	N. 10 W.	2	W., cl.	
	24	9 p.m	1096	29.088	2.224	57	53	47	S. 40 W.	0	Raining	
	25	7 a.m	1056	29.086	2.234	55	58	54	S. 40 W.	1	Wh. cl.	
	25	12 m	1096	29.081	2.238	59	58	56	S. 20 W.	1	9 cir.	
	25	9 p.m	1096	29.082	2.259	60	58	46	S.	1	W., cl.	
	26	7 a.m	1096	29.036	2.261	57	53	47	S.	0	Raining.	
	26	12 m	1095	29.041	2.281	58	58	57	S.	0	Raining	
	26	9 p.m	1096	29.068	2.239	59	58	53	S.	0	Raining	
Camp Alexander	27	7 a.m	1096	29.108	2.200	52	58	44	N. 20 W	1	9 cum.	
At the foot of S. Madra mountains	27,28	7 p.m	1696	28.791	2.422	44	58	46	N. 60 E.	4	9 cum. cir.	
	28	9 p.m	1096	28.794	2.428	45	58	45	N. 40 W.	5	1 stratus.	
	28	7 a.m	1096	28.791	2.436	50	58	49	N. 20 W	4	9 cum.	

APPENDIX C—Continued.

Station.	Date.	Hour.	Number of barometer.	Reading of barometer. Upper vernier.	Reading of barometer. Lower vernier.	Attached thermometer.	Detached thermometer. Wet bulb.	Detached thermometer. Dry bulb.	Wind. Direction.	Wind. Force.	Clouds.	Remarks.
	1857.			Inche.	Inches.	°	°	°				
Camp 29—30	Nov. 29	9 p.m.	1096	29.406	1.998	41	58	40	N. 15 W	3	1 cum.	
In San Francisco cañon	30	7 a. m.	1096	29.392	1.966	40	58	40	N. 15 W	0	3 cir.	
Sea beach, half a mile south of old San Diego, (low water mark.)	11	12.30 p m	1095*	31.042	1.012	66	59	66	SW	1	Cum. str.	* Green's syphon.
Camp Mission, San Diego bottom	12	7 a. m.	1095	30.963	0.898	51	50	51	SW	1	Cum. overcast.	
	12	2.45 p. m.	1095	30.945	0.928	63	61	63	SE.	1	Cum. cir.	
Camp at San Bernardo	13	7.45 a. m.	1095	30.934	0.904	52	51	51	0	0	Nim. over.	
	14	7.30 a. m.	1095	31.314	1.084	45	47	44	0	0	0	
Camp at the Laguna	15	8 a. m.	1095	31.110	1.188	49	44	44	E.	1	0	
Camp at Warner's	16	7.15 a. m.	1055	30.186	1.814	33	44	33	E.	1	0	
Camp at San Felipe	17	7.30 a m	1095	29.636	2.284	54	42	51	E.	2	0	
Camp at San Vallecito	18	7.15 a. m.	1095	29.652	1.338	32	35	31	SW	1	0	
	19	7.30 a. m.	1095	31.136	1.500	50	47	49	0	0	0	
Camp at Indian Wells	20	8 a. m.	1095	31.170	1.494	58	49	55	0	0	0	
	22	6.45 a. m.	1095	31.008	0.534	38	37	38	0	0	1 cir.	
Camp at Alamo Mocho	23	7.30 a. m.	1095	31.000	0.860	52	52	52	0	0	2 cir. str.	
Camp at Cook's Wells	24	8 a. m.	1095	31.222	1.24	58	57	58	0	0	1 cir.	
Camp at Tager's Ferry, Fort Yuma	26	8 a. m.	1095	31.141	1.242	56	54	55	SE	1	2 cir. str.	
	26	4.45 p. m.	1095	31.128	1.504	66	54	66	SW	3	0	
	27	7.30 a. m.	1095	31.136	1.362	50	48	50	0	0	0	
	27	1.15 p. m.	1095	31.180	1.194	71	56	71	SW	2	0	
	27	5.15 p. m.	1095	31.156	1.194	63	51	65	W	1	0	
	28	7.15 a. m.	1095	31.188	1.118	45		46	0	0	Few cir.	
	28	1.30 p. m.	1095	31.225	1.156	70		70	W	1	0	
	29	7 a. m.	1095	31.178	1.114	39		40	E.	1	0	
	30	7.45 a. m.	1095	31.178	1.138	43	44	44	NE.	1	2 cir. str.	
	30	12 m	1095	31.226	1.142	66		66	SE.	1	3 cir. str.	
	30	5 p. m.	1095	31.166	1.172	59		58	0	0	1 cir. str.	
	Dec. 1	7.15 a. m.	1095	31.160	1.126	45		46	NE.	1	7 cir. str.	
	1	1.30 p. m.	1095	31.192	1.174	71	56	69	SW	1	0	
	1	5 p. m.	1095	31.172	1.162	57	51	56	NE.	0	0	
	2	7.15 a. m.	1095	31.156	1.129	43	44	44	NE.	1	3 cir. str.	
	2	12 m	1095	31.190	1.168	64	64	64	NE.	2	2 cir. str.	
	3	5 p. m.	1095	31.146	1.154	64		0	0	0	6 cir. str.	
	3	8 a. m.	1095	31.152	1.148	47		47	NE.	1	6 cir. str.	
	8	7.15 a. m.	1095	31.338	0.994	45		44	SW	1	0	
	8	1.30 p m	1095	31.366	1.020	58		58	N. by W	3	¼ cir. str.	

APPENDIX C—Continued.

Station	Date	Hour	Number of barometer	Reading of barometer. Upper vernier. (Inches.)	Reading of barometer. Lower vernier. (Inches.)	Attached thermometer.	Detached thermometer. Wet bulb.	Detached thermometer. Dry bulb.	Wind. Direction.	Wind. Force.	Clouds.	Remarks.
Camp at Tager's Ferry, Fort Yuma	1857. Dec. 9	7 15 a. m.	1095	31.296	0.998	33	33	37	0	0	2 cir. str	
	9	12 30 p. m.	1095	31.362	1.026	62	46	62	N	1	1 cir. str	
	9	5 p. m.	1095	31.304	1.110	56	40	56	NW	1	1 cir. str	
	10	7.30 a. m.	1095	31.236	1.072	41	35	41	0	0	0	
	10	12.45 p. m.	1095	31.255	1.100	66	46	65	N	2	2 cir. str	
	10	5.15 p. m.	1095	31.224	1.124	58	43	58	N	1	6 cir. str	
	11	7 a. m.	1095	31.196	1.096	36	35	40	0	0	1 cir. str	
	11	2.45 p. m.	1005	31.196	1.048	70	51	70	N	1	1 cir. str	This observation was made with a new syphon barometer tube, the first one used having been found broken.
	12	7.15 a. m.	1095	31.116	1.050	37	34	37	0	0	8 cir. str. and cir. cum..	
	13	7.30 a. m.	1095	31.040	1.142	45	42	45	0	0	C. 5 cir. cum	
	13	3.30 p. m.	1095	31.094	1.138	63	54	62	0	0	0	
	14	7.15 a. m.	1095	31.134	1.018	33	38	33	0	0	0	
	15	7.30 a. m.	1059	31.208	1.004	52	45	51	NW	1	0	
	15	5 p. m.	1095	31.190	1.032	63	52	63	0	0	1 cir. str	
	16	7.30 a. m.	1095	31.140	1.028	41	39	42	NE	1	1 stratus	
	17	7.45 a. m.	1095	31.156	1.044	55	46	55	NE	1	1 stratus	
Camp O, 6 miles W. Fort Yuma	27	9 a. m.	1095	31.145	1.029	44	44	40	SW	1	0	
	27	12 m	1095	31.156	1.054	59	58	50	SW	1	0	Few scattering clouds in southwest.
	27	3 p. m.	1095	31.142	1.065	61	52	62	W	1	W, c.	
	27	6 p. m.	1095	31.128	1.014	53	52	53	0	0	Cum	
	28	9 a. m.	1095	31.176	0.916	50	42	47	0	0	Cum	
	28	12 m	1095	31.200	1.000	62	50	62	S.	1	Cir. cum	
	28	3 p. m.	1095	31.182	1.028	65	56	67	SW	1	Cum	
	28	6 p. m.	1095	31.144	1.017	48	45	50	0	0	Cum	
	28	9 p. m.	1095	31.182	1.008	43	41	41	NW	1	0	
	29	9 a. m.	1095	31.236	0.902	59	45	56	NW	2	Cum	
	29	12 m	1095	31.256	0.936	63	45	62	NW	2	0	
	29	3 p. m.	1095	31.244	0.952	64	44	63	0	0	0	
	29	6 p. m.	1095	31.146	0.902	47	42	45	NW	1	0	
	29	9 p. m.	1095	31.184	0.942	30	30	35	0	0	Cum	
	30	6 a. m.	1095	31.196	0.928	40	34	42	NW	0	0	
	30	9 a. m.	1095	31.262	0.920	61	41	57	NE	1	Cum	
	30	12 m	1095	31.244	0.932	65	47	65	NE	1	Cum	
	30	3 p. m.	1095	31.256	0.984	70	53	70	NE	2	0	
	30	6 p. m.	1095	31.178	1.048	55	43	58	NE	1	0	
	31	6 a. m.	1095	31.674	1.036	33	33	38	N.	1	0	
	31	9 a. m.	1095	31.140	1.037	60	46	57	N.	1	0	

APPENDIX C—Continued.

Station.	Date.	Hour.	Number of barometer.	Reading of barometer. Upper vernier.	Lower vernier.	Attached thermometer.	Detached thermometer. Wet bulb.	Dry bulb.	Wind. Direction.	Force.	Clouds.	Remarks.
	1857.			Inches.	Inches.	°	°	°				
Camp O, 6 miles W. Fort Yuma..........	Dec. 31	12 m	1095	31.136	1.064	71	53	71	NE......	1	0........	
	31	3 p. m.....	1095	31.108	1.112	75	57	75	N.......	1	0........	
	31	6 p. m.....	1095	31.046	1.172	57	49	58	0.......	0	0........	
	1858.											
	Jan. 1	6 a. m.....	1095	31.062	1.022	59	49	57	NW......	1	Cum......	
	1	9 a. m.....	1095	31.183	0.998	66	46	62	NW......	2	Cum......	
	1	3 p. m.....	1095	31.212	0.936	65	45	62	NW......	5	0........	
	1	6 p. m.....	1095	31.204	0.976	57	43	55	NW......	5	0........	
	2	6 a. m.....	1095	31.065	0.983	53	34	53	NW......	2	0........	
	2	9 a. m.....	1095	31.300	0.877	57	38	49	NW......	2	0........	
	2	12 m	1095	31.294	0.884	63	44	61	NW......	3	0........	
	2	3 p. m.....	1095	31.283	0.915	65	47	63	NW......	1	0........	
	2	6 p. m.....	1095	31.248	0.900	48.7	36	47	0.......	0	0........	
	3	6 a. m.....	1095	31.178	0.917	55	39	53	0.......	0	0........	
	3	9 a. m.....	1095	31.262	0.928	65	47	51	0.......	1	0........	
	3	12 m	1095	31.260	0.945	67	50	65	NW......	1	0........	
	3	3 p. m.....	1095	31.237	0.973	49	37	65	NW......	0	0........	
	3	6 p. m.....	1095	31.168	0.990	30	28	48	0.......	0	0........	
	4	6 a. m.....	1095	31.099	0.996	24	28	54	0.......	0	0........	
	4	9 a. m.....	1035	31.160	0.953	55	40	51	0.......	0	0........	
	4	12 m	1035	31.180	1.015	63	46	60	NW......	0	0........	
	4	3 p. m.....	1095	31.177	1.034	67	49	67	0.......	0	0........	
	4	6 p. m.....	1095	31.142	1.034	56	42	55	0.......	0	0........	
	5	6 a. m.....	1095	31.006	1.077	24	28	28	0.......	0	0........	
	5	9 a. m.....	1065	31.192	1.575	52	41	53	NE......	1	0........	
	5	12 m	1035	31.150	1.098	66	54	66	NE......	1	0........	
	5	3 p. m.....	1035	31.127	1.075	66	48	64	NE......	1	1 cir. str........	Cirrus cum. around horizon.
	5	6 p. m.....	1095	31.088	1.063	29	41	53	0.......	0	Cir. cum..........	
Camp three-quarters of a mile west of Fort Yuma....	12	7 a. m.....	1095	31.026	1.080	29	30	30	W.......	¹⁄₁₆	1............	
	12	9 a. m.....	1095	31.042	1.068	58	44	47	NW......	¹⁄₁₆	Cum...........	
	12	12 m	1095	31.110	1.078	68	63	54	NW......	¹⁄₁₆	0........	
	12	3 p. m.....	1095	31.074	1.088	67	57	67	NW......	¹⁄₁₆	0........	
	12	6 p. m.....	1095	31.026	1.040	49	45	49	NW......	¹⁄₁₆	Cum...........	
	13	7 a. m.....	1095	30.980	1.091	28	22	31	NW......	0	0........	
	13	9 a. m.....	1095	31.070	1.094	61	45	59	NW......	¹⁄₁₆	Stratus......	
	13	12 m.....	1095	31.064	1.140	61	46	60	S.......	0	5........	
	13	3 p. m.....	1095	31.038	1.170	59	50	59	S.......	¹⁄₁₆	5........	

APPENDIX C—Continued.

Station.	Date.	Hour.	Number of barometer	Reading of barometer. Upper vernier.	Reading of barometer. Lower vernier.	Attached thermometer.	Detached thermometer. Wet bulb.	Detached thermometer. Dry bulb.	Wind. Direction.	Wind. Force.	Clouds.	Remarks.
Camp three-quarters of a mile west of Fort Yuma....	1858. Jan. 13	6 p. m.......	1095	*Inches.* 31.026	*Inches.* 1.128	54	52	60	S..........	1/4	5..........	
	14	7 a. m.......	1095	31.062	1.040	38	35	39	E........	..	0..........	
	14	9 a. m.......	1095	31.138	1.022	53	44	53	SE.......	1	0..........	
	14	12 m.......	1095	31.140	1.010	62	47	60	NW......	1/4	0..........	
	14	3 p. m.......	1095	31.136	1.028	62	52	63	NW......	1/4	0..........	
	14	6 p. m.......	1095	31.078	1.024	45	39	46	NW......	1/2	0..........	
	15	7 a. m.......	1095	31.132	0.948	33	29	35	W........	1/4	1..........	
	15	9 a. m.......	1095	31.200	0.938	48	45	53	W........	1/2	1..........	
	15	12 m.......	1095	31.184	0.954	64	48	64	W........	1/2	1..........	
	15	3 p. m.......	1095	31.146	1.006	62	47	64	W........	1/4	0..........	
	15	6 p. m.......	1095	31.108	0.986	45	43	46	....	..	1..........	
	16	7 a. m.......	1095	31.082	0.994	39	30	39	W........	1	1..........	
	16	9 a. m.......	1095	31.144	0.980	55	42	55	NW......	1	2..........	
	16	12 m.......	1095	31.110	1.010	56	42	56	NW......	1	5..........	
	16	3 p. m.......	1095	31.100	1.028	62	48	65	NW......	1	1..........	
	16	6 p. m.......	1095	31.044	1.044	45	33	45	NW......	1/4	0..........	
	17	7 a. m.......	1095	31.058	1.036	48	37	46	NW......	1/2	8..........	
	17	9 a. m.......	1095	31.072	1.038	52	40	40	NW......	1/4	8..........	
	17	12 m.......	1095	31.080	1.090	66	52	70	NW......	1/4	1..........	
	17	3 p. m.......	1095	31.064	1.083	68	48	70	NW......	1/4	0..........	
	17	6 p. m.......	1095	31.038	1.088	51	39	49	W........	1/2	1..........	
	18	7 a. m.......	1095	31.017	1.050	39	34	38	W........	1/4	0..........	
	18	9 a. m.......	1095	31.090	1.042	65	39	60	W........	1/4	0..........	
	18	12 m.......	1095	31.096	1.048	68	40	68	W........	1/2	0..........	
	18	3 p. m.......	1095	31.074	1.084	71	52	73	W........	1/4	0..........	
	18	6 p. m.......	1095	31.040	1.082	52	41	52	W........	1/4	0..........	
	19	7 a. m.......	1095	31.036	1.030	38	30	38	W........	1/4	1 cir.....	
	19	9 a. m.......	1095	31.098	1.050	65	44	60	W........	1/2	1 cir.....	
	19	12 m.......	1095	31.122	1.040	70	53	72	W........	1/2	1 cir.....	
	19	3 p. m.......	1095	31.094	1.078	75	53	77	W........	1/2	1 cir.....	
	19	6 p. m.......	1095	31.048	1.074	54	42	53	W........	1/2	1 cir.....	
	20	7 a. m.......	1095	31.022	1.076	39	37	38	NW......	1/2	8 nim.....	
	20	9 a. m.......	1095	31.046	1.066	51	44	53	NW......	1/4	8 nim.....	
	20	12 m.......	1095	31.064	1.084	65	48	64	NW......	1/4	8 nim.....	
	20	3 p. m.......	1095	31.035	1.124	68	49	65	NW......	1/2	8 nim.....	
	20	6 p. m.......	1093	31.022	1.124	52	46	59	NW......	1/2	8 nim.....	
Camp near Fort Yuma........	21	7 a. m.......	1095	31.053	1.081	32	26	31	W........	0		

APPENDIX C—Continued.

Station.	Date.	Hour.	Number of barometer.	Upper vernier.	Lower vernier.	Attached thermometer.	Wet bulb.	Dry bulb.	Direction.	Force.	Clouds.	Remarks.
Camp near Fort Yuma	1858. Jan. 21	9 a. m.	1095	31.054	1.076	65	46	58	W	0		
	21	12 m.	1095	31.060	1.058	69	52	71	W	0		
	21	3 p. m.	1095	31.036	1.126	70	53	72	SW	½	0 cir	
	21	6 p. m.	1095	31.028	1.131	68	48	67	SW	⅛	0 cir	
	22	7 a. m.	1095	31.000	1.073	43	37	42	0		1	
	22	9 a. m.	1095	31.056	1.072	64	42	60	0		1	
	22	12 m.	1095	31.030	1.046	69	56	67	S	1	5	
	22	3 p. m.	1095	30.988	1.032	68	55	68	SW	3	5	
	22	6 p. m.	1095	30.967	1.130	65	50	65	SW	3	8	Rain from 4 p. m. to 6 p. m.
	23	7 a. m.	1095	30.960	1.1.6	43	40	42	0		1	
	23	9 a. m.	1095	31.100	1.090	57	46	53	W	1	1 cum	
	23	12 m.	1095	31.016	1.086	58	49	55	SW	3	1	
	23	3 p. m.	1095	31.013	1.082	59	48	60	SW	3	1	
	23	6 p. m.	1095	30.990	1.104	52	43	49	SW	1	0	
	24	7 a. m.	1095	31.046	0.985	28	31	30	0		0	
	24	9 a. m.	1095	31.136	0.960	48	37	47	0		0	
	24	12 m.	1095	31.153	0.950	58	45	56	W	⅛	Cir	
	24	3 p. m.	1095	31.125	0.912	60	45	59	W	1	1	
	24	6 p. m.	1095	31.198	0.980	50	39	49	0		1	
	25	7 a. m.	1095	31.076	0.984	45	32	37	0		5	
	25	9 a. m.	1095	31.100	0.990	53	40	52	0		5	
	25	12 m.	1095	31.100	0.992	61	45	60	W	1	1	
	25	3 p. m.	1095	31.092	1.080	69	49	69	W	1	1 cir	
	25	6 p. m.	1095	31.054	1.028	50	40	49	0		1	
	26	7 a. m.	1095	31.063	1.024	45	35	45	W	1	1	
	26	9 a. m.	1095	31.118	1.008	58	40	53	W	1	Cir	
	26	12 m.	1095	31.188	0.992	65	49	66	W	⅛	Cir	
	26	3 p. m.	1095	31.124	1.028	70	49	68	W	⅛	Cir	
	26	6 p. m.	1095	31.064	1.011	50	42	49	0		Cir	
	27	7 a. m.	1095	31.058	1.020	48	37	48	W	1	Cir	
	27	9 a. m.	1095	31.066	1.024	52	39	52	W	1	Cir	
	27	12 m.	1095	31.106	1.014	68	48	66	W	1	Cir	
	27	3 p. m.	1095	31.126	1.010	70	50	70	W	1	Cir	
	27	6 p. m.	1095	31.115	1.00	60	46	60	W	1	Cir	
	28	7 a. m.	1095	31.074	1.044	57	46	57	0		8 nim	Raining all day.
	28	9 a. m.	1095	31.060	1.024	57	47	56	0		8 nim	
	28	12 m.	1095	31.076	1.015	56	57	55	0		Nim	

APPENDIX C—Continued.

Station	Date	Hour	Number of barometer	Reading of barometer. Upper vernier.	Reading of barometer. Upper vernier.	Attached thermometer.	Detached thermometer. Wet bulb.	Detached thermometer. Dry bulb.	Wind. Direction.	Wind. Force.	Clouds.	Remarks.
	1858.			*Inches.*	*Inches.*	°	°	°				
Camp near Fort Yuma	Jan. 28	3 p. m.	1095	31.070	1.020	53	51	53	0	0	Nim	
	28	6 p. m.	1095	31.076	1.028	50	48	51	0	0	8 nim	
	29	7 a. m.	1095	31.026	1.028	47	47	47	0	0	5 nim	
	29	9 a. m.	1095	31.062	1.030	55	53	54	0	0	Cir. stratus	
	29	12 m.	1095	31.070	1.025	73	60	75	0	0	Cir	
	29	3 p. m.	1095	31.050	1.030	74	58	73	0	0	Cir	
	29	6 p. m.	1095	31.028	1.074	58	53	57	0	0	Cir	
	30	7 a. m.	1095	31.010	1.010	33	32	32	0		0	
	30	9 a. m.	1095	31.106	1.000	65	54	54	0		0	
	30	12 m.	1095	31.124	1.020	72	53	71	W	½	0	
	30	3 p. m.	1095	31.100	1.032	81	53	77	0	0	0	
	30	6 p. m.	1095	31.062	1.042	59	43	57	W	½	Cir	
	31	7 a. m.	1095	31 081	0.992	45	37	45	W	½	Cum	
	31	9 a. m.	1095	31.135	0.964	53	52	60	W	½	Cum	
	31	12 m.	1095	31.162	0.984	72	50	69	W	½	Cum	
	31	3 p. m.	1095	31.125	0.973	73	47	69	0	0	0	
	31	6 p. m.	1095	31.060	1.020	56	47	55	0	0	0	
Feb.	1	7 a. m.	1095	31.002	1.034	41	32	39	NW	½	0	
	1	9 a. m.	1095	31.048	1.050	60	48	61	0	0	0	
	1	12 m.	1095	31.038	1.088	73	49	69	NW	3	0	
	1	3 p. m.	1095	30.964	1.135	70	50	62	NW	3	Cir	
	1	6 p. m.	1095	30.800	1.180	52	44	52	NW	3	Cir	
	2	7 a. m.	1095	30.938	1.158	54	39	53	NW	3	Cir	
	2	9 a. m.	1095	30.992	1.066	65	47	63	NW	3	0	
	2	12 m.	1095	31.006	1.088	69	48	69	0	0	0	
	2	3 p. m.	1095	31.008	1.090	71	48	69	N.	½	0	
	2	6 p. m.	1095	30.990	1.102	65	43	62	N.	½	0	
	3	7 a. m.	1095	31.034	1.026	45	35	43	N.	½	Cir	
	3	9 a. m.	1095	31.120	0.970	60	44	59	N.	½	0	
	3	12 m.	1095	31.198	0.992	75	53	74	W.	½	0	
	3	3 p. m.	1095	31.190	0.987	71	49	70	W.	½	0	
	3	6 p. m.	1095	31.146	0.978	64	43	63	0	0	0	
	4	7 a. m.	1095	31.084	0.954	31	39	34	0	0	0	
	4	9 a. m.	1095	31.180	0.914	59	47	59	0	0	0	
	4	12 m.	1095	31.170	0.997	72	42	71	0	0	0	
	4	3 p. m.	1095	31.130	0.998	70	50	70	0	0	0	
	4	6 p. m.	1095	31.120	0.976	63	44	62	0	0	0	

APPENDIX C—Continued.

Station.	Date.		Hour.	Number of barometer.	Reading of barometer. Upper vernier.	Reading of barometer. Lower vernier.	Attached thermometer.	Detached thermometer. Wet bulb.	Detached thermometer. Dry bulb.	Wind. Direction.	Wind. Force.	Clouds.	Remarks.
	1858.				Inches.	Inches.	°	°	°				
Camp near Fort Yuma	Feb.	5	7 a. m.	1095	31.030	0.970	28	29	30	0	0	0	
		5	9 a. m.	1095	31.066	0.996	53	46	53	0	0	0	
		5	12 m.	1095	31.096	1.016	71	41	72	W	½	0	
		5	3 p. m.	1095	31.098	1.050	77	53	77	N	½	0	
		5	6 p. m.	1095	31.048	1.052	62	46	59	0	0	0	
		6	7 a. m.	1095	30.980	1.052	30	27	30	0	0	Cum	
		6	9 a. m.	1095	31.086	1.008	55	43	55	0	0	Cir	
		6	12 m.	1095	31.104	1.028	73	49	70	W	½	0	
		6	3 p. m.	1095	31.090	1.052	74	48	69	0	0	0	
		6	6 p. m.	1095	31.010	1.066	57	42	54	0	0	0	
		7	7 a. m.	1095	30.938	1.080	31	28	29	0	0	0	
		7	9 a. m.	1095	30.996	1.066	53	43	55	0	0	0	
		7	12 m.	1095	31.036	1.140	71	57	69	SW	½	0	
		7	3 p. m.	1095	30.990	1.140	74	54	73	SW	½	0	
		7	6 p. m.	1095	30.948	1.150	66	48	66	SW	½	0	
		8	7 a. m.	1095	30.876	1.150	36	32	39	0	0	Cir	
		8	9 a. m.	1095	30.936	1.188	53	43	53	0	0	Nims	
		8	12 m.	1095	30.932	1.182	60	46	60	0	0	Nims	
		8	3 p. m.	1095	30.930	1.176	63	49	64	0	0	Nims	
		8	6 p. m.	1095	30.870	1.164	62	48	60	SW	½	Nims	
		9	7 a. m.	1095	30.912	1.156	49	43	49	0	0	Nims	
		9	9 a. m.	1095	30.950	1.128	53	47	52	0	0	Nims	
		9	12 m.	1095	30.982	1.130	64	50	63	0	0	Nims	
		9	3 p. m.	1095	30.984	1.112	69	48	66	0	0	Nims	
		9	6 p. m.	1095	30.974	1.130	58	46	57	0	0	Nims	
		10	7 a. m.	1095	30.948	1.120	43	38	43	0	0	Nims	
		10	9 a. m.	1095	30.982	1.116	57	45	56	0	0	Nims	
		10	12 m.	1095	31.014	1.080	68	50	68	0	0	Nims	
		10	3 p. m.	1095	31.000	1.100	66	49	64	0	0	Nims	
		10	6 p. m.	1095	30.984	1.114	58	41	58	0	0	Nims	
		11	7 a. m.	1095	30.912	1.132	50	50	50	0	0	Nims	Raining very heavily during the day.
		11	9 a. m.	1095	30.918	1.126	52	52	52	0	0	Nims	
		11	12 m.	1095	30.984	1.110	52	50	51	0	0	Nims	
		11	3 p. m.	1095	30.876	1.210	50	45	50	0	0	Nims	
		11	6 p. m.	1095	30.840	1.228	48	41	48	0	0	Nims	
		12	7 a. m.	1095	30.866	1.166	41	42	42	0	0	0	
		12	9 a. m.	1095	30.968	1.122	54	49	53	0	0	0	

APPENDIX C—Continued.

Station	Date	Hour	Number of barometer	Reading of barometer. Upper vernier.	Reading of barometer. Lower vernier.	Attached thermometer.	Detached thermometer. Wet bulb.	Detached thermometer. Dry bulb.	Wind. Direction.	Wind. Force.	Clouds.	Remarks.
Camp near Fort Yuma	1858. Feb. 12	12 m	1095	30.980	1.124	60	51	55	SE	1/8	0	
	12	3 p. m.	1095	30.968	1.118	65	51	65	SE	1/8	0	
	12	6 p. m.	1095	30.942	1.144	58	50	58	0	0	0	
	13	7 a. m.	1095	30.946	1.080	38	39	39	0	0	0	
	13	9 a. m.	1095	31.058	1.042	65	53	55	0	0	0	
	13	12 m	1095	31.060	1.057	66	52	59	SE	1/8	Cir.	
	13	3 p. m.	1095	31.052	1.064	68	54	65	SE		Cir.	
	13	6 p. m.	1095	31.048	1.054	60	53	60	SE	0	Cir.	
	14	7 a. m.	1095	30.988	1.044	38	43	41	0	0	Cir.	
	14	9 a. m.	1095	31.058	1.048	50	53	55	0	1/8	Cir. str	
	14	12 m	1095	31.044	1.002	65	52	61	SE	1/8	Cir.	
	14	3 p. m.	1095	31.080	1.010	67	54	65	SE	0	Cir.	
	14	6 p. m.	1095	31.036	1.012	59	52	59	0	0	0	
	15	7 a. m.	1095	31.036	1.002	36	37	37	0	1/8	0	
	15	9 a. m.	1095	31.146	1.076	65	57	61	W	1/8	Cir.	
	15	12 m	1095	31.182	0.974	72	58	73	W	1/8	Cir.	
	15	3 p. m.	1095	31.162	0.982	72	53	69	W	1/8	Str.	
	15	6 p. m.	1095	31.120	0.987	57	50	58	W	0	Cir.	
	16	7 a. m.	1095	31.058	0.982	41	41	43	0	0	Cir.	
	16	9 a. m.	1095	31.140	0.996	73	58	67	0		Cir.	
Camp 1	1857. Dec. 23	8 a. m.	1252	30.274		46	47	55	NW	1/8	0	The observations at this camp were taken in the open air, in a northern exposure, in the shade of a pile of stones, 20 feet above low water.
	23	9 a. m.	1252	30.305		45	41	45	NW	1/8	0	
	23	10 a. m.	1253	30.300		48	43	47	NW	1/8	0	
	23	10 a. m.	1255	30.300		48	43	47	NW	1/8	0	
	23	10 a. m.	1256	30.300		48	43	47	NW	1/8	0	
	23	11 a. m.	1253	30.376		59	44	51	NW	1/8	0	
	23	11 a. m.	1255	30.376		52	44	51	NW	1/8	0	
	23	11 a. m.	1256	30.376		52	44	51	NW	1/8	0	
	23	12 m	1253	30.302		56	45	56	NW	1/8	0	
	23	12 m	1255	30.352		56	45	56	NW	1/8	0	
	23	12 m	1256	30.314		56	45	56	NW	1/8	0	
	23	1 p. m.	1252	30.370		58	47	58	NW	1/8	0	
	23	1 p. m.	1255	30.300		58	47	58	NW	1/8	0	
	23	1 p. m.	1256	30.282		58	47	58	NW	1/8	0	
	23	2 p. m.	1252	30.268		63	48	60	NW	1/8	0	
	23	2 p. m.	1255	30.306		62	48	60	NW	1/8	0	

APPENDIX C—Continued.

Station	Date	Hour	Number of barometer	Reading of barometer. Upper vernier. (Inches)	Reading of barometer. Lower vernier. (Inches)	Attached thermometer.	Detached thermometer. Wet bulb.	Detached thermometer. Dry bulb.	Wind. Direction.	Wind. Force.	Clouds.	Remarks.
Camp 1	1857. Dec. 23	2 p. m.	1256	30.262	......	62	48	60	NW	1/16	0	
	23	3 p. m.	1252	30.252	......	61	46	58	NW		0	
	23	3 p. m.	1255	30.290	......	61	46	58	NW		0	
	23	3 p. m.	1256	30.268	......	61	46	58	NW		0	
	23	4 p. m.	1252	30.280	......	58	46	55	NW		0	
	23	4 p. m.	1255	30.280	......	58	46	55	NW		0	
	23	4 p. m.	1256	30.250	......	58	46	55	NW		0	
	23	5 p. m.	1252	30.230	......	55	45	51	NW		0	
	23	5 p. m.	1255	30.278	......	55	45	51	NW		0	
	23	5 p. m.	1256	30.250	......	55	45	51	NW		0	
	23	6 p. m.	1252	30.232	......	52	44	49	NW		0	
	23	6 p. m.	1255	30.300	......	52	44	49	NW		0	
	23	6 p. m.	1256	30.250	......	52	44	49	NW		1 cum.	
	24	7 a. m.	1252	30.234	......	38	38	36	SW		1 cum.	
	24	7 a. m.	1255	30.200	......	38	38	36	SW		1 cum.	
	24	7 a. m.	1256	30.200	......	38	38	36	SW		5 cum.	
	24	8 a. m.	1252	30.224	......	41	39	41	SW		5 cum.	
	24	8 a. m.	1255	30.200	......	41	39	41	SW		5 cum.	
	24	8 a. m.	1256	30.208	......	46	42	46	SW		5 cum.	
	24	9 a. m.	1252	30.250	......	46	42	46	SW		5 cum.	
	24	9 a. m.	1255	30.218	......	46	42	46	SW		5 cum.	
	24	9 a. m.	1256	30.220	......	50	41	51	SW		5 cum.	
	24	10 a. m.	1252	30.266	......	49	41	51	SW		5 cum.	
	24	10 a. m.	1255	30.234	......	50	41	51	SW		5 cum.	
	24	10 a. m.	1256	30.230	......	52	42	50	SW		4 cum.	
	24	11 a. m.	1252	30.262	......	51	42	50	SW		4 cum.	
	24	11 a. m.	1256	20.230	......	52	42	50	SW		4 cum.	
	24	12 m.	1252	30.194	......	56	51	55	SW		6 cum. str	
	24	12 m.	1255	30.234	......	56	51	56	SW		6 cum. str	
	24	12 m.	1256	30.204	......	56	51	56	SE		6 cum. str	
	24	1 p. m.	1252	30.142	......	54	52	56	SE	1	6 cum. str	
	24	1 p. m.	1255	30.178	......	54	52	56	SE	1	6 cum. str	
	24	1 p. m.	1256	30.160	......	54	52	55	SE	1	6 cum. str	
	24	2 p. m.	1252	30.126	......	54	53	56	SE	1	6 cum. str	
	24	2 p. m.	1255	30.166	......	54	53	56	SE	1	6 cum. str	
	24	2 p. m.	1256	30.142	......	55	53	56	SE	1	6 cum. str	

APPENDIX C—Continued.

Station	Date	Hour	Number of barometer.	Upper vernier. Inches.	Lower vernier. Inches.	Attached thermometer.	Wet bulb.	Dry bulb.	Wind. Direction.	Wind. Force.	Clouds.	Remarks.
Camp 1	1857. Dec. 24	3 p. m.	1252	30.172		58	53	58	SE	1	8 nim	
	24	3 p. m.	1255	30.154		58	53	58	SE	1	8 nim	
	24	3 p. m.	1256	30.130		58	53	58	SE	1	8 nim	
	24	4 p. m.	1252	30.162		55	52	55	SE	1	8 nim	
	24	4 p. m.	1255	30.136		53	52	55	SE	1	8 nim	
	24	4 p. m.	1256	30.106		53	52	55	SE	1	8 nim	
	24	5 p. m.	1252	30.102		56	51	54	SE	1	8 nim	
	24	5 p. m.	1255	30.146		56	51	54	SE	1	8 nim	
	24	5 p. m.	1256	30.118		56	51	54	SE	1	8 nim	
	24	6 p. m.	1252	30.000		53	49	52	SE	1	8 nim	
	24	6 p. m.	1255	30.152		53	49	52	SE	1	8 nim	
	24	6 p. m.	1256	30.126		53	49	52	SE	1	6.	
	25	6 a. m.	1252	30.110		46	39	44	W	½	6.	
	25	6 a. m.	1255	30.194		46	39	44	W	½	6.	
	25	6 a. m.	1256	30.110		46	39	44	W	½	5.	
	25	7 a. m.	1252	30.100		45	39	45	W	½	5.	
	25	7 a. m.	1255	30.148		45	39	45	W	½	5.	
	25	7 a. m.	1256	30.100		45	39	45	W	½	1.	
	25	8 a. m.	1252	30.101		46	41	46	W	½	1.	
	25	8 a. m.	1255	30.150		46	41	46	W	½	1.	
	25	8 a. m.	1256	30.115		46	43	46	W	½	1.	
	25	9 a. m.	1252	30.124		51	43	51	W	½	1.	
	25	9 a. m.	1255	30.168		51	43	51	W	½	1.	
	25	9 a. m.	1256	30.142		51	46	56	W	½	1.	
	25	10 a. m.	1252	30.156		55	46	56	W	½	1.	
	25	10 a. m.	1255	30.200		55	46	56	W	½	1.	
	25	10 a. m.	1256	30.172		55	46	56	W	½	1.	
	25	11 a. m.	1252	30.136		56	49	55	W	½	1.	
	25	11 a. m.	1255	30.186		56	49	55	W	½	1.	
	25	11 a. m.	1256	30.150		56	49	55	W	½	1.	
	25	12 m	1252	30.116		58	49	57	W	½	1.	
	25	12 m	1255	30.158		58	49	57	W	½	1.	
	25	12 m	1256	30.128		58	49	57	W	½	1.	
	25	1 p. m.	1252	30.100		58	50	53	W	½	1.	
	25	1 p. m.	1255	30.136		58	50	53	W	½	1.	
	25	1 p. m.	1256	30.113		58	50	53	W	½	1.	
	25	2 p. m.	1252	30.078		57	53	56	W	½	1.	

APPENDIX C—Continued.

Station.	Date.	Hour.	Number of barometer.	Reading of barometer. Upper vernier.	Reading of barometer. Lower vernier.	Attached thermometer.	Detached thermometer. Wet bulb.	Detached thermometer. Dry bulb.	Wind. Direction.	Wind. Force.	Clouds.	Remarks.
	1857.			*Inches.*	*Inches.*	°	°	°				
Camp 1	Dec. 25	2 p. m.	1255	30.117	....	56	52	56	W	½	1	
	25	2 p. m.	1256	30.092	....	57	52	56	W	½	1	
	25	3 p. m.	1252	30.060	....	56	51	58	SE	1	1	
	25	3 p. m.	1255	30.104	....	56	51	58	SE	1	1	
	25	3 p. m.	1256	30.074	....	57	51	58	SE	1	1	
	25	4 p. m.	1252	30.070	....	62	54	60	SE	1	1	
	25	4 p. m.	1255	30.110	....	61	54	60	SE	1	1	
	25	4 p. m.	1256	30.042	....	62	54	60	SE	1	1	
	25	5 p. m.	1252	30.060	....	57	52	55	SE	1	1	
	25	5 p. m.	1255	30.102	....	57	52	55	SE	1	1	
	25	5 p. m.	1256	30.077	....	57	52	55	SE	1	1	
	25	6 p. m.	1252	30.062	....	54	49	52	SE	1	1	
	25	6 p. m.	1255	30.100	....	53	49	52	SE	1	1	
	25	6 p. m.	1256	30.060	....	54	49	52	SE	1	1	
	26	6 a. m.	1252	30.064	....	43	39	42	W	½	1	
	26	6 a. m.	1255	30.106	....	43	39	42	W	½	1	
	26	6 a. m.	1256	30.062	....	43	39	42	W	½	1	
	26	7 a. m.	1252	30.084	....	43	40	42	W	½	1	
	26	7 a. m.	1255	30.125	....	43	40	42	W	½	1	
	26	7 a. m.	1256	30.078	....	43	40	42	W	½	1	
	26	8 a. m.	1252	30.068	....	40	37	40	W	½	1	
	26	8 a. m.	1255	30.094	....	40	37	40	W	½	1	
	26	8 a. m.	1256	30.070	....	40	37	40	W	½	1	
	26	9 a. m.	1252	30.102	....	46	44	47	W	½	1	
	26	9 a. m.	1255	30.152	....	46	44	47	W	½	1	
	26	9 a. m.	1256	30.110	....	47	44	47	W	½	1	
	26	10 a. m.	1252	30.120	....	51	47	50	W	½	1	
	26	10 a. m.	1255	30.142	....	51	47	50	W	½	1	
	26	10 a. m.	1256	30.126	....	51	47	50	W	½	1	
	26	11 a. m.	1252	30.114	....	55	50	55	W	½	1	
	26	11 a. m.	1255	30.143	....	55	50	55	W	½	1	
	26	11 a. m.	1256	30.126	....	56	50	55	W	½	1	
	26	12 m.	1252	30.080	....	56	52	54	NW	½	1	
	26	12 m.	1255	30.114	....	56	52	54	NW	½	1	
	26	12 m.	1256	30.094	....	56	52	54	NW	½	1	
	26	1 p. m.	1252	30.046	....	57	54	56	NW	½	1	
	26	1 p. m.	1255	30.082	....	56	54	56	NW	½	1	

APPENDIX C—Continued.

Station	Date	Hour	Number of barometer	Reading of barometer, Upper vernier (Inches)	Reading of barometer, Lower vernier (Inches)	Attached thermometer	Detached thermometer, Wet bulb	Detached thermometer, Dry bulb	Wind, Direction	Wind, Force	Clouds	Remarks
Camp 1	1857. Dec. 26	1 p. m.	1256	30.060		57	54	56	NW	1/8	1	
	26	2 p. m.	1252	30.028		58	54	57	NW	1/8	1	
	26	2 p. m.	1255	30.066		58	54	57	NW	1/8	1	
	26	2 p. m.	1256	30.038		58	54	57	NW	3/8	1	
	26	3 p. m.	1252	30.030		64	53	61	SE	1/8	5	
	26	3 p. m.	1255	30.072		63	53	61	SE	1	5	
	26	3 p. m.	1256	30.050		60	53	61	SE	1	5	
	26	4 p. m.	1252	30.064		59	53	59	W		8	
	26	4 p. m.	1255	30.090		59	53	59	W		8	
	26	4 p. m.	1256	30.052		59	52	59	W		8	
	26	5 p. m.	1252	30.050		57	52	55	W		1	
	26	5 p. m.	1255	30.074		57	52	55	W		1	
	26	5 p. m.	1256	30.046		57	52	52	W			
	26	6 p. m.	1252	30.024		53	49	52	SE			
	26	6 p. m.	1255	30.008		53	49	52	SE			
	26	6 p. m.	1256	30.012		53	49	52	SE			
	28	6 a. m.	1252	30.246		44	42	44	W	1/2	0	
	28	6 a. m.	1255	30.336		44	42	44	W	1/2	0	
	28	6 a. m.	1256	30.286		44	42	44	W	1/2	0	
	28	7 a. m.	1252	30.228		43	42	44	W	1/2	0	
	28	7 a. m.	1255	30.331		43	42	44	W	1/2	0	
	28	7 a. m.	1256	30.240		43	42	44	W	1/2	0	
	28	8 a. m.	1252	30.296		42	40	42	W	1/2	0	
	28	8 a. m.	1255	30.335		43	40	42	W	1/2	0	
	28	8 a. m.	1256	30.300		44	40	42	W	1/2	0	
	28	9 a. m.	1252	30.310		44	41	44	W	1/2	0	
	28	9 a. m.	1255	30.318		44	41	44	W	1/2	0	
	28	9 a. m.	1256	30.316		45	41	44	W	1/2	0	
	28	10 a. m.	1252	30.346		50	46	49	W	1/2	0	
	28	10 a. m.	1255	30.370		50	46	49	W	1/2	0	
	28	10 a. m.	1256	30.245		50	46	49	W	1/2	0	
	28	11 a. m.	1252	30.342		52	49	52	W	1/2	0	
	28	11 a. m.	1255	30.368		52	49	52	W	1/2	0	
	28	11 a. m.	1256	30.347		53	49	52	W	1/2	0	
	28	12 m.	1252	30.306		55	50	53	W	1/2	0	
	28	12 m.	1255	30.350		55	50	53	W	1/2	0	
	28	12 m.	1256	30.324		55	50	53	W	1/2	0	

APPENDIX C—Continued.

Station.	Date.	Hour.	Number of barometer.	Reading of barometer. Upper Vernier.	Reading of barometer. Lower Vernier.	Attached thermometer.	Detached thermometer. Wet bulb.	Detached thermometer. Dry bulb.	Wind. Direction.	Wind. Force.	Clouds.	Remarks.
	1857.			*Inches.*	*Inches.*	°	°	°				
Camp 1	Dec. 28	1 p. m.	1252	30.286	....	56	50	55	W.	½	0	
	28	1 p. m.	1255	30.324	....	56	50	55	W.	½	0	
	28	1 p. m.	1256	30.300	....	57	50	55	W.	½	0	
	28	2 p. m.	1252	30.264	....	59	50	57	W.	½	0	
	28	2 p. m.	1255	30.314	....	59	50	57	W.	½	0	
	28	2 p. m.	1256	30.276	....	59	50	57	W.	½	0	
	28	3 p. m.	1252	30.264	....	60	51	59	W.	½	0	
	28	3 p. m.	1255	30.310	....	60	51	59	W.	½	0	
	28	3 p. m.	1256	30.278	....	61	51	59	W.	½	0	
	28	4 p. m.	1252	30.262	....	61	50	59	W.	½	0	
	28	4 p. m.	1255	30.316	....	51	50	59	W.	½	0	
	28	4 p. m.	1256	30.278	....	61	50	59	W.	½	0	
	28	5 p. m.	1252	30.264	....	55	49	54	W.	½	0	
	28	5 p. m.	1255	30.310	....	55	49	54	W.	½	0	
	28	5 p. m.	1256	30.278	....	55	49	54	W.	½	0	
	28	6 p. m.	1252	30.206	....	53	48	52	W.	½	0	
	28	6 p. m.	1255	30.320	....	53	48	52	W.	½	0	
	28	6 p. m.	1256	30.290	....	53	48	52	W.	½	0	
	29	6 a. m.	1252	30.340	....	48	38	42	W.	1	0	
	29	6 a. m.	1255	30.366	....	48	38	42	W.	1	0	
	29	6 a. m.	1256	30.345	....	48	38	42	W.	1	0	
	29	7 a. m.	1252	30.380	....	42	39	42	W.	1	0	
	29	7 a. m.	1255	30.446	....	42	39	42	W.	1	0	
	29	7 a. m.	1256	30.390	....	42	39	42	W.	1	0	
	29	8 a. m.	1252	30.408	....	44	40	43	W.	1	0	
	29	8 a. m.	1255	30.448	....	44	40	43	W.	1	0	
	29	8 a. m.	1256	30.430	....	44	40	43	W.	1	0	
	29	9 a. m.	1252	30.428	....	46	42	45	W.	1	0	
	29	9 a. m.	1255	30.464	....	45	42	45	W.	1	0	
	29	9 a. m.	1256	30.446	....	46	42	45	W.	1	0	
	29	10 a. m.	1252	30.486	....	52	40	51	W.	1	0	
	29	10 a. m.	1255	30.520	....	51	40	51	W.	1	0	
	29	10 a. m.	1256	30.502	....	52	40	51	W.	1	0	
Camp 2	31	7.25 a. m.	1252	30.200	....	46	34	54	NW.	1	0	
	31	7.25 a. m.	1255	30.225	....	45	34	54	NW.	1	0	
	31	7.25 a. m.	1256	30.226	....	45	34	54	NW.	1	0	

APPENDIX C—Continued.

Station.	Date.	Hour.	Number of barometer.	Reading of barometer. Upper vernier.	Reading of barometer. Lower vernier.	Attached thermometer.	Detached thermometer. Wet bulb.	Detached thermometer. Dry bulb.	Wind. Direction.	Wind. Force.	Clouds.	Remarks.
				Inches.	Inches.	°	°	°				
Camp 2	1858. Jan. 1	8.53 a. m.	1252	30.432		54	40	51	NW	1/8	0	
	1	8.53 a. m.	1255	30.480		52	40	51	NW	1/8	0	
	1	8.53 a. m.	1256	30.450		53	40	51	NW	1/8	0	
Camp 3	2	8 a. m.	1252	30.494		37	30	38	NW	1/8	0	
	2	8 a. m.	1255	30.526		37	30	38	NW	1/8	0	
	2	8 a. m.	1256	30.496		37	30	38	W	1/8	0	
Camp 4	3	7.49 a. m.	1252	30.380		32	27	32	W	1/8	0	
	3	7.49 a. m.	1255			32	27	32	W	1/8	0	
	3	7.49 a. m.	1256	30.400		32	27	32			0	
Camp 5	4	8.05 a. m.	1252	30.200		34	30	31				
	4	8.05 a. m.	1255	30.200		34	30	31				
	4	8.05 a. m.	1256	30.158		34	30	31			0	
Camp 6	5	8 a. m.	1252	30.151		40	37	41				
	5	8 a. m.	1256	30.060		40	37	41	NW	1/8	0	
Camp 7	6		1256	30.060		47	40	47	NW	1/8		
	7	8.54 a. m.	1252	30.050		47	40	47				
	7	8.54 a. m.	1256	30.036		39	35	38			0	
Camp 8	6	5.15 a. m.	1252	29.992		39	35	47	NE	1/8	0	
	6	5.15 a. m.	1256	29.982		52	41	47				
	7	7.15 a. m.	1252	30.014		53	41	28				
	7	7.15 a. m.	1256	30.020		31	26	28				
Camp 9	7	5.45 p. m.	1252	30.020		30	26	53				
	7	5.45 p. m.	1256	30.030		53	43	53				
	8	7.9 a. m.	1252	30.024		53	43	41				
	8	7.9 a. m.	1256	30.014		43	38	41	NW	1/4	2	
Camp 10	9	7.10 a. m.	1252	29.896		43	38	37	NW	1/4		
	9	7.10 a. m.	1256	29.838		37	35	37				
Camp 23	23	7 a. m.	1256	29.685		47	45	46	N.	2	3 cir. cum.	
	23	7 a. m.	1252	29.672		47	45	46	N.	2	3 cir. cum.	
Station 2,045	23	12 m.	1256	29.709		64	64	56	W.	4 1/2	1/2 cir. cum.	
Camp 24	24	7 a. m.	1252	29.944		34	31	34	0	0	0	
	24	7 a. m.	1256	29.938		34	35	34	0	0	0	
Camp 25	25	7 a. m.	1252	29.952		43	39	45	0	0	10 str. and nim.	
	25	7 a. m.	1256	29.949		43	39	45	0	0	10 str. and nim.	
Camp 26	26	7 a. m.	1256	29.965		39	36	38	0	0	1 stratus	
	26	7 a. m.	1252	29.961		39	36	38	0	0	1 stratus	

APPENDIX C—Continued.

Station.	Date.	Hour.	Number of barometer.	Upper vernier. (Inches)	Lower vernier. (Inches)	Attached thermometer.	Wet bulb.	Dry bulb.	Direction.	Force.	Clouds.	Remarks.
Camp 27	1858. Jan. 27	7 a. m.	1256	29.929	......	38	36	39	0	0	½ stratus	
	27	7 a. m.	1252	29.920	......	38	36	39	0	0	½ stratus	Steamboat shaken very much, and correct observations impossible.
Camp 28	28	7 a. m.	1255	29.916	......	48	43	47	SE.	2	10 str. nim.	
	28	7 a. m.	1252	29.902	......	48	43	47	SE.	2	......	
Camp 29	29	7 a. m.	1255	29.810	......	50	48	50	N.NE.	1½	9½ cir. cum. str	
	29	7 a. m.	1252	29.796	......	50	48	50	N.NE.	1½	9½ cir. cum. str.	
Camp 30	30	7 a. m.	1256	29.818	......	42	40	43	0	0	0	
	30	7 a. m.	1252	29.302	......	42	40	43	0	0	0	
Camp 31	31	7 a. m.	1256	29.905	......	35	35	34	0	0	1 stratus	Hazy to NW., near horizon.
	31	7 a. m.	1252	29.898	......	35	35	34	0	0	1 stratus	
Camp 32	Feb. 1	7 a. m.	1256	29.757	......	43	42	38	S.	½	½ stratus	
	1	7 a. m.	1252	29.745	......	43	42	38	S.	½	½ stratus	Blowing in gust; a little subsiding.
Camp 33	2	7 a. m.	1252	29.632	......	53	44	53	N.NW.	6	0	
	2	7 a. m.	1255	29.632	......	53	44	53	N.N.	6	0	
Camp 34	3	7 a. m.	1252	29.836	......	52	48	51	NW.	6	0	
	3	7 a. m.	1256	29.848	......	52	48	51	NW.	6	0	
Camp 35	4	7 a. m.	1252	29.986	......	41	......	37	0	0	0	
	4	7 a. m.	1256	29.996	......	41	......	37	0	0	0	
Camp 36	5	7 a. m.	1252	29.794	......	38	37	35	0	0	0	
	5	7 a. m.	1256	29.807	......	38	37	35	0	0	0	
Camp 37	6	7 a. m.	1256	29.796	......	40	44	39	W.	1	9 cir. cum. str.	
	6	7 a. m.	1252	29.784	......	40	44	39	W.	1	9 cir. cum. str.	
Camp 38	8	7 a. m.	1256	29.440	......	47	44	46	0	0	2 cir. str.	
	8	7 a. m.	1252	29.428	......	47	44	46	0	0	2 cir. str.	
Camp 39	9	7 a. m.	1252	29.541	......	47	43	46	N.	1	8 cir. cum. str.	
	9	7 a. m.	1256	29.552	......	47	43	46	N.	1	8 cir. cum. str.	
Camp 40	10	7 a. m.	1252	29.663	......	47	42	46	0	0	10 cum. str. and nim.	
	10	7 a. m.	1256	29.672	......	47	42	46	0	0	10 cum. str. and nim.	
Camp 41	11	7 a. m.	1252	29.436	......	51	50	50	0	0	10 cum. and nim.	
	11	7 a. m.	1256	29.450	......	51	50	50	0	0	10 cum. and nim.	
Camp 42	12	7 a. m.	1252	29.363	......	46	43	45	0	0	0	
	12	7 a. m.	1256	29.379	......	46	43	45	0	0	0	
Camp 43	13	7 a. m.	1252	29.552	......	40	41	40	0	0	1 stratus	
	13	7 a. m.	1256	29.568	......	40	41	40	0	0	1 stratus	
Camp 44	15	7 a. m.	1252	29.800	......	39	......	37	W.	1	0	
	15	7 a. m.	1256	29.813	......	39	......	37	W.	1	0	
Camp 45	16	7 a. m.	1252	29.761	......	47	44	45	E.	1½	10 cir. cum. and stratus.	

APPENDIX C—Continued.

Station.	Date.	Hour.	Number of barometer.	Reading of barometer. Upper vernier.	Lower vernier.	Attached thermometer.	Wet bulb.	Dry bulb.	Wind. Direction.	Force.	Clouds.	Remarks.
	1858.			Inches.	Inches.	°	°	°				
Camp 45	Feb. 16	7 a. m.	1256	29.777		47	44	45	E	1½		
Camp 46	17	7 a. m.	1252	29.631		52	50	51	NW	2	5 cir. cum. str.	
	17	7 a. m.	1256	29.645		52	50	51	NW	2	0	
Camp 47	18	7 a. m.	1252	29.714		49	46	48	NW	0	0	
	18	7 a. m.	1256	29.732		49	46	48	0	0	0	
Camp 48	19	7 a. m.	1252	29.655		48	44	46	NW	2	2 cir. str.	
Jesup's Rapids	19	7 a. m.	1256	29.666		48	44	46	NW	2	2 cir. str.	
Camp 49	20	7 a. m.	1252	29.492		57	49	51	NW	2	7 cir. str.	
Five Rapids	20	7 a. m.	1256	29.502		57	49	51	N W	2	7 cir. str.	
Camp 49	21	7 a. m.	1252	29.573		57	49	56	N	3	0	
	21	7 a. m.	1256	29.583		57	49	56	N	3	0	
	21	8 a. m.	1252	29.629		71	63	80	N	6	0	These observations were necessarily taken in the sun.
	21	8 a. m.	1256	29.635		71	62	80	N	6	0	
	21	9 a. m.	1252	29.637		66	57	68	N	8 m	0	
	21	9 a. m.	1256	29.654		66	57	68	N	8 m	0	
	21	10.15 a. m.	1252	29.604		68	58	69	N	10 m	1 cir.	
	21	10.15 a. m.	1256	29.631		68	58	69	N	10 m	1 cir.	
	21	11 a. m.	1252	29.608		69	59	70	N	12 m	1 cir.	
	21	11 a. m.	1256	29.620		69	59	70	N	12 m	1 cir.	
	21	12 m.	1252	29.583		73	61	73	N	12	0	
	21	12 m.	1256	29.601		73	61	73	N	12	0	
	21	3 p. m.	1252	29.535		75	62	75	N	14	0	
	21	3 p. m.	1256	29.550		75	62	75	N	14	0	
	21	4 p. m.	1252	29.520		75	61	74	N	15	0	
	21	4 p. m.	1256	29.530		75	61	74	N	15	0	
	21	5 p. m.	1252	29.540		75	62	75	N	15	0	
	21	5 p. m.	1256	29.550		75	62	75	N	15	0	
	22	7 a. m.	1252	29.696		56	47	54	N	4	1 cum. str.	
	22	7 a. m.	1256	29.710		56	47	54	N	4	1 cum. str.	
	23	7 a. m.	1252	29.485		48	42	47	N	5	0	
	23	7 a. m.	1256	29.498		48	42	47	N	5	0	
	24	7 a. m.	1252	29.787		60	50	59	N	9	4 cum str.	
	24	7 a. m.	1256	29.800		60	50	59	N	9	4 cum. str.	
Camp 50	25	7 a. m.	1252	29.788		58	49	57	NNW	6	0	
	25	7 a. m.	1256	29.800		58	49	57	NNW	6	0	
Camp 51	26	7 a. m.	1252	92.575		46	43	43	0.	0	0	
	26	7 a. m.	1256	29.589		46	43	43	0.	0	0	

APPENDIX C—Continued.

Station	Date	Hour	Number of barometer	Reading of barometer — Upper vernier (Inches)	Reading of barometer — Lower vernier (Inches)	Attached thermometer	Detached thermometer — Wet bulb	Detached thermometer — Dry bulb	Wind — Direction	Wind — Force	Clouds	Remarks
Camp 52	1858. Feb. 27	7 a. m.	1252	29.468		51	48	51	0	0	0	
	27	7 a. m.	1256	29.485		51	48	51	0	0	0	
Camp 53	Mar. 1	7 a. m.	1252	29.792		54	43	52	N	6m	0	
	1	7 a. m.	1256	29.802		54	43	52	N	6m	0	
	2	7 a. m.	1252	29.574		44	38	42	0	0	1 cir.	
	2	7 a. m.	1256	29.586		44	38	42	0	0	1 cir.	
Camp 54	3	7 a. m.	1256	29.459		43	38	42	N	1	6 cir. str.	
	3	7 a. m.	1252	29.472		43	38	42	N	1	6 cir. str.	
Camp 55	3	6 p. m.	1252	29.393		78	...	72	N	1	3 cir. str.	
	3	6 p. m.	1256	29.405		78	...	72	N	1	3 cir. str.	
	4	7 a. m.	1252	29.350		46	42	46	0	0	4 cir. str.	
	4	7 a. m.	1256	29.367		46	42	46	0	0	4 cir. str.	
Camp 56	5	6 p. m.	1252	29.295		76	57	75	N	4	2 cum. str.	
	5	6 p. m.	1256	29.309		76	57	75	N	4	2 cum. str.	
	6	7 a. m.	1252	29.536		59	50	58	N	3	0	
	6	5 p. m.	1256	29.551		59	50	58	N	3	0	
Camp 57	7	8 a. m.	1252	29.436		75	50	75	N	6m	0	
	7	8 a. m.	1256	29.450		75	46	75	N	6m	0	
	8	12.10 p. m.	1252	29.630		56	46	50	N	4m	2 cum. str.	
	8	12.10 p. m.	1256	29.647		56	56	50	N	4m	2 cum. str.	
	8	3 p. m.	1252	29.578		79	56	75	N	4m	10 cir. and nimbus	
	8	3 p. m.	1256	29.594		79	68	75	N	4m	10 cir. and nimbus	
	8	6 p. m.	1252	29.509		75	68	83	0	1	10 cir. and nimbus	
	8	6 p. m.	1256	29.518		75	...	83	0	0	10 cir. and nimbus	
	12	7 a. m.	1252	29.456		63	55	74	0	0	9 cir. and nimbus	
	12	7 a. m.	1256	29.474		63	55	74	0	0	9 cir. and nimbus	
	12	8 a. m.	1252	29.401		61	56	61	0	0	8 cir. and nimbus	
	12	8 a. m.	1256	29.417		61	56	61	0	0	8 cir. and nimbus	
	12	10 a. m.	1252	29.410		61	...	62	S	0		
	12	10 a. m.	1256	29.426		64	54	62	S	0		
	12	12 m.	1252	29.420		64	54	64	S	6m		
	12	12 m.	1256	29.438		69	...	64	S	6m		
	12	2 p. m.	1252	29.396		69	...	69	S	3	8 cir. and nimbus	
	12	2 p. m.	1256	29.414		71	...	69	S	3	8 cir. and nimbus	
	12	……	1252	29.338		71	...	71	S	7m	2 cir.	
	12	……	1256	29.356		...	...	71	S	7m	2 cir.	
Camp 60	24	7 a. m.	1252	27.996		52	41	53	SE.	1m	¼ stratus	

APPENDIX C—Continued.

Station.	Date.	Hour.	Number of barometer.	Upper vernier.	Lower vernier.	Attached thermometer	Wet bulb.	Dry bulb.	Direction.	Force.	Clouds.	Remarks.
	1858.			Inches.	Inches.	°	°	°				
Camp 60	Mar. 24	7 a. m.	1256	28.009		52	41	53	SE	1 m	¼ stratus	
Summit of Sitgreaves's Pass	24	12.30 p. m.	1252	26.540		70				1 m	0	
Camp 61	24	6 p. m.	1252	27.182		63	46	56	NW	1 m	0	
	24	6 p. m.	1256	27.190		61	46	56	NW	1 m	0	Hazy.
	25	6 a. m.	1252	27.153		71	52	72	SE	1 m		Hazy.
	25	6 a. m.	1256	27.166		71	52	72	SE	1 m		Hazy.
	25	6 p. m.	1252	27.080		66	47	63	SE	2 m		Hazy.
	25	6 p. m.	1256	27.022		65	47	63	SE	2 m		
	26	7 a. m.	1252	27.010		46	39	44	E	⅛	2 cir.	
	26	7 a. m.	1256	27.090		51	39	44	E	⅛	2 cir.	
Station between Camps 61 and 62—(see topography)	26	12 m.	1252	27.703		78		62	S	4	6 cir. nim.	
Camp 62	26	6 p. m.	1252	26.735		63		62	S	4	6 cir. nim.	
	26	6 p m	1255	25.744		63		50	0	0	2 cir.	
	27	7.30 a. m.	1252	25.772		58		50				
	27			25.784		60						
Summit of Railroad Pass	26	10.10 a. m.	1252	26.432		69		69				
Camp 65	April 1	8 a. m.	1252	26.022		57			SE			
Camp 66	1	6.30 p. m.	1252	25.742		65	45	62	SE	6 m	7 nim. cum	
	1	6.30 p. m.	1256	25.764		66	45	62	SE	6 m	7 nim. cum	
	2	7 a. m.	1252	25.686		57	39	49	SE	2 m	1 cir. str.	
	2	7 a. m.	1256	25.696		53	39	49	SE	2 m	1 cir. str.	
Camp 67	2	6 p. m.	1252	28.402		69	50	68	SE	3 m	0	
	2	6 p. m.	1256	28.404		70	50	68	SE	3 m	0	
Mouth of Diamond river	3	12.30 p. m.	1252	23.741		73	54	72	NW	1	0	
	3		1256	28.754		74						
Camp 67	3	6 p. m.	1256	28.497		69	51	65	0	0	0	
	3	6 p. m.	1252	28.493		68	51	65	0	0	0	
	4	7 a. m.	1252	28.510		63	50	60	SE	2	0	
	4	7 a. m.	1256	28.626		64	50	60	SE	2	0	
Camp 68	4	6 p. m.	1252	25.885		63	44	59	S	2	1 cir.	
	4	6 p. m.	1256	25.892		63	44	59	S	2	1 cir.	
Camp 69	5	7.30 a. m.	1256	25.922		60	48	59	SE	1	1 cir.	
	5	7.30 a. m.	1252	25.911		61	48	59	SE	1	1 cir.	
	5	6.30 p. m.	1256	24.404		58	47	55	S	2	1 cir.	
	5	6.30 p. m.	1253	24.413		57	47	55	S	2	1 cir.	
	6	7 a. m.	1253	24.314		54	36	45	S	1	2 cir. cum	
	6	7 a. m.	1256	24.329		55	36	45	S	1	2 cir. cum	

APPENDIX C—Continued.

Station.	Date.	Hour.	Number of barometer.	Reading of barometer. Upper vernier.	Lower vernier.	Attached thermometer.	Wet bulb.	Dry bulb.	Wind. Direction.	Force.	Clouds.	Remarks.
				Inches.	Inches.	°	°	°				
Camp 70	1858. April 6	6 p. m.	1256	23.770		50	34	45	W	4	7 cir., 1 cum	
	6	6 p. m.	1252	23.756		49	34	45	W	4		
	7	6 p. m.	1252	23.915		49	35	43	N	2	2 nim. str.	
	7	6 p. m.	1256	23.922		48	35	43	N			
Camp 71	8	7 a. m.	1252	33.800		41	33	38	N	5	4 nim	Snowed and stormed in the morning, cleared up at noon; thunder and lightning from 2 to 4 p. m., and gusts of snow and sleet throughout the day.
	8	7 a. m.	1256	23.812		41	33	38	N	5		
	8	6 p. m.	1256	23.121		33	33	38	W	5	1 cum. nim	
	8	6 p. m.	1252	23.113		33	33	38	W	5		
	9	6 p. m.	1252	23.414		50	34	42	W	8	9 cir. nim	Frequent gusts of light snow during the day.
	9	6 p. m.	1256	23.405		49	34	42	W	8	9 cir. nim	
Camp 72	10	7 a. m.	1256	23.832		56	42	47	W	4	2 stratus	
	10	7 a. m.	1252	23.865		55	42	47	W	4	2 stratus	
	10	6 p. m.	1256	24.401		55	38	48	W	2	1 stratus	
	10	6 p. m.	1252	24.388		51	38	48	W		0	
	11	7 a. m.	1256	24.420		38	42	50	W	2	0	
	11	7 a. m.	1252	24.428		60	42	50	W	2	0	
Hualpais cataract	12	2.45 p. m.	1252	27.576		76	54	72				
	12	2.45 p. m.	1256	27.564		75	54	72				
Camp 73	14	6 p. m.	1236	24.328		57	42	53	SE	2	3 stratus	
	14	6 p. m.	1252	24.315		56	42	53	SE	2	3 stratus	
	15	7 a. m.	1256	24.319		49	44	52	SE	3	4 stratus cum	Sprinkled slightly.
	15	7 a. m.	1252	24.328		49	44	52	SE	3		
Camp 74	18	6 p. m.	1256	23.694		51	33	40	NW	10	1 stratus	Gusts of snow and hail.
	18	6 p. m.	1252	23.686		49	33	40	NW	10	1 stratus	
Camp 75	19	7 a. m.	1256	23.740		53	42	48	N	10	0	
	19	7 a. m.	1252	23.733		52	42	48	N	10		
	19	6 p. m.	1256	24.521		63	44	55	NW	2	2 cir.	
	19	6 p. m.	1252	24.506		60	44	55	NW	2	2 cir.	
Camp 76	20	7 a. m.	1236	24.580		46	41	46	SE	1	0	
	20	7 a. m.	1252	24.580		46	41	46	SE	1		
	20	6 p. m.	1256	24.650		64	44	55	SE	1	¼ cir. str.	
	20	6 p. m.	1252	24.640		62	44	55	SE	1	¼ cir. str.	
Camp 77	21	7 a. m.	1256	24.568		53	40	46	NW	1	¼ cir.	
	21	7 a. m.	1252	24.576		55	40	46	NW		¼ cir.	
	21	6 p. m.	1256	24.370		69	46	61	NW	2	⅛ cir.	
	21	6 p. m.	1252	24.375		68	46	61	NW	2	⅛ cir.	
	22	7 a. m.	1256	24.457		62	52	64	NW	2	¼ cir.	

APPENDIX C—Continued.

Station.	Date. 1858.	Hour.	Number of barometer.	Reading of barometer. Upper vernier. Inches.	Reading of barometer. Lower vernier. Inches.	Attached thermometer. °	Detached thermometer. Wet bulb. °	Detached thermometer. Dry bulb. °	Wind. Direction.	Wind. Force.	Clouds.	Remarks.
Camp 77	April 22	7 a. m.	1252	24.463	.....	64	52	64	NW	2	¼ cir.	
	22	6 p. m.	1256	25.092	.....	75	53	68	NW	4	0	
Camp 78	22	6 p. m.	1252	25.099	.....	76	53	68	NW	4	0	
	23	6 p. m.	1256	25.009	.....	75	49	72	NW	4	0	
	23	6 p. m.	1252	25.000	.....	75	49	72	NW	4	0	
	24	7 a. m.	1256	25.056	.....	57	44	58	NW	2	0	
Camp 79	24	7 a. m.	1252	25.060	.....	57	44	58	NW	2	0	
	24	6 p. m.	1252	24.468	.....	80	52	70	NW	2	¼ str.	
	24	6 p. m.	1256	24.458	.....	78	52	70	NW	2	0	
	25	7 a. m.	1256	24.450	.....	56	48	58	NW	1	0	
Camp 80	25	7 a. m.	1252	24.454	.....	57	48	58	NW	1	½ cir.	
	25	6 p. m.	1252	23.712	.....	69	46	59	NW	2	0	
	25	6 p. m.	1256	23.720	.....	67	46	59	NW	2	0	
	26	7 a. m.	1252	24.700	.....	55	45	58	NW	1	0	
Camp 81	26	7 a. m.	1256	24.714	.....	58	45	58	NW	1	0	
	26	6 p. m.	1252	23.158	.....	70	51	68	SE	2	3 cum. cir.	
	26	6 p. m.	1256	23.150	.....	70	51	68	SE	2	3 cum. cir.	
	27	7 a. m.	1252	23.120	.....	53	45	51	SE	1	4 cir. str.	
Camp 82	27	7 a. m.	1256	23.127	.....	52	45	51	SE	1	4 cir. str.	
	27	6 p. m.	1256	22.904	.....	60	45	52	E	1	4 nim. cum.	
	27	6 p. m.	1252	22.910	.....	60	45	52	E	1	5 nim. cum.	
	28	7 a. m.	1256	22.793	.....	57	41	46	SE	5	5 nim. cum.	
	28	7 a. m.	1252	22.788	.....	57	41	46	SE	5		
Camp 90	May 7	6 p. m.	1256	24.758	.....	59	43	50	N	1	3 cir. nim.	At noon violent SW. gale, with hail and rain; very cold; at 4 p. m. gale abated; became mild.
	7	6 p. m.	1252	24.748	.....	58	43	50	N	1		
Camp 91	9	6 p. m.	1252	24.537	.....	66	46	59	NE	6	0	
	9	6 p. m.	1256	24.545	.....	67	46	59	NE	6	0	
Camp 92	10	7 a. m.	1252	24.597	.....	68	48	62	NW	3	½ cir.	
	10	7 a. m.	1256	24.609	.....	69	48	62	NW	3	½ cir.	
Camp 93	11	7 a. m.	1252	24.420	.....	68	49	65	NW	3	5 cir. cum.	
	11	7 a. m.	1256	24.436	.....	69	49	65	NW	3	5 cir. nim.	
Camp 94	12	7 a. m.	1252	24.490	.....	69	50	65	SW	5	8 cir. nim.	
	12	7 a. m.	1256	24.506	.....	70	50	65	SW	5	10 nim.	
Camp 95	13	6 p. m.	1252	23.991	.....	70	48	66	W	6		
	13	6 p. m.	.....	24.008	.....	70	48	65	W	6	10 nim.	
Camp 96	14	6 p. m.	1252	24.113	.....	74	48	68	SW	6	10 nim.	
	14	6 p. m.	1256	24.121	.....	72	48	68	SW	6		

APPENDIX C—Continued.

Station.	Date.	Hour.	Number of barometer.	Reading of barometer. Upper vernier.	Reading of barometer. Lower vernier.	Attached thermometer.	Detached thermometer. Wet bulb.	Detached thermometer. Dry bulb.	Wind. Direction.	Wind. Force.	Clouds.	Remarks.
	1858.			Inches	Inches	°	°	°				
Camp 99	May 18	7 p. m.	1252	24.039	......	66	45	56	0	0	0	
	18	7 p. m.	1256	24.046	......	65	45	56	0	0	0	
Camp 100	19	7 p. m.	1252	23.857	......	66	45	60	NW	1	0	
	19	7 p. m.	1256	23.859	......	67	45	60	NW	1	0	
Camp 101	21	5 a. m.	1252	23.938	......	44	36	43	NE	3	10 cir. nim	
	21	5 a. m.	1256	23.959	......	44	36	43	NE	3	10 cir. nim	

APPENDIX D.

REMARKS UPON THE CONSTRUCTION OF THE MAPS.

The plan of construction of these maps is in some respects, new. It however embraces a system of topography at one time adopted in France, in which the light is supposed to fall at an oblique angle upon the objects represented; illuminating certain portions, and leaving others in shade

A disadvantage of that system, in copper and steel engraving, was, that it afforded no relief to the light sides of the mountains or ravines, which, in many cases, therefore could not be distinguished from the surrounding plain.

In lithographed maps, printed in black and white, upon tinted paper, this objection could, in a measure, be obviated.

Mr. Egloffstein, the topographer to the expedition, conceived the idea—while sketching the naked mountains, barren plains, and immense gorges that characterized some portion of the region explored—of endeavoring to give to his map the appearance of a small plaster model of the country, with the light falling upon it at a particular angle. Such a model of a bare and rocky region would strongly resemble nature. Portions of the mountain sides and of the edges of the ravines would appear in brilliant light, others in deep shade. Level plateaus and valleys would have a uniform tint; the lightness or darkness of which would depend upon their elevation or depression. Mr. Egloffstein devised the plan of producing the different tints by means of fine parallel lines, drawn upon the plate with a ruling machine; each part of the ruled portion being brought to the requisite shade by exposing it a longer or shorter time to the action of acid. The maps were engraved by him in accordance with this plan. The topography was constructed from the field-notes directly upon the plates. The latter were of steel; it being feared that copper would not be hard enough to give a sufficient number of impressions of the more delicate tints. The topography was first delineated; the lettering was then put on; and afterwards the plates were ruled.

A glance at the result will show how far the experiment has succeeded. There are defects readily to be perceived, and further experience will doubtless suggest many improvements, but I think it will be generally admitted that, for maps of such a character of country, and upon such a scale, this style—which is believed to be new, so far a regards the application of the ruled tints—is, in beauty and effectiveness, much superior to the old. It possesses the power, which the other does not, of exhibiting the comparative altitudes of plateaus of different elevations. This is particularly apparent in map No. 2. The alluvial lands along the Colorado and Flax rivers, being designated by a darker tint, are distinctly defined, as well as the boundaries and extent of the mesas that limit them. The loftier table-lands, by their lighter appearance, may also be distinguished from lower levels. In the old style these effects could not be produced.

This method of representing topography is less conventional than the other, and truer to nature. It is an approximation to a bird's eye view, and is intelligible to every eye.

Another advantage of the system is its economy. Nearly one-half of the most expensive part of map engraving—the *hachures* upon the mountain sides—is dispensed with, and the additional work, the ruling, is attended with little cost.

DATE DUE